MACMILLAN/McGRAW-HILL

Math

Assessment Guide

Grade 4

- Inventory and Final Test
- Chapter Tests
- Unit Tests
- Portfolio and Performance Assessment
- Self-Assessment
- Teacher Interviews
- Journal Writing
- Scoring Rubrics and Prescription Tables
- Teacher Forms

GRADE 4

CONTENTS

How to Use the Assessment Guide

Macmillan/McGraw-Hill Math includes opportunities to assess students' knowledge on both a formal and an informal basis. This Assessment Guide is intended to assist you in developing, organizing, and managing multiple assessment strategies.

It is the philosophy of this series that the primary purpose of assessment is to improve students' learning, not just to grade their work. Assessment should provide an occasion for students to learn and to evaluate their own work. It should be an integral part of instruction, not simply an end point. Therefore, strategies for monitoring progress as well as summative measures, such as chapter tests, are all included in this guide.

The following is a brief description of the seven assessment strategies provided in this program.

Teacher Interview

The Teacher Interview is an informal assessment strategy designed to help you measure your students' understanding of math concepts. This guide includes a **Teacher Interview Questionnaire** (see page 15) that you can use to document your interviews with students. It also provides information on questioning strategies and help with interviewing techniques.

Journal Writing

Journal Writing is another informal assessment strategy. Here students are given the opportunity to write down how they think about math concepts in their journals. The program provides numerous opportunities for journal writing.

Journal Writing: Problem Solving

The problem-solving section of journal writing contains specifically designed problems based on the material covered in each chapter. These problems give students the opportunity to express their math thinking and problem-solving skills in a written setting. You may use these questions as either a formal or informal assessment tool.

How to Use the Assessment Guide *(continued)*

Paper-and-Pencil Tests

Inventory, chapter, unit, and final tests in this Assessment Guide provide a snapshot of the content that the student has mastered. These tests are available in multiple-choice and free-response formats. They are easy to grade, and they measure student understanding, skill level, and problem-solving ability.

Performance Assessment

Each unit test contains a Performance Assessment. Here, students are asked to perform math procedures and make problem-solving decisions that require an understanding of math concepts. The emphasis is on problems set in realistic situations outside of school.

Portfolio Assessment

Portfolios give you a means of evaluating students' understanding of concepts and abilities to reason and communicate mathematically. Blackline Masters are provided for both student and teacher to help with selecting and documenting student portfolios.

Self-Assessment

Self-assessment gives the students opportunity to look at their work and assess how well they are doing. This guide provides a checklist for students to use as they review their work.

Teacher Interview

The **Teacher Interview** is an informal technique designed to be part of the process of monitoring student progress. Interviews can help you assess your students' knowledge of math concepts. The purpose of the interview is to try to discern a student's thinking well enough to determine what to do next. By using questioning strategies, you can learn how each of your students is understanding the concepts you are teaching.

Where to Begin

A generic **Teacher Interview Questionnaire** (see page 15) is included in this Assessment Guide. You may customize this questionnaire to suit your needs. In addition, later in this guide you will find a Teacher Interview section for each chapter. These interview questions focus on the major ideas of each chapter. Another possibility is the **Write About It!** question in each Pupil Edition lesson as a starting point for the interview.

Classroom Management

Select a time when groups of students are engaged in different activities. As students work, you can either interview small groups or individuals at your desk, or move around the room to talk to students. Conduct the interviews in whatever manner best suits your own teaching style. Target a few students each day. Over the course of two weeks, you should be able to interview all the students in your class.

Recordkeeping. One of the most important things to remember is to date the notes you take. In this way a student's progress can be monitored. If you are using the **Teacher Interview Questionnaire** (see page 15), you can write student responses on this form. Another technique would be to keep a class roster with enough space under each student's name for you to take notes about the student's answers to questions.

Some Hints for Questioning Strategies

- Try to ask open-ended questions.
- The question could be a follow-up to work the student has done or to a response the student has made.
- Clarifying Questions: "What do you mean by...?" or "How did you do that?"
- Probing Questions: "Do you think that will always be the case?" or "How can you prove that your answer is right?"
- Challenging Questions: "What if the problem was changed in the following way?"
- Try not to pose questions that lead the students to the correct answer.

Interviewing Techniques

- Try to keep a relaxed atmosphere. Get students off to a positive start with a question you are sure that they can handle.
- Tell the students what you are doing. Explain that you are questioning them so that you can learn how they think when they solve math questions. Emphasize the thinking process as opposed to getting a correct answer.
- Rephrase your question if the student doesn't understand it.
- The interview session is not a time for you to teach or correct a student's errors. Concentrate on learning more about the student's thought processes. You may want to take notes on problems you need to help the student with at another time.
- Observe your student's behavior during the interview. You can often gain insight into a student's thinking through his or her actions.
- After you've asked a question, give the student some time to answer. Your focus should be on observing. Allowing the students to do most of the talking will supply you with a wealth of information on the way they think about math.

See page 15 in this Assessment Guide for the ***Teacher Interview Questionnaire.***

Journal Writing

Journal Writing is the second component of monitoring student progress. Journals provide an opportunity for students to use writing and drawing to show their understanding of math concepts. Math journals can provide you with valuable information about how and what your students are thinking about math.

The Value of Journal Writing

Writing helps students develop thinking skills. Expressing understanding of a concept in writing is also a means of discovering that understanding. Journal writing gives the student the opportunity to clarify, reflect on, and summarize math lessons. Students can pose a question, explore a train of thought, support an argument, or come to a conclusion. Writing can itself be a form of problem solving.

Journal Writing can:

- Help students become comfortable with reflecting on their own learning
- Promote self-assessment of the student's math thinking
- Give students the opportunity to restate information they just learned
- Provide you with information on how a student is thinking about concepts taught

Where to Begin

Macmillan/McGraw-Hill Math provides several opportunities for students to write in their journals. You will find a feature on journal writing for each chapter of this guide. In addition, journal prompts can be found in the **Writing for Math** and **Performance Assessment** sections of the Pupil Edition. All prompts are specific to the material covered in the unit.

Talking to Your Students About Journal Writing

Emphasize clarity and focus, rather than fluency, in math journals. Tell your students that the idea is to explain a math idea, using illustrations when appropriate, in a way that is to the point.

Discuss the prompts and notify the students if any of their journal entries will be seen by their peers.

Classroom Management

Students can use folders, spiral notebooks, or sections of binders in which to keep their journals. Just be sure that they keep their writing together so that you can easily keep up a dialog with the student.

Assessment and Feedback

It would be best to read and respond to the journals at least once each unit. You may want to write directly in the journal. Encourage students to respond to your entries. Try to provide constructive feedback that will help students further their understanding of a particular topic.

Journal Writing: Problem Solving

Problem Solving questions are word problems specifically designed to assess the material covered in each chapter. See the specific chapter sections in this *Assessment Guide* for the **Problem Solving** question for each chapter.

The Intent of Problem Solving Questions

These word problems give students the opportunity to express their math thinking and problem solving skills in a written setting. You may use these questions as either a formal or informal assessment tool.

Scoring Problem Solving Questions

If you would like to have a numerical score for the **Problem Solving** questions, you may want to use the following 4-point holistic scoring rubric.

Scoring Rubric

Category 4
- Shows a full understanding of the problem
- Uses a systematic and effective math strategy
- Develops a solution that is accurate and complete
- Explains math reasoning in a clear and logical way

Category 3
- Shows an understanding of the problem
- Uses a workable strategy
- Forms a solution that is mostly accurate and complete
- Describes reasoning in a way that makes sense

Category 2
- Shows a partial understanding of the problem
- Uses an appropriate strategy
- Forms a solution that is mostly inaccurate and/or incomplete
- Displays little reasoning

Category 1
- Shows little or no understanding of the problem
- Uses an inappropriate strategy or no strategy
- Forms an inaccurate solution or no solution
- Displays no reasoning

Paper-and-Pencil Tests

Macmillan/McGraw-Hill Math includes four levels of paper-and-pencil tests. The **inventory test** is given at the beginning of the school year. **Chapter tests** and **unit tests** are available to measure student progress throughout the school year. The **final test** is designed to assess student understanding of the content of the entire year. *All* tests provide a multiple-choice format (Form A) and a free-response format (Form B) that contain different item content. Both forms test the same objectives and have the same number of items.

By using both the multiple-choice and the free-response formats, you may help ensure that students get practice taking standardized tests and also have an opportunity to demonstrate higher level thinking skills.

Inventory Test

The inventory test is given at the beginning of the school year. Its intent is to provide a measure of individual and class level of performance at the beginning of the program, establishing a baseline. The inventory test for each grade is the equivalent of the final test of the grade previous to it. There are 20 questions in each form. The inventory test is designed to be scored by the previous grade's objectives and by total test.

Chapter Tests

The chapter tests in this Assessment Guide are aligned with the 28 chapters in the **Macmillan/McGraw-Hill Math** Pupil Edition. The chapter tests measure progress on individual chapter objectives as the students progress through the program. There are about 20 questions in each form of every chapter test. Each test is designed to be scored by objective and by total test.

Unit Tests

The unit tests in this Assessment Guide are aligned with the 14 units in the **Macmillan/McGraw-Hill Math** PE, occurring after every 2 chapters. The unit tests measure progress on individual chapter objectives within that particular unit. There are about 40 questions in each form of every unit test. Each test is designed to be scored by objective and by total test.

Final Test

The final test is given at the end of the school year and measures student progress on skills covered throughout the school year. There are 40 questions in each form. The final test is designed to be scored by the year's objectives and by total test.

Administering the Tests

The tests are not timed. In most cases they may be administered in one sitting. For the multiple-choice tests, students may mark their answers on the generic **Student Answer Sheet** (see page 16) or on the test page. Responses to the free-response Form B tests should be marked directly on the test.

It is very important that your students understand exactly what they are supposed to do. Review the directions and the test items before giving the test. During the test, monitor the students to make sure that they are following directions, working on the appropriate task, and indicating their responses correctly.

Try to make the environment as comfortable as possible. Make an effort to minimize distracting noises or activities that might draw the students' attention away from the test.

Evaluating Test Scores

Each test provides an indication of each student's general math achievement at different periods. Achievement on all tests is reported by objective AND by total test. Scores on these tests may indicate if a student has mastered one or more of the math areas tested. The test scores, therefore, can be used to plan further activities, either for reteaching or enrichment.

*See page 16 in this Assessment Guide for the **Student Answer Sheet.***

*See pages 17–18 in this Assessment Guide for the **Monitoring Student Progress** form.*

*See page 19 in this Assessment Guide for the **Monitoring Class Progress** form.*

Performance Assessment

In math, performance assessment emphasizes what the student *does* and *thinks* with problems that involve realistic situations outside of school. Students are asked to perform math procedures and make problem-solving decisions that require an understanding of math concepts.

The Goals of Performance Assessment

The **Performance Assessment** tasks at the end of each unit:

- Assess the "big ideas" in the unit
- Balance concept and process, knowing and doing
- Elicit reasoning
- Provide opportunities for varied learning styles and intelligences
- Set a "real-world" context as often as possible
- May involve teamwork

Where to Begin

At the end of each unit of the Pupil Edition, there is a Performance Assessment task. This task is designed to allow students to apply their knowledge of the unit in a practical situation. The problem-solving, activity-based assignments in each unit also offer important assessment opportunities with more extended time frames and greater potential for students to explore math in engaging situations.

Evaluating Student Performance

Responses in this type of assessment are not simply right or wrong, but rather show a continuum of the degree of understanding. To evaluate students in a fair and consistent way, **Macmillan/McGraw-Hill Math** provides you with scoring rubrics. At the end of each unit in the Teacher Edition you will find a scoring rubric specifically designed for that unit's **Performance Assessment** task. These rubrics are 3-point scales that provide you with specific criteria on which to evaluate students' work. You might want to distribute these rubrics to your students so that they understand how they will be assessed. Students should receive feedback about their performance with respect to the criteria. In this way, assessment will serve to improve student performance, not just monitor it.

Portfolio Assessment

A portfolio is a collection of students' work that can be used as an important assessment tool. Portfolio assessment:

- Focuses attention on performance criteria
- Documents the improvement of students' work over time
- Fosters students' self-assessment and reflection
- Develops students' ownership in learning
- Communicates with students, parents, and other teachers
- Evaluates the instructional program

What Goes in a Portfolio?

The portfolio is a place for student work that highlights their understanding of concepts, problem solving, reasoning, communication, and connection making. Any task that provides evidence of these abilities is a candidate for inclusion in the portfolio. In particular, **Macmillan/McGraw-Hill Math** provides the following features for use in the portfolio:

- Performance Assessment
- Journal Writing
- Write About It!
- Reading Math and Science
- Applying Math and Science
- Decision Making
- Unit Enrichment

One important goal of the portfolio is to foster student ownership of his or her work. Therefore, material to go in the portfolio should always be selected with the student. You may prefer to keep a "working" portfolio where all student work is held. Then every three or four weeks, you and the student can determine which pieces will go in the "showcase" portfolio, which is shared with external audiences, such as parents and next year's teacher.

Selecting the Showcase Portfolio

Selecting the showcase portfolio is very important. It is a significant part of a student's self-assessment. Have your students use **My Portfolio** (see page 20) to write about the selections they've made. In addition, each piece may be annotated by the student or teacher indicating where it demonstrates specific portfolio criteria, such as using appropriate problem-solving criteria. Since portfolios collect student work over time, be sure to include work that shows improvement. Remember to write the date on all work.

You may also want to consider a multimedia portfolio. Here students who are not strong in writing can demonstrate their math proficiency through photographs, audio or video tapes, and computer software.

Classroom Management

Working portfolios need to be used in ongoing instruction and therefore must be accessible to students. Cardboard boxes or milk crates can be used to house working portfolios. As students complete performance tasks and other appropriate exercises, they will need to store drafts of their work. When students revise their work they will need access to their portfolios again. If possible, allow students to move about the room to access their portfolio material. Learning to take responsibility for one's own work can be a fruitful by-product of using a portfolio.

As selections are made for the showcase portfolio, those materials not selected can be sent home to parents or discarded. Showcase portfolios need not be accessible on a daily basis and may be stored in a file cabinet or closet.

Small-Group Strategies

Teachers who use portfolios often find that by using flexible grouping strategies they are able to work intensively with small groups of students on particular topics while other students work independently. Since students generally finish performance-oriented tasks at different rates, this approach works well with portfolio work. It can also free you up to confer with individuals or groups concerning portfolio work.

Reviewing Portfolios

A good strategy for reviewing portfolios is to look at just a few each day. Even if each portfolio is reviewed every two weeks, this schedule can provide you with enough information to meet with students to discuss their portfolios.

See page 20 in this Assessment Guide for the student's ***My Portfolio*** *form.*

See page 21 in this Assessment Guide for the teacher's ***Portfolio Assessment Form.***

Self-Assessment

Self-assessment empowers the students and gives them the sense that they are in control of an important aspect of their school work. Students should be able to look at their work and assess how well they are doing. Self-assessment is an important aspect of the process of selecting a showcase portfolio as well.

Checklist

Macmillan/McGraw-Hill Math provides a checklist for students to use in the self-assessment process. The **Self-Assessment Checklist** (see page 22) uses simplified language to provide students with a means of comparing their work against established criteria. This list correlates to the teacher's blackline master **Portfolio Assessment Form** (see page 21). It is particularly suitable for extended tasks, such as performance assessment tasks. To promote and guide student self-assessment, you might want to attach checklists to the work in the student's portfolio. Then use this information in conferences to improve your student's understanding of classroom standards.

See page 22 in this Assessment Guide for the student's ***Self-Assessment Checklist.***

Teacher Interview Questionnaire

Student Name ______________________ Date __________

Chapter __________ Lesson __________

For Individual Students

Tell how you got your result.

What were some of the things you were thinking when you solved the problem?

Show how to prove that your answer is right.

What would happen if (you changed)...

What have you learned in class that might have helped you solve this problem?

For Students in a Group

How would you solve this problem differently than the other students in your group suggested?

Tell me more about how you would solve this problem.

Student Answer Sheet

Student Name ______________________________ Date ____________

Macmillan/McGraw-Hill Math

GRADE 4

☐ Inventory ☐ Chapter ______ ☐ Unit ______ ☐ Final

Choose One

1.	Ⓐ	Ⓑ	Ⓒ	Ⓓ	**21.**	Ⓐ	Ⓑ	Ⓒ	Ⓓ
2.	Ⓕ	Ⓖ	Ⓗ	Ⓙ	**22.**	Ⓕ	Ⓖ	Ⓗ	Ⓙ
3.	Ⓐ	Ⓑ	Ⓒ	Ⓓ	**23.**	Ⓐ	Ⓑ	Ⓒ	Ⓓ
4.	Ⓕ	Ⓖ	Ⓗ	Ⓙ	**24.**	Ⓕ	Ⓖ	Ⓗ	Ⓙ
5.	Ⓐ	Ⓑ	Ⓒ	Ⓓ	**25.**	Ⓐ	Ⓑ	Ⓒ	Ⓓ
6.	Ⓕ	Ⓖ	Ⓗ	Ⓙ	**26.**	Ⓕ	Ⓖ	Ⓗ	Ⓙ
7.	Ⓐ	Ⓑ	Ⓒ	Ⓓ	**27.**	Ⓐ	Ⓑ	Ⓒ	Ⓓ
8.	Ⓕ	Ⓖ	Ⓗ	Ⓙ	**28.**	Ⓕ	Ⓖ	Ⓗ	Ⓙ
9.	Ⓐ	Ⓑ	Ⓒ	Ⓓ	**29.**	Ⓐ	Ⓑ	Ⓒ	Ⓓ
10.	Ⓕ	Ⓖ	Ⓗ	Ⓙ	**30.**	Ⓕ	Ⓖ	Ⓗ	Ⓙ
11.	Ⓐ	Ⓑ	Ⓒ	Ⓓ	**31.**	Ⓐ	Ⓑ	Ⓒ	Ⓓ
12.	Ⓕ	Ⓖ	Ⓗ	Ⓙ	**32.**	Ⓕ	Ⓖ	Ⓗ	Ⓙ
13.	Ⓐ	Ⓑ	Ⓒ	Ⓓ	**33.**	Ⓐ	Ⓑ	Ⓒ	Ⓓ
14.	Ⓕ	Ⓖ	Ⓗ	Ⓙ	**34.**	Ⓕ	Ⓖ	Ⓗ	Ⓙ
15.	Ⓐ	Ⓑ	Ⓒ	Ⓓ	**35.**	Ⓐ	Ⓑ	Ⓒ	Ⓓ
16.	Ⓕ	Ⓖ	Ⓗ	Ⓙ	**36.**	Ⓕ	Ⓖ	Ⓗ	Ⓙ
17.	Ⓐ	Ⓑ	Ⓒ	Ⓓ	**37.**	Ⓐ	Ⓑ	Ⓒ	Ⓓ
18.	Ⓕ	Ⓖ	Ⓗ	Ⓙ	**38.**	Ⓕ	Ⓖ	Ⓗ	Ⓙ
19.	Ⓐ	Ⓑ	Ⓒ	Ⓓ	**39.**	Ⓐ	Ⓑ	Ⓒ	Ⓓ
20.	Ⓕ	Ⓖ	Ⓗ	Ⓙ	**40.**	Ⓕ	Ⓖ	Ⓗ	Ⓙ

Monitoring Student Progress

GRADE 4

Student Name ______________________________

Inventory Test	Form A		Form B		Comments
	Score	%	Score	%	
	/20		/20		

Chapter	Form A		Form B		Comments
	Score	%	Score	%	
1	/20		/20		
2	/20		/20		
3	/20		/20		
4	/20		/20		
5	/20		/20		
6	/20		/20		
7	/20		/20		
8	/20		/20		
9	/20		/20		
10	/20		/20		
11	/20		/20		
12	/20		/20		
13	/20		/20		
14	/20		/20		
15	/20		/20		
16	/20		/20		
17	/20		/20		
18	/20		/20		
19	/20		/20		
20	/20		/20		
21	/20		/20		
22	/20		/20		
23	/20		/20		
24	/20		/20		
25	/20		/20		
26	/20		/20		
27	/20		/20		
28	/20		/20		

Monitoring Student Progress *(continued)* GRADE 4

Student Name ______________________________

Unit	Form A		Form B		Performance Assessment	Comments
	Score	%	Score	%		
1	/40		/40			
2	/40		/40			
3	/40		/40			
4	/40		/40			
5	/40		/40			
6	/40		/40			
7	/40		/40			
8	/40		/40			
9	/40		/40			
10	/40		/40			
11	/40		/40			
12	/40		/40			
13	/40		/40			
14	/40		/40			

Final Test	Form A		Form B		Comments
	Score	%	Score	%	
	/40		/40		

Monitoring Class Progress

GRADE 4

This chart is to be used in monitoring your class progress unit by unit. Please photocopy this page and use one page for every unit in the **Macmillan/McGraw-Hill Math** program. Fill in the correct chapter and unit numbers in the chart as you complete the columns.

UNIT ____ **PA = Performance Assessment**

Student	Chapter ____		Chapter ____		Unit ____		
	Form A	Form B	Form A	Form B	Form A	Form B	PA

My Portfolio

Student Name ____

Date	Type of Work	Title	I'm including this because...

Portfolio Assessment Form

Student Name ______________________ Grade __________

Teacher ______________________ Date __________

This portfolio shows evidence that the student:	Little Evidence	Partial Evidence	Adequate Evidence	Substantial Evidence
Understands concepts				
Selects appropriate strategies to solve problems				
Provides quality explanations				
Expresses concepts, ideas, and thinking in an organized and clear way				
Uses math representations (models, graphs, charts, pictures, diagrams, numerals, symbols, math vocabulary) appropriately and accurately				
Makes connections to real-world situations, other math ideas, or other subject areas				

I would characterize the quality of the work in this portfolio as —

____

____

This student shows growth in —

____

____

This student would benefit from instruction in —

____

____

Self-Assessment Checklist

Student Name ______________________________

Now you have a chance to look at your work and review it.
Check what you did.

Understanding

☐ My work shows that I understand the big math "idea."

Problem Solving

☐ I answered the whole question.

☐ I showed how I got my answer.

Reasoning

☐ I explained why I did my work the way I did.

☐ I explained why my solution is reasonable.

Communicating

☐ My writing was organized and clear.

☐ I used models, pictures, or charts to organize my work.

Now complete these sentences.

The math strategy I used to solve this problem was —

____

____

From this problem I learned —

____

____

Inventory Test – Monitoring Student Progress

☐ Form A ☐ Form B

Student Name ______________________________ Date ____________

Directions: This test targets selected objectives. For each item that is answered incorrectly, cross out the item number. Then record the number of correct responses in the column labeled **Number of Correct Responses.** Add to find the **Total Number of Correct Responses** and record the total. Use this total to determine the **Total Test Score** and the **Total Percent Correct.**

Strand • Objective(s)	Item Numbers	Number of Correct Responses
Number Sense • Explore numbers through hundred thousands. • Compare and order numbers, money, and decimals. • Add more than two numbers. • Subtract greater numbers. • Multiply and divide by 9. • Multiply 3 numbers. • Estimate sums, products, and quotients. • Multiply multi-digit numbers. • Divide 3-digit numbers. • Read, identify, and write fractions. • Explore equivalent fractions. • Add and subtract fractions and decimals.	1, 2, 3, 4, 5, 6, 9, 11, 13, 14, 16, 17, 18, 19, 24, 25, 26, 27, 30	/19
Algebra & Functions • Relate multiplication to division. • Convert customary units. • Identify and use the Identity and Zero Properties of Multiplication. • Find the missing factors.	10, 12, 20, 38	/4
Measurement and Geometry • Tell time and find elapsed time and ending time. • Estimate temperature in degrees Fahrenheit and degrees Celsius. • Identify 2-dimensional shapes and 3-dimensional figures. • Find the perimeter and area. • Explore symmetry. • Identify congruent and similar figures.	7, 21, 22, 23, 28, 33, 34, 37	/8
Statistics, Data, and Probability • Interpret data in graphs. • Find the mean. • Determine the probability. • Find the range, median, and mode.	8, 15, 29, 39, 40	/5
Mathematical Reasoning • Use skills and strategies to solve problems.	31, 32, 35, 36	/4
Total Number of Correct Responses		
Total Test Score		/40
Total Percent Correct		%

Name ______________________________

INVENTORY
TEST
FORM A
PAGE 1

Read each question carefully. Darken the circle on your answer sheet for the correct answer.

1. What is the standard form of 9 thousands 8 tens 6 ones?

A. 9,860 **C.** 9,086
B. 9,806 **D.** 8,906

2. Order from least to greatest.

$4.65, $5.46, $6.45, $4.56

F. $6.45, $5.46, $4.65, $4.56
G. $4.65, $5.46, $6.45, $4.56
H. $4.65, $4.56, $5.46, $6.45
J. $4.56, $4.65, $5.46, $6.45

3. Estimate.

195 + 439

A. 700 **C.** 400
B. 600 **D.** 200

4.
$$\begin{array}{r} 375 \\ 487 \\ +\ 392 \\ \hline \end{array}$$

F. 1,254 **H.** 1,054
G. 1,154 **J.** 1,044

5. 295 − 187 = ■

A. 118 **C.** 108
B. 110 **D.** 98

6.
$$\begin{array}{r} \$37.25 \\ -\ 11.99 \\ \hline \end{array}$$

F. $26.36 **H.** $25.26
G. $26.26 **J.** $15.26

7. If it is now 8:15 A.M., what time will it be in an hour and forty-five minutes?

A. 11:30 A.M. **C.** 9:45 A.M.
B. 10:00 A.M. **D.** 9:00 A.M.

8. The graph shows that Pete read two times as many books as ■.

F. Quentin **H.** Sean
G. Robert **J.** Tracy

9. 8 × 5 = ■

A. 40 **B.** 32 **C.** 24 **D.** 13

10. 9 × ■ = 63

F. 10 **G.** 9 **H.** 8 **J.** 7

Name ____________________

11. $4 \times 5 \times 6 =$ ■

A. 120 **B.** 100 **C.** 96 **D.** 15

12. Which multiplication sentence is related to this division sentence?

$36 \div 9 = 4$

F. $18 \times 2 = 36$ **H.** $12 \times 3 = 36$
G. $6 \times 6 = 36$ **J.** $4 \times 9 = 36$

13. $25 \div 5 =$ ■

A. 7 **B.** 6 **C.** 5 **D.** 4

14. $45 \div 9 =$ ■

F. 6 **G.** 5 **H.** 4 **J.** 3

15. Find the mean of the following numbers:

3, 4, 3, 6, 4

A. 6 **B.** 5 **C.** 4 **D.** 3

16. Which is the best estimate for $83 \div 8$?

F. 11 **G.** 10 **H.** 9 **J.** 8

17. $452 \div 6 =$ ■

A. 85 R2 **C.** 76 R2
B. 76 R4 **D.** 75 R2

18. Estimate.

475×8

F. 40,000 **H.** 4,000
G. 32,000 **J.** 400

19. 304×9

A. 3,726 **C.** 2,736
B. 3,627 **D.** 1,836

20. Otelia bought a 2-pound bag of flour. How many ounces is that?

F. 8 **G.** 16 **H.** 32 **J.** 48

21. Identify the figure.

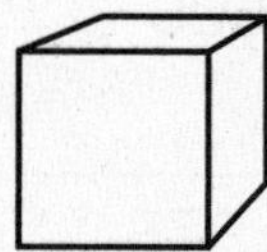

A. pyramid
B. cylinder
C. sphere
D. cube

22. What is the area of the square?

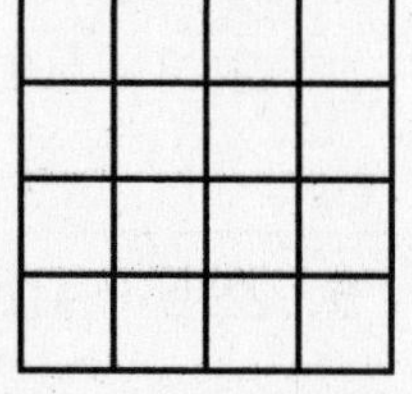

F. 20 square units
G. 16 square units
H. 12 square units
J. 8 square units

GO ON

Name ______________________________

23. Which is a reasonable temperature for a hot summer day?

A. 95°F **B.** 95°C **C.** 50°C **D.** 50°F

24. What is the fraction for the part that is shaded?

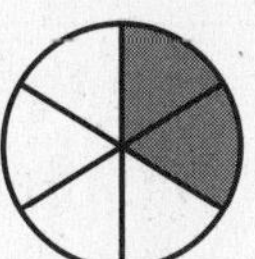

F. $\frac{5}{6}$ **G.** $\frac{2}{3}$ **H.** $\frac{1}{2}$ **J.** $\frac{1}{3}$

25. $\frac{2}{5} + \frac{1}{5} = \square$

A. $\frac{3}{10}$ **B.** $\frac{1}{2}$ **C.** $\frac{3}{5}$ **D.** $\frac{4}{5}$

26. $\frac{7}{10} - \frac{3}{10} = \square$

F. $\frac{2}{5}$ **G.** $\frac{4}{5}$ **H.** 1 **J.** $\frac{4}{0}$

27. $8.3 + 2.6 = \square$

A. 11.9 **B.** 11.3 **C.** 10.9 **D.** 10.3

28. How many lines of symmetry does a square have?

F. 4 **G.** 3 **H.** 2 **J.** 1

29. A cube has 3 blue faces and 3 yellow faces. What is the probability that a yellow face will be tossed?

A. $\frac{1}{3}$ **B.** $\frac{1}{2}$ **C.** $\frac{2}{3}$ **D.** $\frac{1}{4}$

30. Write the long jumpers in order from the shortest jump to the longest jump.

The Longest Jumps

Name	Distance Jumped
Bob Beamon	8.90 meters
Robert Emmiyan	8.86 meters
Carl Lewis	8.87 meters
Mike Powell	8.95 meters
Eric Walder	8.74 meters

F. Walder, Lewis, Powell, Beamon, Emmiyan

G. Beamon, Powell, Walder, Lewis, Emmiyan

H. Powell, Beamon, Lewis, Emmiyan, Walder

J. Walder, Emmiyan, Lewis, Beamon, Powell

31. The Math Club is taking a trip to the museum. There are 35 people in the club. If each car can hold 4 students, how many cars are needed?

A. 7 cars **C.** 9 cars

B. 8 cars **D.** 10 cars

32. Lisa buys a kitten with a 100-dollar bill. With her change she buys cat toys for $11. She now has $32. How much did the kitten cost?

F. $32 **G.** $43 **H.** $57 **J.** $68

33. What is the perimeter if all sides are equal?

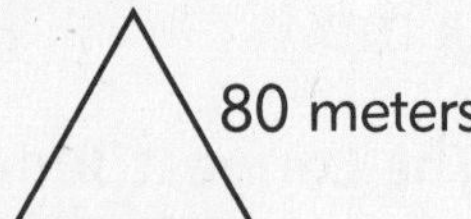

A. 320 meters **C.** 160 meters
B. 240 meters **D.** 80 meters

34. Identify.

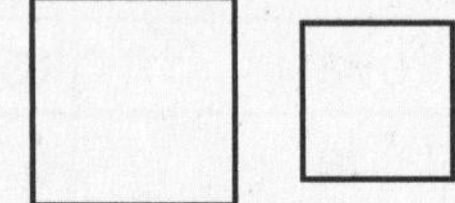

F. similar, but not congruent
G. congruent, but not similar
H. congruent and similar
J. neither congruent nor similar

35. There are 8 seats in each row. There are 4 rows. How many seats are there?

A. 2 seats **C.** 12 seats
B. 4 seats **D.** 32 seats

36. The Olympics were held in Los Angeles 52 years after the first time they were there. When were the Olympics first held in Los Angeles? What information do you need to solve the problem?

F. The current year.
G. When the Olympics were last held in Los Angeles.
H. The year of the first Olympics.
J. You have all the information you need.

37. What time does the clock show?

A. 5:07 **B.** 7:05 **C.** 7:25 **D.** 8:25

38. Use the Identity Property of Multiplication to complete.

$\square \times 81 = 81$

F. 0 **G.** 1 **H.** 3 **J.** 9

Use the graph for problems 39–40.

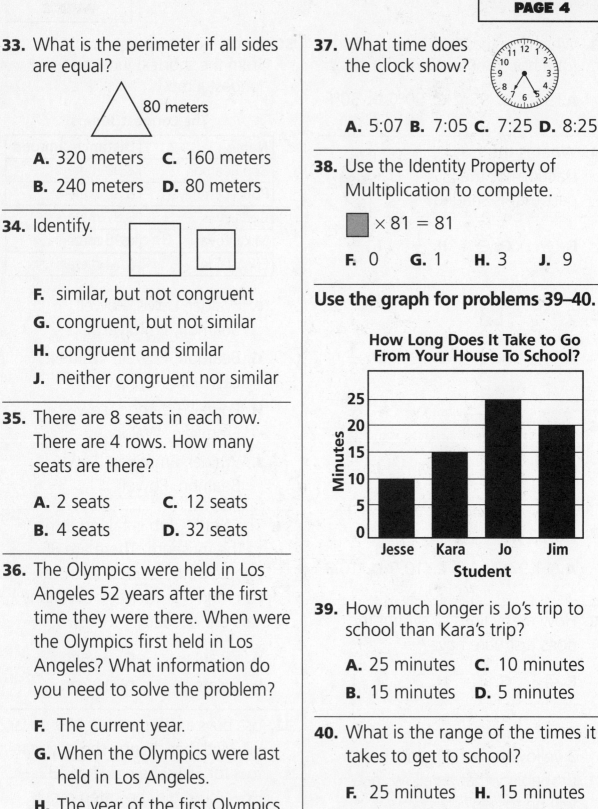

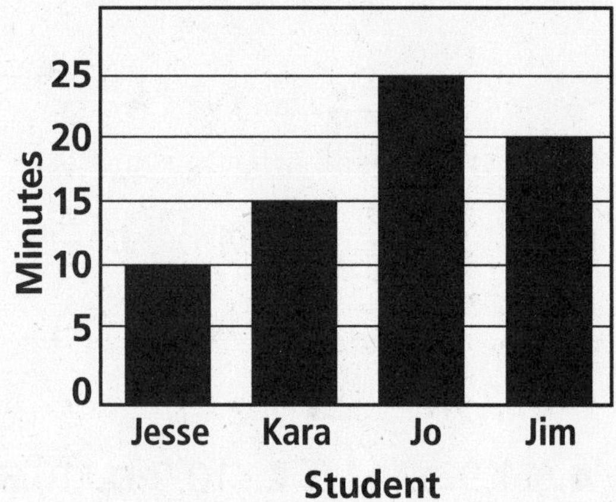

39. How much longer is Jo's trip to school than Kara's trip?

A. 25 minutes **C.** 10 minutes
B. 15 minutes **D.** 5 minutes

40. What is the range of the times it takes to get to school?

F. 25 minutes **H.** 15 minutes
G. 20 minutes **J.** 10 minutes

STOP

Name ____________________

Read each question carefully. Fill in the correct answer in the space provided.

1. What is the standard form of 8 thousands 6 tens 4 ones?

____

2. Write in order from least to greatest.

$5.25, $4.46, $6.54, $4.65

____

3. Estimate.

185 + 429

____

4.
```
  352
  435
+ 533
```

5. 286 − 177 = __________

6.
```
  $56.35
−  24.99
```

7. If it is now 7:15 A.M., what time will it be in an hour and thirty-five minutes?

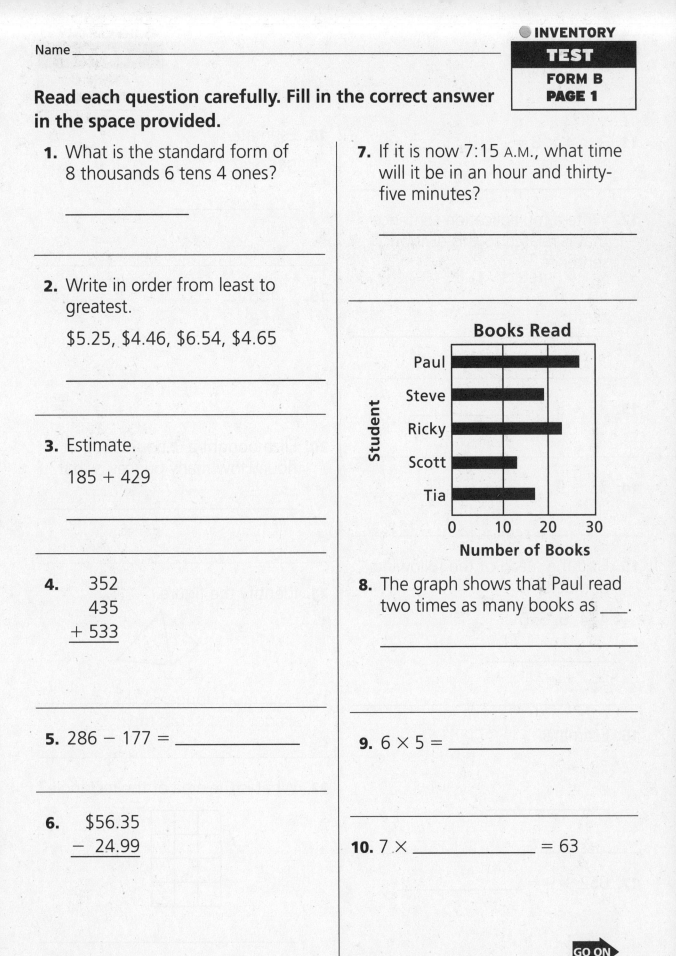

____

Books Read

Student	Number of Books
Paul	
Steve	
Ricky	
Scott	
Tia	

Number of Books: 0, 10, 20, 30

8. The graph shows that Paul read two times as many books as ___.

____

9. 6 × 5 = __________

10. 7 × __________ = 63

GO ON

Name ______________________________

11. $3 \times 4 \times 8 =$ __________

12. Write a multiplication sentence that is related to this division sentence.

$56 \div 8 = 7$

____

13. $35 \div 5 =$ __________

14. $72 \div 9 =$ __________

15. Find the mean of the following numbers:

4, 4, 6, 5, 6

____

16. Estimate.

$72 \div 7$

____

17. $652 \div 9 =$ __________

18. Estimate.

575×7

____

19.

$$\begin{array}{r} 408 \\ \times \quad 8 \\ \hline \end{array}$$

20. Eliza bought a 3-pound bag of flour. How many ounces is that?

____

21. Identify the figure.

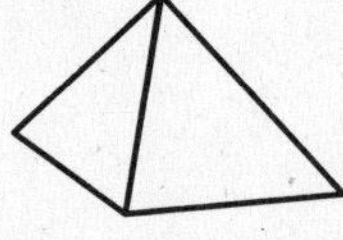

____

22. What is the area of the rectangle?

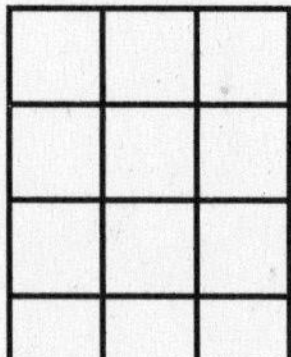

____

GO ON

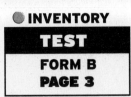

Name ________________________________

23. What is a reasonable temperature in degrees Fahrenheit for a hot summer day?

____

24. Write a fraction for the part that is shaded.

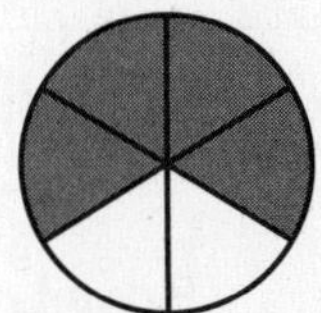

____

25. $\frac{3}{5} + \frac{1}{5} =$ ____________

26. $\frac{9}{10} - \frac{7}{10} =$ ____________

27. 7.3 + 4.4 = ____________

28. How many lines of symmetry does a rectangle that is not a square have?

____

29. A cube has 3 red faces and 3 green faces. What is the probability that a green face will be tossed?

____

30. Write the players in order from the lowest ERA to the highest ERA.

Low ERAs

Name	Best ERA
Greg Maddux	1.56
Pedro Martinez	1.74
Tom Seaver	1.76
Bob Gibson	1.12
Luis Tiant	1.60

____

____

____

31. The Science Club is taking a trip to the science center. There are 37 people in the club. If each car can hold 5 students, how many cars are needed?

____

32. Marie buys a puppy with a 100-dollar bill. With her change she buys dog toys for $17. She now has $12. How much did the puppy cost?

____

GO ON

33. What is the perimeter if all sides are equal?

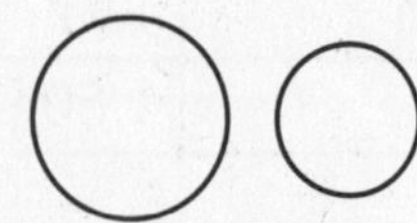

____

34.

Are the circles *similar, congruent,* or *both*?

____

35. There are 7 seats in each row. There are 6 rows. How many seats are there?

____

36. The Olympics were held in Lake Placid, New York, 48 years after the first time they were there. When were they first held in Lake Placid? What information do you need to solve the problem?

____

____

37. What time does the clock show?

____

38. Use the Identity Property of Multiplication to complete.

____________ $\times 78 = 78$

Use the graph for problems 39–40.

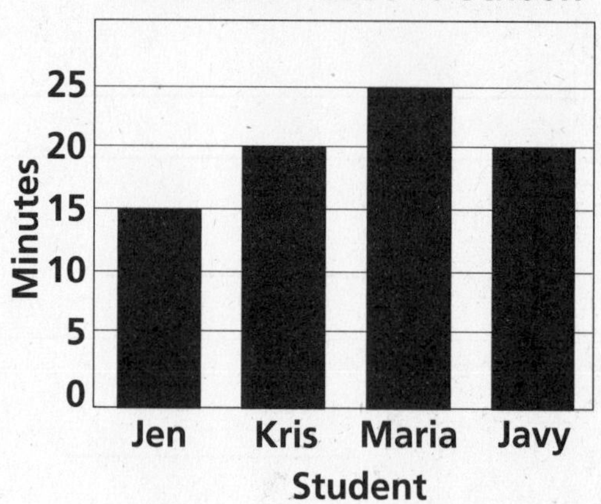

39. How much longer is Maria's trip to school than Kris's trip?

____

40. What is the mode of the times it takes to get to school?

____

STOP

Chapter 1 – Teacher Interview

Core Concept: ***Place Value***

Student Activity: Students demonstrate an ability to read and write whole numbers in the millions and identify the value of each place. Present students with a number such as 60,035,072.

Teacher Question 1:

- What is the value of the 6 in this number?

Understanding Student Response	Practice and Improvement
Students who say 6,000,000.	Review lesson 4 to help students practice with larger numbers.
Students who say 600,000.	Review lesson 2 to help students recognize that it is the position of a number which gives it its place value.

Teacher Question 2:

- What is the place value of the 3 in this number?

Understanding Student Response	Practice and Improvement
Students who say thousands.	Review lesson 2 to help students differentiate between the places in the thousands period.
Students who say hundred thousands.	Review lesson 2 to help students recognize the ten thousands place.

Chapter 1 – Journal Writing

Encourage students to generate their own journal entries related to math ideas in general or to concepts in this chapter. For students requiring guidance, present the following journal prompt:

- When you are comparing whole numbers, why is it important to focus on the place value of the left-most digit? How will that help you to compare whole numbers?

  (Responses should include that the place value of the left-most digit of a whole number will initially determine if any one number is less than the others; if place value is equal, then the left-most digit will determine the greatest or least number, and so on.)

JOURNAL WRITING/PROBLEM SOLVING

The students of Ms. Green's math class are making a chart of how many people visited the Jackson Aquarium during June, July, and August. There were 29,685 people who visited the aquarium in June; 30,791 people visited in July; and 3,002 people visited the aquarium in August. Order the number of people visiting the aquarium last summer from greatest to least.

Read

Have students find the answer to the problem. Then ask them to write a few sentences telling—

- what number they eliminated first
- how they determined the greater of the remaining numbers

Have students make up another problem with different information for which they would have to follow the same procedure. Then have students solve the problem and supply the correct response.

Plan

Students must know the place-value chart, be able to compare the single digit numbers, and follow through correctly on the procedure.

Solve

The correct response to the assigned problem is 30,791; 29,865; 3,002. Students had to first determine that 3,002 had fewer place values than the other two numbers. They then had to scrutinize the left-most digit of the remaining whole numbers and determine that 3 has a greater value than 2.

Look Back

A correct response demonstrates the ability to determine which number has the least place value, compare the value of the left-most digits of the remaining numbers and respond with the greatest whole number. (See scoring rubric on page 7.)

Chapter 1 – Monitoring Student Progress

☐ Form A ☐ Form B

Name _______________ Date _______________

Directions: For each item that is answered incorrectly, cross out the item number. Then record the number of correct responses in the appropriate Student Score column. If the student has not met the Criterion Score for an objective, circle the student's score. Recommended assignments are listed in the Prescription Table on the next page.

Objective	Item Numbers	Criterion Score	Student Score
A. Use benchmark numbers.	1, 16	1/2	/2
B. Read and write whole numbers in millions.	2, 4, 5, 7, 8, 10, 11, 12	7/8	/8
C. Compare and order whole numbers.	3, 6, 9, 13, 14, 15	5/6	/6
D. Use skills and strategies to solve problems.	17, 18, 19, 20	3/4	/4
Total Test Score		16/20	/20
Total Percent Correct			%

Chapter 1 – Prescription Table

The following chart correlates the tested objectives for this chapter to supplementary materials that meet the individual needs of the students. The Reteach and Practice pages are designed for students who need further instruction in the math concepts taught in this chapter. The Enrich pages are designed for students who need advanced challenges.

Objective	Reteach	Practice	Enrich
A. Use benchmark numbers.	1	2	3
B. Read and write whole numbers in millions.	7, 10	8, 11	9,12
C. Compare and order whole numbers.	13	14	15
D. Use skills and strategies to solve problems.	16	17	18

Name ______________________________

CHAPTER 1 TEST
FORM A
PAGE 1

Read each question carefully. Darken the circle on your answer sheet for the correct answer.

1. Use a benchmark number to help you decide the number of stars on the right.

50 Stars

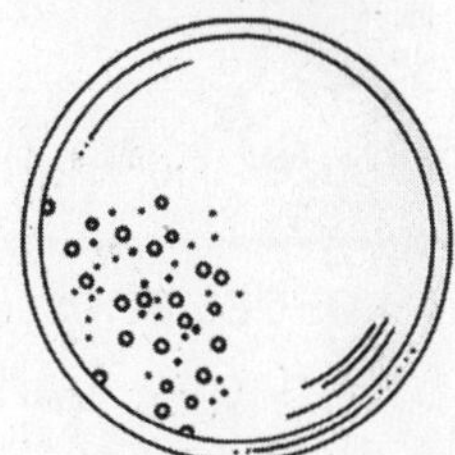
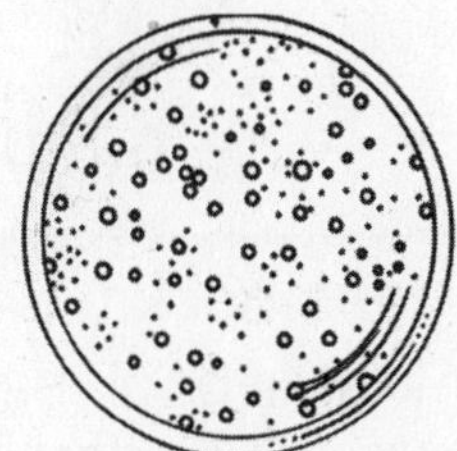

A. 50 **B.** 200 **C.** 500 **D.** 2,000

2. What is the standard form of eight million, three hundred fifteen thousand, forty-three?

F. 8,315,043 **H.** 80,315,043
G. 8,315,403 **J.** 803,015,043

3. Order from greatest to least.

31,114; 31,600; 30,533

A. 30,533; 31,114; 31,600
B. 31,600; 30,533; 31,114
C. 31,600; 31,114; 30,533
D. 31,114; 31,600; 30,533

4. What is the standard form of fifty-six million, thirty-three thousand?

F. 56,033,000 **H.** 56,303,000
G. 56,300,000 **J.** 56,330,000

5. What is the standard form of 900,000 + 600 + 80 + 2?

A. 9,682 **C.** 906,082
B. 900,682 **D.** 900,000,682

6. Order from least to greatest.

11,679; 10,850; 12,039

F. 11,679; 12,039; 10,850
G. 10,850; 12,039; 11,679
H. 12,039; 10,850; 11,679
J. 10,850; 11,679; 12,039

7. What is the name for 2,046,701?

A. two million, four hundred-six thousand, seven hundred one
B. two million, forty-six thousand, seventy-one
C. two million, forty-six thousand, seven hundred one
D. two million, forty-six thousand, seven hundred ten

8. What is the expanded form of 73,011?

F. 70,000 + 3,000 + 100 + 1
G. 70,000 + 3,000 + 10 + 1
H. 700,000 + 3,000 + 10 + 1
J. 70,000 + 3,000 + 100 + 10

9. Which digit makes the sentence true?

$4{,}518 < 4{,}\blacksquare18$

A. 3 **B.** 4 **C.** 5 **D.** 6

GO ON

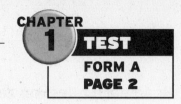

10. What is the standard form of 300,000,000 + 40,000,000 + 800,000 + 200 + 30 + 6?

F. 348,236 **H.** 3,408,236
G. 3,048,236 **J.** 340,800,236

11. What is the standard form of twenty million, six hundred thousand, four hundred thirty-nine?

A. 26,439 **C.** 20,600,439
B. 2,600,439 **D.** 20,604,039

12. What is the standard form of 90,000,000 + 700,000 + 30,000 + 1,000 + 600 + 5?

F. 973,165 **H.** 90,731,065
G. 9,731,605 **J.** 90,731,605

13. Which digit makes the sentence true?

8,375 = 8,3 ▢ 5

A. 8 **B.** 7 **C.** 5 **D.** 3

14. Order from greatest to least.

389,042; 389,402; 398,042

F. 398,042; 389,402; 389,042
G. 389,402; 389,042; 398,042
H. 398,042; 389,042; 389,402
J. 389,042; 389,402; 398,042

15. Order from least to greatest.

24, 421; 24, 412; 42, 241

A. 42, 241; 24, 412; 24, 421
B. 42, 241; 24, 421; 24, 412
C. 24, 421; 24, 412; 42, 241
D. 24, 412; 24, 421; 42, 241

16. Use a benchmark number to help you decide which is the more reasonable number of marbles.

F. 400 **G.** 200 **H.** 40 **J.** 20

17. Jen's book has 619 pages and Matt's book has 594 pages. Carl's book has 835 pages and Terry's book has 1,023 pages. Whose book has the least number of pages?

A. Jen **B.** Matt **C.** Carl **D.** Terry

18. The distance between the Earth and the Sun is about 93,000,000 miles. What is this distance written as a short word name?

F. 93 trillion **H.** 93 million
G. 93 billion **J.** 93 thousand

19. Maria went on four plane trips last year. The spring trip was 738 miles long and the summer trip was 593 miles long. The fall trip was 1,058 miles long and the winter trip was 783 miles long. Which season's trip was the longest?

A. spring **C.** fall
B. summer **D.** winter

20. Amy sells cookies. She sold 136 boxes in May, 179 in June, 139 in July, and 152 in August. In which month did she sell the least?

F. May **H.** July
G. June **J.** August

STOP

Name ____________________

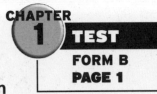

Read each question carefully. Fill in the correct answer in the space provided.

1. Use a benchmark number to help you decide which is the more reasonable number. 1,500 Grapes or 150 Grapes?

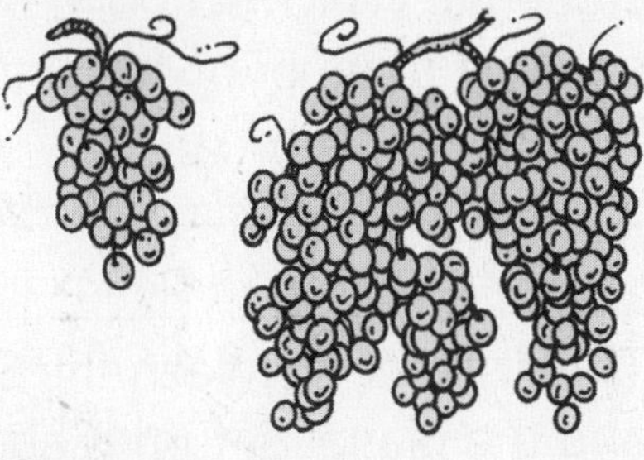

30 grapes

____

2. What is the standard form of four million, six hundred twenty-five thousand, seven hundred nine?

____

3. Order from greatest to least.

   307,574; 307,754; 370,574

____

4. What is the standard form of seven hundred thirty-two million, ninety-four thousand, sixty-two?

____

5. What is the standard form?

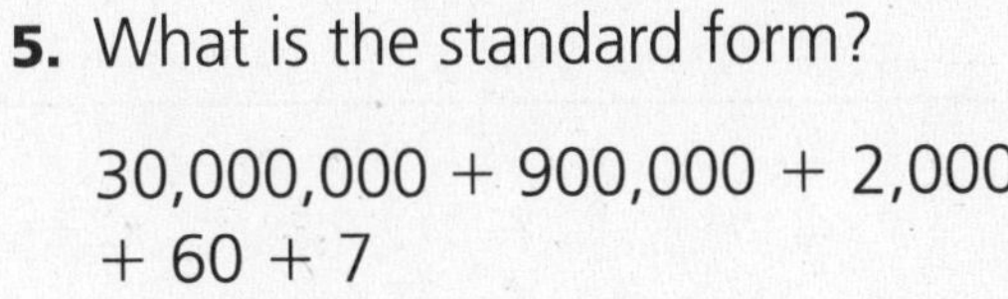

   30,000,000 + 900,000 + 2,000 + 60 + 7

____

6. Order from least to greatest.

   89,982; 98,892; 89,892

____

7. What is the word name for 56,702,058?

____

8. What is the expanded form of 4,880,540?

____

9. Which symbol makes the sentence true: >, <, or = ?

   3,518 ◯ 3,218

____

10. What is the standard form?

    70,000,000 + 3,000,000 + 50,000 + 100 + 90 + 2

____

GO ON

Name ______________________________

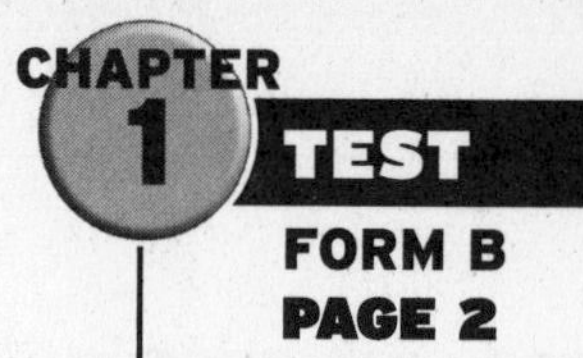

11. What is the standard form of twenty-three million, four hundred thousand, five hundred sixty-seven?

____

12. What is the standard form?

30,000,000 + 800,000 + 10,000 + 4,000 + 60 + 2

____

13. Which symbol makes the sentence true: >, <, or = ?

2,108 ● 2,108

____

14. Order from greatest to least.

542,180; 524,180; 542,018

____

15. Order from least to greatest.

37,380,092; 37,380,091; 37,380,910

____

16. Use a benchmark number to help you decide which is the more reasonable number 240 pennies or 2,400 pennies?

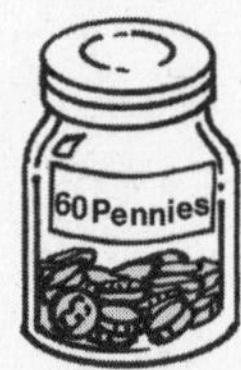

____

17. Heightstown Middle School has 874 students. Sparta Middle School has 947 students. East Orange Middle School has 1,293 students. Middleneck Middle School has 849 students. Which school has the greatest number of students?

____

18. The distance between the Sun and the planet Saturn is about 886,000,000 miles. What is this distance written as a short word name?

____

19. Georgia read four magazine articles about art. The first article had 1,428 words and the second had 1,782 words. The third article had 1,274 words and the fourth had 1,872 words. Which article had the least number of words?

____

20. Exit 9 clothing store sold 734 pairs of jeans last year. They also sold 437 t-shirts, 873 pairs of socks, and 783 hats. Which kind of clothing did Exit 9 sell the greatest number of last year?

____

STOP

Chapter 2 – Teacher Interview

Core Concept: ***Place Value and Money***

Student Activity: The students demonstrate an understanding of how to count money when given two $5 bills, two $1 bills, two quarters, two dimes, three nickels, and one penny.

Teacher Question 1:

- What is the value of the money?

Understanding Student Response	Practice and Improvement
Students who compute the number of dollars correctly, but fail to count the change correctly.	Review lesson 1 to help students review how to count change.
Students who compute the money amount correctly, but do not know how to write money amounts.	Review lesson 1 to help students review how to write money amounts.

Teacher Question 2:

- Round $35.68 to the nearest dollar.

Understanding Student Response	Practice and Improvement
Students who estimate $40.	Review lesson 3 to help students differentiate between rounding to the nearest dollar and the nearest ten dollars.
Students who answer $35.	Review lesson 3 to help students review rounding money.
Students who estimate $30.	Review lesson 3 to help students learn how to estimate.

Chapter 2 – Journal Writing

Encourage students to generate their own journal entries related to math ideas in general or to concepts in this chapter. For students requiring guidance, present the following journal prompt:

- What do you do differently to compare and order a list of prices and to compare and order a list of numbers? What do you do the same way for both lists?

  (Responses should include the idea that to compare prices they must be lined up at the decimal point, while numbers must be lined up by the ones column. Both must be examined place by place, starting with the left-most digit.)

JOURNAL WRITING/PROBLEM SOLVING

Anita uses a $20 bill to buy a CD that costs $15.29. Choon uses a $10 bill to pay for apples and pears that cost $4.78. Who goes home with more money?

Read

Have students find the answer to the problem. Then ask them to write a few sentences telling —

- how they found the amount of change each person received
- how they compared the two amounts

Have students make up another problem with different information for which they would have to follow the same procedure. Then have students solve the problem and supply the correct responses.

Plan

Students must know how to count up to find the amount of change, and must know how to order money amounts.

Solve

The correct response to the assigned problem is Choon. He has $5.22 in change, while Anita has $4.71. Students had to count up to find the amount of change each person received, then align and compare the two amounts.

Look Back

A correct response demonstrates the ability to know how to make change, and how to compare and order money amounts. (See scoring rubric on page 7.)

Chapter 2 – Monitoring Student Progress

☐ **Form A** ☐ **Form B**

Name ____________________ Date ____________

Directions: For each item that is answered incorrectly, cross out the item number. Then record the number of correct responses in the appropriate Student Score column. If the student has not met the Criterion Score for an objective, circle the student's score. Recommended assignments are listed in the Prescription Table on the next page.

Objective	Item Numbers	Criterion Score	Student Score
A. Count money and make change.	1, 3, 5, 6, 7, 10, 12, 14	7/8	/8
B. Compare, order, and round whole numbers and money.	2, 4, 8, 9, 11, 13, 15, 16	7/8	/8
C. Use skills and strategies to solve problems	17, 18, 19, 20	3/4	/4
Total Test Score		17/20	/20
Total Percent Correct			%

Chapter 2 – Prescription Table

The following chart correlates the tested objectives for this chapter to supplementary materials that meet the individual needs of the students. The Reteach and Practice pages are designed for students who need further instruction in the math concepts taught in this chapter. The Enrich pages are designed for students who need advanced challenges.

Objective	Reteach	Practice	Enrich
A. Count money and make change.	19	20	21
B. Compare, order, and round whole numbers and money.	22, 25	23, 26	24, 27
C. Use skills and strategies to solve problems.	28, 29	30	

Name ______________________________

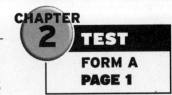

Read each question carefully. Darken the circle on your answer sheet for the correct answer.

1. Find the amount of change.

Price: $2.68
Amount given: $5.00

A. $2.32 **C.** $2.68
B. $2.38 **D.** $3.32

2. Round to the nearest hundred thousand.

8,361,319

F. 8,300,000 **H.** 8,361,300
G. 8,361,000 **J.** 8,400,000

3. Find the amount of change.

Price: $0.79
Amount given: $1.00

A. $0.21 **C.** $1.21
B. $0.31 **D.** $1.79

4. Round $172.52 to the nearest dollar.

F. $170.00 **H.** $173.00
G. $172.00 **J.** $180.00

5. Find the amount of change.

Price: $3.24
Amount given: $10.00

A. $6.76 **C.** $7.86
B. $7.76 **D.** $13.24

6. How much money is shown?

F. $2.35 **H.** $6.30
G. $6.35 **J.** $10.35

7. Find the amount of change.

Price: $3.39
Amount given: $5.00

A. $0.61 **C.** $1.61
B. $0.71 **D.** $1.71

8. Round to the nearest million.

80,830,485

F. 79,000,000 **H.** 81,000,000
G. 80,000,000 **J.** 90,000,000

9. Which digit makes the sentence true?

$43,273.48 > $43,2  3.48

A. 9 **B.** 8 **C.** 7 **D.** 6

10. Find the amount of change.

Price: $4.03
Amount given: $10.00

F. $5.97 **H.** $6.07
G. $6.03 **J.** $6.97

GO ON

Name ____________________

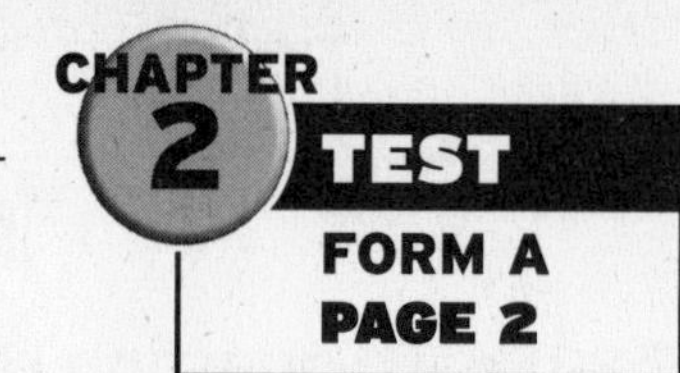

11. Round $19.38 to the nearest ten cents.

A. $19.30 **C.** $20.38
B. $19.40 **D.** $20.40

12. Find the amount of change.

Price: $0.68
Amount given: $1.00

F. $0.32 **H.** $1.32
G. $0.42 **J.** $1.42

13. Which digit makes the sentence true?

$23,581.27 = $23,5 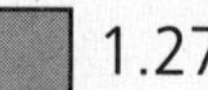 1.27

A. 9 **B.** 8 **C.** 7 **D.** 6

14. How much money is shown?

F. $3.35 **H.** $7.35
G. $3.40 **J.** $7.40

15. Round $3,089.56 to the nearest dollar.

A. $3,089.00 **C.** $3,090.00
B. $3,089.60 **D.** $3,090.60

16. Which digit makes the sentence true?

$68,84 ▢ .38 < $68,842.38

F. 4 **G.** 3 **H.** 2 **J.** 1

17. Kai bought a DVD for $12.75. She paid with a $20.00 bill. How much change will she receive?

A. $7.25 **C.** $8.25
B. $7.35 **D.** $8.35

18. Rusty, David, Arnold, and Jules each play a different musical instrument; either drums, bass, keyboards, or guitar. Rusty plays drums. Jules doesn't play drums or bass. David plays guitar. What instrument does Arnold play?

F. drums **H.** keyboards
G. bass **J.** guitar

19. Jody buys a breakfast meal for $4.72. She pays with a $10.00 bill. How much change does she receive?

A. $5.28 **C.** $5.38
B. $6.38 **D.** $6.72

20. Kelly buys a package of guitar strings for $5.95. Lester pays $6.05 in a second store. Marian pays $4.25 in a third store. Wendell pays $5.45 in a fourth store. Who paid the least?

F. Kelly **H.** Marian
G. Lester **J.** Wendell

STOP

Name ____________________

Read each question carefully. Fill in the correct answer in the space provided.

1. Find the amount of change.

Price: $7.63
Amount given: $10.00

______

2. Round to the nearest hundred thousand.

9,513,572

______

3. Find the amount of change.

Price: $0.71
Amount given: $1.00

______

4. Round $381.25 to the nearest dollar.

______

5. Find the amount of change.

Price: $3.44
Amount given: $20.00

______

6. How much money is shown?

______

7. Find the amount of change.

Price: $3.92
Amount given: $5.00

______

8. Round to the nearest million.

78,538,188

______

9. Which symbol makes the sentence true: < , > , or = ?

$84,371.08  $84, 471.08

______

10. Find the amount of change.

Price: $7.22
Amount given: $10.00

______

GO ON

Name ______________________

CHAPTER 2 TEST
FORM B
PAGE 2

11. Round $53.28 to the nearest ten cents.

______

12. Find the amount of change.

Price: $0.39

Amount given: $1.00

______

13. Which symbol makes the sentence true: <, >, or = ?

$58,150.79 ⬤ $58,150.79

______

14. How much money is shown?

______

15. Round $875.37 to the nearest dollar.

______

16. Which symbol makes the sentence true: <, >, or = ?

$43,238.16 ⬤ $46,238.16

______

17. Julia bought a book for $13.95. She paid with a $20.00 bill. How much change will she receive?

______

18. Una, Trent, Frank, and Michael each have a different favorite color; either blue, green, purple, or orange. Una likes orange. Frank doesn't like green or purple. Michael likes green. What is Trent's favorite color?

______

19. Oliver buys a comic book for $3.29. He pays with a $10.00 bill. How much change does he receive?

______

20. Harry buys a computer program for $18.89. Jack pays $17.55 in a second store. Gina pays $18.67 in a third store. Misty pays $16.99 in a fourth store. Who paid the most?

______

STOP

Unit 1 Performance Assessment

Supersize My Numbers!

- ***Target Skill:*** Compare and order whole numbers.
- ***Additional Skills:*** Read and write whole numbers in millions.

Task Description: This task requires students to write numbers from thousands to hundred millions by using a number cube and a spinner. The students then compare numbers at the end of each round, write the word name for the greater number, and then order the numbers at the end of the game.

Preparing: You may want to review the concept of place value with students. Have the students make the 0–9 spinner and the 4–9 number cube before starting.

Materials	Group Size	Time on Task
Spinner Number cube	2 to 4 students	1–2 days

Guiding: Remind students that to compare numbers, start with the greatest place and if that number is the same, move to the next greatest place.

Observing/ Monitoring: As you move among the students, pose the following questions:
What strategy did you use to place the numbers?
How can you compare numbers that have the same number of places?

Unit 1 Performance Assessment Scoring Rubric

Supersize My Numbers!

Score	Explanation
3	Students demonstrate an efficient strategy and a thorough approach that enables them to solve the problem completely. A satisfactory answer: • shows a knowledge of where to place numbers during the game; • writes all of the word names for the numbers; • correctly orders the numbers at the end of the game from least to greatest. Students are able to complete the problem quickly and have all of the above correct solutions.
2	Students demonstrate a strategy that enables them to solve most of the problem correctly. The strategy is somewhat disorganized, making it less efficient. A solution is found but errors are contained. Students may: • not have compared and ordered all of the numbers correctly; • write most of the word names correctly; • display a strategy for making the greatest number possible. Students may have some difficulty determining all solutions correctly but demonstrate an understanding of general concepts.
1	Students demonstrate a confused strategy, which leads to difficulty solving the problem. Most answers are incorrect, but students demonstrate knowledge of at least one concept being assessed. Students may: • write some of the word names correctly; OR • order numbers with a different number of places correctly.

Name ____

Unit 1 Performance Assessment Student Activity

Supersize My Numbers!

You will need
- 0–9 spinner
- index cards
- 4–9 number cube

Play with a partner.

1. Toss the number cube. The number that is tossed is the number of places in your number. On your score card, shade in the places you will not need. A sample card for a toss is shown below.

Beth							■	■	■
Sanjay								■	■

Number word name: ____________________________

2. Take turns spinning the spinner. Place the number that is spun in one of the places of your number.

   In the sample card, Beth tossed a 6, and Sanjay tossed a 7. Beth spun a 4. She decided to place the 4 in the hundreds place.

3. Repeat until the cards are filled. The player who makes the greater number can write the word name of the number. Each correctly written word name is worth 1 point.

4. Repeat. Play until someone has 3 points.

5. Record all the numbers that you make at the end of a round on a separate sheet of paper. Order them from least to greatest.

Unit I – Monitoring Student Progress

☐ Form A ☐ Form B

Name ______________________________ Date ________________

Directions: This test targets selected objectives. For each item that is answered incorrectly, cross out the item number. Then record the number of correct responses in the column labeled **Number of Correct Responses.** Add to find the **Total Number of Correct Responses** and record the total. Use this total to determine the **Total Test Score** and the **Total Percent Correct.**

Strand • Objective(s)	Item Numbers	Number of Correct Responses
Number Sense, Concepts, and Operations • Use benchmark numbers. • Read and write whole numbers in millions. • Compare, order, and round whole numbers and money. • Use skills and strategies to solve problems.	1, 2, 4, 5, 6, 7, 8, 10, 11, 12, 13, 16, 17, 18, 19, 21, 22, 24, 25, 26, 27, 29, 30, 31, 32, 33, 36, 37, 38, 39	/30
Measurement • Count money and make change. • Use skills and strategies to solve problems.	3, 9, 14, 15, 20, 23, 28, 34, 35, 40	/10
Total Number of Correct Responses		
Total Test Score		/40
Total Percent Correct		%

Name ____________________

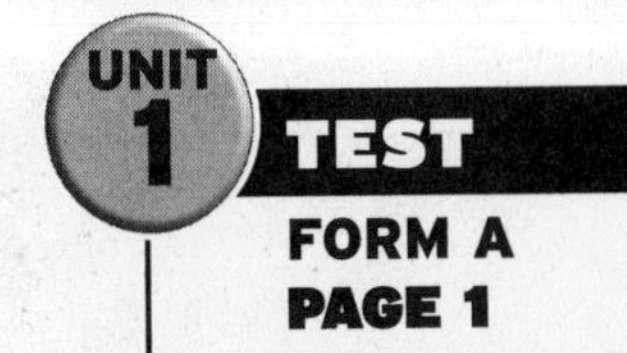

Read each question carefully. Darken the circle on your answer sheet for the correct answer.

1. What is the standard form of six million, three hundred eighteen thousand, forty-five?

A. 6,318,045 **C.** 60,318,045
B. 6,318,405 **D.** 603,018,045

---

2. Order from greatest to least.

21,214; 21,700; 20,549

F. 20,549; 21,214; 21,700
G. 21,700; 20,549; 21,214
H. 21,700; 21,214; 20,549
J. 21,214; 21,700; 20,549

---

3. Find the amount of change.

Price: $3.48
Amount given: $5.00

A. $1.52 **C.** $2.58
B. $2.48 **D.** $2.62

---

4. What is the standard form of fifty-nine million, thirty-six thousand, one hundred two?

F. 59,036,102 **H.** 59,306,102
G. 59,036,120 **J.** 59,360,102

---

5. Which symbol makes the sentence true?

15,741  15,471

A. = **B.** > **C.** < **D.** +

---

6. Estimate the number of sheets in the right stack using the left stack as a benchmark?

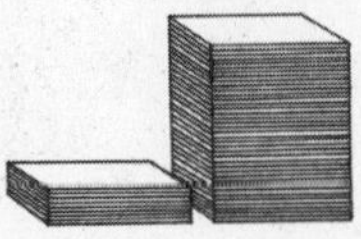

100 sheets

F. 200 sheets **H.** 1000 sheets
G. 500 sheets **J.** 1500 sheets

---

7. What is the standard form?

800,000 + 400 + 50 + 2

A. 8,452 **C.** 804,052
B. 800,452 **D.** 800,000,452

---

8. Round to the nearest hundred thousand.

7,351,426

F. 7,000,000 **H.** 7,400,000
G. 7,300,000 **J.** 8,000,000

---

9. Find the amount of change.

Price: $0.89
Amount given: $1.00

A. $0.11 **C.** $1.11
B. $0.21 **D.** $1.89

---

10. Which symbol makes the sentence true?

466,127  466,127

F. = **G.** > **H.** < **J.** +

Name ____

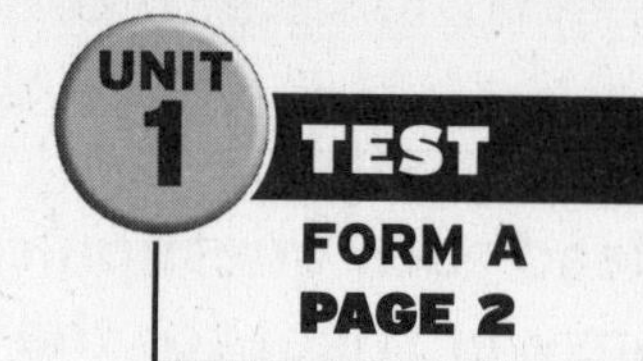

11. What is the standard form?

70,000,000 + 500,000 + 90,000 + 1,000 + 10 + 5

A. 759,115 **C.** 70,591,015
B. 7,591,105 **D.** 700,591,015

12. Which has the least value?
5,309,493; 5,300,000; 5,298,001; 5,310,017

F. 5,298,001 **H.** 5,309,493
G. 5,300,017 **J.** 5,310,000

13. Round $185.62 to the nearest dollar.
A. $180.00 **C.** $186.00
B. $185.00 **D.** $190.00

14. Find the amount of change.
Price: $1.27
Amount given: $10.00

F. $8.73 **H.** $9.83
G. $9.73 **J.** $11.27

15. How much money is shown?

A. $1.45 **C.** $5.50
B. $5.45 **D.** $10.45

16. Which digit makes the sentence true?
5,882 < 5,8  2

F. 6 **G.** 7 **H.** 8 **J.** 9

Solve.
Use the tally chart for problems 17–18.

This tally chart shows students' favorite ways of getting to school.

Favorite Way of Going to School	
Bike	𝍸
Walk	||||
In-line Skate	𝍸 |

17. Which way of going to school got the least votes?

A. bike **C.** in-line skates
B. walk **D.** bike and walk (tied)

18. How many chose in-line skates as their favorite way of going to school?
F. 4 students **H.** 6 students
G. 5 students **J.** 7 students

19. Dictionary W has 619 pages and Dictionary X has 594 pages. Dictionary Y has 835 pages and Dictionary Z has 1,023 pages. Which dictionary has the least number of pages?
A. W **B.** X **C.** Y **D.** Z

20. Toni buys a sandwich for $3.58. She pays with a $10.00 bill. How much change does she receive?
F. $6.42 **H.** $7.42
G. $6.58 **J.** $7.58

Name ______________________________

UNIT 1 TEST
FORM A
PAGE 3

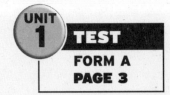

21. What is the standard form of two million, forty-six thousand, seven hundred one?

A. 2,046,071 **C.** 2,460,710
B. 2,046,701 **D.** 246,000,701

22. Order from least to greatest.

$116.79; $108.50; $120.39

F. $108.50; $116.79; $120.39
G. $108.50; $120.39; $116.79
H. $120.39; $108.50; $116.79
J. $116.79; $120.39; $108.50

23. Find the amount of change.

Price: $4.59
Amount given: $5.00

A. $0.41 **C.** $1.41
B. $0.51 **D.** $1.51

24. What is the standard form of eighty million, five hundred thousand, one hundred thirty-nine?

F. 85,139 **H.** 80,500,139
G. 8,500,139 **J.** 80,501,039

25. Round to the nearest dollar.

$61.63

A. $62.60 **C.** $61.60
B. $62.00 **D.** $61.00

26. What is the standard form of 3,000,000 + 70,000 + 3,000 + 10 + 1?

F. 37,311 **H.** 3,073,011
G. 301,311 **J.** 3,073,101

27. Round to the nearest million.

20,720,685

A. 19,000,000 **C.** 21,000,000
B. 20,000,000 **D.** 30,000,000

28. Find the amount of change.

Price: $6.03
Amount given: $10.00

F. $3.97 **H.** $4.07
G. $4.03 **J.** $4.97

29. Which symbol makes the sentence true?

8,422,611  8,471,906

A. = **B.** < **C.** > **D.** +

30. What is the standard form of 400,000,000 + 90,000,000 + 800,000 + 700 + 50 + 6?

F. 498,756 **H.** 4,908,756
G. 4,098,756 **J.** 490,800,756

31. Which has the least value?

$55.00; $54.99; $54.51; $54.12

A. $54.99 **C.** $54.12
B. $55.00 **D.** $54.51

Name ______________________________

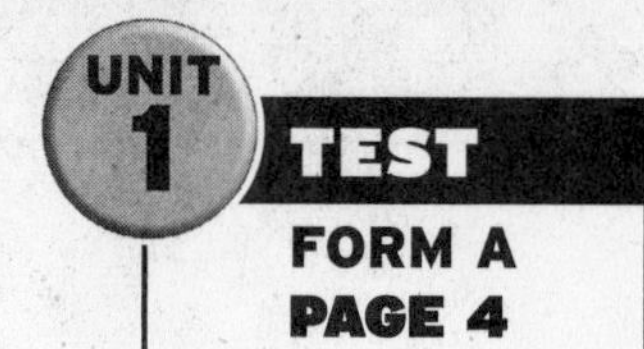

32. Which has the greatest value?

$23.55; $23.61; $22.29; $23.00

F. $23.55 **H.** $23.61
G. $23.00 **J.** $22.29

---

33. Round $49.17 to the nearest ten cents.

A. $49.10 **C.** $49.20
B. $50.17 **D.** $50.20

---

34. Find the amount of change.
Price: $0.42
Amount given: $1.00

F. $0.48 **H.** $1.42
G. $0.58 **J.** $1.58

---

35. How much money is shown?

A. $ 3.35 **C.** $12.40
B. $12.35 **D.** $30.35

---

36. Which symbol makes the sentence true?

$512.35  $511.55

F. = **G.** < **H.** > **J.** +

Solve.
Use the tally chart for problems 37–38.

This tally chart shows students' pets.

Pets Students Own	
Cat	𝍷𝍷𝍷𝍷
Dog	𝍸
Fish	𝍷𝍷𝍷
Bird	𝍷𝍷

37. Which pet is owned by the least number of students?

A. cat **B.** dog **C.** fish **D.** bird

---

38. How many students own a dog?

F. 2 students **H.** 4 students
G. 3 students **J.** 5 students

---

39. Maria saw a CD on sale in 4 stores. The prices of the CD were: $12.69 at Acme; $11.39 at Ben's; $11.91 at CD Heaven; and $12.05 at Downtown. What store charged the least amount for the CD?

A. Acme **C.** CD Heaven
B. Ben's **D.** Downtown

---

40. Casey bought a book for $15.65. He paid with a $20.00 bill. How much change will he receive?

F. $4.35 **H.** $5.35
G. $4.45 **J.** $5.45

STOP

Name ____________________

UNIT 1 **TEST** FORM B PAGE 1

Read each question carefully. Fill in the correct answer in the space provided.

1. What is the standard form of three million, four hundred twelve thousand, and fifty-four?

____

2. Order from greatest to least.

34,440; 25,440; 34,611

____

3. Find the amount of change.
Price: $8.67
Amount given: $10.00

____

4. What is the standard form of forty-two million, fifty-seven thousand, three hundred six?

____

5. Which symbol makes the sentence true?

24,506 ● 24,506

____

Use the diagram for item 6.

6. Estimate the amount of water in the right glass using the left glass as a benchmark.

____

7. What is the standard form of 700,000 + 4000 + 300 + 5?

____

8. Round to the nearest thousand.

16,543,788

____

9. Find the amount of change.
Price: $2.14
Amount given: $5.00

____

10. Which symbol makes the sentence true?

322,989 ● 321,899

____

GO ON

Name ______________________________

11. What is the standard form of 90,000,000 + 300,000 + 40,000 + 2,000 + 20 + 7?

____

12. Which has the least value?

235,899; 250,032; 235,143; 241,887

____

13. Round $236.43 to the nearest dollar.

____

14. Find the amount of change.
Price: $0.65
Amount given: $1.00

____

15. How much money is shown?

____

16. Which symbol makes the sentence true?

61,503  61,403

____

Use the tally chart for items 17–18.

The tally chart shows students' favorite meals at the cafeteria.

Favorite Meals at School

Meals	Tally
Pizza	𝍸 II
Cheeseburgers	𝍸 I
Spaghetti	III
Tuna Sandwiches	II

17. Which meal got the least votes?

____

18. How many chose pizza as their favorite meal?

____

19. John has 432 pennies, George has 428 pennies, Rico has 576 pennies, and Paul has 711 pennies. Who has the least number of pennies?

____

20. Jill buys a lunch that costs $3.92. She pays with a $20.00 bill. How much change should she receive?

____

GO ON

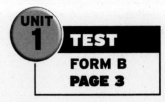

21. What is the standard form of six million, seventy-eight thousand, four hundred ninety-three?

___

22. Order from least to greatest.

$92.88; $90.67; $90.82

___

23. Find the amount of change.
Price: $5.65
Amount given: $10.00

___

24. What is the standard form of sixty-two million, seven hundred four thousand, two hundred eleven?

___

25. Round to the nearest dollar.

$5.88

___

26. What is the standard form of 5,000,000 + 40,000 + 6,000 + 20 + 7?

___

27. Round to the nearest million.

46,710,034

___

28. Find the amount of change.
Price: $1.34
Amount given: $2.00

___

29. Which symbol makes the sentence true?

14,675,423 ⬤ 4,675,324

___

30. What is the standard form of 900,000,000 + 30,000,000 + 600,000 + 3000 + 200 + 70 + 5?

___

GO ON

Name ______________________________

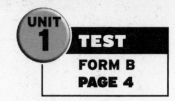

31. Which has the least value?
$81.91; $82.00; $81.22; $81.89

____

32. Which has the greatest value?
$37.88; $35.98; $34.05; $37.92

____

33. Round $67.28 to the nearest ten cents.

____

34. Find the amount of change.
Price: $0.88
Amount given: $1.00

____

35. How much money is shown?

____

36. Which symbol makes the sentence true?
$78.99 ◯ $79.12

____

Use the tally chart for items 37–38.

The tally chart shows students' favorite seasons.

Favorite Seasons

Seasons	Tally
Winter	//
Spring	~~////~~
Summer	~~////~~ ////
Fall	////

37. Which season is the favorite of the most students?

____

38. How many students chose fall as their favorite season?

____

39. Julia saw a CD on sale in 4 stores. The prices on the CD were $14.66 at Acme; $13.88 at Carey's; $15.22 at CD Basement; and $14.12 at Uptown. Which store charged the least amount for the CD?

____

40. Johnny bought a book for $13.52. He paid with a $20.00 bill. How much change will he receive?

____

STOP

Chapter 3 – Teacher Interview

Core Concept: ***Addition and Subtraction***

Student Activity: Students demonstrate an understanding of addition facts and regrouping. Assign an addition problem such as 697 + 2,340.

Teacher Question 1:

- How would you set up this addition problem?

Understanding Student Response	Practice and Improvement
Students who set it up as shown. 6 97 + 2,340	Review lesson 4 to help students learn addition with different place values.

Teacher Question 2:

- What is the sum of 697 + 2,340?

Understanding Student Response	Practice and Improvement
Students who say 2,917.	Review lesson 4 to help students with the steps in regrouping.
Students who say 2,017.	Review lesson 4 to help students with the steps in regrouping.
Students with sums other than the above sums.	Review lesson 2 to help students review addition properties.

Chapter 3 – Journal Writing

Encourage students to generate their own journal entries related to math ideas in general or to concepts in this chapter. For students requiring guidance, present the following journal prompt:

- How can knowing the Commutative and Associative Properties of Addition help you to add sums?

  (Responses should mention that the Associative Property allows you to find tens to simplify addition; the Commutative Property allows you to regroup addends.)

JOURNAL WRITING/PROBLEM SOLVING

The Salt Brook School's Earth Club has 113 members in grade 4, and 149 members in grades 1 to 3. If there are a total of 217 members in grades 5 and 6, how many club members are there in grades 4 to 6? How many club members are there in grades 1 to 6?

Read

Have students find the answer to the problem. Then ask them to write a few sentences telling —

- how they organized the information
- which properties of addition they used

Have students make up another problem with different information for which they would have to follow the same procedure. Then have students solve the problem and supply the correct response.

Plan

Students must know how to arrange the information to give them the correct response for each grouping of grades, and must know how to use the Associative Property of Addition to regroup to find the sum.

Solve

The correct responses are 330 members in grades 4 to 6, and 479 members in grades 1 to 6. Students had to be able to combine the correct number of members in each grouping of grades and be able to add 3-digit numbers correctly.

Look Back

A correct response demonstrates the ability to organize the information correctly, and to use the Associative and Commutative Properties to regroup addends properly and do the sum. (See scoring rubric on page 7.)

Chapter 3 – Monitoring Student Progress

☐ **Form A** ☐ **Form B**

Name ______________________ Date ______________

Directions: For each item that is answered incorrectly, cross out the item number. Then record the number of correct responses in the appropriate Student Score column. If the student has not met the Criterion Score for an objective, circle the student's score. Recommended assignments are listed in the Prescription Table on the next page.

Objective	Item Numbers	Criterion Score	Student Score
A. Write and solve addition expressions and solve equations.	1, 6, 11	2/3	/3
B. Use patterns and properties of addition.	2, 7, 12	2/3	/3
C. Estimate sums.	3, 8, 13, 16,	3/4	/4
D. Add whole numbers and money amounts.	4, 5, 9, 10, 14, 15	5/6	/6
E. Use skills and strategies to solve problems.	17, 18, 19, 20	3/4	/4
Total Test Score		15/20	/20
Total Percent Correct			%

Chapter 3 – Prescription Table

The following chart correlates the tested objectives for this chapter to supplementary materials that meet the individual needs of the students. The Reteach and Practice pages are designed for students who need further instruction in the math concepts taught in this chapter. The Enrich pages are designed for students who need advanced challenges.

Objective	Reteach	Practice	Enrich
A. Write and solve addition expressions and solve equations.	33	34	35
B. Use patterns and properties of addition.	36, 39	37, 40	38, 41
C. Estimate sums.	48	49	50
D. Add whole numbers and money amounts.	42	43	44
E. Use skills and strategies to solve problems.	45, 51	46, 52	47, 53

Name ______________________________

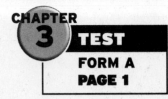

Read each question carefully. Darken the circle on your answer sheet for the correct answer.

1. Find the value of the expression.

$18 + d$ for $d = 4$

A. 4 **C.** 18
B. 14 **D.** 22

---

2. What number makes the sentence true?

$38 + x = 63$

F. 23 **H.** 33
G. 25 **J.** 38

---

3. Which is the best estimate?

39,829 + 7,457

A. 40,000 **C.** 47,000
B. 41,000 **D.** 50,000

---

4. $\begin{array}{r} \$4.78 \\ +\ 3.62 \\ \hline \end{array}$

F. \$7.30 **H.** \$8.30
G. \$7.40 **J.** \$8.40

---

5. $\begin{array}{r} 5{,}462 \\ -\ 875 \\ \hline \end{array}$

A. 4,587 **C.** 4,697
B. 4,687 **D.** 5,697

---

6. Find the value of the expression.

$23 + g$ for $g = 12$

F. 35 **H.** 12
G. 23 **J.** 11

---

7. What number makes the sentence true?

$43 + z = 76$

A. 43 **C.** 33
B. 36 **D.** 23

---

8. Which is the best estimate?

419,926 + 208,837

F. 400,000 **H.** 600,000
G. 500,000 **J.** 700,000

---

9. $\begin{array}{r} \$35{,}326 \\ +\ \ 3{,}908 \\ \hline \end{array}$

A. \$38,224 **C.** \$39,234
B. \$38,234 **D.** \$39,324

---

10. $\begin{array}{r} 316{,}077 \\ +\ 44{,}841 \\ \hline \end{array}$

F. 350,818 **H.** 360,818
G. 356,918 **J.** 360,918

GO ON

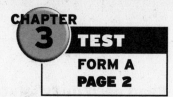

11. Find the value of the expression.

$56 + k$ for $k = 37$

A. 37 **B.** 56 **C.** 83 **D.** 93

12. What number makes the sentence true?

$28 + c = 61$

F. 89 **G.** 43 **H.** 33 **J.** 29

13. Which is the best estimate?

$26.39 + $17.92

A. $30.00 **C.** $50.00
B. $40.00 **D.** $60.00

14. $226.85
+ 156.33

F. $36.14 **H.** $383.18
G. $372.18 **J.** $472.18

15. 792,082
+ 116,474

A. 808,556 **C.** 908,556
B. 908,456 **D.** 918,556

16. Which is the best estimate?

174,456 + 597,006

F. 600,000 **H.** 800,000
G. 700,000 **J.** 900,000

17. Rob had 26 model cars in his collection. He built another 16 models. How many model cars did he have then? Choose the number sentence that shows how to solve this problem.

A. $42 + 16 = 58$ models
B. $26 + 16 = 42$ models
C. $26 - 16 = 10$ models
D. $42 - 16 = 26$ models

18. An ice cream parlor has 18 tables outside and 24 tables inside. How many tables does it have altogether? Choose the number sentence that shows how to solve this problem.

F. $24 - 18 = 6$ tables
G. $18 + 24 = 32$ tables
H. $18 + 42 = 60$ tables
J. $24 + 18 = 42$ tables

19. Lucy bought a skirt for $13.19 and socks for $8.29. About how much did she spend?

A. $10 **B.** $15 **C.** $20 **D.** $25

20. Henrietta bought a shirt for $20.99 and a hat for $11.05. How much did she spend altogether?

F. $3.24 **H.** $32.04
G. $9.94 **J.** $32.90

STOP

Name ______________________________

CHAPTER 3 TEST
FORM B
PAGE 1

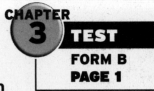

Read each question carefully. Fill in the correct answer in the space provided.

1. Find the value of the expression.

$52 + j$ for $j = 19$

____

2. Write the number that makes the sentence true.

$64 + x = 81$

____

3. Estimate.

74,581 + 9,805

____

4.

$$\begin{array}{r} \$7.62 \\ +\ 5.76 \\ \hline \end{array}$$

5.

$$\begin{array}{r} 5,927 \\ +\ 785 \\ \hline \end{array}$$

6. Find the value of the expression.

$49 + r$ for $r = 32$

____

7. Solve for p.

$51 + p = 94$

____

8. Estimate.

438,135 + 487,180

____

9.

$$\begin{array}{r} \$67,109 \\ +\ 6,710 \\ \hline \end{array}$$

10.

$$\begin{array}{r} 517,008 \\ +\ 53,938 \\ \hline \end{array}$$

GO ON

Name ______________________________

CHAPTER 3 TEST
FORM B
PAGE 2

11. Find the value of the expression.

$29 + y$ for $y = 52$

____

12. Solve for e.

$74 + e = 89$

____

13. Estimate.

\$62.07 + \$28.95

____

14.

$$\begin{array}{r} \$521.18 \\ +\ 453.76 \\ \hline \end{array}$$

15.

$$\begin{array}{r} 445{,}554 \\ +\ 234{,}187 \\ \hline \end{array}$$

16. Estimate.

697,078 + 218,741

____

17. Greg had 26 pages of reading to do for his reading class on Monday. He also had to read 13 pages for his history class on Monday. How many total pages of reading did Greg have to do for Monday? Write a number sentence to solve.

____

18. Hal taught 33 students during his 6 o'clock martial arts class on Thursday. He also taught 29 students during his 7 o'clock class on Thursday. How many total students did he teach during the two classes? Write a number sentence to solve.

____

19. Melissa bought a backpack for \$18.74 and a set of 3-ring binders for \$8.67. About how much did she spend?

____

20. Jose spent 278 minutes working on his painting. After the artwork was finished, he spent 29 minutes framing it, and 11 minutes attaching picture wire so he could hang it. How many total minutes did Jose spend painting and preparing to hang his artwork?

____

STOP

Chapter 4 – Teacher Interview

Core Concept: *Subtraction*

Student Activity: Students demonstrate an understanding of subtraction facts and regrouping. Assign a subtraction problem such as 3,258 – 889.

Teacher Question 1:

- How would you use regrouping in this subtraction problem?

Understanding Student Response	Practice and Improvement
Students who say that regrouping is not necessary.	Review lesson 3 to help students learn the steps involved in regrouping.
Students give some of the places that need regrouping, but not all of them.	Review lesson 3 to help students review the steps involved in regrouping.

Teacher Question 2:

- What is the difference of 3,258 – 889?

Understanding Student Response	Practice and Improvement
Students who say 2,000 or 2,400.	Review lesson 3 to help students subtract multi-digit numbers.
Students who give an incorrect answer because of a failure to regroup.	Review lesson 3 to help students review the steps involved in regrouping.
Students who give an incorrect answer because of a computation error.	Review lesson 3 to help the student practice subtracting multi-digit numbers.

Chapter 4 – Journal Writing

Encourage students to generate their own journal entries related to math ideas in general or to concepts in this chapter. For students requiring guidance, present the following journal prompt:

- When you estimate in a subtraction problem, why is it important to use rounding? Why is estimating useful when subtracting with greater numbers?

  (Responses should include the concept that rounding enables us to get a quick estimate of the difference in a subtraction problem which is helpful with greater numbers.)

JOURNAL WRITING/PROBLEM SOLVING

Blue Mountain Middle School had 5,392 students. There were 2,914 students in the 5th grade. Estimate the number of students in the remaining grades.

Read

Have students find the answer to the problem. Then ask them to write a few sentences telling—

- how they used rounding in this problem
- how rounding made solving the problem easier

Have students make up another problem with different information for which they would have to follow the same procedure. Then have students solve the problem and supply the correct response.

Plan

Students must know how to round both numbers to the greatest place value, and remember to subtract and compute correctly.

Solve

The correct response to the assigned problem is 2,000. Students had to round both numbers to the greatest place value. Then they had to subtract these numbers correctly.

Look Back

A correct response demonstrates the ability to know how to round numbers to the greatest place value and subtract these rounded numbers correctly. (See scoring rubric on page 7.)

Chapter 4 – Monitoring Student Progress

☐ **Form A** ☐ **Form B**

Name ______________________ Date ______________

Directions: For each item that is answered incorrectly, cross out the item number. Then record the number of correct responses in the appropriate Student Score column. If the student has not met the Criterion Score for an objective, circle the student's score. Recommended assignments are listed in the Prescription Table on the next page.

Objective	Item Numbers	Criterion Score	Student Score
A. Write and solve subtraction expressions and solve equations.	8, 11	1/2	/2
B. Use patterns of subtraction.	2, 6	1/2	/2
C. Estimate differences.	1, 3, 7, 13, 15	4/5	/5
D. Subtract whole numbers and money amounts.	4, 5, 9, 10, 12, 14	5/6	/6
E. Use skills and strategies to solve problems.	16, 17, 18, 19, 20	4/5	/5
Total Test Score		15/20	/20
Total Percent Correct			%

Chapter 4 – Prescription Table

The following chart correlates the tested objectives for this chapter to supplementary materials that meet the individual needs of the students. The Reteach and Practice pages are designed for students who need further instruction in the math concepts taught in this chapter. The Enrich pages are designed for students who need advanced challenges.

Objective	Reteach	Practice	Enrich
A. Write and evaluate subtraction expressions and solve equations.	54	55	56
B. Use patterns of subtraction.	57	58	59
C. Estimate differences.	69	70	71
D. Subtract whole numbers and money amounts.	60	61	62
E. Use skills and strategies to solve problems.	63, 66, 72	64, 67, 73	65, 68, 74

Name ______________________________

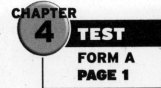

Read each question carefully. Darken the circle on your answer sheet for the correct answer.

1. Which is the best estimate?

561,426 − 238,705

A. 100,000 **C.** 300,000
B. 200,000 **D.** 400,000

2. Which number makes the sentence true?

600 − x = 300

F. 100 **H.** 300
G. 250 **J.** 200

3. Which is the best estimate?

$6.27 − $2.12

A. $2 **C.** $4
B. $3 **D.** $5

4. $34.68
− 17.92

F. $16.76 **H.** $27.76
G. $17.66 **J.** $52.60

5. 35,274
− 16,632

A. 18,642 **C.** 28,642
B. 19,642 **D.** 29,642

6. Which number makes the sentence true?

16,000 − 2,000 = g

F. 18,000 **H.** 4,000
G. 14,000 **J.** 21,400

7. Which is the best estimate?

9,003 − 2,941

A. 6,000 **C.** 8,000
B. 7,000 **D.** 9,000

8. Solve for y.

68 − y = 24

F. 92 **H.** 44
G. 86 **J.** 32

9. $75,503
− 44,726

A. $30,777 **C.** $31,777
B. $30,887 **D.** $31,887

10. 230,625
− 103,941

F. 126,624 **H.** 127,784
G. 126,684 **J.** 127,984

GO ON

Name ___________________________

11. Solve for *b*.

$37 - b = 9$

A. 19 **B.** 28 **C.** 39 **D.** 48

---

12. 635
− 386

F. 349 **G.** 319 **H.** 249 **J.** 239

---

13. Which is the best estimate?
$7.19 − $2.83

A. $6.00 **C.** $5.00
B. $4.00 **D.** $7.00

---

14. $122.35
− 47.39

F. $185.06 **H.** $74.96
G. $75.04 **J.** $74.06

---

15. Which is the best estimate?
589,293 − 168,312

A. 300,000 **C.** 500,000
B. 400,000 **D.** 600,000

---

16. Nicole has 47 CDs. Petra has 85 CDs. How many more CDs does Petra have? Write a number sentence to solve.

F. 47 + 132 = 179 more CDs
G. 85 + 47 = 132 more CDs
H. 85 − 38 = 47 more CDs
J. 85 − 47 = 38 more CDs

---

17. Company A spent $145,890 on commercials. Company B spent $325,600 on commercials. How much more did Company B spend than Company A?

A. $179,710 **C.** $180,290
B. $179,810 **D.** $180,710

---

18. Last year Kate's sister was 52 inches tall. This year she is 61 inches tall. How much has she grown? Write a number sentence to solve.

F. 52 + 61 = 113 inches
G. 61 − 52 = 9 inches
H. 52 + 9 = 61 inches
J. 113 − 52 = 61 inches

---

19. Alec earned $67 mowing lawns. He spent $29. How much does he have left?

A. $48 **B.** $42 **C.** $38 **D.** $32

---

20. On Saturday, 14,215 people visited the park. On Sunday, 6,287 people visited the park. How many more people visited the park on Saturday than Sunday?

F. 8,928 people
G. 8,038 people
H. 8,072 people
J. 7,928 people

STOP

Name ___

CHAPTER 4 TEST
FORM B
PAGE 1

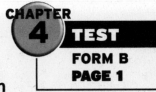

Read each question carefully. Fill in the correct answer in the space provided.

1. Estimate.

687,075 − 337,150

___

2. Solve for t.

$54 - t = 27$

___

3. Estimate.

$18.27 − $9.14

___

4. $98.06
− 39.47

5. 61,287
− 48,058

6. Solve for r.

$623 - r = 326$

___

7. Estimate.

28,501 − 6,076

___

8. Solve for p.

$85 - p = 32$

___

9. $76,075
− 63,842

10. 809,564
− 237,870

GO ON

Name ____________________

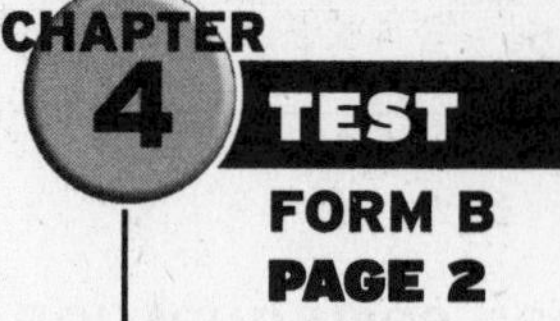

11. Solve for w.

$952 - w = 681$

____

12.
$$\begin{array}{r} 854 \\ -\ 385 \\ \hline \end{array}$$

13. Estimate.

\$68.39 – \$48.32

____

14.
$$\begin{array}{r} \$382.19 \\ -\ \ 89.27 \\ \hline \end{array}$$

15. Estimate.

933,567 – 794,250

____

16. Jesse has 89 baseball cards. Eric has 52 baseball cards. How many more baseball cards does Jesse have than Eric? Write a number sentence to solve.

____

17. Louie's Autos spent \$685,237 on new cars for January. Phil's Autos spent \$518,372 on new cars for January. How much more did Louie's Autos spend than Phil's Autos on new cars for January?

____

18. Last year there were 1,375 students in Alan's school. This year there are 1,526 students. How many more students are there this year? Write a number sentence to solve.

____

19. Mary has \$243 in her savings account. She withdraws \$87. How much does she have left in her account?

____

20. During opening week, 389,047 people bought tickets for the new movie "Vermont Getaway." During the movie's second week 241,283 people bought tickets. How many more people bought tickets for the movie during the opening week than the second week?

____

STOP

Unit 2 Performance Assessment

Setting Up the Home Office

- ***Target Skill:*** Add and subtract money amounts.
- ***Additional Skills:*** Use skills and strategies to solve problems.

Task Description: This task requires students to add and subtract sums to set up a home office.

Preparing: You may wish to have students work in pairs or alone. Discuss which operation they should use to find the amount spent so far and the amount left.

Materials	Group Size	Time on Task
Calculator (optional)	1 to 2 students	1 day

Guiding: Remind students to line up the decimal points when adding and subtracting money amounts.

Observing/ Monitoring: As you move among the students, pose the following questions:

How do you know you added the costs correctly?

How do you know you subtracted the costs correctly?

Unit 2 Performance Assessment Scoring Rubric

Setting Up the Home Office

Score	Explanation
3	Students demonstrate an efficient strategy and a thorough approach that enables them to solve the problem completely. A satisfactory answer: • correctly adds and subtracts all the sums and differences. Students are able to complete the problem quickly and have all of the above correct solutions.
2	Students demonstrate a strategy that enables them to solve most of the problem correctly. The strategy is somewhat disorganized, making it less efficient. A solution is found but errors are contained. Students may: • add correctly but not know how much money is left; • use an incorrect sum to correctly calculate the amount of money remaining. Students may have some difficulty determining all solutions correctly but demonstrate an understanding of general concepts.
1	Students demonstrate a confused strategy, which leads to difficulty solving the problem. Most answers are incorrect, but students demonstrate knowledge of at least one concept being assessed, such as adding or subtracting money amounts.

Name ______________________________

Unit 2 Performance Assessment Student Activity

Setting Up the Home Office

You will need
- calculator (optional)

You have $3,000 to spend to buy office supplies. The supplies are listed below.

Item	Cost
Laptop	$1,799.95
Software	$795.49
Printer	$289.99
Cables	$34.59
CDs	$29.99
Paper	$49.45

1. How much does the laptop and the software cost?

____

2. How much will be left over after buying the laptop and software?

____

3. What is the total cost of the remaining supplies?

____

4. How much will be left over after buying all the supplies?

____

Unit 2 – Monitoring Student Progress

☐ Form A ☐ Form B

Name ______________________ Date ______________

Directions: This test targets selected objectives. For each item that is answered incorrectly, cross out the item number. Then record the number of correct responses in the column labeled **Number of Correct Responses.** Add to find the **Total Number of Correct Responses** and record the total. Use this total to determine the **Total Test Score** and the **Total Percent Correct.**

Strand • Objective(s)	Item Numbers	Number of Correct Responses
Number Sense, Concepts, and Operations • Write and solve addition expressions and solve equations. • Use patterns and properties of addition. • Estimate sums. • Add whole numbers and money amounts. • Write and solve subtraction expressions and solve equations. • Estimate differences. • Use patterns of subtraction. • Subtract whole numbers and money amounts. • Use skills and strategies to solve problems.	1, 2, 3, 4, 5, 6, 7, 8, 9, 10, 11, 12, 13, 14, 15, 16, 17, 18, 19, 20, 21, 22, 23, 24, 25, 26, 27, 28, 29, 30, 31, 32, 33, 34, 35, 36, 37, 38, 39, 40	/40
Total Number of Correct Responses		
Total Test Score		/40
Total Percent Correct		%

Name ____________________

Read each question carefully. Darken the circle on your answer sheet for the correct answer.

1. 705 + 146 = ■

A. 841 **B.** 846 **C.** 851 **D.** 941

---

2. 9,808 − 563 = ■

F. 4,178 **H.** 9,345
G. 9,245 **J.** 9,365

---

3. 497 + 223 = ■

A. 274 **B.** 610 **C.** 700 **D.** 720

---

4. Which is the best estimate?

29,838 + 7,392

F. 30,000 **H.** 37,000
G. 31,000 **J.** 40,000

---

5. 563 − 309 = ■

A. 164 **B.** 254 **C.** 263 **D.** 264

---

6. $\begin{array}{r} 87{,}434 \\ -\ 73{,}852 \\ \hline \end{array}$

F. 13,582 **H.** 14,582
G. 14,422 **J.** 14,682

---

7. 912 − 682 = ■

A. 190 **C.** 330
B. 230 **D.** 390

---

8. 691 + 4,052 = ■

F. 1,043 **H.** 5,643
G. 4,743 **J.** 10,962

---

9. $\begin{array}{r} \$4.39 \\ +\ 2.82 \\ \hline \end{array}$

A. $1.57 **C.** $7.11
B. $6.11 **D.** $7.21

---

10. Which is the best estimate?

581,315 − 240,905

F. 100,000 **H.** 300,000
G. 200,000 **J.** 400,000

---

11. $\begin{array}{r} 6{,}442 \\ +\ 975 \\ \hline \end{array}$

A. 6,317 **C.** 7,317
B. 6,417 **D.** 7,417

---

12. $\begin{array}{r} \$45{,}316 \\ +\ 2{,}905 \\ \hline \end{array}$

F. $47,211 **H.** $48,221
G. $47,22 **J.** $48,311

---

13. $\begin{array}{r} 749{,}286 \\ -\ 672{,}477 \\ \hline \end{array}$

A. 76,809 **C.** 137,211
B. 77, 819 **D.** 177,819

GO ON

Name ______________________________

14. Which is the best estimate?

$4.37 − $1.52

F. $2 **H.** $6
G. $4 **J.** $7

15. $65.68 − 27.92

A. $37.76 **C.** $48.76
B. $42.36 **D.** $93.60

16. Which is the best estimate?

435,874 + 213,198

F. 400,000 **H.** 600,000
G. 500,000 **J.** 700,000

Solve.

17. A pizza parlor has 12 tables outside and 29 tables inside. How many tables does it have altogether? Write a number sentence to solve.

A. 29 − 12 = 17 tables
B. 12 + 29 = 41 tables
C. 12 + 31 = 43 tables
D. 29 + 31 = 60 tables

18. Tom has 56 channels with his cable TV service. Pedro has 95 channels with his cable TV service. How many more channels does Pedro have? Write a number sentence to solve.

F. 56 + 151 = 217 more channels
G. 95 + 56 = 151 more channels
H. 39 + 95 = 134 more channels
J. 95 − 56 = 39 more channels

19. Wen bought a shirt for $22.19 and socks for $5.59. About how much did he spend?

A. $6 **C.** $28
B. $17 **D.** $35

20. Company A spent $125,690 on computers. Company B spent $220,800 on computers. How much more money did Company B spend than Company A?

F. $95,110 **H.** $345,490
G. $95,210 **J.** $346,490

GO ON

Name ______________________________

TEST
FORM A
PAGE 3

21. 210 + 358 = ■

A. 148 **B.** 548 **C.** 568 **D.** 578

---

22. $181.35 – $65.39 = ■

F. $115.96 **H.** $126.06
G. $124.04 **J.** $246.74

---

23. 191 + 639 = ■

A. 720 **B.** 800 **C.** 830 **D.** 839

---

24. Which is the best estimate?

$27.59 + $18.64

F. $40.00 **H.** $50.00
G. $47.00 **J.** $55.00

---

25. 735 – 419 = ■

A. 316 **B.** 320 **C.** 324 **D.** 326

26.
$$\begin{array}{r} 320{,}865 \\ -\ 105{,}972 \\ \hline \end{array}$$

F. 214,893 **H.** 225,893
G. 225,113 **J.** 225,993

---

27. 822 – 578 = ■

A. 200 **C.** 244
B. 240 **D.** 254

28. 2,179 + 9,348 = ■

F. 11,417 **H.** 11,527
G. 11,517 **J.** 12,527

29.
$$\begin{array}{r} \$0.87 \\ +\ 0.75 \\ \hline \end{array}$$

A. $0.12 **C.** $1.52
B. $0.16 **D.** $1.62

---

30. Which is the best estimate?

9,126 – 2,873

F. 6,000 **H.** 8,000
G. 7,000 **J.** 9,000

31.
$$\begin{array}{r} 116{,}097 \\ +\ 14{,}821 \\ \hline \end{array}$$

A. 26,518 **C.** 130,818
B. 110,818 **D.** 130,918

32.
$$\begin{array}{r} \$209.66 \\ +\ 173.52 \\ \hline \end{array}$$

F. $36.14 **H.** $383.18
G. $372.18 **J.** $472.18

33.
$$\begin{array}{r} \$78{,}418 \\ -\ 42{,}549 \\ \hline \end{array}$$

A. $35,869 **C.** $36,879
B. $36,131 **D.** $36,979

GO ON

Name ____________________

34. Which is the best estimate?

$7.45 − $2.78

F. $4.00 **H.** $5.00
G. $6.00 **J.** $7.00

35.
$$\begin{array}{r} 609 \\ -\ 291 \\ \hline \end{array}$$

A. 318 **C.** 498
B. 418 **D.** 900

36. Which is the best estimate?

168,312 + 589,293

F. 600,000 **H.** 760,000
G. 700,000 **J.** 800,000

Solve.

37. Last year there were 42 teachers in Jan's school. This year there are 51 teachers. How many more teachers are there this year? Write a number sentence to solve.

A. 42 + 51 = 93 more teachers
B. 51 − 42 = 9 more teachers
C. 51 + 9 = 60 more teachers
D. 93 − 42 = 51 more teachers

38. Phil had 34 customers on his paper route. He took over another route with 18 customers. How many customers did he have then? Write a number sentence to solve.

F. 52 + 18 = 70 customers
G. 34 + 18 = 52 customers
H. 70 − 52 = 18 customers
J. 34 − 18 = 16 customers

39. Alana has $93 in her savings account. She withdraws $29. How much does she have left in her account?

A. $64 **C.** $76
B. $74 **D.** $122

40. On Friday the attendance at the stadium was 54,319. On Saturday the attendance was 41,768. How many people attended the games on Friday and Saturday?

F. 12,551 people
G. 95,077 people
H. 96,077 people
J. 96,087 people

STOP

Name ______________________________

UNIT 2 **TEST** FORM B PAGE 1

Read each question carefully. Fill in the correct answer in the space provided.

1. 643 + 119 = ____________

____

2. 6704 − 681 = ____________

____

3. 512 + 394 = ____________

____

4. Estimate.

39,221 + 6,156

____

____

5. 674 − 261 = ____________

6.
```
  42,564
− 21,783
```

____

7. 943 − 725 = ____________

____

8. 847 + 3,035 = ____________

____

9.
```
  $3.56
+  1.63
```

____

10. Estimate.

721,889 − 381,324

____

GO ON

Name ____________________

UNIT 2 TEST
FORM B
PAGE 2

11. $\begin{array}{r} 4{,}219 \\ +\ 454 \\ \hline \end{array}$

12. $\begin{array}{r} \$23{,}754 \\ +\ 7{,}182 \\ \hline \end{array}$

13. $\begin{array}{r} 563{,}215 \\ -\ 254{,}891 \\ \hline \end{array}$

14. Estimate.

$4.21 – $1.56

15. $\begin{array}{r} \$45.23 \\ -\ 21.76 \\ \hline \end{array}$

16. Estimate.

674,221 + 132,994

Solve.

17. A restaurant has 18 tables inside and 23 tables outside. How many tables does it have altogether? Write a number sentence to solve.

18. Wally has 27 channels with his cable TV service. Juan has 94 channels with his cable TV service. How many more channels does Juan have than Wally? Write a number sentence to solve.

19. Edwina bought a shirt for $24.65 and socks for $6.24. About how much did she spend?

20. Company A spent $43,870 on insurance. Company B spent $124,500 on insurance. How much more money did Company B spend than Company A?

GO ON

21. 429 + 324 = ____________

22. $213.75 − $87.47 = ____________

23. 167 + 543 = ____________

24. Estimate.

$42.23 + $19.87

____

25. 834 − 319 = ____________

26.

```
   523,841
 − 101,671
```

27. 722 − 551 = ____________

28. 4,213 + 9,541 = ____________

29.

```
   $0.74
 + $0.68
```

30. Estimate.

8,167 − 3,912

____

GO ON

Name ______________________________

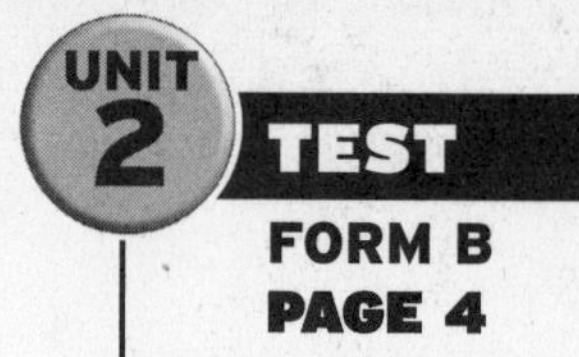

31. 167,710
+ 45,251

______

32. $277.23
+ 38.18

______

33. $67,670
− 26,190

______

34. Estimate.

$8.12 − $6.89

______

35. 861
− 237

______

36. Estimate.

219,012 + 623,561

______

Solve.

37. Last year there were 46 teachers in Ian's school. This year there are 54 teachers. How many more teachers are there this year? Write a number sentence to solve.

______

38. Jenny had 26 customers on her paper route. She took over another route with 17 customers. How many customers did she have then? Write a number sentence to solve.

______

39. Antoine had $78 dollars in his bank account. He withdrew $49. How much does he have left in his account?

______

40. On Friday the attendance at the stadium was 42,910. On Saturday the attendance was 56,132. What was the total attendance at the stadium on Friday and Saturday?

______

STOP

Chapter 5 – Teacher Interview

Core Concept: *Interpretation of Data*

Student Activity: Students demonstrate an understanding of the organization and interpretation of data given, such as the number of soccer goals scored by a team in its first five games: 1; 3; 2; 1; and 7.

Teacher Question 1:

- What is the range of this data?

Understanding Student Response	Practice and Improvement
Students who say 1 or 3.	Review lesson 4 to help students find the range of a set of data.
Students who say 7.	Review lesson 4 to help the student understand that the range is a measure of the difference between the greatest number and the least.

Teacher Question 2:

- How would you organize this data in a tally chart?

Understanding Student Response	Practice and Improvement
Students who don't think it's necessary to organize the raw data.	Review lesson 5 to help students summarize the data in a tally chart.

Teacher Question 3:

- In how many games did the team score only 1 goal?

Understanding Student Response	Practice and Improvement
Students who say once.	Review lesson 5 to help students organize their data better by using a tally chart.

Chapter 5 – Journal Writing

Encourage students to generate their own journal entries related to math ideas in general or to concepts in this chapter. For students requiring guidance, present the following journal prompt:

- When you are finding the median for a set of data, why is it important to organize your data? How can you find the middlemost piece of data?

  (Responses should include the concept of organizing the data in either ascending or descending order, with the goal being to discover the middlemost data.)

JOURNAL WRITING/PROBLEM SOLVING

Jill kept a record of the number of saves she made as goalie in her soccer games: 10, 6, 4, 5, and 7. What is the median number of saves that she made?

Read

Have students find the answer to the problem. Then ask them to write a few sentences telling—

- how they organized the data
- by what means they found the median

Have students make up another problem with different information for which they would have to follow the same procedure. Then have the students solve the problem and supply the correct response.

Plan

Students must be able to arrange their data in order, determine what would be the middlemost score, and correctly identify that number.

Solve

The correct response to the assigned problem is 6. Students had to arrange the data in order, and determine that the third number was the middlemost number of saves.

Look Back

A correct response demonstrates the ability to organize data in order, determine what is the middlemost number, and identify this number correctly. (See scoring rubric on page 7.)

Chapter 5 – Monitoring Student Progress

☐ **Form A** ☐ **Form B**

Name ______________________ Date ______________

Directions: For each item that is answered incorrectly, cross out the item number. Then record the number of correct responses in the appropriate Student Score column. If the student has not met the Criterion Score for an objective, circle the student's score. Recommended assignments are listed in the Prescription Table on the next page.

Objective	Item Numbers	Criterion Score	Student Score
A. Tell time and find elapsed time.	1, 4, 7, 8	3/4	/4
B. Find range, median, and mode.	5, 6, 11, 12, 13, 14, 15	6/7	/7
C. Collect and organize data.	2, 3, 9, 10	3/4	/4
D. Use skills and strategies to solve problems.	16, 17, 18, 19, 20	4/5	/5
Total Test Score		16/20	/20
Total Percent Correct			%

Chapter 5 – Prescription Table

The following chart correlates the tested objectives for this chapter to supplementary materials that meet the individual needs of the students. The Reteach and Practice pages are designed for students who need further instruction in the math concepts taught in this chapter. The Enrich pages are designed for students who need advanced challenges.

Objective	Reteach	Practice	Enrich
A. Tell time and find elapsed time.	76, 79, 82	77, 80, 83	78, 81, 84
B. Find range, median, and mode.	85	86	87
C. Collect and organize data.	88	89	90
D. Use skills and strategies to solve problems.	91	92	93

Name ____________________

CHAPTER 5 TEST
FORM A
PAGE 1

Read each question carefully. Darken the circle on your answer sheet for the correct answer.

1. What time is shown on the clock?

A. 1:17
B. 1:32
C. 3:06
D. 3:11

Use the line plot for items 2–3.

Number of Points Scored

1	2	3	4	5
	X			
	X			
X	X			
X	X	X		
X	X	X		X
X	X	X	X	X

2. How many people did the data include?

F. 5 **G.** 6 **H.** 15 **J.** 16

3. How many people attended exactly 3 games?

A. 1 **B.** 2 **C.** 3 **D.** 4

4. How much time has passed?
Start: 8:25 A.M. **End:** 10:15 A.M.

F. 1 h 50 min **H.** 2 h 40 min
G. 2 h 10 min **J.** 2 h 50 min

Use this set of data for items 5–6.

6, 2, 4, 8, 7, 2, 6, 6, 5, 8

5. What is the range of this data set?

A. 4 **B.** 6 **C.** 8 **D.** 10

6. What is the mode of the data?

F. 2 **G.** 4 **H.** 6 **J.** 8

7. What time is shown?

A. a quarter to seven
B. half-past seven
C. 2 minutes before eight
D. 23 minutes before seven

8. How much time has passed?
Start: 7:50 P.M. **End:** 1:30 A.M.

F. 5 h 20 min **H.** 6 h 20 min
G. 5 h 40 min **J.** 6 h 40 min

Use the tally table for exercises 9–10.

Time Spent Practicing for Recital

Number of Hours per Week	Tally
1	||||
2	~~||||~~ ||
3	~~||||~~ ||||
4	~~||||~~ |||
5 or more	||

9. The fourth-graders practiced singing for their school recital. The tally table shows how many hours they sang each week. How many fourth-graders practiced for the recital?

A. 4 **B.** 9 **C.** 20 **D.** 30

10. How many students practiced for exactly 4 hours each week?

F. 2 **G.** 8 **H.** 9 **J.** 30

GO ON

Name ____________________

CHAPTER 5 TEST
FORM A
PAGE 2

Use this set of data for items 11–12.

Money Paul earned:
$8, $12, $7, $9, $12, $6, $8, $12, $9

11. What is the median?

A. $6 **B.** $8 **C.** $9 **D.** $12

---

12. What is the range?

F. $6 **G.** $8 **H.** $10 **J.** $12

Use this set of data for items 13-15.

Number of hours Koki listened to the radio: 2, 5, 3, 2, 1, 4, 4, 1, 2

13. What is the mode of this data set?

A. 2 **B.** 3 **C.** 4 **D.** 5

---

14. What is the range of the data?

F. 2 **G.** 3 **H.** 4 **J.** 5

---

15. What is the median of the data?

A. 1 **B.** 2 **C.** 3 **D.** 4

---

16. Jerry wants to leave his house by 9:15 A.M. He needs 40 minutes to wash and dress and 10 minutes to eat breakfast. For what time should he set his alarm?

F. 7:35 A.M. **H.** 8:25 A.M.
G. 7:45 A.M. **J.** 8:45 A.M.

---

17. Lisa hikes from 2:15 P.M. to 4:40 P.M. How long does she hike?

A. 2 h 55 min **C.** 2 h 25 min
B. 2 h 35 min **D** 2 h 15 min

Use this information for items 18–19.

A new sofa costs $845. The manufacturer is also giving a discount of $50 with a mail-in rebate. Last year the same sofa cost $805.

18. How much does the new sofa cost after the discount is included?

F. $755 **H.** $855
G. $795 **J.** $895

---

19. What information is not needed to solve problem 18?

A. the discount of $50
B. the current price of the sofa
C. the cost of the sofa last year
D. all of the information is needed

---

20. James is making ice cream for his class. He wants each student to have enough to eat. There are 22 students altogether. There are 11 girls in the class. How many gallons of ice cream will James have to make?

What information that is necessary to solve this problem is missing?

F. the number of quarts in a gallon
G. the amount of ice cream each student will eat
H. the number of cups in a pint
J. the number of boys in the class

STOP

Name ______________________________

CHAPTER 5 TEST
FORM B
PAGE 1

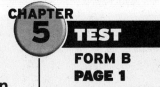

Read each question carefully. Fill in the correct answer in the space provided.

1. What time is shown on the clock?

____

Use the line plot for items 2–3.

Number of Hours of Homework

1	2	3	4	5
	X X			
X X	X X	X		
X X	X X	X X	X	
X X	X X	X X	X	X
X X	X X	X X	X	X

2. How many students did the data include?

____

3. How many students worked for exactly 3 hours on the homework?

____

4. How much time has passed?
Start: 11:05 A.M. End: 3:20 P.M.

____

Use this set of data for items 5–6.

Teresa earned: $11, $6, $9, $12, $9, $15, $8, $9, $13

5. What is the range of this data set?

____

6. What is the mode of the data?

____

7. What time is shown on the clock?

____

8. How much time has passed?
Start: 9:35 P.M. End: 1:05 A.M

____

Use the tally table for items 9–10.

Time Spent Exercising

Number of Hours per Week	Tally
4	𝍷𝍷𝍷
8	𝍸 𝍸
12	𝍸 𝍸 𝍸
16	𝍸 𝍷
20 or more	𝍷

9. The tally table shows how many hours a group of fourth-graders exercised in one week. How many fourth-graders were in the group?

____

10. How many students exercised for exactly eight hours each week?

____

GO ON

Name ______________________________

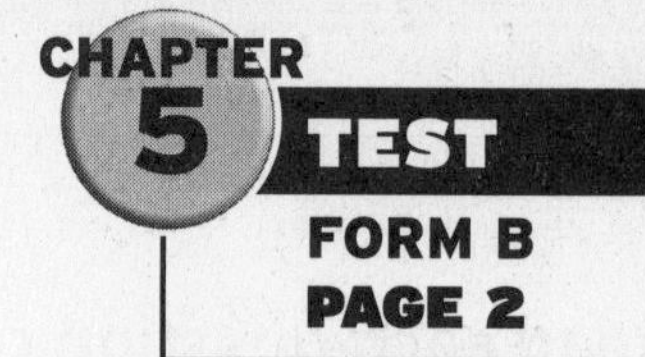

Use this set of data for items 11–12.

Points Matt scored on tests:
98, 76, 85, 98, 94, 89, 98, 87, 91

11. What is the median?

____

12. What is the range?

____

Use this set of data for items 13–15.

Miles jogged by Coreen:
4 mi, 7 mi, 5 mi, 5 mi, 2 mi,
3 mi, 2 mi, 1 mi, 2 mi

13. What is the mode?

____

14. What is the range of the data?

____

15. What is the median of the data?

____

16. Mona wants to finish her homework by 8:45 P.M. Her homework takes 50 minutes to complete. At what time should she begin?

____

17. Damon wants to spend exactly 1 hour 30 minutes exercising. He begins at 5:40 P.M. At what time will Damon stop exercising?

____

Use this information for items 18–19.

The price of a new scooter is $1,225. The manufacturer is also giving a discount of $260 cash back with purchase. Last year the same scooter cost $1,795.

18. How much does the new scooter cost with the discount?

____

19. What information about the scooter is not needed to solve problem 18?

____

20. Celia needs to fill her empty swimming pool. It takes Celia 6 hours to fill her pool using a hose. How many gallons of water does the hose carry to Celia's pool every hour?

What information that is necessary to solve this problem is missing?

____

STOP

Chapter 6 – Teacher Interview

Core Concept: ***Reading Graphs***

Student Activity: Students demonstrate an understanding of how to use ordered pairs to read a line graph.

Teacher Question 1:

- Starting from the point (0, 0) on a coordinate graph, how would you get to point (2, 5)?

Understanding Student Response	Practice and Improvement
Students who say 5 places to the right and 2 places up.	Review lesson 4 to help students review how to write ordered pairs.
Students who give any other incorrect answer.	Review lesson 4 to students learn how to read and write ordered pairs.

Teacher Question 2:

- Maria is making a line graph using this data: March: 100; April: 150; May: 200; June: 250; July: 300. Which data will be on the bottom of the graph, and which will be on the side?

Understanding Student Response	Practice and Improvement
Students who cannot say how to display the data.	Review lessons 5 and 6 to reinforce the idea that units of time are typically shown on the horizontal axis, or the bottom, of a line graph.
Students who say that the months will be on the side of the graph and the numbers will be on the bottom.	Review lessons 5 and 6 to reinforce the idea that units of time are typically shown on the horizontal axis, or the bottom, of a line graph.

Teacher Question 3:

- For the data set 100, 150, 200, 250, 300, what scale should Maria use for her line graph?

Understanding Student Response	Practice and Improvement
Students who answer anything other than 25, 50, or 100.	Review lessons 5 and 6 to help students learn how to write appropriate scales.

Chapter 6 – Journal Writing

Encourage students to generate their own journal entries related to math ideas in general or to concepts in this chapter. For students requiring guidance, present the following journal prompt:

- What kind of problem is most easy to solve by organizing the data using a Venn diagram? Show why.

  (Responses should mention that a problem in which the data falls into more than one category is best organized with a Venn diagram, because a Venn diagram lets you see the overlap. Students should draw a Venn diagram to illustrate their point.)

JOURNAL WRITING/PROBLEM SOLVING

Roxanne keeps track of the temperature for four months. She discovers that the average temperature in October was 64°F, in November it was 54°F, in December it was 44°F, and in January it was 34°F. Draw a line graph showing the average temperatures for those months in Fahrenheit.

Read

Have students find the answer to the problem. Then ask them to write a few sentences telling —

- how they organized the data and created ordered pairs
- how they labeled the graphs and decided on scale

Have students make up another problem with different information for which they would have to follow the same procedure. Then have students solve the problem and supply the correct responses.

Plan

Students must be able to organize the data into ordered pairs, set up the graph, and plot the data.

Solve

The correct response to the assigned problem is a line graph with the months along the x-axis and temperatures on the y-axis, and with the given data points plotted correctly. Students had to create ordered pairs, label graphs, understand what scale to use, and plot the data points.

Look Back

Correct responses demonstrate the ability to properly organize data, create ordered pairs from data, understand the appropriate scale, and plot data points correctly. (See scoring rubric on page 7.)

Chapter 6 – Monitoring Student Progress

☐ **Form A** ☐ **Form B**

Name ______________________ Date ______________

Directions: For each item that is answered incorrectly, cross out the item number. Then record the number of correct responses in the appropriate Student Score column. If the student has not met the Criterion Score for an objective, circle the student's score. Recommended assignments are listed in the Prescription Table on the next page.

Objective	Item Numbers	Criterion Score	Student Score
A. Collect and organize data in tables and graphs.	4, 7, 8,13, 14, 15, 16	6/7	/7
B. Read and interpret data.	1, 2, 3, 5, 6, 9, 10, 11, 12	8/9	/9
C. Display data in different graphs.	19, 20	1/2	/2
D. Use skills and strategies to solve problems.	17, 18	1/2	/2
Total Test Score		16/20	/20
Total Percent Correct			%

Chapter 6 – Prescription Table

The following chart correlates the tested objectives for this chapter to supplementary materials that meet the individual needs of the students. The Reteach and Practice pages are designed for students who need further instruction in the math concepts taught in this chapter. The Enrich pages are designed for students who need advanced challenges.

Objective	Reteach	Practice	Enrich
A. Collect and organize data in tables and graphs.	94, 97, 106	95,98, 107	96,99, 108
B. Read and interpret data.	103, 109	104, 110	105, 111
C. Display data in different graphs.	112	113	114
D. Use skills and strategies to solve problems.	100	101	102

Name ____

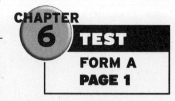

Read each question carefully. Darken the circle on your answer sheet for the correct answer.

Use the bar graph for items 1–4.

1. How many votes did vanilla get?

   A. 1 **B.** 2 **C.** 4 **D.** 5

2. Which flavor did girls like most?

   F. vanilla **H.** mint
   G. chocolate **J.** strawberry

3. How many boys like strawberry?

   A. 1 **B.** 4 **C.** 8 **D.** 12

4. If 3 times as many girls voted for mint as is on the graph, what would be a good scale to use?

   F. 0-3 **G.** 0-12 **H.** 0-20 **J.** 0-30

Use the pictograph for items 5–8.

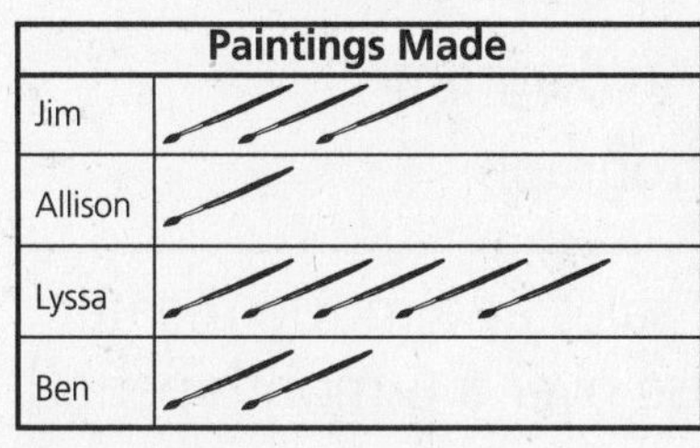

5. How many more paintings did Jim make than Allison?

   A. 2 **B.** 3 **C.** 4 **D.** 6

6. Who made the most paintings?

   F. Jim **H.** Lyssa
   G. Allison **J.** Ben

7. Erika made 18 paintings. How many brushes would be next to her name?

   A. 6 **B.** 9 **C.** 12 **D.** 18

8. If the number of brushes next to Lyssa represented 15 paintings instead of 10, how many paintings made would each picture represent in the key?

   F. 1 **G.** 2 **H.** 3 **J.** 4

Use the line graph for items 9–12.

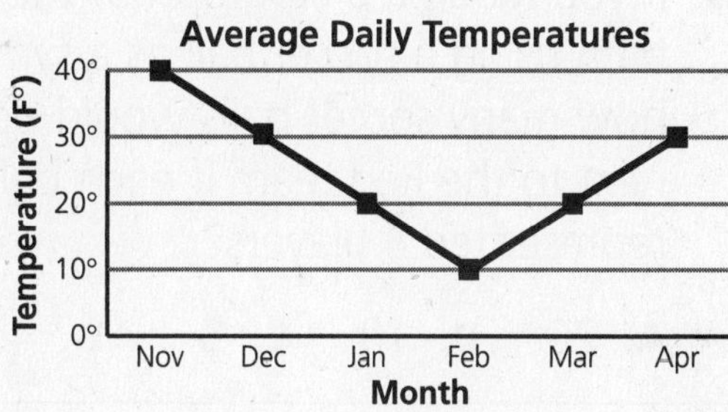

9. What was the average daily temperature for February?

   A. 10° **B.** 20° **C.** 30° **D.** 40°

10. How much higher was the average daily temperature in December than in February?

    F. 10° **G.** 20° **H.** 30° **J.** 40°

GO ON

Name ______________________________

11. What was the average daily temperature for all six months?

A. 15° **B.** 16° **C.** 25° **D.** 30°

12. October had an average daily temperature of 50°. By how much would the range change if you added October to the graph?

F. 10° **G.** 15° **H.** 20° **J.** 25°

Use this set of data for items 13–16.

Number of Players on Each Soccer Team	
Green	24
Blue	12
Black	16
Red	20

13. If you made a pictograph of the data using a soccer ball as a symbol, how many soccer balls would be next to the Red team if each ball represented 4 players?

A. 20 **B.** 10 **C.** 5 **D.** 4

14. How many soccer balls would be next to the Green team if each ball represented 8 players?

F. 4 **G.** 3 **H.** 16 **J.** 2

15. If you made a bar graph of the data, which would be the best scale?

A. 0-4 **B.** 0-12 **C.** 0-24 **D.** 0-48

16. If you made a line graph of the data, which team would correspond to the lowest point on the line?

F. Green **H.** Black
G. Blue **J.** Red

For 17–20, choose the best graph.

17. Four students compare the number of boxes of cookies they sold. Each cookie symbol represents 3 boxes.

A. line graph
B. double bar graph
C. Venn diagram
D. pictograph

18. 32 students play baseball, soccer or track. 18 play 2 of the sports, and 5 play all 3 sports.

F. line graph
G. double bar graph
H. Venn diagram
J. pictograph

19. Ben and Amy compare their math and reading scores.

A. line graph
B. double bar graph
C. Venn diagram
D. pictograph

20. Ticket sales at a movie theater increase over a 6-month period.

F. line graph
G. double bar graph
H. Venn diagram
J. pictograph

STOP

Name ___

CHAPTER 6 TEST
FORM B
PAGE 1

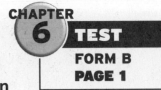

Read each question carefully. Fill in the correct answer in the space provided.

Use the bar graph for items 1–4.

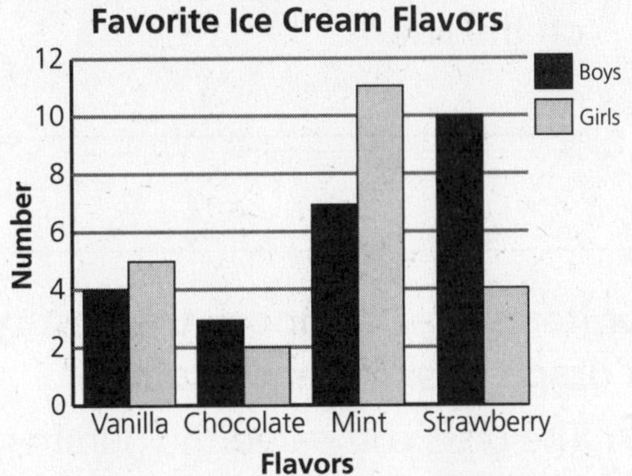

1. How many votes did mint get?

___

2. Which flavor had the most votes by boys?

___

3. How many girls like vanilla best?

___

4. If 4 times as many boys voted for strawberry as shown on the graph, what would be a good scale?

___

Use the pictograph for items 5–8.

Points Scored	
Jason	
Alice	
Francis	
Louis	

Each (basketball) means 2 points scored.

5. How many more points did Alice score than Jason?

___

6. Who scored the least points?

___

7. William scored 14 points. How many basketballs would you put next to his name?

___

8. If the number of basketballs next to Francis represented 12 points instead of 8, how many points would each picture represent in the key?

___

Use the line graph for items 9–12.

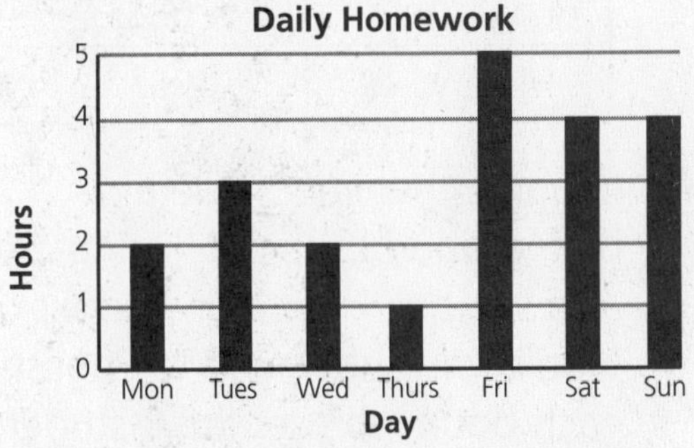

9. The graph shows how many hours of homework Kevin had for each day of the week. How many hours did he have on Tuesday?

___

10. How many more hours of homework did Kevin have on Friday than on Thursday?

___

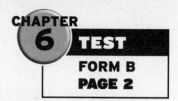

11. What was the average number of hours of homework for all seven days?

____

12. If Kevin had 6 hours of homework on Sunday, by how much would the range change if you changed this data in the graph?

____

Use this set of data for items 13–16.

Students Favorite School Subjects	
Math	42
Science	35
English	63
History	56

13. Imagine that you made a pictograph of the data using a book as a symbol. How many books would you show next to English if each book represented 7 students?

____

14. How many books would be next to History if each book represented 8 students?

____

15. If you made a bar graph of the data, which would be the best scale to use?

0–7, 0–35, or 0–70

____

16. If you made a line graph of the data in the table, which subject would correspond to the highest point on the line?

____

For items 17–20, choose the best type of graph to show each data set.

17. The class compared the number of pizza slices they ate. Each pizza pie symbol represents 2 slices.

____

18. 24 students enjoy action movies, comedies, or cartoons. Some enjoy only action, some only comedies, others like all three.

____

19. Matt and Jasira earn money each week working at their summer jobs.

____

20. Daily sales at Morgan's Hardware Store increase over a 3-month period.

____

STOP

Unit 3 Performance Assessment

Game Time!

- ***Target Skill:*** Organize and represent data in tables and graphs.
- ***Additional Skills:*** Find the range, mode, and median for a set of data. Add whole numbers.

Task Description: This task requires students to create a table and bar graph for a set of scores from a game and find the range, mode, and median for the set.

Preparing: You may wish to have students write out the definition of range, mode, and median before they begin.

Materials	Group Size	Time on Task
Graph paper	3 to 4 students	1–2 days

Guiding: Remind students that when creating bar graphs, the bars should be equal width.

Remind students of the difference between mode and median.

Suggest that the students put the scores in ascending order before finding the median.

Tell students that all values should be whole numbers.

Observing/ Monitoring: As you move among the students, pose the following questions:

What other ways could you represent the scores from the game?

What other comparisons can you make between the friends' scores?

Unit 3 Performance Assessment Scoring Rubric

Game Time!

Score	Explanation
3	Students demonstrate an efficient strategy and a thorough approach that enables them to solve the problem completely. A sufficient answer: • has a table with labels and the correct score for each boy; • identifies the range as 15; the mode as 60; and the median as 55, with work shown for each computation; • has a complete bar graph with labels and the correct score for each boy. Students are able to complete the problem quickly and have all of the above correct solutions.
2	Students demonstrate a strategy that enables them to solve most of the problem correctly. The strategy is somewhat disorganized, making it less efficient. A solution is found but errors are contained. Students may: • confuse mode and median; • not label bar graph correctly; • confuse scores for boys. Students may have some difficulty determining all solutions correctly but demonstrate an understanding of general concepts.
1	Students demonstrate a confused strategy, which leads to difficulty solving the problem. Most answers are incorrect, but students demonstrate knowledge of at least one concept being assessed. Students may: • create a table without the data; OR • set up a bar graph without labels or data; OR • only calculate the range, the median, or the mode.

Name ____________________

Unit 3 Performance Assessment Student Activity

Game Time!

You will need
- Colored pencils or markers
- Graph paper

Tom bought a new game. He and his friends got the following scores the first time they played: Tom—50; Allen—45; Raul—60; and Seth—60.

1. In the space below, make a table of the boys' scores.
2. In the space below, make a bar graph of the scores.

Table	**Bar Graph**

3. What are the range, the mode, and the median of the scores? Show your work.

Range ____________________

Mode ____________________

Median ____________________

Unit 3 – Monitoring Student Progress

☐ **Form A** ☐ **Form B**

Name ______________________ Date ______________

Directions: This test targets selected objectives. For each item that is answered incorrectly, cross out the item number. Then record the number of correct responses in the column labeled **Number of Correct Responses.** Add to find the **Total Number of Correct Responses** and record the total. Use this total to determine the **Total Test Score** and the **Total Percent Correct.**

Strand • Objective(s)	Item Numbers	Number of Correct Responses
Measurement • Tell time and find elapsed time. • Use skills and strategies to solve problems.	1, 4, 8, 9, 10, 16, 17, 21, 24, 28, 29, 30, 36, 37	/14
Data Analysis and Probability • Find range, median, and mode. • Collect and organize data in tables and graphs. • Read and interpret data. • Display data in different graphs. • Use skills and strategies to solve problems.	2, 3, 5, 6, 7, 11, 12, 13, 14, 15, 18, 19, 20, 22, 23, 25, 26, 27, 31, 32, 33, 34, 35, 38, 39, 40	/26
Total Number of Correct Responses		
Total Test Score		/40
Total Percent Correct		%

Name ______________________________________

UNIT 3 **TEST**
FORM A
PAGE 1

Read each question carefully. Darken the circle on your answer sheet for the correct answer.

1. What time is shown on the clock?

A. 1:23
B. 1:43
C. 2:20
D. 4:05

Use the line plot for exercises 2–3.

Number of Games Attended

	X			
X	X			
X	X	X		
X	X	X		
X	X	X	X	
X	X	X	X	X
1	**2**	**3**	**4**	**5**

2. The data included ▢ people.

F. 7 **G.** 8 **H.** 18 **J.** 15

---

3. ▢ people attended 3 games.

A. 4 **B.** 5 **C.** 6 **D.** 7

---

4. Which time is shown?

F. a quarter to nine
G. half-past eight
H. 17 minutes before nine
J. 42 minutes before eight

Use the bar graph for exercises 5–7.

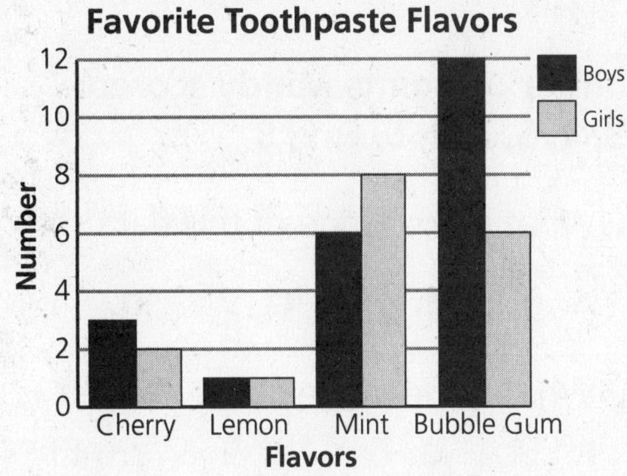

5. Cherry got ▢ votes all together.

A. 2 **B.** 3 **C.** 5 **D.** 6

---

6. Girls liked ▢ flavor best.

F. cherry **H.** lemon
G. mint **J.** bubble gum

---

7. ▢ boys liked bubble gum best.

A. 6 **B.** 8 **C.** 11 **D.** 12

---

8. 120 minutes = ▢ hours

F. 2 **G.** 3 **H.** 10 **J.** 12

---

9. 45 minutes = ▢ quarter hours

A. 2 **B.** 3 **C.** 5 **D.** 6

---

10. How much time has passed?

Start: 10:35 A.M. **End:** 1:15 P.M.

F. 2 h 20 min **H.** 2 h 40 min
G. 2 h 30 min **J.** 9 h 20 min

Name ____________________

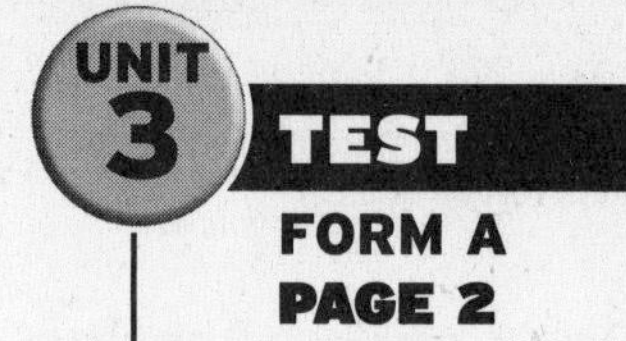

Use this set of data for exercises 11–12.

Number of points Mindy scored: 5, 3, 4, 5, 7, 2, 5, 6, 9, 8

11. What is the range of this data set?

A. 5 **B.** 7 **C.** 9 **D.** 11

12. What is the mode of the data?

F. 5 **G.** 6 **H.** 9 **J.** 11

Use this set of data for exercises 13–15.

Number of hours Sean watched TV: 2, 7, 3, 2, 1, 5, 4, 3, 2

13. What is the mode of this data set?

A. 2 **B.** 4 **C.** 6 **D.** 7

14. What is the range of the data?

F. 2 **G.** 4 **H.** 6 **J.** 7

15. What is the median of the data?

A. 2 **B.** 3 **C.** 4 **D.** 7

Solve.

16. Tom wants to leave his house by 8:45 A.M. He needs 30 minutes to wash and dress and 20 minutes to eat breakfast. For what time should he set his alarm?

F. 7:55 A.M. **H.** 8:15 A.M.
G. 8:05 A.M. **J.** 8:25 A.M.

17. Carmen hikes from 1:20 P.M. to 3:15 P.M. How long does she hike?

A. 2 h 55 min **C.** 1 h 55 min
B. 2 h 5 min **D.** 1 h 35 min

Use this information for problems 18–19.

A new TV costs $935. Last year the same TV cost $905. The manufacturer is giving a discount of $40.

18. How much does the new TV cost with the discount?

F. $875 **G.** $895 **H.** $965 **J.** $975

19. What information is not needed to solve problem 18?

A. the discount of $40
B. the current price of the TV
C. the cost of the TV last year
D. the difference in price between the TVs

20. Tim is making punch for his class. He wants each student to have enough to drink. There are 30 students all together. There are 15 girls in the class. How many gallons of punch will Tim have to make?
What information that is necessary to solve this problem is missing?

F. the number of quarts in a gallon
G. the amount of punch each student will drink
H. the number of cups in a pint
J. the number of boys in the class

Name ____________________

UNIT 3 TEST
FORM A
PAGE 3

21. What time is shown on the clock?

A. 6:45
B. 6:48
C. 9:30
D. 10:30

Use the pictograph for exercises 22–23.

Books Read	
Tim	
Alex	
Lauren	
Keesha	

Each ▯ means 2 books read.

22. Tim read ■ more books than Alex.

F. 2 **G.** 3 **H.** 4 **J.** 6

23. Who read the most books?

A. Alex
B. Keesha
C. Tim
D. Lauren

24. What time is shown?

F. ten minutes after one
G. quarter past one
H. ten minutes to one
J. five minutes after two

Use the line graph for exercises 25–27.

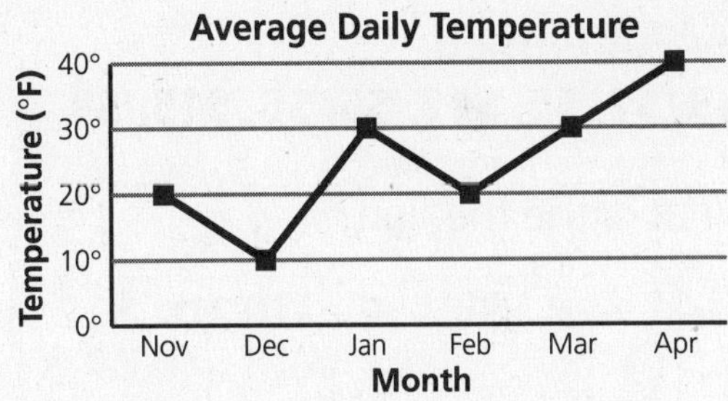

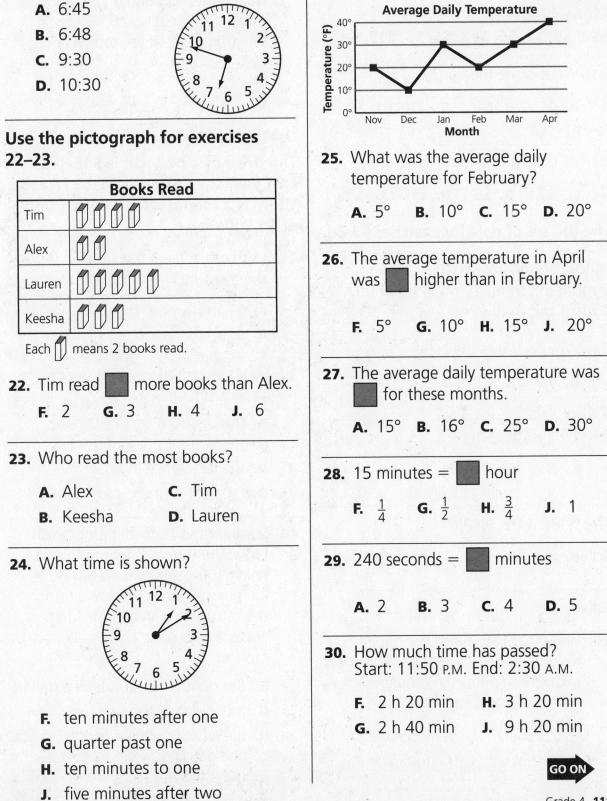

25. What was the average daily temperature for February?

A. 5° **B.** 10° **C.** 15° **D.** 20°

26. The average temperature in April was ■ higher than in February.

F. 5° **G.** 10° **H.** 15° **J.** 20°

27. The average daily temperature was ■ for these months.

A. 15° **B.** 16° **C.** 25° **D.** 30°

28. 15 minutes = ■ hour

F. $\frac{1}{4}$ **G.** $\frac{1}{2}$ **H.** $\frac{3}{4}$ **J.** 1

29. 240 seconds = ■ minutes

A. 2 **B.** 3 **C.** 4 **D.** 5

30. How much time has passed?
Start: 11:50 P.M. End: 2:30 A.M.

F. 2 h 20 min
G. 2 h 40 min
H. 3 h 20 min
J. 9 h 20 min

Name ____________________

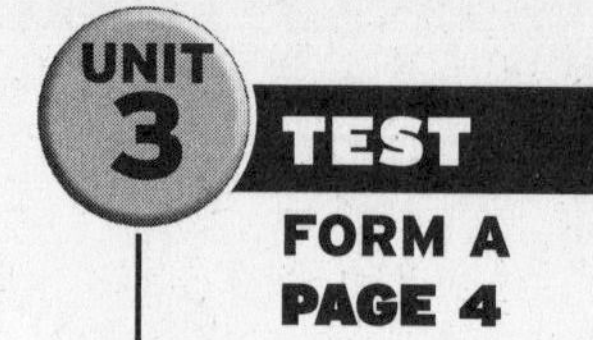

Use this set of data for exercises 31–32.

Money Pat earned:
$10, $5, $7, $5, $12, $5, $8, $15, $9

31. What is the median?

A. $5 **B.** $8 **C.** $10 **D.** $12

32. What is the range?

F. $5 **G.** $8 **H.** $10 **J.** $12

Use this set of data for exercises 33–35.

Miles jogged by Kristi:
2 mi, 8 mi, 6 mi, 10 mi, 4 mi, 9 mi, 2 mi, 1 mi, 2 mi

33. What is the mode?

A. 10 **B.** 8 **C.** 2 **D.** 1

34. What is the range?

F. 2 **G.** 6 **H.** 8 **J.** 9

35. What is the median?

A. 2 **B.** 4 **C.** 8 **D.** 10

Solve.

36. Linda wants to finish her paper route by 8:15 A.M. Her paper route takes 50 minutes to complete. At what time should she leave?

F. 7:25 A.M. **H.** 7:55 A.M.
G. 7:45 A.M. **J.** 9:05 A.M.

37. Dave wants to spend exactly 1 hour 30 minutes working on his science project. He begins at 6:55 P.M. At what time will Dave stop working?

A. 7:35 P.M. **C.** 8:25 P.M.
B. 7:55 P.M. **D.** 8:35 P.M.

Use this information for problems 38–39.

The price of a new car is $18,395. Last year the same car cost $17,295. There is a manufacturer's discount of $1,500.

38. How much does the car cost with the discount?

F. $13,395 **H.** $17,295
G. $16,895 **J.** $18,395

39. What information is not needed to solve problem 38?

A. the discount of $1,500
B. the current price of the car
C. the difference in price
D. the cost of the car last year

40. Susan needs to fill her empty fish tank. The tank is 2 feet high and holds 100 gallons of water. How long will Susan have to wait until the tank is full? What information necessary to solve this problem is missing?

F. the number of quarts in a gallon
G. the width of the tank
H. the amount of time needed to add one gallon of water to the tank
J. the number of fish

STOP

Name ____________________

UNIT 3 **TEST**
FORM B
PAGE 1

Read each question carefully. Fill in the correct answer in the space provided.

1. What time is shown?

____

Use the line plot for items 2–3.

Number of Games Attended

	X			
X	X			
X	X	X		X
X	X	X	X	X
X	X	X	X	X
1	2	3	4	5

2. How many people does the data include?

____

3. How many people attended exactly 2 games?

____

4. What time is shown?

____

Use the bar graph for items 5–7.

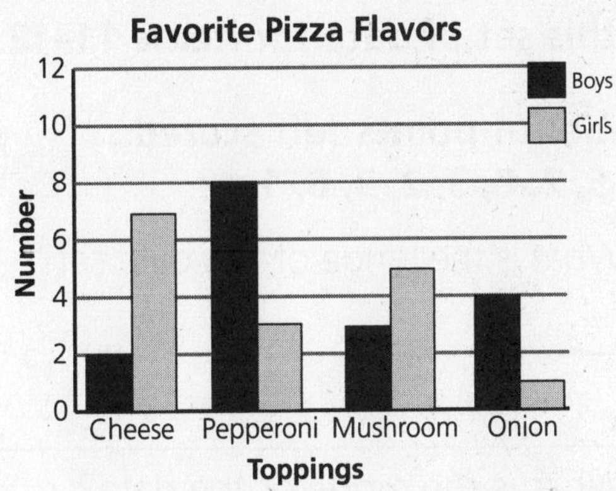

5. How many votes did pepperoni get altogether?

____

6. Which topping did girls like best?

____

7. How many boys liked mushroom best?

____

8. 180 minutes = ______ hours

9. 75 minutes = ______ quarter hours

10. How much time has passed?

Start: 11:30 A.M. End: 2:25 P.M.

____

Name ______________________________

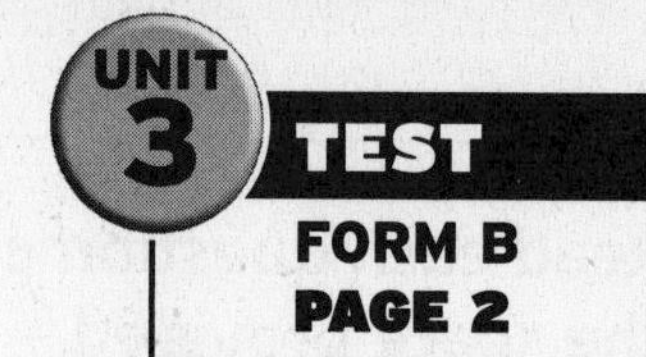

Use this set of data for items 11–12.

Number of points Jeff scored:
3, 4, 5, 2, 8, 3, 2, 3, 6, 1

11. What is the range of this data set?

____

12. What is the mode of the data?

____

Use this set of data for items 13–15.

Number of pages Chanae read:
11, 6, 3, 4, 2, 9, 1, 7, 2

13. What is the mode of this data set?

____

14. What is the range of this data set?

____

15. What is the median of the data?

____

16. Bill wants to leave his house by 7:55 A.M. He needs 25 minutes to wash and dress and 15 minutes to eat breakfast. For what time should he set his alarm?

____

17. Carol rides her bike from 2:30 P.M. to 4:05 P.M. How long does she ride her bike?

____

Use this information for items 18–19.

A new TV costs $235. The manufacturer is giving a discount of $20. A new DVD player costs $250.

18. How much does the new TV cost with the discount?

____

19. What is given but not needed to solve problem 18?

____

20. Kelly is making cookies for class. She wants to be sure each student has enough to eat. There are 24 students in her class. There are 15 girls in her class. How many cookies should she make?

What information that is necessary to solve this problem is missing?

____

Name ________________________________

UNIT 3 **TEST**
FORM B
PAGE 3

21. What time is shown?

____

Use the pictograph for items 22–23.

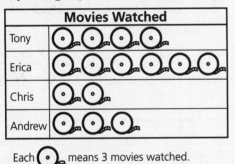

Movies Watched	
Tony	
Erica	
Chris	
Andrew	

Each (film reel) means 3 movies watched.

22. How many more movies did Tony watch than Chris?

____

23. Who watched the most movies?

____

24. What time is shown?

____

Use the line graph for items 25–27.

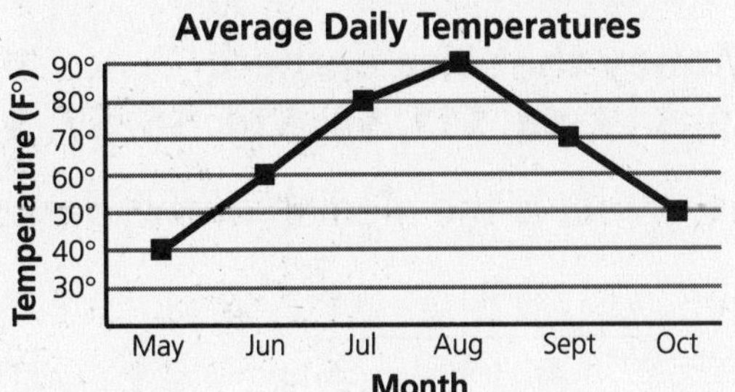

25. What was the average daily temperature in July?

____

26. How much higher was the average temperature in September than in May?

____

27. What was the average temperature during these months?

____

28. 45 minutes = ________ hour

29. 300 seconds = ______ minutes

30. How much time has passed?

Start: 10:15 P.M. End: 2:35 A.M.

____

GO ON

Name ______________________________

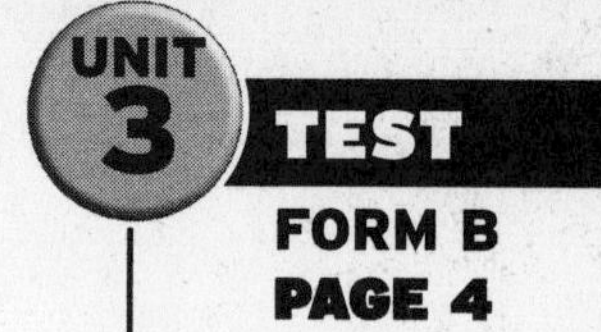

Use this data set for items 31–32.

Money that Lisa earned:
$9, $15, $8, $11, $4, $14, $6, $7, $16

31. What is the median of this data set?

____

32. What is the range of this data set?

____

Use this data set for items 33–35.

Home runs hit per game:
2, 1, 5, 3, 0, 1, 2, 4, 1

33. What is the mode of this data set?

____

34. What is the range of the data?

____

35. What is the median of this data set?

____

36. Andy wants to finish mowing his lawn by 4:30 P.M. The mowing takes 55 minutes to complete. At what time should he start?

____

37. Seth wants to play video games for 1 hour 20 minutes. He starts at 7:45 P.M. At what time does he stop playing?

____

Use this information for items 38–39.

The price of a new van is $24,050. Last year the same van cost $23,220. The dealership is offering a discount of $1,200.

38. How much does the new car cost with the discount?

____

39. What piece of information is given to you but not needed for problem 38?

____

40. Tom needs to fill his empty swimming pool. The pool is 4 feet deep and contains 10,000 gallons of water. He wants to go swimming when it is full. How long will Tom have to wait?

What information that is necessary to solve this problem is missing?

____

STOP

Chapter 7 – Teacher Interview

Core Concept: *Multiplication Facts*

Student Activity: Students demonstrate an understanding of multiplication facts through 12. Assign a problem such as 7 × 8.

Teacher Question 1:

- What is the product of 7 × 8?

Understanding Student Response	Practice and Improvement
Students who say 54, 63, or 64.	Review lesson 1 to help the student understand multiplication facts.

Teacher Question 2:

- 7 × 8 = 56. What other multiplication sentence could you write using the Commutative Property?

Understanding Student Response	Practice and Improvement
Students who say 7 × 0 = 0.	Review lesson 2 to help the student understand the Commutative Property.
Students who say 7 × 1 = 1.	Review lesson 2 to help the student understand the Commutative Property.

Teacher Question 3:

- How can you show this multiplication fact as an addition expression?

Understanding Student Response	Practice and Improvement
Students who say 7 + 8.	Review lesson 1 to help students understand the relationship between addition and multiplication.

Chapter 7 – Journal Writing

Encourage students to generate their own journal entries related to math ideas in general or to concepts in this chapter. For students requiring guidance, present the following journal prompt:

- How can the Commutative Property of Multiplication help you learn fact families?

  (Reponses should state that if you know one fact, all you have to do is change the order of the factors to get another.)

JOURNAL WRITING/PROBLEM SOLVING

Andy bought 4 packs of baseball cards with 6 cards in each. Katie bought 6 packs of baseball cards with 4 cards in each. Who had more cards, Andy or Katie?

Read

Have students find the answer to the problem. Then ask them to write a few sentences about:

- what information they needed to solve the problem
- how they used properties of multiplication to help them solve the problem

Have students make up another problem for which they would have to follow the same procedure, but with different information. Students should also supply the correct response.

Plan

Students must understand that to find the total number of cards each boy has they must multiply the number of cards in each pack by the number of packs. They must then either solve each equation and compare, or use the commutative property to compare equations and draw a conclusion about the products.

Solve

The correct response to the problem is that both Andy and Katie have the same amount, 24 cards. Students can either solve both equations, 4×6 and 6×4, and then compare products, or they can use the Commutative Property to compare equations and to get the answer.

Look Back

A correct response demonstrates the ability to understand what the problem is asking and to use the appropriate process for finding the answer. A correct response also demonstrates an understanding of how to use the Commutative Property of Multiplication to compare equations and draw conclusions. (See scoring rubric on page 7.)

Chapter 7 – Monitoring Student Progress

☐ **Form A** ☐ **Form B**

Name ______________________ Date ______________________

Directions: For each item that is answered incorrectly, cross out the item number. Then record the number of correct responses in the appropriate Student Score column. If the student has not met the Criterion Score for an objective, circle the student's score. Recommended assignments are listed in the Prescription Table on the next page.

Objective	Item Numbers	Criterion Score	Student Score
A. Use properties of multiplication.	1, 4, 5, 8, 9, 11, 13	6/7	/7
B. Multiply facts through 12.	2, 3, 7, 10, 12, 14	5/6	/6
C. Review patterns in a multiplication table.	6, 15	1/2	/2
D. Use skills and strategies to solve problems.	16, 17, 18, 19, 20	4/5	/5
Total Test Score		16/20	/20
Total Percent Correct			%

Chapter 7 – Prescription Table

The following chart correlates the tested objectives for this chapter to supplementary materials that meet the individual needs of the students. The Reteach and Practice pages are designed for students who need further instruction in the math concepts taught in this chapter. The Enrich pages are designed for students who need advanced challenges.

Objective	Reteach	Practice	Enrich
A. Use properties of multiplication.	120	121	122
B. Multiply facts through 12.	117, 123 126, 132	118, 124 127, 133	119, 125 128, 134
C. Review patterns in a multiplication table.	135	136	137
D. Use skills and strategies to solve problems.	129	130	131

Name ____________________

CHAPTER 7 TEST
FORM A
PAGE 1

Read each question carefully. Darken the circle on your answer sheet for the correct answer.

1. 3×1

A. 0 **B.** 1 **C.** 3 **D.** 31

2. $9 \times 7 = \square$

F. 48 **G.** 54 **H.** 63 **J.** 28

3. $4 \times 8 = \square$

A. 12 **B.** 24 **C.** 28 **D.** 32

4. Use the Commutative Property to find a related multiplication sentence.

$5 \times 7 = 35$

F. $5 + 7 = 12$
G. $7 - 5 = 2$
H. $7 \times 7 = 49$
J. $7 \times 5 = 35$

5. 8×0

A. 0 **C.** 8
B. 1 **D.** 9

6. Complete the table.

2	3	4	5
4	9	16	■

F. 20 **G.** 24 **H.** 25 **J.** 30

7. $7 \times 6 = \square$

A. 13 **B.** 21 **C.** 42 **D.** 48

8. Use the Commutative Property to find a related multiplication sentence.

$10 \times 3 = 30$

F. $10 + 3 = 13$
G. $3 \times 10 = 30$
H. $10 - 3 = 7$
J. $15 \times 2 = 30$

9. Use the Commutative Property to find a related multiplication sentence.

$4 \times 6 = 24$

A. $6 + 4 = 24$
B. $4 + 6 = 10$
C. $6 \times 4 = 24$
D. $24 - 6 = 18$

10. 2×4

F. 2 **H.** 8
G. 6 **J.** 10

GO ON

11. $\begin{array}{r} 9 \\ \times\ 1 \\ \hline \end{array}$

A. 1 **B.** 8 **C.** 9 **D.** 10

12. $6 \times 3 = \blacksquare$

F. 9 **G.** 12 **H.** 18 **J.** 24

13. Use the Commutative Property to find a related multiplication sentence.

$12 \times 5 = 60$

A. $12 + 5 = 17$
B. $5 \times 12 = 60$
C. $12 - 5 = 7$
D. $5 \times 5 = 25$

14. $\begin{array}{r} 11 \\ \times\ 7 \\ \hline \end{array}$

F. 4 **G.** 11 **H.** 18 **J.** 77

15. Complete the table.

1	2	3	4
8	16	24	■

A. 30 **B.** 32 **C.** 48 **D.** 56

16. Lola bought 4 markers. Each marker cost $5. Which number sentence shows how much she spent all together?

F. 4 + $5 = $9
G. 4 × $5 = $20
H. $5 − 4 = $1
J. $5 × $5 = $25

17. Gene bought 5 packs of cookies. Each pack contained 3 cookies. What would you use to find how many cookies Gene bought all together?

A. subtraction
B. division
C. addition, then subtraction
D. multiplication

18. Joey earned $2 a day walking his neighbor's dog. Which number sentence shows how much money Joey earned after 10 days?

F. $2 × $2 = $4
G. $2 + 10 = $12
H. 10 − $2 = $8
J. $2 × 10 = $20

19. Mrs. Martin had 18 pencils. She gave the same number of pencils to each of her 6 students. What operation would you use to find how many pencils Mrs. Martin gave to each student?

A. addition
B. division
C. multiplication
D. division, then addition

20. Ms. Li worked with her students on an experiment. There were 8 equal groups of students. If each group had 4 students, how many total students worked on the experiment?

F. 4 **G.** 8 **H.** 12 **J.** 32

STOP

Name ______________________

CHAPTER 7 **TEST** FORM B PAGE 1

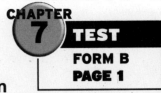

Read each question carefully. Fill in the correct answer in the space provided.

1. $\begin{array}{r} 7 \\ \times 1 \\ \hline \end{array}$

____

2. $9 \times 6 =$ ______________

____

3. $2 \times 3 =$ ______________

____

4. Use the Commutative Property to write a related multiplication sentence.

$7 \times 3 = 21$

____

5. $\begin{array}{r} 0 \\ \times 9 \\ \hline \end{array}$

6. Complete the table.

5	6	7	8
35	42	49	■

____

____

7. $6 \times 2 =$ ______________

____

8. Use the Commutative Property to find a related multiplication sentence.

$11 \times 5 = 55$

____

9. Use the Commutative Property to find a related multiplication sentence.

$7 \times 5 = 35$

____

10. $\begin{array}{r} 8 \\ \times 9 \\ \hline \end{array}$

GO ON

Name ____________________

11. $1 \times 5 =$ ________

12. $4 \times 4 =$ ________

13. Use the Commutative Property to find a related multiplication sentence.

$8 \times 5 = 40$

____

14. $\begin{array}{r} 4 \\ \times 7 \\ \hline \end{array}$

15. Complete the table.

2	4	6	8	10
4	16	36	64	■

____

16. Zoe bought 6 comic books. Each comic book cost $5. Write a number sentence that shows how much she spent all together.

____

17. Hannah bought 9 packages of game cards. Each package contained 6 cards. What operation would you use to find how many game cards Hannah bought all together?

____

18. Ben runs 2 laps around the track every day after school. Write a number sentence that shows how much Ben runs after 8 days.

____

19. Jill had $32 in her bank account. She deposited an additional $12. What operation would you use to find out how much money Jill has in her account now?

____

20. Frank ordered CDs from a music club. He ordered CDs from 4 different categories and 8 CDs in each category. How many total CDs did Frank order?

____

STOP

Chapter 8 – Teacher Interview

Core Concept: *Division Facts*

Student Activity: Students demonstrate an understanding of division facts through 12, such as 63 ÷ 9.

Teacher Question 1:

- What is the quotient of 63 ÷ 9?

Understanding Student Response	Practice and Improvement
Students who don't get 7 as their answer.	Review lessons 2 and 3 to help students understand division facts.

Teacher Question 2:

- What is a related multiplication fact?

Understanding Student Response	Practice and Improvement
Students who say 63 ÷ 7 = 9.	Review lesson 2 to help students understand related multiplication facts.
Students who answer with a multiplication problem not using the numbers 7, 9, and 63.	Review lessons 2–4 to help students understand fact families.

Teacher Question 3:

- What is the value of the expression (30 ÷ 6) × 5?

Understanding Student Response	Practice and Improvement
Students who answer 1.	Review lesson 6 to help students learn how to evaluate expressions.
Students who answer 5.	Review lesson 6 to help students learn how to evaluate expressions.

Chapter 8 – Journal Writing

Encourage students to generate their own journal entries related to math ideas in general or to concepts in this chapter. For students requiring guidance, present the following journal prompt:

- When you are finding a related fact in the same fact family as a multiplication fact, why is it important to recognize that division is related to multiplication?

  (Responses should include an understanding that multiplication and division are "opposite" operations.)

JOURNAL WRITING/PROBLEM SOLVING

Keisha has 6 shelves in her bookcase. Each shelf has 7 books. Keisha has 42 books in all. If she moved her books to another bookcase with 7 shelves and wanted an equal number of books on each shelf, how many books would Keisha place on each shelf of her other bookcase?

Read

Have students find the answer to the problem. Then ask them to write a few sentences telling—

- which numbers they used in the related fact
- which operation they used in the related fact

Have students make up another problem with different information for which they would have to follow the same procedure. Then have students solve the problem and supply the correct response.

Plan

Students must realize that a related fact for a multiplication fact is a division fact, and that the related fact employs the same numbers as the given fact.

Solve

The correct response to the assigned problem is $42 \div 6 = 7$ or $42 \div 7 = 6$. Students had to use the given numbers in a division problem.

Look Back

A correct response demonstrates the ability to recognize that a division fact is related to any given multiplication fact and the given numbers are used in the division fact. (See scoring rubric on page 7.)

Chapter 8 – Monitoring Student Progress

☐ Form A ☐ Form B

Name ______________________ Date ______________

Directions: For each item that is answered incorrectly, cross out the item number. Then record the number of correct responses in the appropriate Student Score column. If the student has not met the Criterion Score for an objective, circle the student's score. Recommended assignments are listed in the Prescription Table on the next page.

Objective	Item Numbers	Criterion Score	Student Score
A. Divide facts through 12.	1, 4, 7, 10, 12, 15, 16	6/7	/7
B. Use inverse operations of multiplication and division.	2, 5, 9, 13	3/4	/4
C. Use expressions to multiply and divide.	3, 6, 8, 11, 14	4/5	/5
D. Use skills and strategies to solve problems.	17, 18, 19, 20	3/4	/4
Total Test Score		16/20	/20
Total Percent Correct			%

Chapter 8 – Prescription Table

The following chart correlates the tested objectives for this chapter to supplementary materials that meet the individual needs of the students. The Reteach and Practice pages are designed for students who need further instruction in the math concepts taught in this chapter. The Enrich pages are designed for students who need advanced challenges.

Objective	Reteach	Practice	Enrich
A. Divide facts through 12.	138, 144	139, 145	140, 146
B. Use inverse operations of multiplication and division.	141, 147	142, 148	143, 149
C. Use expressions to multiply and divide.	153	154	155
D. Use skills and strategies to solve problems.	150	151	152

Name ______________________________

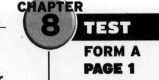

Read each question carefully. Darken the circle on your answer sheet for the correct answer.

1. $24 \div 8 = \square$

A. 3 **B.** 4 **C.** 5 **D.** 6

2. Find a related fact in the same fact family.

$5 \times 6 = 30$

F. $30 \div 5 = 6$
G. $30 \div 2 = 15$
H. $30 \div 3 = 10$
J. $30 \div 1 = 30$

3. Find the missing number.

$35 \div 5 = t$

A. 4 **B.** 5 **C.** 6 **D.** 7

4. $6\overline{)72} = \square$

F. 9 **G.** 10 **H.** 11 **J.** 12

5. Find a related fact in the same fact family.

$9 \times 5 = 45$

A. $9 + 5 = 14$
B. $9 - 5 = 4$
C. $45 \times 1 = 45$
D. $45 \div 9 = 5$

6. Find the missing number.

$36 \div 3 = x$

F. 12 **G.** 11 **H.** 10 **J.** 9

7. $7\overline{)21} = \square$

A. 2 **B.** 3 **C.** 4 **D.** 5

8. Find the missing number.

$54 \div 6 = a$

F. 8 **G.** 9 **H.** 10 **J.** 11

9. Find a related fact in the same fact family.

$2 \times 8 = 16$

A. $16 \div 4 = 4$
B. $16 \div 1 = 16$
C. $16 \div 4 = 5$
D. $16 \div 2 = 8$

10. $49 \div 7 = \square$

F. 6 **G.** 7 **H.** 8 **J.** 9

GO ON

Name ______________________________

11. Find the missing factor.

$d \times 12 = 96$

A. 7 **B.** 8 **C.** 9 **D.** 10

12. $4\overline{)24} = \square$

F. 6 **G.** 7 **H.** 8 **J.** 9

13. Find a related fact in the same fact family.

$6 \times 4 = 24$

A. $4 + 6 = 10$
B. $6 - 4 = 3$
C. $12 \times 2 = 22$
D. $24 \div 6 = 4$

14. Find the missing factor.

$f \times 10 = 60$

F. 0 **G.** 1 **H.** 6 **J.** 10

15. $3\overline{)33} = \square$

A. 8 **B.** 9 **C.** 10 **D.** 11

16. $72 \div 9 = \square$

F. 6 **G.** 7 **H.** 8 **J.** 9

17. There are 21 climbers signed up for rope lessons. Each teacher will take 3 climbers. How many teachers are needed?

A. 7 teachers **C.** 24 teachers
B. 81 teachers **D.** 63 teachers

18. Glen had 8 magnets. Then his mother gave him some packages of magnets. Each package had 4 magnets. Now Glen has 36 magnets. How many packages of magnets did Glen's mother give him?

F. 7 packages **H.** 5 packages
G. 6 packages **J.** 4 packages

19. Trina has 12 CDs. She put them into 6 CD cases. Each case held the same number of CDs. How many CDs did each case hold? Write a number sentence to solve.

A. $12 \div 6 = 2$
B. $12 - 6 = 6$
C. $12 + 6 = 18$
D. $12 \times 6 = 72$

20. There are 48 children signed up to play softball. There are 4 teams. How many players are on each team?

F. 10 players **H.** 12 players
G. 11 players **J.** 13 players

STOP

Name ______________________________

CHAPTER 8 TEST
FORM B
PAGE 1

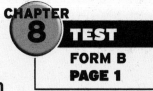

Read each question carefully. Fill in the correct answer in the space provided.

1. $64 \div 8 =$ ______________

2. Write a related division fact in the same fact family.

$5 \times 9 = 45$

____

3. Find the missing number.

$72 \div 6 = s$

____

4. $8\overline{)56} =$ ______________

5. Write a related division fact in the same fact family.

$8 \times 3 = 24$

____

6. Find the missing number.

$44 \div 11 = a$

____

7. $5\overline{)60} =$ ______________

8. Find the missing number.

$81 \div 9 = z$

____

9. Write a related division fact in the same fact family.

$9 \times 11 = 99$

____

10. $108 \div 12 =$ ______________

GO ON

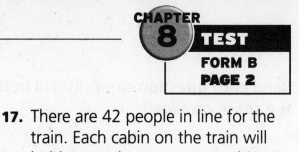

11. Find the missing factor.

$d \times 7 = 63$

12. $8\overline{)88}$ = ____________

13. Write a related division fact in the same fact family.

$6 \div 3 = 18$

____

14. Find the missing factor.

$j \times 7 = 84$

____

15. $5\overline{)55}$ = ____________

16. $24 \div 4$ = ____________

17. There are 42 people in line for the train. Each cabin on the train will hold 6 people. How many cabins will all 42 people fill?

____

18. Marcy had 3 pencils. Then her sister gave her some packages of pencils. Each package had 6 pencils. Now Marcy has 33 pencils. How many packages of pencils did Marcy's sister give her?

____

19. Marty has 15 soccer trophies. He would like to place an equal number of trophies on each of 5 shelves. How many trophies should he put on each shelf? Write a number sentence to solve.

____

20. There are 36 students going on a field trip. The children are split into groups. There are 9 groups. How many students are in each group?

____

STOP

Unit 4 Performance Assessment

Mix and Match

- ***Target Skill:*** Skill: Divide facts through 12.
- ***Additional Skills:*** Use inverse operations of multiplication and division. Multiply facts through 10.

Task Description: This task requires students to match a divisor, dividend, and a quotient from 3 columns of 10 rows. There is only one match for each. Students will then write a multiplication sentence to check their division.

Preparing: You may wish to review fact families with students.

Materials	Group Size	Time on Task
Paper Pencil	1 to 2 students	1 day

Guiding: Remind students that when dividing facts there should be no remainder.

Observing/ Monitoring: As you move among the students, pose the following questions:

How do you know that your division facts are correct?

How can you check your answers?

Unit 4 Performance Assessment Scoring Rubric

Mix and Match!

Score	Explanation
3	Students demonstrate an efficient strategy and a thorough approach that enables them to solve the problem completely. A satisfactory answer: • has a match for each divisor, dividend, and quotient; • checks each quotient with a multiplication sentence. Students are able to complete the problem quickly and have all of the above correct solutions.
2	Students demonstrate a strategy that enables them to solve most of the problem correctly. The strategy is somewhat disorganized, making it less efficient. A solution is found but errors are contained. Students may: • divide correctly but not match each quotient; • check division with a multiplication sentence for each quotient. Students may have some difficulty determining all solutions correctly but demonstrate an understanding of general concepts.
1	Students demonstrate a confused strategy, which leads to difficulty solving the problem. Most answers are incorrect, but students demonstrate knowledge of at least one concept being assessed, such as dividing or multiplying correctly.

Name ______________________________

Unit 4 Performance Assessment Student Activity

Mix and Match

You will need

- Pencil
- Paper

Take one number from each column to make division problems.

All of the numbers should divide evenly.

Divisors	Dividends	Quotients
2	12	3
5	15	4
6	44	6
7	48	7
10	63	8
11	70	9
12	132	11

1. Match a divisor to a dividend and a quotient. Use each number only once.

____

2. Write a related multiplication sentence to check your division.

____

Unit 4 – Monitoring Student Progress

☐ **Form A** ☐ **Form B**

Name ______________________ Date ______________

Directions: This test targets selected objectives. For each item that is answered incorrectly, cross out the item number. Then record the number of correct responses in the column labeled **Number of Correct Responses.** Add to find the **Total Number of Correct Responses** and record the total. Use this total to determine the **Total Test Score** and the **Total Percent Correct.**

Strand • Objective(s)	Item Numbers	Number of Correct Responses
Number Sense, Concepts, and Operations • Use properties of multiplication. • Multiply facts through 12. • Review patterns in a multiplication table. • Divide facts through 12. • Use inverse operations of multiplication and division. • Use expressions to multiply and divide. • Use skills and strategies to solve problems.	1, 2, 3, 4, 5, 6, 7, 8, 9, 10, 11, 12, 13, 14, 15, 16, 17, 18, 19, 20, 21, 22, 23, 24, 25, 26, 27, 28, 29, 30, 31, 32, 33, 34, 35, 36, 37, 38, 39, 40	/40
Total Number of Correct Responses		
Total Test Score		/40
Total Percent Correct		%

Name ______________________________

Read each question carefully. Darken the circle on your answer sheet for the correct answer.

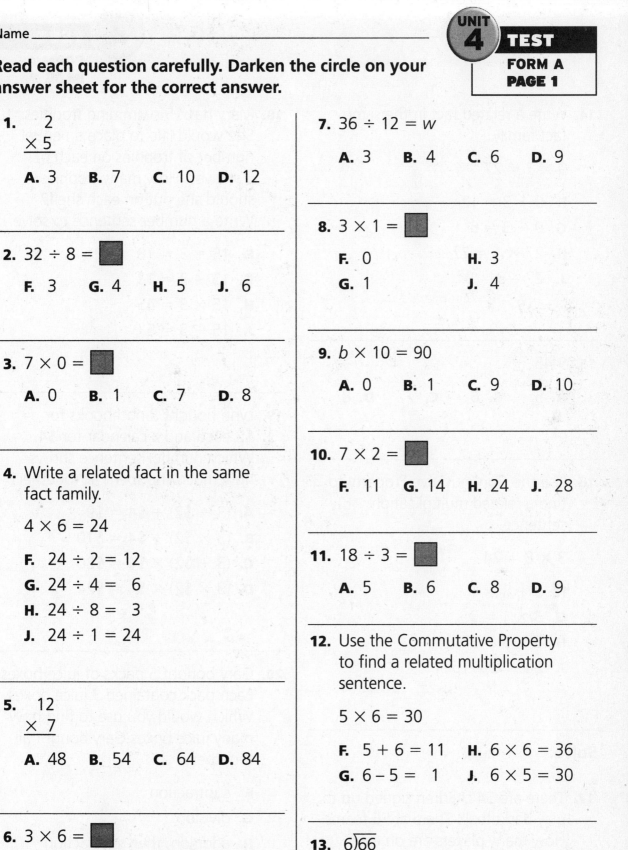

1. $\begin{array}{r} 2 \\ \times 5 \\ \hline \end{array}$

A. 3 **B.** 7 **C.** 10 **D.** 12

2. 32 ÷ 8 = ■

F. 3 **G.** 4 **H.** 5 **J.** 6

3. 7 × 0 = ■

A. 0 **B.** 1 **C.** 7 **D.** 8

4. Write a related fact in the same fact family.

4 × 6 = 24

F. 24 ÷ 2 = 12
G. 24 ÷ 4 = 6
H. 24 ÷ 8 = 3
J. 24 ÷ 1 = 24

5. $\begin{array}{r} 12 \\ \times 7 \\ \hline \end{array}$

A. 48 **B.** 54 **C.** 64 **D.** 84

6. 3 × 6 = ■

F. 13 **G.** 18 **H.** 42 **J.** 72

7. 36 ÷ 12 = *w*

A. 3 **B.** 4 **C.** 6 **D.** 9

8. 3 × 1 = ■

F. 0 **H.** 3
G. 1 **J.** 4

9. *b* × 10 = 90

A. 0 **B.** 1 **C.** 9 **D.** 10

10. 7 × 2 = ■

F. 11 **G.** 14 **H.** 24 **J.** 28

11. 18 ÷ 3 = ■

A. 5 **B.** 6 **C.** 8 **D.** 9

12. Use the Commutative Property to find a related multiplication sentence.

5 × 6 = 30

F. 5 + 6 = 11 **H.** 6 × 6 = 36
G. 6 − 5 = 1 **J.** 6 × 5 = 30

13. $6\overline{)66}$

A. 9 **B.** 10 **C.** 11 **D.** 12

GO ON

Name ____________________

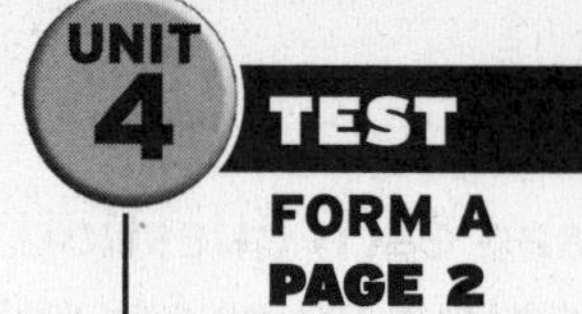

14. Write a related fact in the same fact family.

$9 \times 3 = 27$

F. $9 + 3 = 12$
G. $9 - 3 = 6$
H. $27 \times 1 = 27$
J. $27 \div 3 = 9$

---

15. $9\overline{)45}$

A. 5 **B.** 6 **C.** 7 **D.** 8

---

16. Use the Commutative Property to find a related multiplication sentence.

$3 \times 8 = 24$

F. $3 + 8 = 1$
G. $3 \times 1 = 3$
H. $8 \times 3 = 24$
J. $24 - 8 = 16$

Solve.

17. There are 54 children signed up to play basketball. There are 6 teams. How many players are on each team?

A. 7 players **C.** 9 players
B. 8 players **D.** 10 players

18. Mary has 15 swimming trophies. She would like to place an equal number of trophies on each of 3 shelves. How many trophies should she put on each shelf? Write a number sentence to solve.

F. $15 + 3 = 18$
G. $15 - 2 = 13$
H. $15 \times 3 = 45$
J. $15 \div 3 = 5$

---

19. Lynn bought 3 notebooks for \$2 each and a calendar for \$4. Which number sentence shows how much she spent all together?

A. $(3 + \$2) + \$4 = \$9$
B. $(3 \times \$2) + \$4 = \$10$
C. $(3 + \$2) \times \$4 = \$20$
D. $(3 \times \$2) \times \$4 = \$24$

---

20. Gary bought 5 packs of juice boxes. Each pack contained 3 juice boxes. Which would you use to find how many juice boxes Gary bought all together?

F. subtraction
G. division
H. addition, then subtraction
J. multiplication

GO ON

Name ______________________________

21. $\begin{array}{r} 6 \\ \times 3 \\ \hline \end{array}$

A. 2 **B.** 3 **C.** 9 **D.** 18

22. 42 ÷ 6 = ■

F. 6 **G.** 7 **H.** 8 **J.** 9

23. 12 ÷ 1 = ■

A. 0 **B.** 1 **C.** 12 **D.** 13

24. Write a related fact in the same fact family.

6 × 8 = 48

F. 48 ÷ 2 = 24
G. 48 ÷ 3 = 16
H. 48 ÷ 4 = 12
J. 48 ÷ 6 = 8

25. $\begin{array}{r} 12 \\ \times 9 \\ \hline \end{array}$

A. 96 **B.** 98 **C.** 99 **D.** 108

26. 3 × 3 = ■

F. 0 **G.** 6 **H.** 9 **J.** 12

27. Find the missing number.

$35 \div 7 = t$

A. 4 **B.** 5 **C.** 6 **D.** 7

28. 8 × 1 = ■

F. 0 **G.** 1 **H.** 8 **J.** 9

29. Find the missing factor.

$c \times 8 = 96$

A. 8 **B.** 9 **C.** 11 **D.** 12

30. 9 × 4 = ■

F. 5 **G.** 13 **H.** 36 **J.** 49

31. 72 ÷ 8 = ■

A. 6 **B.** 7 **C.** 8 **D.** 9

32. Use the Commutative Property to find a related multiplication sentence.

10 × 7 = 70

F. 7 × 10 = 70 **H.** 10 − 7 = 3
G. 10 + 7 = 17 **J.** 35 × 2 = 70

33. $7\overline{)49}$

A. 6 **B.** 7 **C.** 8 **D.** 9

Name ____________________

UNIT 4 TEST
FORM A
PAGE 4

34. Write a related fact in the same fact family.

$7 \times 4 = 28$

F. $4 + 7 = 11$
G. $7 - 4 = 3$
H. $14 \times 2 = 28$
J. $28 \div 7 = 4$

35. $5\overline{)30}$

A. 4 **B.** 6 **C.** 8 **D.** 10

36. Use the Commutative Property to find a related multiplication sentence.

$6 \times 3 = 18$

F. $6 + 3 = 9$
G. $6 - 3 = 3$
H. $3 \times 6 = 18$
J. $18 - 3 = 6$

37. There are 21 campers signed up for canoe lessons. Each canoe will hold 3 campers. How many canoes are needed?

A. 63 canoes
B. 18 canoes
C. 7 canoes
D. 3 canoes

38. Tyler has 32 CDs. He put them into 4 CD wallets. Each wallet had the same number of CDs. How many CDs did each wallet have? Write a number sentence to solve.

F. $32 \div 4 = 8$ **H.** $32 + 4 = 36$
G. $32 - 4 = 28$ **J.** $32 \times 4 = 128$

39. Mario bought 2 bags of apples for \$3 each and a container of orange juice for \$4. Which number sentence shows how much he spent all together?

A. $(2 \times 3) \times \$4 = \$24$
B. $(2 + 3) + \$4 = \$9$
C. $(2 \times \$3) + \$4 = \$10$
D. $(2 + 3) \times \$4 = \$20$

40. Lisa had 16 pencils. She gave the same number of pencils to each of 8 students. What operation would you use to find how many pencils Lisa gave to each student?

F. addition
G. division
H. multiplication
J. division, then addition

STOP

Name ______________________________

TEST
FORM B
PAGE 1

Read each question carefully. Fill in the correct answer in the space provided.

1. $\begin{array}{r} 3 \\ \times\ 6 \\ \hline \end{array}$

____

2. 36 ÷ 9 = ______

____

3. 11 × 0 = ______

____

4. Write a related fact in the same fact family.

5 × 3 = 15

____

____

5. $\begin{array}{r} 14 \\ \times\ 5 \\ \hline \end{array}$

6. 4 × 7 = ______

____

7. 48 ÷ 4 = ______

____

8. 5 × 1 = ______

____

9. Write the missing factor.

b × 10 = 60

____

____

10. 7 × 7 = ______

GO ON

Name ____________________

UNIT 4 TEST
FORM B
PAGE 2

11. $14 \div 2 =$ ______

12. Use the Commutative Property to write a related multiplication sentence.

$4 \times 7 = 28$

______

13. $6\overline{)48} =$ ______

14. Write a related fact in the same fact family.

$6 \times 4 = 24$

______

15. $7\overline{)35} =$ ______

16. Use the Commutative Property to write a related multiplication sentence.

$12 \times 8 = 96$

______

17. There are 60 children signed up to play baseball. There are 5 teams. How many players are on each team?

______

18. Mary has 20 swimming trophies. She would like to place an equal number of trophies on each of 4 shelves. How many trophies should she place on each shelf?

Write a number sentence to solve.

______

19. David bought 4 notebooks for \$3 each and a calendar for \$5. Write a number sentence that shows how much money he spent all together.

______

20. Eddie bought 4 packs of batteries. Each pack contained 6 batteries. What operation would you use to find out how many batteries Eddie bought all together?

______

STOP

Name ____________________

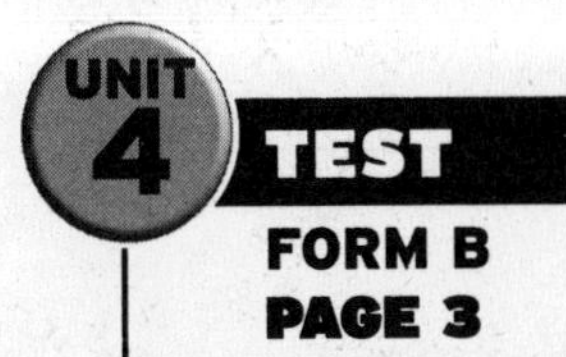

21. $\begin{array}{r} 7 \\ \times\ 3 \\ \hline \end{array}$

____

22. $66 \div 6 =$ ______

____

23. $15 \div 1 =$ ______

____

24. Write a related fact in the same fact family.

$7 \times 9 = 63$

____

____

25. $\begin{array}{r} 12 \\ \times\ 7 \\ \hline \end{array}$

26. $5 \times 2 =$ ______

____

27. Write the missing number.

$64 \div 8 = t$

____

____

28. $19 \times 1 =$ ______

____

29. Write the missing factor.

$c \times 4 = 44$

____

____

30. $9 \times 11 =$ ______

GO ON

Name ______________________

UNIT 4 TEST
FORM B
PAGE 4

31. $56 \div 7 =$ ______

____

32. Use the Commutative Property to write a related multiplication sentence.

$9 \times 8 = 72$

____

____

33. $5\overline{)25} =$ ______

____

34. Write a related fact in the same fact family.

$2 \times 9 = 18$

____

____

35. $4\overline{)12} =$ ______

____

36. Use the Commutative Property to write a related multiplication sentence.

$5 \times 6 = 30$

____

37. There are 22 campers signed up to go canoeing. Each canoe will hold 2 campers. How many canoes are needed?

____

____

38. Scott has 45 CDs. He put them into 5 CD wallets. Each wallet has the same number of CDs. How many CDs does each wallet hold?

Write a number sentence to solve.

____

____

39. Luigi bought 2 boxes of doughnuts for $5 each and a cup of coffee for $1. Write a number sentence that shows how much he spent all together.

____

____

40. Patricia had 18 markers. She gave the same number of markers to each of 6 students. What operation would you use to find out how many markers Patricia gave to each student?

____

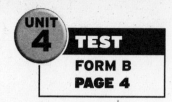

STOP

Chapter 9 – Teacher Interview

Core Concept: *Multiplying by 1-Digit Numbers*

Student Activity: Students demonstrate an understanding of multiplying by a 1-digit number when asked to solve an expression such as 780 × 4.

Teacher Question 1:

- What is the product of 10 × 4?

Understanding Student Response	Practice and Improvement
Students who say 4 or 10.	Review lesson 2 to help students practice multiplying.

Teacher Question 2:

- Which operation do you use to find the product of 78 and 4?

Understanding Student Response	Practice and Improvement
Students who say addition, subtraction, or division.	Review Chapter 7 lesson 1 to help students recognize the terms associated with multiplication.

Teacher Question 3:

- What is the product of 780 × 4?

Understanding Student Response	Practice and Improvement
Students who say 28,320.	Review lesson 3 to help students review regrouping when multiplying.
Students who say 2,832.	Review lesson 3 to help students review regrouping when multiplying.

Chapter 9 – Journal Writing

Encourage students to generate their own journal entries related to math ideas in general or to concepts in this chapter. For students requiring guidance, present the following journal prompt:

- If you are estimating when multiplying by a 1-digit number, how is rounding used? How is the number of zeroes in the product determined?

  (Responses should indicate that rounding is used with the number that has the greatest place value; the number of zeroes in that number will give a good indication of the number of zeroes in the product.)

JOURNAL WRITING/PROBLEM SOLVING

There are 57 pencils in each of 4 boxes in the school bookstore. Estimate the total number of pencils in the bookstore.

Read

Have students find the answer to the problem. Then ask them to write a few sentences telling—

- how they used rounding in the problem
- if the number of zeroes in the product equal the number of zeroes in the number being multiplied

Have students make up another problem with different information for which they would have to follow the same procedure. Then have students solve the problem and supply the correct response.

Plan

Students must know how to round the number being multiplied to the largest place value and remember to include the correct number of zeroes in the product.

Solve

The correct response to the assigned problem is 240. Students had to round the number being multiplied to the nearest ten and then multiply correctly.

Look Back

A correct response demonstrates the ability to know how to round numbers to the greatest place value and multiply by a 1-digit number correctly. (See scoring rubric on page 7.)

Chapter 9 – Monitoring Student Progress

☐ **Form A** ☐ **Form B**

Name ____________________ Date ____________

Directions: For each item that is answered incorrectly, cross out the item number. Then record the number of correct responses in the appropriate Student Score column. If the student has not met the Criterion Score for an objective, circle the student's score. Recommended assignments are listed in the Prescription Table on the next page.

Objective	Item Numbers	Criterion Score	Student Score
A. Multiply multiples of 10, 100, and 1,000.	1, 4, 7, 10, 13, 15	5/6	/6
B. Multiply multi-digit numbers.	3, 6, 9, 12	3/4	/4
C. Estimate products, including money.	2, 5, 8, 11, 14, 16	5/6	/6
D. Use skills and strategies to solve problems.	17, 18, 19, 20	3/4	/4
Total Test Score		16/20	/20
Total Percent Correct			%

Chapter 9 – Prescription Table

The following chart correlates the tested objectives for this chapter to supplementary materials that meet the individual needs of the students. The Reteach and Practice pages are designed for students who need further instruction in the math concepts taught in this chapter. The Enrich pages are designed for students who need advanced challenges.

Objective	Reteach	Practice	Enrich
A. Multiply multiples of 10, 100, and 1,000.	157	158	159
B. Multiply multi-digit numbers.	160, 163	161, 164	162, 165
C. Estimate products, including money.	166	167	168
D. Use skills and strategies to solve problems.	169	170	171

Name ______________________________

Read each question carefully. Darken the circle on your answer sheet for the correct answer.

1. $\begin{array}{r} 30 \\ \times\ 5 \\ \hline \end{array}$

A. 15 **C.** 1,500
B. 150 **D.** 15,000

2. Which is the best estimate?

5 × 64

F. 300 **H.** 500
G. 400 **J.** 600

3. 8 × 32 = ☐

A. 240 **C.** 250
B. 246 **D.** 256

4. $\begin{array}{r} 800 \\ \times\ 2 \\ \hline \end{array}$

F. 160 **H.** 16,000
G. 1,600 **J.** 160,000

5. Which is the best estimate?

5 × 323

A. 1,000 **C.** 2,000
B. 1,500 **D.** 2,500

6. 9 × 44 = ☐

F. 366 **H.** 386
G. 376 **J.** 396

7. $\begin{array}{r} 300 \\ \times\ 9 \\ \hline \end{array}$

A. 27 **C.** 2,700
B. 270 **D.** 27,000

8. Which is the best estimate?

7 × $18.95

F. $30 **H.** $140
G. $50 **J.** $200

9. 8 × 74 = ☐

A. 542 **C.** 572
B. 562 **D.** 592

10. $\begin{array}{r} 4{,}000 \\ \times\ 3 \\ \hline \end{array}$

F. 120 **H.** 12,000
G. 1,200 **J.** 120,000

GO ON

Name ______________________________

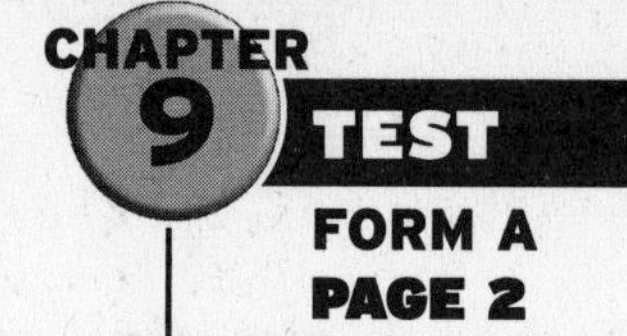

11. Which is the best estimate?

3 × 9,398

A. 2,700 **C.** 27,000
B. 3,000 **D.** 30,000

---

12. 5 × 79 = ■

F. 350 **H.** 385
G. 355 **J.** 395

13.
$$\begin{array}{r} 70 \\ \times\ 6 \\ \hline \end{array}$$

A. 420 **C.** 42,00
B. 4,200 **D.** 420,000

---

14. Which is the best estimate?

8 × 829

F. 1,600 **H.** 7,200
G. 6,400 **J.** 10,000

15.
$$\begin{array}{r} 4{,}000 \\ \times\ \ \ 5 \\ \hline \end{array}$$

A. 200 **C.** 20,000
B. 2,000 **D.** 200,000

---

16. Which is the best estimate?

5 × $32.75

F. $40 **H.** $150
G. $80 **J.** $200

---

17. Sally earned $2,209 every month. About how much did she earn in 5 months?

A. $10,000 **C.** $20,000
B. $15,000 **D.** $30,000

---

18. A factory can produce 8,000 small parts every day. How many small parts can be processed in 9 days?

F. 720,000 small parts
G. 72,000 small parts
H. 7,200 small parts
J. 720 small parts

---

19. Ken made 9 bowls to sell. Each bowl cost $18.79. About how much did Ken earn?

A. $200 **C.** $60
B. $100 **D.** $30

---

20. A magazine had 92,670 subscribers. Each subscriber pays a bill of $4 per month. About how much does the magazine collect from its subscribers each month?

F. $900,000
G. $400,000
H. $360,000
J. $90,000

STOP

Name ______________________________

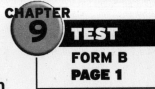

Read each question carefully. Fill in the correct answer in the space provided.

1. $\begin{array}{r} 70 \\ \times \ 8 \\ \hline \end{array}$

____

2. Estimate.

8×47

____

3. $4 \times 87 =$ ______

____

4. $\begin{array}{r} 600 \\ \times \quad 3 \\ \hline \end{array}$

____

5. Estimate.

3×986

____

6. $7 \times 54 =$ ______

____

7. $400 \times 9 =$ ______

____

8. Estimate.

$8 \times \$37.42$

____

9. $\begin{array}{r} 91 \\ \times \ 6 \\ \hline \end{array}$

____

10. $\begin{array}{r} 9{,}000 \\ \times \quad 5 \\ \hline \end{array}$

GO ON

Name ____________________

CHAPTER 9 TEST
FORM B
PAGE 2

11. Estimate.

2 × 918

____

12. 8 × 36 = ______

13.

$$\begin{array}{r} 400 \\ \times \quad 7 \\ \hline \end{array}$$

14. Estimate.

3 × 425

____

15.

$$\begin{array}{r} 6{,}000 \\ \times \quad 9 \\ \hline \end{array}$$

16. Estimate.

7 × $81.85

____

Solve.

17. Belle earned $2,234 every month. About how much did she earn in 8 months?

____

18. A factory makes 7,000 widgets every month. How many widgets can the company make in 3 months?

____

19. Ruth bought 6 comic books to read. Each book cost $3.85. About how much did Ruth spend?

____

20. Harry set a goal of writing 34 pages of his novel per week. If he maintains that pace, how many pages will he write in 9 weeks?

____

STOP

Chapter 10 – Teacher Interview

Core Concept: *Functions*

Student Activity: Students demonstrate an understanding of writing an equation to describe data given in a word problem or in a function table.

Teacher Question 1:

- It takes Chris 18 minutes to ride to the park. It takes Megan 6 minutes. It takes Chris 27 minutes to ride to school. It takes Megan 9 minutes. It takes Chris 39 minutes to ride to the lake. It takes Megan 13 minutes. Write an equation you can use to figure out how many minutes *y* it takes Chris to ride to the baseball field if it takes Megan *x* minutes to ride the same distance.

Understanding Student Response	Practice and Improvement
Students who answer that Chris takes three times as long as Megan.	Review lesson 4 to help students write an equation from data given.
Students who are unable to answer the question.	Review lesson 4 to help students learn how to make and read a function table and write an equation to represent the data.

Teacher Question 2:

- It takes Megan 12 minutes to ride to the baseball field. How long does it take Chris to ride the same distance?

Understanding Student Response	Practice and Improvement
Students who say 4 minutes.	Review lesson 5 to help students understand how to evaluate a function.
Students who give an answer other than 36 or the one above.	Review lesson 5 to help students learn how to substitute a known value for a variable.

Teacher Question 3:

- How can you graph the equation $y = 3x$ for $x = 12$?

Understanding Student Response	Practice and Improvement
Students whose answers places the point at (36, 12)	Review lesson 5 to help students understand how to graph a function.
Students who answer with any other incorrect point.	Review lesson 5 to help students learn how to substitute a known value for a variable.

Chapter 10 – Journal Writing

Encourage students to generate their own journal entries related to math ideas in general or to concepts in this chapter. For students requiring guidance, present the following journal prompt:

- Given an equation, what steps do you have to take to graph a function?

  (Responses should include substituting the known values for x and then using a coordinate graph to plot the points. Students should know that x is the first coordinate and y is the second coordinate.)

JOURNAL WRITING/PROBLEM SOLVING

Billy works on a fishing boat during the summer. He earns $1,256 each week for 9 weeks. How much money does he make altogether?

Read

Have students find the answer to the problem. Then ask them to write a few sentences about—

- what information they needed to solve the problem
- how they used regrouping to find the product

Have students make up another problem for which they would have to follow the same procedure, but with different information. Students should also supply the correct response.

Plan

Students must understand that Billy earns $1,256 each week for nine weeks, so they need to multiply to find the total amount of money that he earned.

Solve

The correct response to the problem is $11,304. They need to multiply each place by 9, to get 54 + 450 + 1,800 + 9,000 = 11,304.

Look Back

A correct response demonstrates the ability to understand the requirements of the problem, and to use the appropriate process for solving the problem. In addition, a correct response demonstrates an understanding of how to use regrouping to multiply larger numbers by a 1-digit number. (See scoring rubric on page 7.)

Chapter 10 – Monitoring Student Progress

☐ **Form A** ☐ **Form B**

Name ______________________ Date ______________

Directions: For each item that is answered incorrectly, cross out the item number. Then record the number of correct responses in the appropriate Student Score column. If the student has not met the Criterion Score for an objective, circle the student's score. Recommended assignments are listed in the Prescription Table on the next page.

Objective	Item Numbers	Criterion Score	Student Score
A. Multiply multi-digit numbers.	1, 2, 3, 4, 5, 7, 8, 9, 10, 11, 13, 14, 16	12/13	/13
B. Use and graph functions.	6, 12, 15	2/3	/3
C. Use skills and strategies to solve problems.	17, 18, 19, 20	3/4	/4
Total Test Score		17/20	/20
Total Percent Correct			%

Chapter 10 – Prescription Table

The following chart correlates the tested objectives for this chapter to supplementary materials that meet the individual needs of the students. The Reteach and Practice pages are designed for students who need further instruction in the math concepts taught in this chapter. The Enrich pages are designed for students who need advanced challenges.

Objective	Reteach	Practice	Enrich
A. Multiply multi-digit numbers.	172, 175, 178	173, 176, 179	174, 177, 180
B. Use and graph functions.	181, 184	182, 185	183, 186
C. Use skills and strategies to solve problems.	187, 188	189	

Name ______________________________

CHAPTER 10 TEST
FORM A
PAGE 1

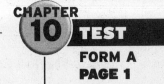

Read each question carefully. Darken the circle on your answer sheet for the correct answer.

1. $53.28
× 4

A. $212.32 **C.** $213.12
B. $212.82 **D.** $213.32

2. 400,297
× 2

F. 800,494 **H.** 800,604
G. 800,594 **J.** 900,594

3. 6 × 5,000 = ■

A. 300 **C.** 30,000
B. 3,000 **D.** 300,000

4. 4 × 23,623 = ■

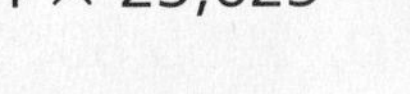

F. 94,492 **H.** 92,482
G. 92,492 **J.** 82,482

5. $162.74
× 5

A. $800.50 **C.** $813.50
B. $800.70 **D.** $813.70

6. Annette drinks 1 bottle of water for every 2 miles she runs. How far does she run when she drinks 4 bottles?

x	1	2	3	4
y	2	4	6	■

F. 7 **G.** 8 **H.** 9 **J.** 10

7. 82,981
× 7

A. 580,867 **C.** 581,767
B. 580,887 **D.** 581,867

8. $92.15 × 6 = ■

F. $550.90 **H.** $555.60
G. $552.90 **J.** $558.30

9. 5 × 400 = ■

A. 2 **C.** 200
B. 20 **D.** 2,000

10. 53,206
× 4

F. 212,804 **H.** 214,804
G. 212,824 **J.** 214,824

GO ON

Name ____________________

11. $\begin{array}{r} \$60{,}840 \\ \times \quad 8 \\ \hline \end{array}$

A. $480,420 **C.** $486,432
B. $486,270 **D.** $486,720

---

12. Complete the table for $c = 4d$.

d	1	2	3	4
c	4	8	12	■

F. 16 **G.** 18 **H.** 20 **J.** 24

---

13. 38,042 × 3 = ■

A. 114,126 **C.** 112,126
B. 114,120 **D.** 112,120

---

14. $45,280 × 8 = ■

F. 360,240 **H.** 362,240
G. 362,200 **J.** 362,440

---

15. Complete the table for $s = 4t - 2$

t	1	2	3	4	5
s	2	6	10	14	■

A. 10 **B.** 15 **C.** 18 **D.** 22

---

16. 93,498 × 4 = ■

F. 373,992 **H.** 376,992
G. 374,992 **J.** 382,992

---

17. For a concert, there are 3 chairs in the first row, 7 chairs in the second row, and 11 chairs in the third row. If the pattern continues, how many chairs will there be in the fifth row?

A. 15 chairs **C.** 19 chairs
B. 17 chairs **D.** 21 chairs

---

18. The first year of his garden, Mr. Kolesar planted 3 rows of carrots. During the second year, he planted 5 rows of carrots. The third year he planted 7 rows of carrots. If he continues this pattern how many rows of carrots will he plant the fourth year? Describe the pattern.

F. 9 rows; the number of rows is increased by 2 each year.

G. 9 rows; the number of rows is increased by 3 each year.

H. 10 rows; the number of rows is increased by 3 each year.

J. 11 rows; the number of rows is increased by 4 each year.

---

19. Mr. Wurtzel bought bicycles for each of his 4 children. Each bicycle cost $238.95. What was the total cost for all of the bicycles?

A. $950.80 **C.** $955.80
B. $955.00 **D.** $965.80

---

20. The cost of Louis's auto insurance is $382.39 each month. What is the total cost for 6 months of insurance?

F. $2,290.34 **H.** $2,294.30
G. $2,292.30 **J.** $2,294.34

STOP

Name ______________________

Read each question carefully. Fill in the correct answer in the space provided.

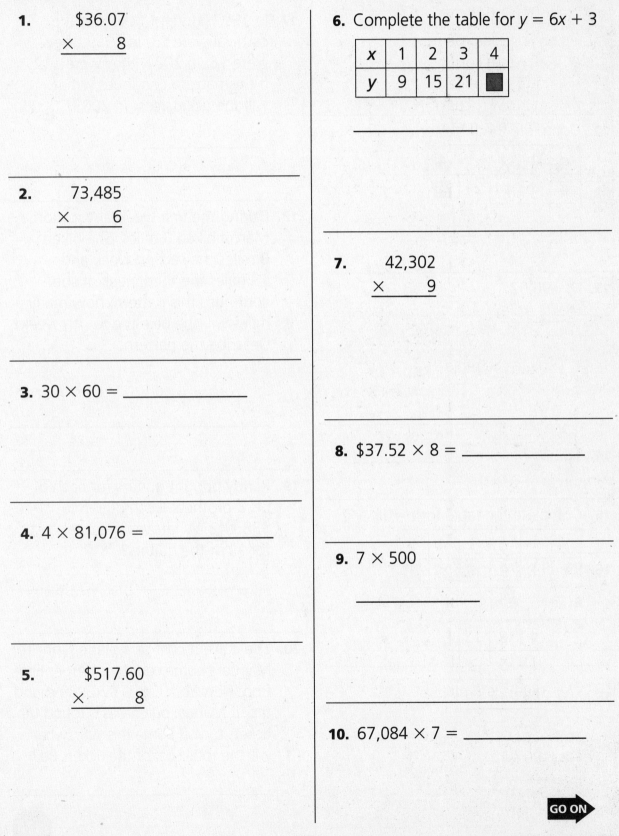

1. $36.07
× 8

____

2. 73,485
× 6

____

3. $30 \times 60 =$ ______________

____

4. $4 \times 81{,}076 =$ ______________

____

5. $517.60
× 8

6. Complete the table for $y = 6x + 3$

x	1	2	3	4
y	9	15	21	■

____

____

7. 42,302
× 9

____

8. $37.52 × 8 = ______________

____

9. 7×500

____

____

10. $67{,}084 \times 7 =$ ______________

GO ON

Name ______________________

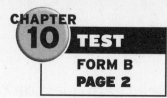

11. $\$45,132 \times 6$

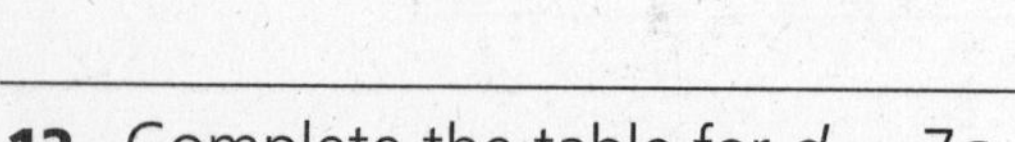

12. Complete the table for $d = 7c$.

d	1	2	3	4
c	7	14	21	■

____

13. $90,027 \times 5$

14. $\$82,651 \times 9 =$ ______________

15. Complete the table for $t = 8s - 7$.

s	1	2	3	4	5
t	1	9	17	25	■

____

16. $407,213 \times 2 =$ ______________

Solve.

17. In 1997, student tickets to the carnival were $3. In 1999, they were $6. In 2001, they were $12. If this pattern continues, what will the tickets cost in 2003?

____

18. During the first week of vacation, Marcia biked 3 miles. She biked 8 miles the second week and 13 miles the third week. If she continues this pattern, how many miles will she bike the fourth week? Describe the pattern.

____

19. Randy bought guitars for each of his 3 brothers. Each guitar cost $383.42. What was the total cost for all of the guitars?

____

20. The current cost of a plane flight to Manuel's home country of Argentina from New York City is $742.38 round trip. If Manual purchases 4 round trip tickets to visit home this year, what will the total cost of the tickets be?

____

STOP

Unit 5 Performance Assessment

A Fun Project!

- ***Target Skill:*** Multiply multi-digit numbers.
- ***Additional Skills:*** Multiply multiples of 10, 100, and 1,000; collect and organize data in tables and graphs.

Task Description: This task requires students to calculate the cost of printing different books based on book length and the number of copies to be printed.

Preparing: You may wish to have students talk about the costs of printing a book. Note that some costs, such as buying paper and ink, are related to the number of books. Ask students to list costs that might not change with the number of books printed. Introduce the concept of bulk buying: the more you buy, the less each unit costs. Ask how this would affect the prices they calculate in this activity.

Materials	Group Size	Time on Task
Calculator (optional)	2 to 3 students	1–2 days

Guiding: Remind students that when multiplying a whole number by 10, you simply add one zero. When multiplying by 100, simply add two zeros, and when multiplying by 1,000, simply add three zeros.

Tell students that the costs of printing the books should include dollar and cents amounts (such as $0.79, $20.34, etc.) change.

Observing/ Monitoring: As you move among the students, pose the following questions:

What additional information from class can help you solve this problem?

How can the Commutative Property of Multiplication be used?

Unit 5 Performance Assessment Scoring Rubric

A Fun Project!

Score	Explanation
3	Students demonstrate an efficient strategy and a thorough approach that enables them to solve the problem completely. A satisfactory answer: • has the table filled in correctly; • shows work and calculates that the cost of the copies of "A New School" was $19.11; • shows work and calculates that 89 copies of "Keeping Friends" produces 2,848 sheets of paper at $0.07 per copy, which will cost $199.36. Students are able to complete the problem quickly and have all of the above correct solutions.
2	Students demonstrate a strategy that enables them to solve most of the problem correctly. The strategy is somewhat disorganized, making it less efficient. A solution is found, but errors are contained. Students may: • be unable to determine how many sheets of paper are needed for 89 copies of "Keeping Friends"; • confuse multiples of 10, 100, and 1,000; • use division instead of multiplication once. Students may have some difficulty determining all solutions correctly, but demonstrate an understanding of general concepts.
1	Students demonstrate a confused strategy, which leads to difficulty solving the problem. Most answers are incorrect, but students demonstrate knowledge of at least one concept being assessed. Students may: • understand multiples of 10, or multiplying decimals; OR • complete the table correctly; OR • calculate one cost correctly.

Name ______________________________

Unit 5 Performance Assessment Student Activity

A Fun Project!

You will need

- Pencil
- Paper

David Jenkins has written several books for younger students for a school project. *A New School* is a 5-page book, while *Brothers and Sisters* is a 12-page book. *Keeping Friends* is a 32-page book.

David made a table to find out how many sheets of paper he needs for different amounts of copies. He determined that it costs him $0.13 to make each copy of *A New School*. He made 147 copies of this book for the younger students in his district. After that he decided that he also wanted to print 89 copies of *Keeping Friends*.

1. Fill in the table below to show how many sheets of paper he needs to make different amounts of copies.

Number of Sheets of Paper Needed			
Book	**Number of Copies**		
	10	**100**	**1,000**
A New School			
Brothers and Sisters			
Keeping Friends			

2. How much did it cost David to print the 147 copies of *A New School*? Show your work.

3. Use the printing table below. Which cost per sheet amount should he use to print 89 copies of *Keeping Friends*? Determine how much it will cost David to print these copies. Show your work.

Number of Sheets of Paper Needed	Cost per Sheet to Print
1–2,000	$0.09
2,001–5,000	$0.07
5,001–10,000	$0.05

Unit 5 – Monitoring Student Progress

☐ **Form A** ☐ **Form B**

Name ______________________________ Date ________________

Directions: This test targets selected objectives. For each item that is answered incorrectly, cross out the item number. Then record the number of correct responses in the column labeled **Number of Correct Responses.** Add to find the **Total Number of Correct Responses** and record the total. Use this total to determine the **Total Test Score** and the **Total Percent Correct.**

Strand • Objective(s)	Item Numbers	Number of Correct Responses
Number Sense, Concepts, and Operations • Multiply multiples of 10, 100, and 1,000. • Multiply multi-digit numbers. • Estimate products, including money. • Use and graph functions. • Use skills and strategies to solve problems.	1, 2, 3, 4, 5, 6, 7, 8, 9, 10, 11, 12, 13, 14, 15, 16, 17, 18, 19, 20, 21, 22, 23, 24, 25, 26, 27, 28, 29, 30, 31, 32, 33, 34, 35, 36, 37, 38, 39, 40	/40
Total Number of Correct Responses		
Total Test Score		/40
Total Percent Correct		%

Name ____

UNIT 5 TEST
FORM A
PAGE 1

Read each question carefully. Darken the circle on your answer sheet for the correct answer.

1. 40×5

A. 20 **C.** 2,000
B. 200 **D.** 20,000

2. $\$73.29 \times 4$

F. $280.16 **H.** $292.11
G. $282.86 **J.** $293.16

3. Which is the best estimate?

4×72

A. 280 **B.** 320 **C.** 360 **D.** 400

4. A baker uses 1 bag of chocolate chips for every 2 cakes. How many cakes can be baked with 4 bags?

x	1	2	3	4
y	2	4	6	■

F. 7 **G.** 8 **H.** 9 **J.** 10

5. 700×9

A. 63 **C.** 6,300
B. 630 **D.** 63,000

6. $8 \times 312 =$ ■

F. 2,400 **H.** 2,496
G. 2,486 **J.** 2,500

7. Which is the best estimate?

9×413

A. 3,600 **C.** 4,500
B. 4,000 **D.** 5,000

8. One number is 4 more than another number. Find the missing number.

a	1	2	3	4	5
b	5	6	7	8	■

F. 9 **G.** 10 **H.** 11 **J.** 12

9. $2 \times 800 =$ ■

A. 160 **C.** 16,000
B. 1,600 **D.** 160,000

10. $9 \times 64 =$ ■

F. 546 **G.** 566 **H.** 576 **J.** 596

11. Which is the best estimate?

$6 \times \$19.95$

A. $40 **C.** $120
B. $50 **D.** $200

12. Complete the table for $y = 3x$.

x	1	2	3	4
y	3	6	9	■

F. 1 **G.** 7 **H.** 9 **J.** 12

GO ON

Name ______________________________

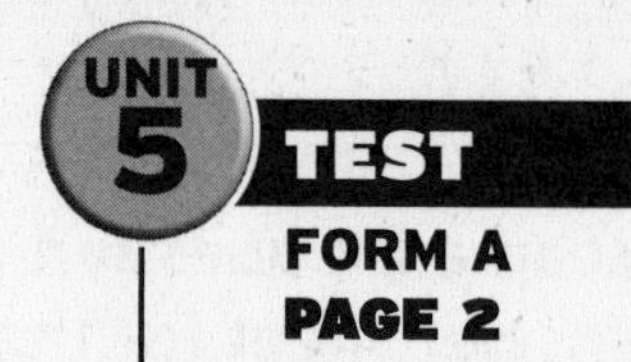

13. $600 \times 3 = \blacksquare$

A. 1,800 **C.** 180,000
B. 18,000 **D.** 1,800,000

---

14. $\begin{array}{r} 300{,}698 \\ \times \quad 2 \\ \hline \end{array}$

F. 600,286 **H.** 602,396
G. 601,396 **J.** 700,396

---

15. Which is the best estimate?

3×986

A. 1,500 **C.** 3,000
B. 2,000 **D.** 6,000

---

16. Complete the table for $p = 2r + 1$.

r	1	2	3	4	5
p	3	5	7	9	■

F. 3 **G.** 6 **H.** 9 **J.** 11

Solve.

17. For a recital, there are 5 chairs in the third row, 9 chairs in the fourth row, and 13 chairs in the fifth row. If the pattern continues, how many chairs will there be in the seventh row?

A. 14 chairs
B. 17 chairs
C. 21 chairs
D. 25 chairs

18. The first year of his garden, Mr. Ramirez planted 2 rows of corn. During the second year, he planted 5 rows of corn. The third year, he planted 8 rows of corn. If he continues this pattern, how many rows of corn will he plant the fourth year? Describe the pattern.

F. 10 rows; the number of rows is increased by 2 each year.
G. 11 rows; the number of rows is increased by 3 each year.
H. 16 rows; the number of rows is doubled each year.
J. 24 rows; the number of previous rows is multiplied by 3.

---

19. Tara bought 8 mugs to paint. Each mug cost $2.75. About how much did Tara spend?

A. $16 **B.** $24 **C.** $30 **D.** $32

---

20. A company can process 2,000 small parts every day. How many small parts can be processed in 7 days?

F. 140 small parts
G. 1,400 small parts
H. 14,000 small parts
J. 140,000 small parts

GO ON

Name ______________________________

UNIT 5 TEST
FORM A
PAGE 3

21. $\begin{array}{r} 80 \\ \times\ 3 \\ \hline \end{array}$

A. 240 **B.** 2,400 **C.** 24,000 **D.** 240,000

---

22. $6 \times 43{,}819 = \blacksquare$

F. 242,864 **G.** 248,864 **H.** 262,914 **J.** 262,964

---

23. Which is the best estimate?

2×918

A. 1,800 **B.** 2,000 **C.** 2,500 **D.** 3,000

---

24. One number is 2 less than another number. Find the missing number.

c	3	4	5	6	7
d	1	2	3	4	■

F. 5 **G.** 6 **H.** 7 **J.** 8

---

25. $\begin{array}{r} 5{,}000 \\ \times\ \ \ \ 2 \\ \hline \end{array}$

A. 100 **B.** 1,000 **C.** 10,000 **D.** 100,000

---

26. $8 \times 74 = \blacksquare$

F. 542 **G.** 562 **H.** 572 **J.** 592

---

27. Which is the best estimate?

7×329

A. 1,400 **B.** 1,600 **C.** 2,100 **D.** 2,800

---

28. Haley packed 3 juice boxes for each scout on the trip. How many juice boxes did she pack for 5 scouts?

x	1	2	3	4	5
y	3	6	9	12	■

F. 10 **G.** 11 **H.** 12 **J.** 15

---

29. $9 \times 400 = \blacksquare$

A. 360 **B.** 3,600 **C.** 36,000 **D.** 360,000

---

30. $2 \times 699 = \blacksquare$

F. 1,288 **G.** 1,298 **H.** 1,388 **J.** 1,398

---

31. Which is the best estimate?

$8 \times 6{,}398$

A. 4,800 **B.** 42,000 **C.** 48,000 **D.** 56,000

---

32. Complete the table for $d = 5c$.

c	1	2	3	4
d	5	10	15	■

F. 16 **G.** 17 **H.** 20 **J.** 25

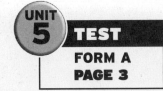

Name ____________________

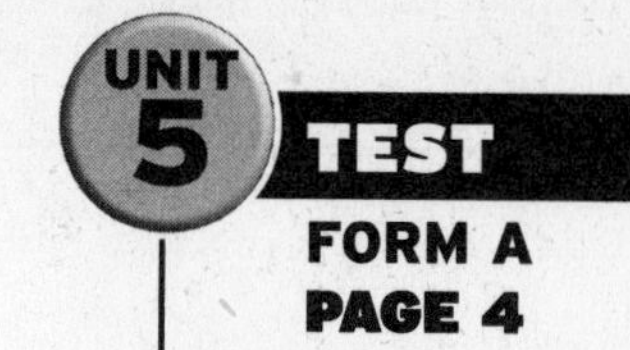

33. $6 \times 7{,}000 = \blacksquare$

A. 420 **C.** 42,000
B. 4,200 **D.** 420,000

---

34. $173.84 × 5

F. $555.40 **H.** $865.42
G. $865.40 **J.** $869.20

---

35. Which is the best estimate for $5 \times \$28.65$?

A. $50 **C.** $150
B. $100 **D.** $200

---

36. Complete the table for $t = 3s - 1$.

s	1	2	3	4	5
t	2	5	8	11	■

F. 12 **G.** 14 **H.** 15 **J.** 16

Solve.

37. In 1995, student tickets to the high school basketball game were $2. In 1997, they were $4. In 1999, they were $6. If this pattern continues, what will the tickets cost in 2001?

A. $7 **C.** $9
B. $8 **D.** $10

38. During the first week of vacation, Mandy read 3 books. She read 5 books the second week and 7 books the third week. If she continues this pattern, how many books will she read the fourth week? Describe the pattern.

F. 9 books; the number of books is increased by 2 each week.
G. 10 books; the number of books is doubled plus 2 each week.
H. 11 books; the number of books is tripled minus 1 each week.
J. 12 books; the number of books is tripled each week.

---

39. Susan earned $3,185 every month. About how much did she earn in 6 months?

A. $12,000 **C.** $24,000
B. $18,000 **D.** $30,000

---

40. The basic cable TV service in Brian's town serves 12,620 users. Each user pays a cable TV bill of $9 per month. How much does the cable TV service collect for basic cable per month?

F. $90,000 **H.** $108,580
G. $98,480 **J.** $113,580

STOP

Name ____________________

UNIT 5 TEST
FORM B
PAGE 1

Read each question carefully. Fill in the correct answer in the space provided.

1. $\begin{array}{r} 80 \\ \times\ 5 \\ \hline \end{array}$

2. $\begin{array}{r} \$63.39 \\ \times\ \quad 3 \\ \hline \end{array}$

3. Estimate.

4×83

____

4. A baker uses 1 bag of chocolate chips for every 3 cakes. How many cakes can be baked with 4 bags?

x	1	2	3	4
y	3	6	9	■

____

5.

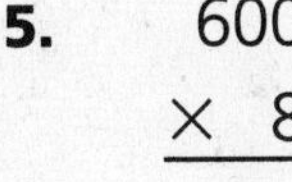

$\begin{array}{r} 600 \\ \times\ 8 \\ \hline \end{array}$

6. $3 \times 812 =$ ________

7. Is 4,500 or 5,000 a better estimate for 9×489 ?

____

8. One number is 6 more than another number. Find the missing number.

a	1	2	3	4	5
b	7	8	9	■	11

____

9. $4 \times 700 =$ ______________

10. $7 \times 64 =$ ______________

GO ON

Name ____________________

UNIT 5 TEST
FORM B
PAGE 2

11. Estimate.

$7 \times \$19.89$

____

12. Complete the table for $y = 6x$

x	1	2	3	4
y	6	12	18	■

____

13. $700 \times 6 =$ ______________

14.

$$\begin{array}{r} 300{,}756 \\ \times \quad\quad 2 \\ \hline \end{array}$$

____

15. Estimate.

$4 \times 1{,}013$

____

16. Complete the table for $p = 2r - 1$

r	1	2	3	4	5
p	1	3	5	7	■

____

17. For a recital, there are 6 chairs in the third row, 11 chairs in the fourth row, and 16 chairs in the fifth row. If the pattern continues, how many chairs will there be in the seventh row?

____

18. When Jorge's dog was one year old she weighed 10 pounds. When she turned two she weighed 14 pounds. When she turned three, she weighed 18 pounds. If she continues this pattern, how much will Jorge's dog weigh when she turns four?

____

19. Tyra pays $4.75 for 1 bag of clay. About how much would she pay for 7 bags of clay?

____

20. A toy company can produce 3,000 die-cast cars each day. How many cars can be produced in 7 days?

____

GO ON

Name ________________________________

21. $\begin{array}{r} 90 \\ \times\ 3 \\ \hline \end{array}$

____

22. 7 × 34,819 = ____________

____

23. Estimate.

2 × 819

____

____

24. One number is 3 less than another number. Find the missing number.

c	3	4	5	6	7
d	0	1	2	3	■

____

____

25. $\begin{array}{r} 6{,}000 \\ \times\ \ \ \ 2 \\ \hline \end{array}$

26. 7 × 81 = ____________

____

27. Is 2,500 or 2,800 a better estimate?

7 × 369

____

____

28. Haley packed 3 granola bars for each scout on the trip. How many granola bars did she pack for 7 scouts?

a	3	4	5	6	7
b	9	12	15	18	■

____

____

29. 4 × 900 = ____________

____

30. 2 × 599 = ____________

GO ON

Name ____________________

31. Estimate.

$8 \times 5,989$

______

32. Complete the table for $q = 9p$

p	1	2	3	4
q	9	18	27	■

______

33. $7 \times 7,000 =$ ______

34.

$$\begin{array}{r} \$134.75 \\ \times \quad 4 \\ \hline \end{array}$$

______

35. Is $100 or $120 a better estimate?

$4 \times \$28.17$

______

36. Complete the table for $t = 4s - 2$

s	1	2	3	4	5
t	2	6	10	14	■

______

37. In 1997, tickets to the high school play were $2. In 1999, they were $5. In 2001 they were $8. If this pattern continues, what will the tickets cost in 2003?

______

38. During the first week of vacation, Tyrone biked 8 miles each day. During the second week he biked 10 miles each day. During the third week he biked 12 miles each day. If this pattern continues, how many miles will Tyrone bike each day during the fifth week of vacation?

______

39. Amy earned $4,885 every month. About how much did she earn in 6 months?

______

40. The local newspaper company in Justin's town has 13,592 subscribers. Each subscriber pays $7.00 per month. How much does the newspaper company collect from the subscribers each month?

______

STOP

Chapter 11 – Teacher Interview

Core Concept: *Multiplying by 2-Digit Numbers*

Student Activity: The student demonstrates an understanding of multiplying by a 2-digit number when asked to solve an expression such as 5,360 × 93.

Teacher Question 1:

- What numeral will be in the ones place of the product of 5,360 and 93?

Understanding Student Response	Practice and Improvement
Students who answer any numeral other than 0.	Review lesson 1 to help students practice multiplying with multiples of 1,000.

Teacher Question 2:

- What is the product of 5,360 and 93?

Understanding Student Response	Practice and Improvement
Students who say 64,320.	Review lesson 5 to help students practice aligning partial products when multiplying a multi-digit number by a 2-digit number.
Students who say 473,380.	Review lesson 5 to help students practice situations with regrouping in multiplication.
Students who say 498,380 or 473,480.	Review lesson 4 to help students understand the importance of regrouping.
Students who say a number other than 498,480 or the above incorrect answers.	Review Chapter 10 to help students practice with multiplication expressions on larger numbers.

Chapter 11 – Journal Writing

Encourage students to generate their own journal entries related to math ideas in general or to concepts in this chapter. For students requiring guidance, present the following journal prompt:

- When you multiply a multiple of 1,000 by a multiple of 10, how do you keep track of the number of zeros in the product?

  (Responses should indicate that the number of zeros in the product are accounted for by the number of zeros in the numbers being multiplied.)

JOURNAL WRITING/PROBLEM SOLVING

Peter ordered 20 boxes of nails for Susan's Hardware Store. There are 8,000 nails per box. How many nails did Peter order in total?

Read

Have students find the answer to the problem. Then ask them to write a few sentences telling—

- how many zeros were in the first number
- how many zeros were in the second number

Have students make up another problem with different information for which they would have to follow the same procedure. Then have students solve the problem and supply the correct response.

Plan

Students must be able to show that the number of zeros in the product are dependent on the number of zeros in both the numbers in the multiplication expression, and be able to multiply correctly.

Solve

The correct response to the assigned problem is 160,000. Students had to account for the correct number of zeros in the product and multiply correctly.

Look Back

A correct response demonstrates the ability to multiply a multiple of 1,000 by a multiple of 10 correctly, with the appropriate amount of zeros present in the product. (See scoring rubric on page 7.)

Chapter 11 – Monitoring Student Progress

☐ Form A ☐ Form B

Name ______________________ Date ______________

Directions: For each item that is answered incorrectly, cross out the item number. Then record the number of correct responses in the appropriate Student Score column. If the student has not met the Criterion Score for an objective, circle the student's score. Recommended assignments are listed in the Prescription Table on the next page.

Objective	Item Numbers	Criterion Score	Student Score
A. Use patterns of multiplication.	1, 4, 7, 10, 13	4/5	/5
B. Multiply by multiples of 10.	2, 5, 8, 11, 14	4/5	/5
C. Multiply by 2-digit numbers.	3, 6, 9, 12, 15	4/5	/5
D. Use skills and strategies to solve problems.	16, 17, 18, 19, 20	4/5	/5
Total Test Score		16/20	/20
Total Percent Correct			%

Chapter 11 – Prescription Table

The following chart correlates the tested objectives for this chapter to supplementary materials that meet the individual needs of the students. The Reteach and Practice pages are designed for students who need further instruction in the math concepts taught in this chapter. The Enrich pages are designed for students who need advanced challenges.

Objective	Reteach	Practice	Enrich
A. Use patterns of multiplication.	192	193	194
B. Multiply by multiples of 10.	195	196	197
C. Multiply by 2-digit numbers.	198, 201	199, 202	200, 203
D. Use skills and strategies to solve problems.	204	205	206

Name ____________________

CHAPTER 11 TEST
FORM A
PAGE 1

Read each question carefully. Darken the circle on your answer sheet for the correct answer.

1. $\begin{array}{r} 500 \\ \times \ 60 \\ \hline \end{array}$

A. 300 **C.** 30,000
B. 3,000 **D.** 300,000

2. 40 × 57 = ■

F. 228 **H.** 2,280
G. 2,028 **J.** 20,280

3. 31 × 47 = ■

A. 1,247 **C.** 1,447
B. 1,257 **D.** 1,457

4. $\begin{array}{r} 7,000 \\ \times \ \ \ 20 \\ \hline \end{array}$

F. 140 **H.** 14,000
G. 1,400 **J.** 140,000

5. 40 × 357 = ■

A. 1,428 **C.** 12,080
B. 1,208 **D.** 14,280

6. 38 × 72 = ■

F. 2,736 **H.** 2,836
G. 2,763 **J.** 2,763

7. 30 × 6,000 = ■

A. 180 **C.** 18,000
B. 1,800 **D.** 180,000

8. $\begin{array}{r} 1,482 \\ \times \ \ \ 30 \\ \hline \end{array}$

F. 4,460 **H.** 44,460
G. 44,400 **J.** 46,460

9. 62 × 28 = ■

A. 1730 **C.** 1,763
B. 1,736 **D.** 17,360

10. 80 × 4,000 = ■

F. 320,000 **H.** 3,200
G. 32,000 **J.** 320

GO ON

Name ______________________________

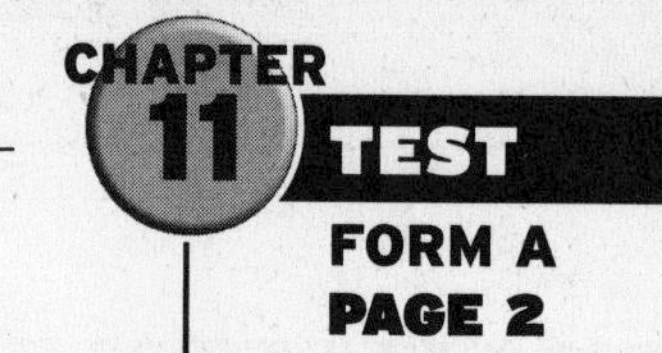

11. 2,489 × 70 = ▢

A. 172,340 **C.** 174,230
B. 173,420 **D.** 174,320

12. 37 × 84 = ▢

F. 3,018 **H.** 3,180
G. 3,108 **J.** 30,108

13. 50 × 3,000 = ▢

A. 1,500 **C.** 150,000
B. 15,000 **D.** 1,500,000

14. 60 × 56 = ▢

F. 3,030 **H.** 3,063
G. 3,036 **J.** 3,360

15. 29 × 67 = ▢

A. 1,943 **C.** 1,493
B. 1,893 **D.** 1,439

16. There are 8 cans of soup in a pack. There are 4 packs in a stack and 6 stacks in a case. Each can is $0.55. How much is a case?

F. $20.90 **H.** $105.60
G. $73.00 **J.** $192.00

17. A warehouse received its first shipment of 11,350 shirts. Then it sent out two shipments of 3,240 shirts each. It then received 4,250 shirts. How many shirts are in the warehouse now?

A. 3,860 shirts **C.** 12,360 shirts
B. 9,120 shirts **D.** 18,840 shirts

18. 34 buses set out together on a trip from New York to Montreal. Each bus held 48 people. How many people took the trip from New York to Montreal?

F. 1,632 people
G. 1,432 people
H. 1,302 people
J. 1,236 people

19. A volunteer can gather 84 signatures per day for an environmental campaign. How many signatures can 25 volunteers gather per day?

A. 2,010 signatures
B. 2,100 signatures
C. 2,200 signatures
D. 20,100 signatures

20. Tickets to a concert cost $18 for adults and $12 for senior citizens. How much will it cost for 22 adults and 34 senior citizens to buy tickets for the concert?

F. $408 **H.** $804
G. $612 **J.** $1,680

STOP

Name ____________________

Read each question carefully. Fill in the correct answer in the space provided.

1. 80 × 90 = ________

2. 60 × 73 = ________

3. 19 × 64 = ________

4.
$$\begin{array}{r} 400 \\ \times\ 70 \\ \hline \end{array}$$

5. 50 × 362 = ________

6. 85 × 61 = ________

7. 8,000 × 30 = ________

8.
$$\begin{array}{r} 4,813 \\ \times\ \ 20 \\ \hline \end{array}$$

9. 73 × 45 = ________

10. 4,000 × 90 = ________

11. 50 × 7,078 = ________

12. 62 × 93 = ________

GO ON

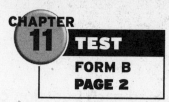

13. $70 \times 6{,}000 =$ ____________

14. $987 \times 30 =$ ____________

15. $24 \times 74 =$ ____________

16. There are 5 pendants in a package. There are 6 packages in a box and 18 boxes in a case. Each pendant sells for $0.25. How much is the case worth?

____

17. A clothing store received its first shipment of 490 pairs of jeans. Then it sent out two shipments of 140 pairs of jeans each. Then the store received 320 more pairs of jeans. How many pairs of jeans does the clothing store have now?

____

18. 24 planes fly each day from Boston to Chicago. Each plane can hold 88 people. If each flight on Monday was full, how many people flew from Boston to Chicago on Monday?

____

19. A bookstore had 49 customers on Wednesday. If each customer spent an average of $32, what was the total amount of money that all of the customers spent on Wednesday at the bookstore?

____

20. Tickets for an art exhibit cost $15 for adults and $11 for children. On Friday, 63 adults and 81 children went to the exhibit. What was the total cost of the tickets sold for the art exhibit on Friday?

____

STOP

Chapter 12 – Teacher Interview

Core Concept: ***Multiply Greater Numbers***

Student Activity: Students demonstrate an understanding of multiplying by a 2-digit number when asked to solve 4,125 × 64.

Teacher Question 1:

- What are the steps needed to find the product?

Understanding Student Response	Practice and Improvement
Students who do not include "add the products" in their answer.	Review lesson 2 to help students review the steps in multiplying with greater numbers.
Students who do not know to multiply 4,125 by the ones and then by the tens.	Review lesson 2 to help students practice with multiplication algorithms of a multi-digit number multiplied by a 2-digit number.

Teacher Question 2:

- What is the product of 4,125 × 64?

Understanding Student Response	Practice and Improvement
Students who say 41,250.	Review lesson 2 to help students practice aligning partial products when multiplying a multi-digit number by a 2-digit number.
Students who say 253,000 or 254,000.	Review lesson 2 to help students practice situations with regrouping in multiplication.
Students who say a number other than the above incorrect answers.	Review lesson 1 to help students estimate a product and to check for reasonableness. Review lesson 2 for practice with multiplication algorithms of a multi-digit number multiplied by a 2-digit number.

Chapter 12 – Journal Writing

Encourage students to generate their own journal entries related to math ideas in general or to concepts in this chapter. For students requiring guidance, present the following journal prompt:

- What steps should you use to multiply a 3-digit number by a 2-digit number? How can you check that your answer is reasonable?

  (Responses should indicate that you multiply each place by the ones, regroup if needed, then multiply each place by the tens, regroup if needed, and add the partial products. Students should indicate that the product can be estimated by rounding one or both of the factors.)

JOURNAL WRITING/PROBLEM SOLVING

Jamal has 73 customers on his Sunday paper route. The Sunday paper costs $3.50. If he delivers papers on all 52 Sundays in a year, how many papers does he deliver? Use the Distributive Property to make your work easier.

Read

Have students find the answer to the problem. Then ask them to write a few sentences telling—

- what information they needed and did not need to solve the problem
- how they used the Distributive Property to solve the problem

Have students make up another problem with different information for which they would have to follow the same procedure. Students should also supply the correct response.

Plan

Students must organize the information that they need to find the product, and use the Distributive Property.

Solve

The correct response to the assigned problem is 3,796 papers. Students must expand 52 to 50 + 2, and then multiply (73 × 50) + (73 × 2), and add the partial products.

Look Back

A correct response demonstrates that students understand how to use the Distributive Property, and how to select the appropriate information to find the product. (See scoring rubric on page 7.)

Chapter 12 – Monitoring Student Progress

☐ **Form A** ☐ **Form B**

Name ______________________ Date ______________

Directions: For each item that is answered incorrectly, cross out the item number. Then record the number of correct responses in the appropriate Student Score column. If the student has not met the Criterion Score for an objective, circle the student's score. Recommended assignments are listed in the Prescription Table on the next page.

Objective	Item Numbers	Criterion Score	Student Score
A. Estimate products.	1, 5, 8, 11, 14	4/5	/5
B. Multiply by greater numbers.	2, 4, 6, 7, 9, 10, 12, 13, 16	8/9	/9
C. Use mental math to multiply.	3, 15	1/2	/2
D. Use skills and strategies to solve problems.	17, 18, 19, 20	3/4	/4
Total Test Score		16/20	/20
Total Percent Correct			%

Chapter 12 – Prescription Table

The following chart correlates the tested objectives for this chapter to supplementary materials that meet the individual needs of the students. The Reteach and Practice pages are designed for students who need further instruction in the math concepts taught in this chapter. The Enrich pages are designed for students who need advanced challenges.

Objective	Reteach	Practice	Enrich
A. Estimate products.	207	208	209
B. Multiply by greater numbers.	210	211	212
C. Use mental math to multiply.	216, 219	217, 220	218, 221
D. Use skills and strategies to solve problems.	213, 214	215	

Name ______________________________

Read each question carefully. Darken the circle on your answer sheet for the correct answer.

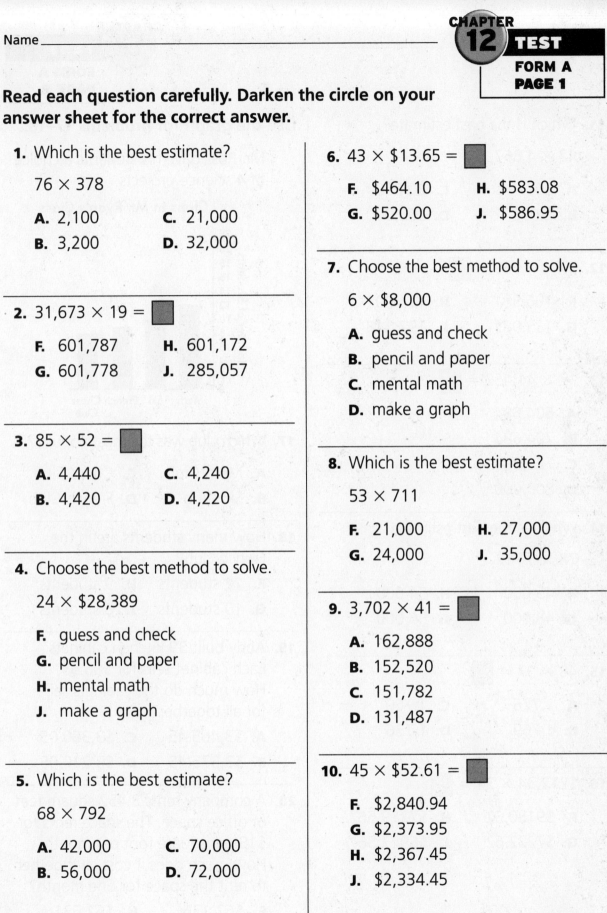

1. Which is the best estimate?

76 × 378

A. 2,100 **C.** 21,000
B. 3,200 **D.** 32,000

2. 31,673 × 19 = ■

F. 601,787 **H.** 601,172
G. 601,778 **J.** 285,057

3. 85 × 52 = ■

A. 4,440 **C.** 4,240
B. 4,420 **D.** 4,220

4. Choose the best method to solve.

24 × $28,389

F. guess and check
G. pencil and paper
H. mental math
J. make a graph

5. Which is the best estimate?

68 × 792

A. 42,000 **C.** 70,000
B. 56,000 **D.** 72,000

6. 43 × $13.65 = ■

F. $464.10 **H.** $583.08
G. $520.00 **J.** $586.95

7. Choose the best method to solve.

6 × $8,000

A. guess and check
B. pencil and paper
C. mental math
D. make a graph

8. Which is the best estimate?

53 × 711

F. 21,000 **H.** 27,000
G. 24,000 **J.** 35,000

9. 3,702 × 41 = ■

A. 162,888
B. 152,520
C. 151,782
D. 131,487

10. 45 × $52.61 = ■

F. $2,840.94
G. $2,373.95
H. $2,367.45
J. $2,334.45

GO ON

Name ____________________

11. Which is the best estimate?

42 × 4,867

A. 200 **C.** 20,000
B. 2,000 **D.** 200,000

12. 27 × 4,963 = ▢

F. 106,581 **H.** 134,001
G. 133,981 **J.** 197,248

13. 17 × 41,452 = ▢

A. 604,684
B. 704,684
C. 731,684
D. 800,000

14. Which is the best estimate?

78 × 3 712

F. 45,000 **H.** 54,000
G. 48,000 **J.** 56,000

15. 48 × 37 = ▢

A. 1,776 **C.** 1,760
B. 1,769 **D.** 1,726

16. $212.34 × 34 = ▢

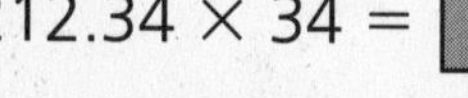

F. $9130.62 **H.** $7219.56
G. $7222.62 **J.** $6927.56

Use the graph for problems 17–18.

Mr. Ross gave his students a choice of 4 science projects.

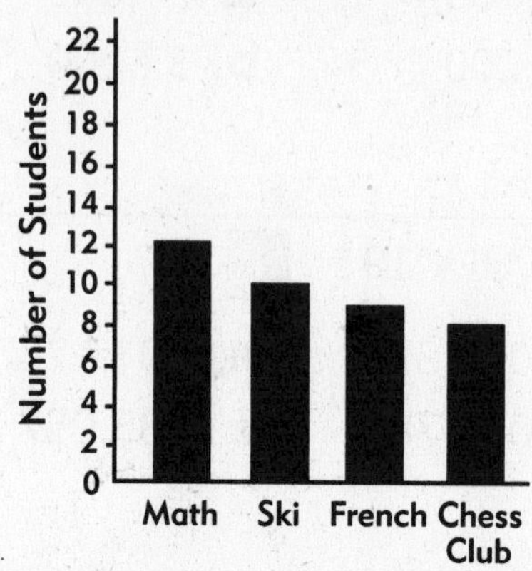

17. Which club was the most popular?

A. Math Club **C.** Chess Club
B. Ski Club **D.** French Club

18. How many students are in the French club?

F. 12 students **H.** 9 students
G. 10 students **J.** 8 students

19. Andy built 39 kitchen cabinets. Each cabinet sells for $86.55. How much do the cabinets sell for all together?

A. $3,465.45 **C.** $3,360.05
B. $3,375.45 **D.** $3,210.05

20. A company rents 3,452 square feet of office space. The space rents for $18 per square foot per month. How much does it cost all together to rent the space for one month?

F. $62,136 **H.** $62,631
G. $62,316 **J.** $63,136

STOP

Name ____________________

CHAPTER 12 TEST
FORM B
PAGE 1

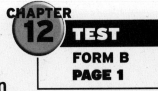

Read each question carefully. Fill in the correct answer in the space provided.

1. Estimate.

37 × 1,297

____

2. 8,190 × 72 = __________

3. 25 × 50 = __________

4. Solve. Write the best method to use.

30 × $8,000

____

5. Estimate.

62 × 407

____

6. 27 × $63.71 = __________

7. Choose the best method to solve.

641 × 34,295

____

8. Estimate.

19 × 2,897

____

9. 538 × 74 = __________

10. 82 × $43.18 = __________

GO ON

Name ___________________________________

CHAPTER 12 TEST
FORM B
PAGE 2

11. Estimate.

57 × 8,234

____

12. 73 × 9,184 = ___________

13. 38 × 62,107 = ___________

14. Estimate.

38 × 2,168

____

15. 75 × 50 = ___________

16. $967.45 × 62 = ___________

Use the graph for problems 17–18.

Ticket Sales

Under 8	3½ tickets
8-15	1 ticket
16-40	5½ tickets
Over 40	2 tickets
Key:	Each full ticket stands for 100 tickets Each half ticket stands for 50 tickets

17. To which age group were the most tickets sold?

____

18. How many tickets were sold all together?

____

19. A store has 82 laptop computers in stock. Each computer sells for $1,249. How much do the computers sell for all together?

____

20. A concert hall sponsors a series of 36 concerts. The hall holds 1,684 people. If the entire series is sold out, how many people attended the concerts?

____

STOP

Unit 6 Performance Assessment

Office Manager

- ***Target Skill:*** Multiply by greater numbers.
- ***Additional Skills:*** Multiply by two-digit numbers; estimate products.

Task Description: This task requires students to calculate the amount of money that part-time employees make in a year and estimate the amount of money they would make if they worked the entire year.

Preparing: You may wish to discuss with students the difference between an estimate and an exact answer.

Materials	Group Size	Time on Task
Calculator (optional)	2 to 3 students	1–2 days

Guiding: Remind students that an estimate can be used to check that an answer is reasonable. There is no perfect way to estimate, so it is acceptable that not everyone's estimates are the same

Observing/ Monitoring: As you move among the students, pose the following questions:

How do you know that you multiplied correctly?

Which numbers did you use for your estimates?

Unit 6 Performance Assessment Scoring Rubric

Office Manager

Score	Explanation
3	Students demonstrate an efficient strategy and a thorough approach that enables them to solve the problem completely. A satisfactory answer: • shows a complete and correct chart; • uses reasonable estimates to find the amount of money each employee would have made in a year. Students are able to complete the problem quickly and have all of the above correct solutions.
2	Students demonstrate a strategy that enables them to solve most of the problem correctly. The strategy is somewhat disorganized, making it less efficient. A solution is found, but errors are contained. Students may: • complete the chart correctly; • make some reasonable estimates. Students may have some difficulty determining all solutions correctly, but demonstrate an understanding of general concepts.
1	Students demonstrate a confused strategy, which leads to difficulty solving the problem. Most answers are incorrect, but students demonstrate knowledge of at least one concept being assessed, such as multiplication or estimating products.

Name ____________________

Unit 6 Performance Assessment Student Activity

Office Manager

You will need

- Pencil
- Paper

How much do people earn in a year? You are the manager of an office. You have four employees. In the chart are their weekly salaries. Find how much each person earns in a year.

Name of Employee	Weekly Pay	Number of Weeks Worked	Yearly Pay
Ryan	$475.00	38	
Sue	$612.35	42	
Mitch	$507.28	45	
Millie	$361.95	31	

1. Find how much money each employee will make in a year. Show your work. Complete the chart.

2. Estimate to find out how much each person would make working all 52 weeks in a year.

____

____

____

____

Unit 6 – Monitoring Student Progress

☐ Form A ☐ Form B

Name ______________________ Date ______________

Directions: This test targets selected objectives. For each item that is answered incorrectly, cross out the item number. Then record the number of correct responses in the column labeled **Number of Correct Responses.** Add to find the **Total Number of Correct Responses** and record the total. Use this total to determine the **Total Test Score** and the **Total Percent Correct.**

Strand • Objective(s)	Item Numbers	Number of Correct Responses
Number Sense, Concepts, and Operations • Use patterns of multiplication. • Multiply by multiples of 10. • Multiply by 2-digit numbers. • Estimate products. • Multiply by greater numbers. • Use mental math to multiply. • Use skills and strategies to solve problems.	1, 2, 3, 4, 5, 6, 7, 8, 9, 10, 11, 12, 13, 14, 15, 16, 17, 18, 19, 20, 21, 22, 23, 24, 25, 26, 27, 28, 29, 30, 31, 32, 33, 34, 35, 36, 37, 38, 39, 40	/40
Total Number of Correct Responses		
Total Test Score		/40
Total Percent Correct		%

Name ______________________________

UNIT 6 **TEST** FORM A PAGE 1

Read each question carefully. Darken the circle on your answer sheet for the correct answer.

1. 80×70

A. 560 **C.** 56,000
B. 5,600 **D.** 560,000

2. 50 × 400 = ■

F. 200 **H.** 20,000
G. 2,000 **J.** 200,000

3. 423×64

A. 4,200 **C.** 27,072
B. 26,972 **D.** 255,492

4. Which is the best estimate?

95 × 408

F. 3,000 **H.** 32,000
G. 4,000 **J.** 40,000

5. 90 × 3,000 = ■

A. 270 **C.** 27,000
B. 2,700 **D.** 270,000

6. 72 × 819 = ■

F. 7,371 **H.** 58,968
G. 58,358 **J.** 58,998

7. 58 × $17.35 = ■

A. $235.55 **C.** $995.30
B. $641.90 **D.** $1,006.30

8. $6{,}000 \times 20$

F. 120 **H.** 12,000
G. 1,200 **J.** 120,000

9. 30 × 87 = ■

A. 261 **C.** 2,610
B. 2,410 **D.** 24,210

10. $43{,}693 \times 16$

F. 305,851 **H.** 698,088
G. 675,578 **J.** 699,088

11. 29 × 7,182 = ■

A. 79,002 **C.** 208,278
B. 107,278 **D.** 215,460

12. Which is the best estimate?

68 × 792

F. 56,000 **H.** 72,000
G. 70,000 **J.** 100,000

13. Which is the best estimate?

12 × 37

A. 100 **C.** 300
B. 200 **D.** 400

GO ON

Name ______________________________

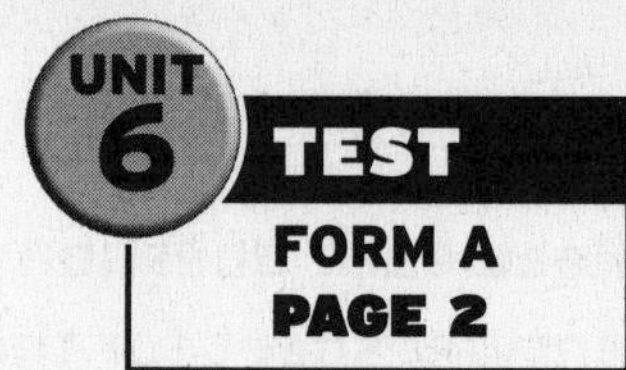

14. $1.38 × 12

F. $11.14 **H.** $16.56
G. $13.56 **J.** $38.76

---

15. Which is the best estimate?

44 × 621

A. 20,000 **C.** 32,000
B. 24,000 **D.** 35,000

---

16. 4,708 × 36

F. 17,208 **H.** 145,488
G. 42,372 **J.** 169,488

Solve.

Use the graph for problems 17–18.

Mr. Ross gave his students a choice of 4 science projects.

Science Kits in Mr. Ross's Class

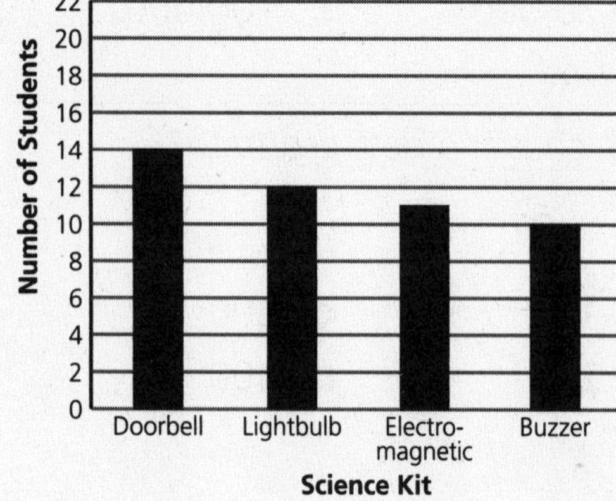

17. Which kit was the most popular?

A. doorbell kit
B. lightbulb kit
C. electromagnetic kit
D. buzzer kit

---

18. How many students chose the electromagnetic kit?

F. 10 students
G. 11 students
H. 12 students
J. 13 students

---

19. There are 6 cups of fruit in a pack. There are 8 packs in a stack and 3 stacks in a case. Each cup of fruit sells for $0.75. How much is the case worth?

A. $35 **C.** $135
B. $108 **D.** $192

---

20. A warehouse received its first shipment of 52,370 books. Then it sent out two shipments of 9,580 books each. The warehouse then received 17,659 books. How many books are in the warehouse now?

F. 15,551 books
G. 33,210 books
H. 50,869 books
J. 61,950 books

Name ____________________

21. 40×30

A. 120 **C.** 12,000
B. 1,200 **D.** 120,000

22. 94 × 628 = ▇

F. 59,032 **H.** 61,032
G. 60,000 **J.** Not Here

23. 600×50

A. 300 **C.** 30,000
B. 3,000 **D.** 300,000

24. Which is the best estimate?

211 × 52

F. 1,000 **H.** 10,000
G. 2,000 **J.** 20,000

25. 90 × 7,000 = ▇

A. 630 **C.** 63,000
B. 6,300 **D.** 630,000

26. 75 × 847 = ▇

F. 10,164 **H.** 63,525
G. 61,525 **J.** 64,000

27. 69 × $52.98 = ▇

A. $3,500.00 **C.** $3,655.62
B. $3,544.62 **D.** $4,200.00

28. $5{,}809 \times 34$

F. 20,026 **H.** 197,406
G. 40,663 **J.** 197,506

29. 80 × 647 = ▇

A. 4,826 **C.** 48,260
B. 5,176 **D.** 51,760

30. $41{,}452 \times 17$

F. 604,684 **H.** 731,684
G. 704,684 **J.** 800,000

31. 80 × 2,000 = ▇

A. 160 **C.** 16,000
B. 1,600 **D.** 160,000

32. Which is the best estimate?

32 × 4,739

F. 150 **H.** 15,000
G. 1,500 **J.** 150,000

33. Which is the best estimate?

19 × 28

A. 600
B. 800
C. 900
D. 1,000

GO ON

34. $2.39
× 16

F. $16.73 **H.** $38.24
G. $36.74 **J.** $48.00

---

35. Which is the best estimate?

87 × 632

A. 45,000 **C.** 54,000
B. 48,000 **D.** 56,000

---

36. 52 × 3,206 = ■

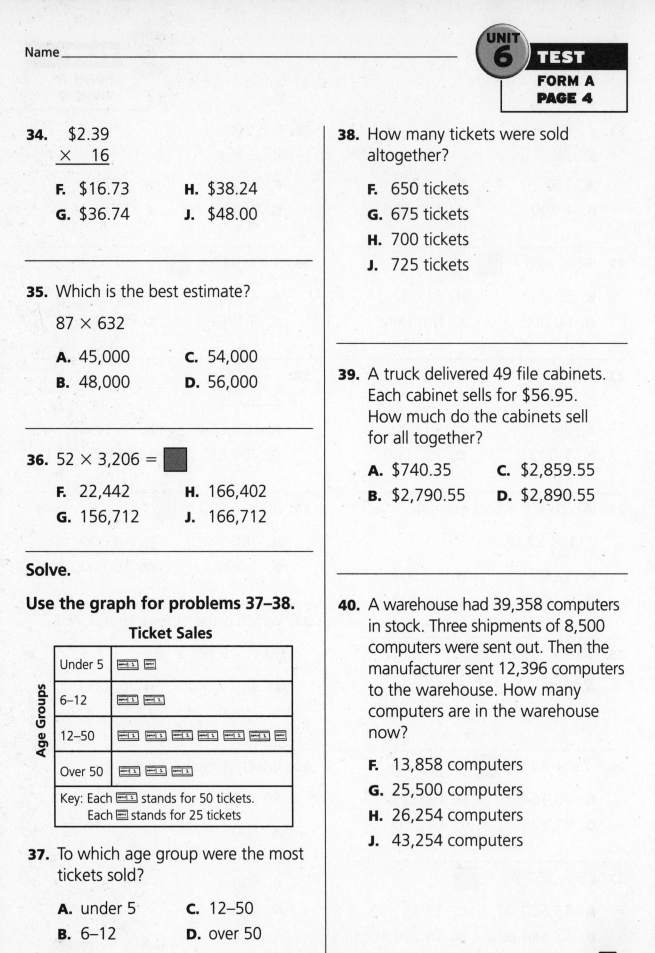

F. 22,442 **H.** 166,402
G. 156,712 **J.** 166,712

Solve.

Use the graph for problems 37–38.

Ticket Sales

Age Groups	
Under 5	ADMIT 1 ADMIT
6–12	ADMIT 1 ADMIT 1
12–50	ADMIT 1 ADMIT 1 ADMIT 1 ADMIT 1 ADMIT 1 ADMIT 1 ADMIT
Over 50	ADMIT 1 ADMIT 1 ADMIT 1
Key: Each stands for 50 tickets. Each stands for 25 tickets	

37. To which age group were the most tickets sold?

A. under 5 **C.** 12–50
B. 6–12 **D.** over 50

38. How many tickets were sold altogether?

F. 650 tickets
G. 675 tickets
H. 700 tickets
J. 725 tickets

---

39. A truck delivered 49 file cabinets. Each cabinet sells for $56.95. How much do the cabinets sell for all together?

A. $740.35 **C.** $2,859.55
B. $2,790.55 **D.** $2,890.55

---

40. A warehouse had 39,358 computers in stock. Three shipments of 8,500 computers were sent out. Then the manufacturer sent 12,396 computers to the warehouse. How many computers are in the warehouse now?

F. 13,858 computers
G. 25,500 computers
H. 26,254 computers
J. 43,254 computers

STOP

Name ______________________

TEST
FORM B
PAGE 1

Read each question carefully. Fill in the correct answer in the space provided.

1. 90
× 70

____

2. 40 × 500 = ____________

____

3. 354
× 33

____

4. Estimate.

102 × 498

____

____

5. 80 × 4,000 = ____________

6. 73 × 612 = ____________

____

7. 47 × $16.45 = ____________

____

8. 7,000
× 20

____

9. 40 × 76 = ____________

____

10. 44,583
× 17

GO ON

Name ______________________________

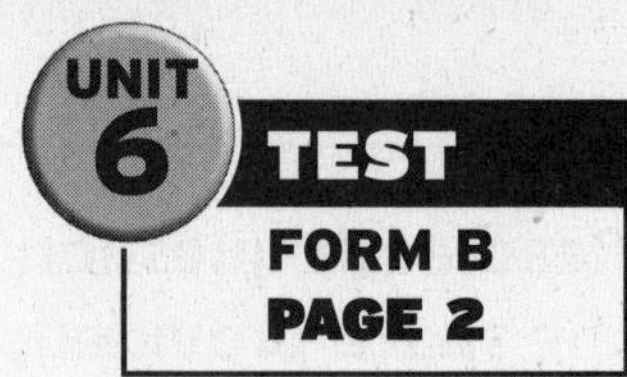
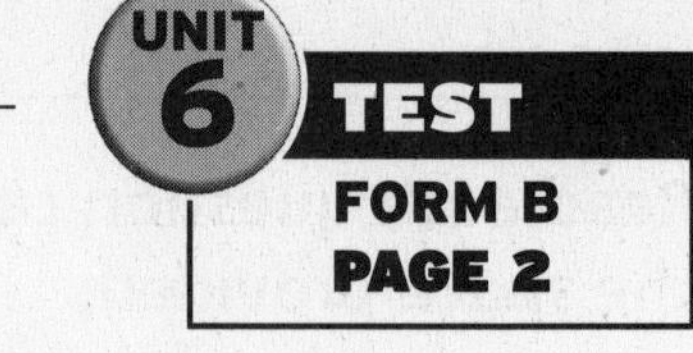

11. $29 \times 6{,}193 =$ ____________

12. Estimate.

57×797

____

13. Is 300 or 500 a better estimate?

12×42

____

14. $\$1.29 \times 13$

15. Estimate.

34×590

____

16. $5{,}706 \times 34$

Use the graph for problems 17–18.

Mr. Crane gave his students a choice of four U.S. history report topics.

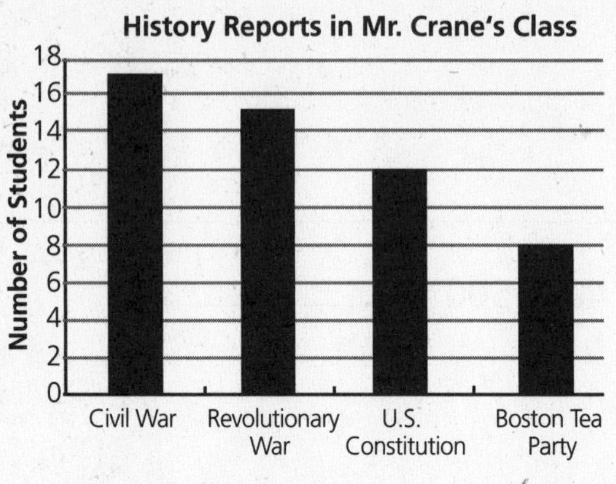

17. Which topic was most popular?

____

18. How many students chose the Revolutionary War?

____

19. There are 8 pickles in a jar. There are 7 jars in a box and 4 boxes in a case. Each pickle sells for \$0.75. How much is the case worth?

____

20. The town library had 63,460 books. 17,720 were destroyed in a flood. The library then received two donations of 9,670 new books each. How many books are now in the library?

____

Name ____________________

21. $\begin{array}{r} 50 \\ \times\ 30 \\ \hline \end{array}$

22. 74 × 829 = ____________

23. $\begin{array}{r} 700 \\ \times\ \ 50 \\ \hline \end{array}$

24. Estimate.

311 × 49

____

25. 70 × 8,000 = ____________

26. 85 × 747 = ____________

27. 59 × $48.26 = ____________

28. $\begin{array}{r} 4{,}786 \\ \times\ \ \ \ 44 \\ \hline \end{array}$

29. 90 × 547 = ____________

30. $\begin{array}{r} 41{,}763 \\ \times\ \ \ \ \ 16 \\ \hline \end{array}$

GO ON

Name ______________________________

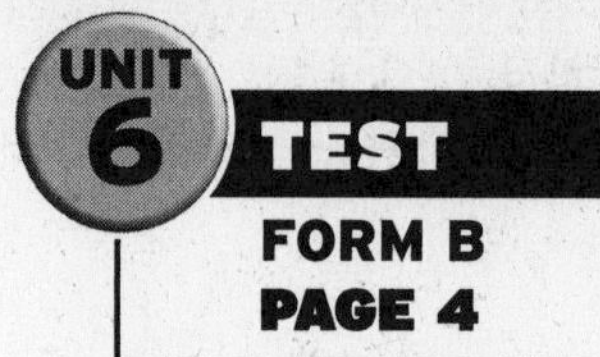

31. $70 \times 2{,}000 =$ ______________

32. Estimate.

$44 \times 4{,}897$

____

33. Is 900 or 1100 a better estimate?

18×48

____

34.

$$\begin{array}{r} \$2.49 \\ \times \quad 17 \\ \hline \end{array}$$

35. Estimate.

77×532

____

36. $48 \times 3{,}302 =$ ______________

Use the graph for problems 37–38.

Ticket Sales

Age Groups	
Under 5	🎟 (half)
6–12	🎟 🎟 🎟 🎟 🎟 🎟
12–50	🎟 🎟 🎟 🎟 (half)
Over 50	🎟 🎟 🎟 🎟
Key: Each 🎟 stands for 50 tickets. Each (half) stands for 25 tickets	

37. To which age group were the most tickets sold?

____

38. How many tickets were sold all together?

____

39. A department store sold 37 chairs. Each chair sold for $47.95. How much did the department store sell all together?

____

40. A warehouse had 37,962 computers in stock. Four shipments of 6,500 computers were sent out. Then the manufacturer sent 11,796 computers to the warehouse. How many computers are in the warehouse now?

____

STOP

Chapter 13 – Teacher Interview

Core Concept: ***Dividing by 1-Digit Numbers***

Student Activity: Students demonstrate an understanding of dividing by a 1-digit number when asked to solve an algorithm such as $8\overline{)304}$.

Teacher Question 1:

- Will the quotient have a 0 in the ones place?

Understanding Student Response	Practice and Improvement
Students who say *yes*.	Review lesson 1 to help students practice dividing with multiples of 10.
Students who say *yes*.	Review lesson 3 to help students practice division in situations where regrouping is necessary.

Teacher Question 2:

- Does the quotient have a remainder?

Understanding Student Response	Practice and Improvement
Students who say *yes*.	Review lesson 3 to help students practice regrouping when dividing.

Teacher Question 3:

- What is the quotient when 304 is divided by 8?

Understanding Student Response	Practice and Improvement
Students who say a quotient other than 38.	Review lesson 4 to help students focus on the procedure to use when dividing a multi-digit number by a 1-digit number, involving regrouping.

Chapter 13 – Journal Writing

Encourage students to generate their own journal entries related to math ideas in general or to concepts in this chapter. For students requiring guidance, present the following journal prompt:

- When you are estimating the quotient of a number by a 1-digit number, why is it a good idea to use an estimate for the dividend that is close to the given dividend?
  (Responses should indicate that the estimate should be easily divisible by the divisor and should be compared as close as possible to the given dividend.)

JOURNAL WRITING/PROBLEM SOLVING

The Kerstein Auditorium has 500 seats arranged in 7 sections. Estimate the number of seats in each section.

Read

Have students find the answer to the problem. Then ask them to write a few sentences telling—

- what estimate they used for the dividend
- why they chose that estimate

Have students make up another problem with different information for which they would have to follow the same procedure. Then have students solve the problem and supply the correct response.

Plan

Students must know their division facts to determine what would be a close estimate for a given dividend, and to correctly divide.

Solve

The correct response to the assigned problem is 70. Students had to determine that 490 would be a close estimate of the given dividend and then had to divide correctly.

Look Back

A correct response demonstrates the ability to judge what would be a close estimate of the given dividend and to divide correctly. (See scoring rubric on page 7.)

Chapter 13 – Monitoring Student Progress

☐ **Form A** ☐ **Form B**

Name ______________________ Date ______________

Directions: For each item that is answered incorrectly, cross out the item number. Then record the number of correct responses in the appropriate Student Score column. If the student has not met the Criterion Score for an objective, circle the student's score. Recommended assignments are listed in the Prescription Table on the next page.

Objective	Item Numbers	Criterion Score	Student Score
A. Divide multiples of 10.	1, 4, 7, 10, 13	4/5	/5
B. Divide multi-digit numbers by 1-digit numbers.	3, 6, 9, 12, 15	4/5	/5
C. Estimate quotients.	2, 5, 8, 11, 14	4/5	/5
D. Use skills and strategies to solve problems.	16, 17, 18, 19, 20	4/5	/5
Total Test Score		16/20	/20
Total Percent Correct			%

Chapter 13 – Prescription Table

The following chart correlates the tested objectives for this chapter to supplementary materials that meet the individual needs of the students. The Reteach and Practice pages are designed for students who need further instruction in the math concepts taught in this chapter. The Enrich pages are designed for students who need advanced challenges.

Objective	Reteach	Practice	Enrich
A. Divide multiples of 10.	223	224	225
B. Divide multi-digit numbers by 1-digit numbers.	229, 232, 238	230, 233, 239	231, 234, 240
C. Estimate quotients.	226	227	228
D. Use skills and strategies to solve problems.	235	236	237

Name ____________________

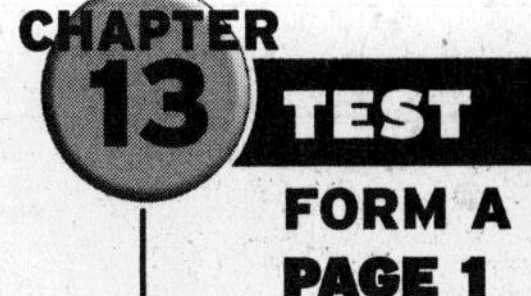

Read each question carefully. Darken the circle on your answer sheet for the correct answer.

1. 440 ÷ 2 = ■

A. 22 **C.** 2,200
B. 220 **D.** 22,000

---

2. Which is the best estimate?

173 ÷ 3

F. 6 **H.** 60
G. 7 **J.** 70

---

3. 7)603

A. 9 **C.** 86 R1
B. 76 R1 **D.** 96 R1

---

4. 3,500 ÷ 5 = ■

F. 7 **H.** 700
G. 70 **J.** 7,000

---

5. Which is the best estimate?

323 ÷ 8

A. 4 **C.** 40
B. 5 **D.** 50

---

6. 8)496

F. 59 **H.** 61
G. 60 **J.** 62

---

7. 1,600 ÷ 4 = ■

A. 4 **C.** 400
B. 40 **D.** 4,000

---

8. Which is the best estimate?

478 ÷ 7

F. 60 **H.** 80
G. 70 **J.** 90

---

9. 5)326

A. 61 R1 **C.** 71 R1
B. 65 R1 **D.** 76 R1

---

10. 480 ÷ 8 = ■

F. 60 **H.** 6,000
G. 600 **J.** 60,000

GO ON

Name ______________________________

11. Which is the best estimate?

8,104 ÷ 5

A. 1,200 **C.** 1,600
B. 1,400 **D.** 1,800

---

12. $7\overline{)837}$

F. 151 **H.** 119
G. 119 R4 **J.** 109 R5

---

13. 300 ÷ 5 = ■

A. 30 **C.** 50
B. 40 **D.** 60

---

14. Which is the best estimate?

437,872 ÷ 5

F. 10,000 **H.** 50,000
G. 25,000 **J.** 90,000

---

15. 682 ÷ 9 = ■

A. 75 R7 **C.** 70 R5
B. 75 R5 **D.** 70 R4

---

16. 6,000 ÷ n = 1,000

F. 4 **H.** 6
G. 5 **J.** 8

---

17. The theatre sold $2,800 worth of tickets on Monday. If each ticket cost $7, how many people went to the circus?

A. 4,000 people **C.** 400 people
B. 500 people **D.** 300 people

---

18. There are 70 band members going to a parade. They are going in vans that seat 8 passengers. How many vans do they need?

F. 6 vans **H.** 8 vans
G. 7 vans **J.** 9 vans

---

19. The aquarium sold $1,950 worth of tickets on Tuesday. If each ticket cost $3, how many people went to the theater?

A. 550 people **C.** 750 people
B. 650 people **D.** 850 people

---

20. Joseph has a collection of 576 baseball cards. He keeps them in 9 card cases. Each case holds the same amount of cards. How many cards are in each case?

F. 60 cards **H.** 70 cards
G. 64 cards **J.** 74 cards

STOP

Name ______________________________

CHAPTER 13 TEST
FORM B
PAGE 1

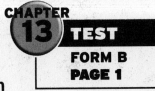

Read each question carefully. Fill in the correct answer in the space provided.

1. 400 ÷ 8 = ______

2. Estimate.

427 ÷ 6

______

3. $5\overline{)372}$

______

4. 7,200 ÷ 8 = ______

5. Estimate.

6,279 ÷ 7

______

6. $7\overline{)923}$

______

7. 3,500 ÷ 5 = ______

8. Estimate.

5,328 ÷ 6

______

9. 747 ÷ 8 = ______

10. 840 ÷ 7 = ______

GO ON

Name ______________________________

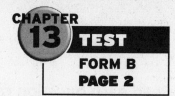

11. Estimate.

3,519 ÷ 9

____

12. $6\overline{)429}$

____

13. 640 ÷ 8 = ______

14. Estimate.

398,156 ÷ 8

____

15. $5\overline{)571}$

____

16. 3,200 ÷ *n* = 800

____

17. The comic book store sold $1,500 worth of comic books on Saturday. If each comic costs $3, how many comics did they sell?

____

18. There are 58 seniors going on a trip together. They are going in vans that seat 7 passengers. How many vans do they need?

____

19. The concert hall sold $3,500 worth of tickets on Friday. If each ticket cost $5, how many people went to the concert hall?

____

20. Lars has a collection of 748 comic books. He keeps them in plastic sleeves. Each sleeve holds 6 comic books. How many sleeves does he need?

____

STOP

Chapter 14 – Teacher Interview

Core Concept: *Find the Mean*

Student Activity: Students demonstrate an understanding of the process of finding the mean of a set of numbers. Ask students to find the mean of a set of numbers: 66, 63, 50, 64, and 49.

Teacher Question 1:

- What are the steps involved in finding the mean of this data set?

Understanding Student Response	Practice and Improvement
Students who say to add the numbers only.	Review lesson 6 to help students understand the process of finding the mean.
Students who say to find the middle number.	Review lesson 5 to help students learn the definition of the mean.
Students who say to divide by any number other than 5.	Review lesson 5 to help students review how to find the divisor when finding the mean of a set of data.

Teacher Question 2:

- What is the mean of this data set?

Understanding Student Response	Practice and Improvement
Students who answer 292.	Review lesson 6 to help students understand that the mean is the sum of the addends divided by the number of addends.
Students who answer 58 or 59.	Review lesson 6 to help students practice finding the mean beyond the whole number part of the quotient.
Students who say 63.	Review lesson 5 to help students learn the definition of the mean.
Students who say a number other than the above incorrect answers.	Review lesson 5 to help students learn the process of finding the mean.

Chapter 14 – Journal Writing

Encourage students to generate their own journal entries related to math ideas in general or to concepts in this chapter. For students requiring guidance, present the following journal prompt:

- If you know the mean of seven numbers, and you know only five of the numbers, can you find the other two numbers? Can you find the mean of the other two numbers?

  (Responses should indicate that knowing the mean and the number of addends allows you to find the total, and subtracting the total of the known numbers only gives you the total of the unknown numbers. You cannot find out what the numbers are, but dividing by two gives you their mean.)

JOURNAL WRITING/PROBLEM SOLVING

Alix will travel with her family to take her older brother to college. The family will stay in a hotel for three nights. Alix checks prices, and learns that the Riverside offers rooms for $415 a week, the Central offers rooms for $279.95 for five nights, and the Cityview offers rooms for $169.99 for two nights. If each hotel offers its rooms for an equal rate no matter how many nights guests stay, which hotel offers the least expensive room per night?

Read

Have students find the answer to the problem. Then ask them to write a few sentences telling—

- how they organized the information
- how they found the unit prices for the rooms

Have students make up another problem for which they would have to follow the same procedure, but with different information. Students should also supply the correct response.

Plan

Students must know how to divide money, find a unit price, and determine the best buy.

Solve

The correct response to the assigned problem is the Central, which offers rooms for $55.99 a night. Students had to divide money amounts correctly, and compare the results to determine which price per night is lowest.

Look Back

A correct response demonstrates an ability to divide money amounts, find unit prices, and understand which is the best buy. (See scoring rubric on page 7.)

Chapter 14 – Monitoring Student Progress

☐ **Form A** ☐ **Form B**

Name ______________________ Date ______________

Directions: For each item that is answered incorrectly, cross out the item number. Then record the number of correct responses in the appropriate Student Score column. If the student has not met the Criterion Score for an objective, circle the student's score. Recommended assignments are listed in the Prescription Table on the next page.

Objective	Item Numbers	Criterion Score	Student Score
A. Divide greater numbers.	1, 5, 7, 10, 12, 13, 15	6/7	/7
B. Find the better buy.	2, 16	1/2	/2
C. Find the mean.	3, 4, 6, 8, 9, 11, 14	6/7	/7
D. Use skills and strategies to solve problems.	17, 18, 19, 20	3/4	/4
Total Test Score		16/20	/20
Total Percent Correct			%

Chapter 14 – Prescription Table

The following chart correlates the tested objectives for this chapter to supplementary materials that meet the individual needs of the students. The Reteach and Practice pages are designed for students who need further instruction in the math concepts taught in this chapter. The Enrich pages are designed for students who need advanced challenges.

Objective	Reteach	Practice	Enrich
A. Divide greater numbers.	241	242	243
B. Find the better buy.	250	251	252
C. Find the mean.	253, 256	254, 257	255, 258
D. Use skills and strategies to solve problems.	247, 248	249	

Name ______________________________

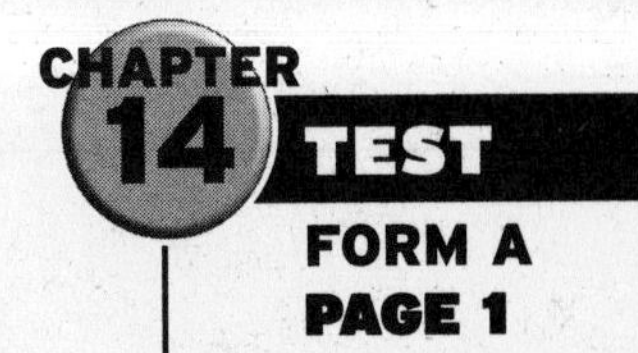

Read each question carefully. Darken the circle on your answer sheet for the correct answer.

1. 4,928 ÷ 7 = ▢

A. 70
B. 704
C. 704 R3
D. 740

2. Which is the best buy?

F. 9 ounces for $3.33
G. 7 ounces for $2.52
H. 5 ounces for $1.75
J. 3 ounces for $1.11

3. What is the mean of 211, 313, 256, and 308?

A. 242
B. 252
C. 272
D. 1,088

4. Which of the following is a correct method to determine the mean?

F. Add 614, 752, 431 and 907, and divide the sum by 3.
G. Add 1,005, 456, and 201 and divide the sum by 3.
H. Add 32, 55, 19, 94, and 31 and divide the sum by 6.
J. Add 20, 25, 35, and 25 and divide the sum by 3.

5. 13,489 ÷ 7 = ▢

A. 1,927
B. 1,729
C. 1,729 R4
D. 1,279

6. What is the mean of 32, 45, 38, 37, and 53?

F. 27 **G.** 31 **H.** 37 **J.** 41

7. 7,498 ÷ 9 = ▢

A. 689
B. 833 R1
C. 833 R6
D. 388 R6

8. What is the mean of 305, 0, 297, 416, 376, 601, and 210?

F. 315
G. 320 R1
H. 335
J. 367 R3

9. Which of the following is a correct method to determine the mean?

A. Add 360, 980, 1,016, and 10 and divide the sum by 3.
B. Add 17, 17, 26, and 30 and divide the sum by 3.
C. Add 37, 99, 28, 66, and 19 and divide the sum by 6.
D. Add 18, 15, and 11 and divide the sum by 3.

10. 6,683 ÷ 8 = ▢

F. 835
G. 835 R3
H. 853
J. 853 R3

GO ON

Name ____________________

11. What is the mean of 30, 16, 51, 23, and 20?

A. 20 **B.** 28 **C.** 30 **D.** 38

12. 34,872 ÷ 7 = ■

F. 4,891 R5
G. 4,981
H. 4,981 R5
J. 5,981 R4

13. 82,379 ÷ 5 = ■

A. 16,475 R3 **C.** 16,754 R4
B. 16,475 R4 **D.** 16,754 R5

14. What is the mean of 116, 128, 115, and 221?

F. 145 **G.** 140 **H.** 125 **J.** 120

15. 14,829 ÷ 6 = ■

A. 2,417
B. 2,417 R3
C. 2,471
D. 2,471 R3

16. Which is the best buy?

F. 8 pounds for $5.25
G. 10 pounds for $6.05
H. 4 pounds for $2.85
J. 3 pounds for $2.03

17. If Lee spent $6.03 on 9 pens and each pen cost the same amount, how much did 1 pen cost?

A. $0.58 **C.** $0.62
B. $0.60 **D.** $0.67

18. A package of 6 donuts costs $1.50. How much does each donut cost?

F. $0.20 **H.** $0.30
G. $0.25 **J.** $0.35

19. Together Ron and Tori have 35 trading cards. Ron has 9 more than Tori. How many does Ron have?

A. 26 cards **C.** 13 cards
B. 22 cards **D.** 9 cards

20. If Tami spent $38.97 on 3 CDs and each CD cost the same amount, how much did 1 CD cost?

F. $12.49 **H.** $13.49
G. $12.99 **J.** $13.99

STOP

Name ____________________

CHAPTER 14 TEST
FORM B
PAGE 1

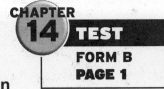

Read each question carefully. Fill in the correct answer in the space provided.

1. 7,124 ÷ 8 = ________

2. Which is the best buy: 8 pounds for $15.43 or 4 pounds for $7.79?

____

3. What is the mean of 323, 374, 184, and 575?

____

4. If you add a 0 to a set of 5 different numbers, how does that change the method you would use to find the mean of all of the numbers?

____

____

____

5. 23,451 ÷ 5 = ________

6. What is the mean of 36, 42, 39, 48, and 50?

____

7. 7,045 ÷ 8 = ________

8. What is the mean of 752, 148, 0, 18, 478, 657, and 894?

____

9. What is a correct method of determining the mean of 16, 12, 14, 7, 6, and 17?

____

____

____

10. 82,125 ÷ 6 = ________

GO ON

Name ____________________

11. What is the mean of 534, 1, 962, 456, and 187?

____

12. 48,453 ÷ 9 = ________

13. 61,075 ÷ 8 = ________

14. What is the mean of 327, 418, 166, and 489?

____

15. 36,187 ÷ 7 = ________

16. Which is the best buy: 6 apples for $3.45 or 2 apples for $0.98?

____

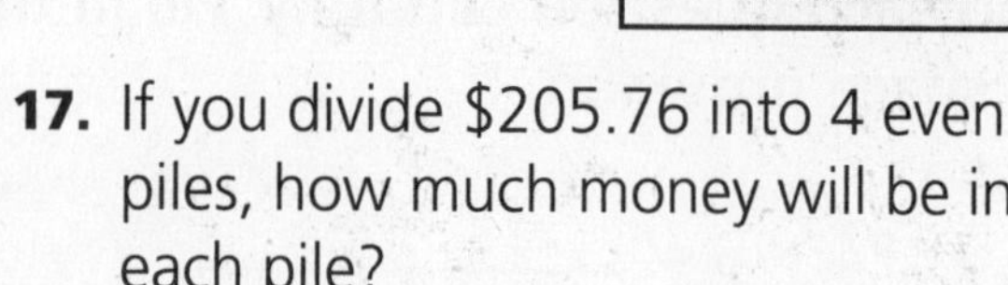
17. If you divide $205.76 into 4 even piles, how much money will be in each pile?

____

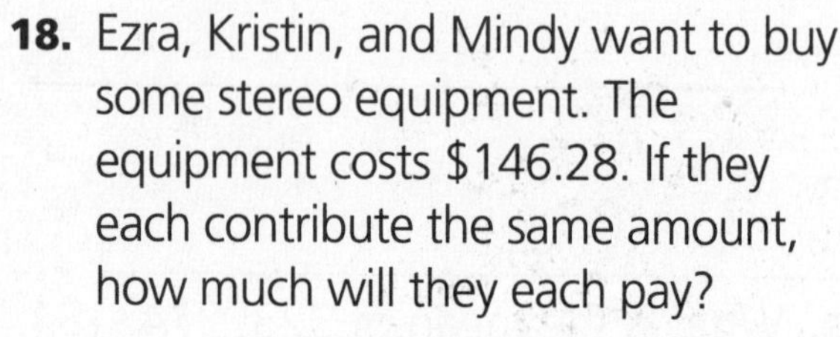
18. Ezra, Kristin, and Mindy want to buy some stereo equipment. The equipment costs $146.28. If they each contribute the same amount, how much will they each pay?

____

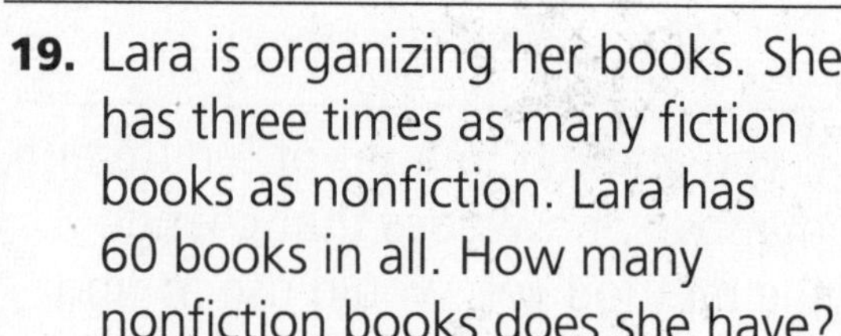
19. Lara is organizing her books. She has three times as many fiction books as nonfiction. Lara has 60 books in all. How many nonfiction books does she have?

____

20. Altogether, Jonas, Kareem, Ben, and Allie earned $77.48. If they shared the money evenly, how much would each of them receive?

____

STOP

Unit 7 Performance Assessment

A Smart Shopper

- ***Target Skill:*** Find the better buy.
- ***Additional Skills:*** Find the mean; divide greater numbers; divide multi-digit numbers by 1-digit divisors; estimate quotients.

Task Description: This task requires students to compare the unit costs of various items and pick the one that is the better buy.

Preparing: You may wish to discuss with students how to find the unit cost of an item. Talk about how this knowledge can be used by shoppers to save money.

Materials	Group Size	Time on Task
Calculator (optional)	2 to 3 students	1–2 days

Guiding: Remind students that an estimate can be used as a first step to find the better buy. If the estimate results in the same numbers, tell students to find an exact answer.

Observing/ Monitoring: As you move among the students, pose the following questions:

How did you use an estimate to find the better buy?

How do you know which items are the better buy?

How can you check your answers?

Unit 7 Performance Assessment Scoring Rubric

A Smart Shopper

Score	Explanation
3	Students demonstrate an efficient strategy and a thorough approach that enables them to solve the problem completely. A satisfactory answer: • names all of the items that are the better buy—6-pack of soda, 2-lb box of cereal, 3-lb box of detergent, 6-oz can of tuna; • states that 4¢ per ounce can be saved by buying the 6-ounce can of tuna. Students are able to complete the problem quickly and have all of the above correct solutions.
2	Students demonstrate a strategy that enables them to solve most of the problem correctly. The strategy is somewhat disorganized, making it less efficient. A solution is found, but errors are contained. Students may: • name 3 of the 4 items that are the better buy; • calculate the amount saved by buying the 6-ounce can of tuna. Students may have some difficulty determining all solutions correctly, but demonstrate an understanding of general concepts.
1	Students demonstrate a confused strategy, which leads to difficulty solving the problem. Most answers are incorrect, but students demonstrate knowledge of at least one concept being assessed such as division or estimating quotients.

Name ____________________

Unit 7 Performance Assessment Student Activity

A Smart Shopper

You will need

- Calculator (optional)

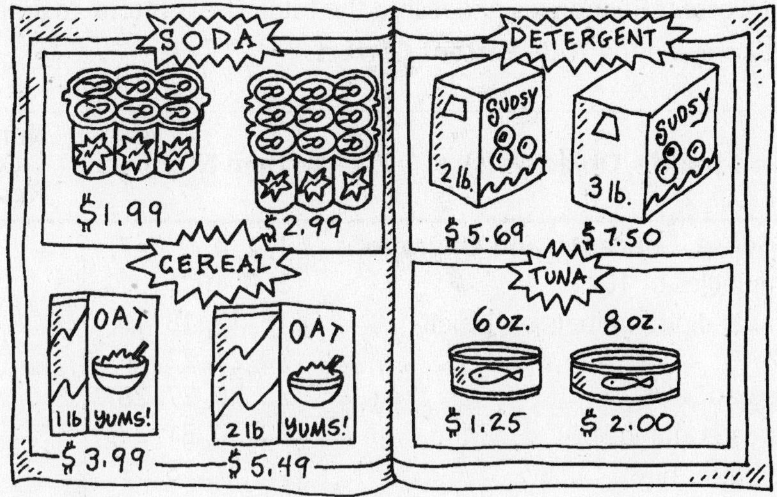

Use the store brochure to answer the following questions.

1. Which package of soda is the better buy: the 6-pack or the 9-pack?

____

2. Which box of cereal is the better buy: the 1-pound box or the 2-pound box?

____

3. Which box of detergent is the better buy: the 2-pound box or the 3-pound box?

____

4. Which can of tuna fish is the better buy: the 6-ounce can or the 8-ounce can?

____

5. About how much money did you save per ounce by buying the less expensive can of tuna?

____

Unit 7 – Monitoring Student Progress

☐ **Form A** ☐ **Form B**

Name ______________________ Date ______________

Directions: This test targets selected objectives. For each item that is answered incorrectly, cross out the item number. Then record the number of correct responses in the column labeled **Number of Correct Responses.** Add to find the **Total Number of Correct Responses** and record the total. Use this total to determine the **Total Test Score** and the **Total Percent Correct.**

Strand • Objective(s)	Item Numbers	Number of Correct Responses
Number Sense, Concepts, and Operations • Divide multiples of 10. • Divide multi-digit numbers by 1-digit numbers. • Estimate quotients. • Divide greater numbers. • Find the better buy. • Use skills and strategies to solve problems.	1, 2, 4, 5, 6, 7, 8, 9, 10, 11, 12, 16, 17, 18, 19, 20, 21, 22, 24, 25, 26, 27, 28, 29, 30, 31, 32, 36, 37, 38, 39, 40	/32
Data Analysis and Probability • Find the mean. • Use skills and strategies to solve problems.	3, 13, 14, 15, 23, 33, 34, 35	/8
Total Number of Correct Responses		
Total Test Score		/40
Total Percent Correct		%

Name ______________________________

Read each question carefully. Darken the circle on your answer sheet for the correct answer.

1. 240 ÷ 2 = ■

A. 12 **C.** 460
B. 120 **D.** 1,200

2. Which is the best estimate?

213 ÷ 3

F. 6 **G.** 7 **H.** 60 **J.** 70

3. What is the mean of 12, 25, 17, 15, and 31?

A. 16 **B.** 17 **C.** 19 **D.** 20

4. 4,500 ÷ 5 = ■

F. 9 **H.** 900
G. 90 **J.** 9,000

5. $4.38 ÷ 6 = ■

A. $0.73 **C.** $0.78
B. $0.75 **D.** $0.79

6. If Lee spent $6.03 on 9 pens and each pen cost the same amount, how much did 1 pen cost?

F. $0.58 **H.** $0.62
G. $0.60 **J.** $0.67

7. Which is the best buy?

A. 8 ounces for $7.82
B. 6 ounces for $5.98
C. 4 ounces for $3.71
D. 2 ounces for $1.92

8. 506 ÷ 7 = ■

F. 8 **H.** 75 R1
G. 72 R2 **J.** 80 R2

9. Which is the best estimate?

332 ÷ 8

A. 40 **B.** 50 **C.** 60 **D.** 70

10. Which is the best estimate?

$96 ÷ 2

F. $30 **H.** $50
G. $40 **J.** $60

11. Which is the best estimate?

597 ÷ 9

A. 5 **B.** 6 **C.** 50 **D.** 60

12. 1,600 ÷ 4 = ■

F. 4 **H.** 400
G. 40 **J.** 4,000

13. What is the mean of 279, 344, 286, and 311?

A. 295
B. 298
C. 300
D. 305

GO ON

Name ______________________________

14. Which of the following is a correct method to determine the mean?

F. Add 987, 942, 931, and 997, and divide the sum by 2.
G. Add 1,025, 1,456, and 2,207, and divide the sum by 3.
H. Add 69, 79, 21, 54, and 71, and divide the sum by 4.
J. Add 80, 85, 95, and 85, and divide the sum by 3.

---

15. What is the mean of 500, 0, 395, 423, 476, 503, and 510?

A. 401 **C.** 468
B. 407 **D.** 476

---

16. 480 ÷ 8 = ■

F. 60 **H.** 6,000
G. 600 **J.** 60,000

Solve.

17. A package of 4 pairs of socks costs $9.20. How much does each pair of socks cost?

A. $2.05 **C.** $2.50
B. $2.30 **D.** $2.55

18. Together Tom and Adam have 25 new quarters. Tom has 7 more than Adam. How many does Adam have?

F. 7 quarters
G. 9 quarters
H. 16 quarters
J. 25 quarters

---

19. The circus sold $2,400 worth of tickets on Monday. If each ticket cost $8, how many people went to the circus?

A. 4,000 people
B. 500 people
C. 400 people
D. 300 people

---

20. There are 72 band members going to a parade. They are going in vans that seat 8 passengers. How many vans do they need?

F. 6 vans
G. 7 vans
H. 8 vans
J. 9 vans

GO ON

Name ____________________

UNIT 7 **TEST**
FORM A
PAGE 3

21. $40 \div 8 = \square$

A. 4 **B.** 5 **C.** 6 **D.** 7

---

22. Which is the best estimate?

$7\overline{)\$650.00}$

F. $70.00 **H.** $110.00
G. $90.00 **J.** $130.00

---

23. What is the mean of 276, 348, 115, and 541?

A. 256 **B.** 320 **C.** 640 **D.** 1,280

---

24. $8{,}000 \div n = 1{,}000$

F. 4 **H.** 6
G. 5 **J.** 8

---

25. $9\overline{)459}$

A. 45 **B.** 50 **C.** 51 **D.** 60

---

26. If Tami spent $38.97 on 3 CDs and each CD cost the same amount, how much did 1 CD cost?

F. $12.49 **H.** $13.49
G. $12.99 **J.** $13.99

---

27. If you divide $205.76 into 4 even piles, how much money will be in each pile?

A. $51.14 **C.** $54.04
B. $51.44 **D.** $54.14

---

28. $4\overline{)331}$

F. 80 **H.** 82 R3
G. 81 R5 **J.** 83 R5

---

29. Which is the best estimate?

$9{,}138 \div 6$

A. 900 **C.** 1,500
B. 1,000 **D.** 1,800

---

30. Which is the best estimate?

$487{,}961 \div 5$

F. 5,000 **H.** 50,000
G. 25,000 **J.** 100,000

---

31. Which is the best estimate?

$33.00 ÷ 5

A. $4.00 **C.** $7.00
B. $5.00 **D.** $8.00

---

32. $200 \div 5 = \square$

F. 10 **H.** 40
G. 30 **J.** 50

---

33. What is the mean of 10, 26, 31, 43, and 10?

A. 13 **B.** 24 **C.** 26 **D.** 30

Name ____________________

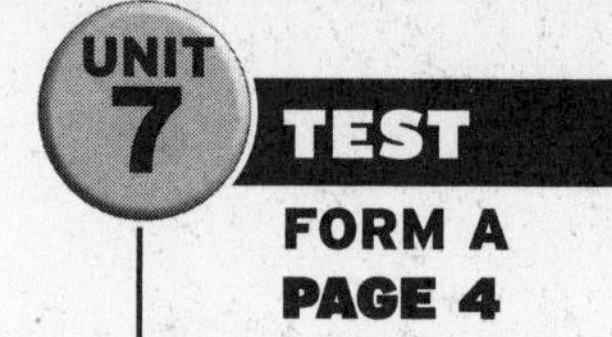

34. Which of the following is a correct method to determine the mean?

F. Add 420, 1,300, 2,046, and 50, and divide the sum by 2.

G. Add 80, 80, 60, and 90, and divide the sum by 3.

H. Add 56, 49, 92, 76, and 38, and divide the sum by 4.

J. Add 93, 65, and 51, and divide the sum by 3.

---

35. What is the mean of 16, 12, 14, 7, 6, and 17?

A. 5 **B.** 7 **C.** 12 **D.** 14

---

36. How many zeros will there be in the quotient?

2,000,000 ÷ 4

F. 3 zeros

G. 4 zeros

H. 5 zeros

J. 6 zeros

Solve.

37. Ezekial, Shameka, and Mona want to buy some baseball equipment. The equipment costs $89.16. If they each contribute the same amount, how much will each pay?

A. $28.73 **C.** $29.23

B. $29.00 **D.** $29.72

38. Sara is organizing the 12 medals she won at track meets. She has twice as many gold medals as silver medals. How many gold medals does Sara have?

F. 4 gold medals

G. 8 gold medals

H. 9 gold medals

J. 12 medals

---

39. The movie theater sold $1,500 worth of tickets on Tuesday. If each ticket cost $6, how many people went to the theater?

A. 220 people **C.** 240 people

B. 230 people **D.** 250 people

---

40. All together, Jonah, Kasey, Arturo, and Amber earned $68.72. If they shared the money evenly, how much would each of them receive?

F. $17.02

G. $17.18

H. $17.38

J. $17.52

STOP

Name ________________________________

UNIT 7 **TEST** FORM B PAGE 1

Read each question carefully. Fill in the correct answer in the space provided.

1. 630 ÷ 9 = ____________

2. Estimate.

239 ÷ 4

____

3. What is the mean of 13, 21, 15, 29, and 32?

____

4. 3,500 ÷ 5 = ____________

5. $5.46 ÷ 7 = ____________

6. If Myra spent $5.22 on 9 pens and each pen cost the same amount, how much did 1 pen cost?

____

7. Which is the better buy?

8 ounces for $6.78

4 ounces for $3.99

____

8. 539 ÷ 8 = ____________

9. Estimate.

361 ÷ 7

____

10. Estimate.

$87 ÷ 2

____

GO ON

Name ____________________

UNIT 7 TEST
FORM B
PAGE 2

11. Estimate.

897 ÷ 9

____

12. 2,500 ÷ 5 = ____________

13. What is the mean of 417, 301, 375, and 367?

____

14. Describe how to find the mean for the following numbers: 999, 872, 782, and 1003.

____

____

____

15. What is the mean of 600, 0, 295, 323, 576, 403, and 610?

____

16. 560 ÷ 70 = ____________

17. A package of five T-shirts costs $20.25. How much does each T-shirt cost?

____

18. Together Andre and Sam have 25 trading cards. Sam has 9 more than Andre. How many does Andre have?

____

19. The carnival sold $2,700 worth of tickets on Monday. If each ticket cost $9, how many people went to the carnival?

____

20. There are 112 football players going to the game. They are going in vans that seat 14 passengers. How many vans do they need?

____

GO ON

Name ______________________

UNIT 7 TEST
FORM B
PAGE 3

21. $45 \div 9 =$ ______

22. Estimate.

$7\overline{)680}$

______

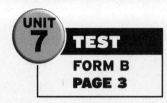

23. What is the mean of 331, 360, 127, and 206?

______

24. If $7{,}000 \div n = 1{,}000$; then $n =$

______

25. $7\overline{)427}$

______

26. If Ellen spent $47.97 on three DVDs and each DVD cost the same amount, how much did one DVD cost?

______

27. If you divide $204.56 into 4 even piles, how much money will be in each pile?

______

28. $5\overline{)363}$

______

29. Estimate.

$8{,}119 \div 4$

______

30. Estimate.

$392{,}792 \div 5$

______

GO ON

Name ____________________

UNIT 7 TEST
FORM B
PAGE 4

31. Estimate.

$37.00 ÷ 5

____

32. 800 ÷ 4 = ____________

33. What is the mean of 33, 41, 26, 19, and 21?

____

34. Describe how to find the mean for the following numbers: 560, 671, and 489.

____

____

____

35. What is the mean of 14, 19, 11, 5, 19, and 10?

____

36. How many zeros will there be in the quotient?

4,000,000 ÷ 5

____

37. Ezekial, Barbara, and Horace went to buy some basketball equipment. The equipment costs $87.69. If they each contribute the same amount, how much will each pay?

____

38. Shameka is organizing her 16 gold and silver swimming medals. She has three times as many gold medals as silver medals. How many silver medals does Shameka have?

____

39. The hot dog vendor sold $1,800 worth of hot dogs on Saturday. If each hot dog cost $3.00, how many hot dogs were sold?

____

40. All together, Calvin, Lamont, Cecil, and Georgia earned $73.52. If they shared the money evenly, how much would each of them receive?

____

STOP

Chapter 15 – Teacher Interview

Core Concept: ***Understand Dividing by 2-Digit Numbers***

Student Activity: Students demonstrate an understanding of dividing a multi-digit number by a 2-digit number when asked to solve an algorithm such as $35\overline{)1{,}018}$.

Teacher Question 1:

- Will the quotient have a 0 in the ones place?

Understanding Student Response	Practice and Improvement
Students who say yes.	Review lesson 1 to help students practice dividing with multiples of 10.
Students who say yes.	Review lesson 3 to help students practice division in situations where regrouping is necessary.

Teacher Question 2:

- Will the quotient have a remainder?

Understanding Student Response	Practice and Improvement
Students who say no.	Review lesson 3 to help students practice regrouping when dividing.

Teacher Question 3:

- What is the quotient when 1,018 is divided by 35?

Understanding Student Response	Practice and Improvement
Students who say a quotient other than 29 R3.	Review lesson 5 to help students focus on the procedure to use when dividing a multi-digit number by a 2-digit divisor, involving regrouping.

Chapter 15 – Journal Writing

Encourage students to generate their own journal entries related to math ideas in general or to concepts in this chapter. For students requiring guidance, present the following journal prompt:

- How can you use both overestimation and underestimation to check if a quotient you have calculated is reasonable?

  (Responses should indicate that overestimation gives you an estimate that is too high, and underestimation gives you an estimate that is too low, so that if your quotient is between those two estimates it makes sense.)

JOURNAL WRITING/PROBLEM SOLVING

Sanjay and Nassar are planning a trip to India over winter break. The route they have mapped out is 3,920 miles long. They have 28 days to travel in India, and they have budgeted $700 for food. How much can they each spend on food each day to keep to their food budget?

Read

Have students find the answer to the problem. Then ask them to write a few sentences telling—

- how they organized the information
- what information they needed to ignore
- how they used 2-digit division to solve the problem

Have students make up another problem for which they would have to follow the same procedure, but with different information. Students should also supply the correct response.

Plan

Students must know how to set up the solution, and how to perform 2-digit division.

Solve

The correct response to the assigned problem is $12.50 per person each day. Students must divide the amount in the food budget by the number of available days, and that quotient by two people.

Look Back

A correct response to the assigned problem demonstrates an ability to organize information and perform 2-digit division. (See scoring rubric on page 7.)

Chapter 15 – Monitoring Student Progress

☐ **Form A** ☐ **Form B**

Name ______________________ Date ______________________

Directions: For each item that is answered incorrectly, cross out the item number. Then record the number of correct responses in the appropriate Student Score column. If the student has not met the Criterion Score for an objective, circle the student's score. Recommended assignments are listed in the Prescription Table on the next page.

Objective	Item Numbers	Criterion Score	Student Score
A. Divide multiples of 10 by 2-digit numbers.	1, 2, 4, 7, 11, 14, 15	6/7	/7
B. Divide a multidigit number by 2-digit numbers.	5, 6, 9, 13, 16	4/5	/5
C. Estimate quotients.	3, 8, 10, 12	3/4	/4
D. Use skills and strategies to solve problems.	17, 18, 19, 20	3/4	/4
Total Test Score		16/20	/20
Total Percent Correct			%

Chapter 15 – Prescription Table

The following chart correlates the tested objectives for this chapter to supplementary materials that meet the individual needs of the students. The Reteach and Practice pages are designed for students who need further instruction in the math concepts taught in this chapter. The Enrich pages are designed for students who need advanced challenges.

Objective	Reteach	Practice	Enrich
A. Divide multiples of 10 by 2-digit numbers.	261	262	263
B. Divide a multidigit number by 2-digit numbers.	270, 273	271, 274	272, 275
C. Estimate quotients.	264	265	266
D. Use skills and strategies to solve problems.	276	277	278

Name ____________________

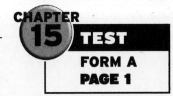

Read each question carefully. Darken the circle on your answer sheet for the correct answer.

1. 84,000 ÷ 70 = ■

A. 20
B. 120
C. 1,200
D. 12,000

2. 3,600 ÷ 90 = ■

F. 40,000
G. 4,000
H. 400
J. 40

3. Estimate.

623 ÷ 87

A. 7
B. 9
C. 70
D. 90

4. $40\overline{)28,000}$

F. 70,000
G. 7,000
H. 700
J. 70

5. $92.46 ÷ 23 = ■

A. $4.02
B. $4.20
C. $40.02
D. $40.20

6. 3,849 ÷ 45 = ■

F. 84 R29
G. 85 R2
H. 85 R24
J. 805 R2

7. $60\overline{)540,000}$

A. 90,000
B. 9,000
C. 900
D. 90

8. Estimate.

592 ÷ 19

F. 30
G. 30 R3
H. 31 R3
J. 300

9. 8,432 ÷ 53 = ■

A. 59 R5
B. 25 R9
C. 159
D. 159 R5

10. Estimate.

5,587 ÷ 72

F. 80
G. 70
H. 8
J. 7

GO ON

Name ______________________________

11. $32,000 \div 16 = \square$

A. 20 **C.** 2,000

B. 200 **D.** 20,000

---

12. Estimate.

$494 \div 57$

F. 8

G. 9

H. 80

J. 90

---

13. $495 \div 61 = \square$

A. 8 **C.** 80 R7

B. 8 R7 **D.** 87

---

14. $8,100 \div x = 90$

F. 9 **G.** 90 **H.** 900 **J.** 9,000

---

15. $64,000 \div 80 = \square$

A. 80 **C.** 8,000

B. 800 **D.** 80,000

---

16. $34\overline{)\$7,378}$

F. 214 **H.** 216

G. 215 **J.** 217

---

17. Mr. Matto decorates the walkway from the street to his hilltop house with paper lanterns each month. A lantern is placed every 15 feet along the right side of the 384-foot walkway. How many lanterns are needed?

A. 250 lanterns

B. 52 lanterns

C. 25 lanterns

D. 5 lanterns

---

18. The local library held a food drive and collected 864 cans of food. They packed the cans into boxes of 32. How many boxes did they use?

F. 260 boxes **H.** 27 boxes

G. 270 boxes **J.** 26 boxes

---

19. John spent \$438 for 84 square yards of carpeting. About how much did each square yard cost?

A. \$4 per square yard

B. \$5 per square yard

C. \$8 per square yard

D. \$10 per square yard

---

20. Jamie is placing flags every 16 feet along the 628-foot perimeter of his backyard. How many flags are needed?

F. 38 flags **H.** 40 flags

G. 39 flags **J.** 48 flags

STOP

Name ____________________

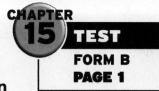

Read each question carefully. Fill in the correct answer in the space provided.

1. 96,000 ÷ 80 = ____________

2. 4,200 ÷ 70 = ____________

3. Estimate.

263 ÷ 33

____

4. $60\overline{)72,000}$

____

5. \$80.85 ÷ 35 = ____________

6. 4,838 ÷ 35 = ____________

7. $70\overline{)490,000}$

____

8. Estimate.

363 ÷ 74

____

9. 4,032 ÷ 28 = ____________

10. Estimate.

8,417 ÷ 93

____

GO ON

Name ____________________

11. 26,000 ÷ 13 = ____________

12. Estimate.

774 ÷ 47

____

13. 624 ÷ 78 = ____________

14. 6,400 ÷ 80 = ____________

15. 63,000 ÷ 90 = ____________

16. 41)$6,232

____

17. Phillip places a marker every 16 feet along a 496-foot walkway. How many markers will he use?

____

18. The students collected 583 empty bottles while cleaning up the local park. They packed the bottles in boxes of 48. How many boxes did they use?

____

19. Elaine spent $352 for 28 square feet of fabric for a dress. About how much did each square foot cost?

____

20. Harold is planting flowers every 12 feet along a 842-foot walkway in the park. How many flowers does he plant?

____

STOP

Chapter 16 – Teacher Interview

Core Concept: ***Order of Operations***

Student Activity: Students demonstrate an understanding of the order of operations by simplifying an expression with two or more operations such as $(3 + 5) \times 8 \div (4 - 2)$.

Teacher Question 1:

- What rules do you follow to simplify expressions?

Understanding Student Response	Practice and Improvement
Students who say first multiply, then divide, then add, then subtract.	Review lesson 4 to help students learn the proper order of operations. Point out that the operations are paired: multiply and divide, then add and subtract.
Students who do not describe performing operations within parentheses first or working from left to right.	Review lesson 4 to help students learn the proper order of operations.

Teacher Question 2:

- What is the first step in simplifying this expression?

Understanding Student Response	Practice and Improvement
Students who say multiply 5×8.	Review lesson 4 to help the student learn the proper order of operations.
Students who say $8 \div 4$.	Review lesson 4 to help the student learn the proper order of operations.

Teacher Question 3:

- Simplify the expression.

Understanding Student Response	Practice and Improvement
Students who answer 8 worked from left to right.	Review lesson 4 to help students learn to perform the operation in parentheses first.
Students who answer 11 ignored the parentheses, but otherwise followed the order of operations.	Review lesson 4 to help students learn the proper order of operations.

Chapter 16 – Journal Writing

Encourage students to generate their own journal entries related to math ideas in general or to concepts in this chapter. For students requiring guidance, present the following journal prompt:

- When you are performing a series of operations, why is it important to follow a specific order of operations? Which operation is performed first?

  (Responses should include that an order has to be followed so that the same answer will result. Operations in parentheses should be performed first.)

JOURNAL WRITING/PROBLEM SOLVING

Ten classmates from the Clark School are attending Running Creek Summer Camp. Each child must bring 4 outfits. Then 2 more classmates decide to go to the camp. All the campers are told to bring an additional 2 outfits. How many outfits in all will the classmates now bring to camp?

Read

Have students find the answer to the problem. Then ask them to write a few sentences telling—

- which operation they performed first
- which operations they performed next

Have students make up another problem with different information for which they would have to follow the same procedure. Then have students solve the problem and supply the correct response.

Plan

Students must know the order of operations and how to apply it.

Solve

The correct response to the assigned problem is 72. Students had to first add $10 + 2$ and then $4 + 2$. Students then had to multiply 12×6.

Look Back

A correct response demonstrates the ability to perform the operations according to the steps in the order of operations. (See scoring rubric onpage 7.)

Chapter 16 – Monitoring Student Progress

☐ **Form A** ☐ **Form B**

Name ______________________ Date ______________

Directions: For each item that is answered incorrectly, cross out the item number. Then record the number of correct responses in the appropriate Student Score column. If the student has not met the Criterion Score for an objective, circle the student's score. Recommended assignments are listed in the Prescription Table on the next page.

Objective	Item Numbers	Criterion Score	Student Score
A. Adjust the quotient.	1, 2, 4, 5	3/4	/4
B. Evaluate expressions and use the proper order of operations.	3, 6, 10, 12, 15	4/5	/5
C. Divide by 2-digit numbers.	7, 8, 9, 11, 13, 14, 16	6/7	/7
D. Use skills and strategies to solve problems.	17, 18, 19, 20	3/4	/4
Total Test Score		16/20	/20
Total Percent Correct			%

Chapter 16 – Prescription Table

The following chart correlates the tested objectives for this chapter to supplementary materials that meet the individual needs of the students. The Reteach and Practice pages are designed for students who need further instruction in the math concepts taught in this chapter. The Enrich pages are designed for students who need advanced challenges.

Objective	Reteach	Practice	Enrich
A. Adjust the quotient.	279	280	281
B. Evaluate expressions and use the proper order of operations.	288	289	290
C. Divide by 2-digit numbers.	282	283	284
D. Use skills and strategies to solve problems.	285, 286	287	

Name ____________________

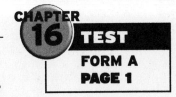

Read each question carefully. Darken the circle on your answer sheet for the correct answer.

1. 139 ÷ 9 = ■

A. 14 **C.** 15
B. 14 R4 **D.** 15 R4

2. 308 ÷ 7 = ■

F. 44 **H.** 43 R7
G. 43 R7 **J.** 42

3. Use order of operations to simplify.
4 × (5 + 9)

A. 56 **C.** 18
B. 29 **D.** 11

4. $6\overline{)149}$

F. 23 R5 **H.** 24 R5
G. 24 **J.** 25

5. 173 ÷ 9 = ■

A. 19 R2
B. 19
C. 18 R2
D. 18

6. Use order of operations to simplify.
42 ÷ (2 + 5) × 6

F. 156 **H.** 7
G. 36 **J.** 1

7. $54\overline{)429}$

A. 80
B. 70 R1
C. 8 R51
D. 7 R51

8. 473 ÷ 39 = ■

F. 12 **H.** 13
G. 12 R5 **J.** 13 R5

9. 29,394 ÷ 18 = ■

A. 1,633
B. 1,633 R4
C. 1,733
D. 1,733 R3

10. Use order of operations to simplify.
(5 × 3) × (1 + 5)

F. 20 **H.** 80
G. 21 **J.** 90

GO ON

Name ________________________________

CHAPTER 16 TEST
FORM A
PAGE 2

11. 297 ÷ 31 = ■

A. 9 **C.** 10
B. 9 R18 **D.** 10 R18

---

12. Use order of operations to simplify.

(8 + 3) × 4 + 7

F. 22 **G.** 27 **H.** 51 **J.** 121

---

13. 58,273 ÷ 41 = ■

A. 142 **C.** 1,421 R12
B. 1,421 **D.** 10,421 R12

---

14. 387 ÷ 52 = ■

F. 7 R23 **H.** 6 R32
G. 7 **J.** 5

---

15. Use order of operations to simplify.

(4 × 9) ÷ (8 − 2)

A. 3 **B.** 6 **C.** 36 **D.** 216

---

16. 63)72,398

F. 1,148 **H.** 1,149
G. 1,148 R11 **J.** 1,149 R11

---

17. The Weintraubs have a flowerbed that measures 52 feet by 18 feet. They are building a fence around the flowerbed. The fence comes in 6-foot sections. How many sections are needed around the flowerbed?

A. 20 sections **C.** 24 sections
B. 23 sections **D.** 30 sections

---

18. Joseph is leasing a new computer. The computer costs a total of $1,449.72. He will make equal payments over 36 months. How much will each monthly payment be?

F. $40 per month
G. $40.27 per month
H. $41.27 per month
J. $52.38 per month

---

19. A parking lot measures 420 feet by 180 feet. The fence comes in 12-foot sections. How many sections are needed to build a fence around the entire parking lot?

A. 10 sections
B. 100 sections
C. 120 sections
D. 1,000 sections

---

20. A company spent $4,829.08 on 58 filing cabinets. How much did each filing cabinet cost?

F. $80 per cabinet
G. $82.00 per cabinet
H. $82.36 per cabinet
J. $83.26 per cabinet

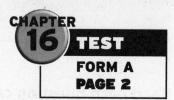

STOP

Name ___________________________________

CHAPTER 16 TEST
FORM B
PAGE 1

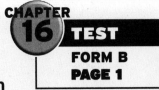

Read each question carefully. Fill in the correct answer in the space provided.

1. 794 ÷ 9 = __________

2. 4,853 ÷ 6 = __________

3. Use order of operations to simplify.

7 × (6 + 8)

____

4. $7\overline{)831}$

____

5. 381 ÷ 8 = __________

6. Use order of operations to simplify.

56 ÷ (1 + 7) × 3

____

7. $62\overline{)518}$

____

8. 813 ÷ 28 = __________

9. 83,067 ÷ 47 = __________

10. Use order of operations to simplify.

(2 × 8) × (7 − 2)

____

GO ON

Name ____________________

CHAPTER 16 TEST

FORM B

PAGE 2

11. $381 \div 44 =$ ________

12. Use order of operations to simplify.

$(6 + 9) \times 7 - 12$

____

13. $71,018 \div 25 =$ ________

14. $586 \div 74 =$ ________

15. Use order of operations to simplify.

$(8 \times 7) \div (9 - 5)$

____

16. $55\overline{)94,751}$

____

17. The Jacobsens have a pool that measures 82 feet by 24 feet. They are building a fence around the pool. The fencing comes in 15-foot sections. How many sections are needed around the pool?

____

18. Zoe spends $2,398.30 on 58 art prints. If each print costs the same amount, how much did she pay for each print?

____

19. A schoolyard measures 640 feet by 280 feet. The fencing comes in 18-foot sections. How many sections are needed around the schoolyard?

____

20. A company spent $6,180.72 on 24 desks. How much did each desk cost?

____

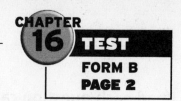

STOP

Unit 8 Performance Assessment

Who's Showing Up?

- ***Target Skill:*** Divide a multi-digit number by a 2-digit number.
- ***Additional Skills:*** Find the mean; divide greater numbers; divide multiples of 10; compare and order numbers.

Task Description: This task requires students to find the attendance of 8 teams in a league and then order the figures from greatest to least.

Preparing: You may wish to discuss with students that teams play home games and away games. Ask them if they know about any professional teams in their area.

Materials	Group Size	Time on Task
Calculator (optional)	2 to 3 students	1–2 days

Guiding: Remind students of the process of regrouping to divide by two-digit numbers.

Tell students to ignore the remainders in their answers.

Tell students they will have enough money to buy the items and they will be paying more than the cost. This means they will receive change.

Observing/ Monitoring: As you move among the students, pose the following questions:

How did you find the attendance for each team?

Is there a team that had an attendance under 1,000 per game?

How can you check your answers?

Unit 8 Performance Assessment Scoring Rubric

Who's Showing Up?

Score	Explanation
3	Students demonstrate an efficient strategy and a thorough approach that enables them to solve the problem completely. A satisfactory answer: • shows a completed and correct chart; • places the attendance figures in proper order and states that the Spiders win the award; • states that multiplication can be used to check a quotient. Students are able to complete the problem quickly and have all of the above correct solutions.
2	Students demonstrate a strategy that enables them to solve most of the problem correctly. The strategy is somewhat disorganized, making it less efficient. A solution is found, but errors are contained. Students may: • have mostly correct quotients; • correctly order the attendance figures; • know how to check a quotient. Students may have some difficulty determining all solutions correctly, but demonstrate an understanding of general concepts.
1	Students demonstrate a confused strategy, which leads to difficulty solving the problem. Most answers are incorrect, but students demonstrate knowledge of at least one concept being assessed such as division or ordering numbers.

Name ________________________________

Unit 8 Performance Assessment Student Activity

Who's Showing Up?

You will need

- Calculator (optional)

The South League awards a trophy to the team with the best average attendance each year. Commissioner Gordon hands out the trophy each year. Help the commissioner award the trophy to the right team.

The season is not yet over. Here are the attendance figures as of today.

Team	Home Games	Attendance	Average Attendance
Lumberjacks	32	46,254	
Spiders	24	48,488	
Whipcords	30	52,830	
Knights	22	12,438	
Zephyrs	30	45,538	
Robins	26	50,182	
Explorers	28	31,436	
Wildcats	34	55,122	

1. Find the attendance for each team. Ignore any remainders.

____

2. How can you check your answer for the Wildcats?

____

3. Order the averages you calculate from greatest to least.

____

____

4. If the season ended today, to which team will Commissioner Gordon hand the trophy?

____

Unit 8 – Monitoring Student Progress

☐ Form A ☐ Form B

Name ____________________ Date ____________

Directions: This test targets selected objectives. For each item that is answered incorrectly, cross out the item number. Then record the number of correct responses in the column labeled **Number of Correct Responses.** Add to find the **Total Number of Correct Responses** and record the total. Use this total to determine the **Total Test Score** and the **Total Percent Correct.**

Strand • Objective(s)	Item Numbers	Number of Correct Responses
Number Sense, Concepts, and Operations • Divide multiples of 10 by 2-digit numbers. • Divide a multi-digit number by 2-digit numbers. • Estimate quotients. • Adjust the quotient. • Evaluate expressions and use the proper order of operations. • Divide by 2-digit numbers. • Use skills and strategies to solve problems.	1, 2, 3, 4, 5, 6, 7, 8, 9, 10, 11, 12, 13, 14, 15, 16, 17, 18, 19, 20, 21, 22, 23, 24, 25, 26, 27, 28, 29, 30, 31, 32, 33, 34, 35, 36, 37, 38, 39, 40	/40
Total Number of Correct Responses		
Total Test Score		/40
Total Percent Correct		%

Name ______________________________

TEST
FORM A
PAGE 1

Read each question carefully. Darken the circle on your answer sheet for the correct answer.

1. 56,000 ÷ 70 = ▇

A. 80,000 **C.** 800
B. 8,000 **D.** 80

2. 2,400 ÷ 40 = ▇

F. 60,000 **H.** 600
G. 6,000 **J.** 60

3. Which is the best estimate?

882 ÷ 31

A. 40
B. 30
C. 4
D. 3

4. $20\overline{)14{,}000}$

F. 70,000 **H.** 700
G. 7,000 **J.** 70

5. $19\overline{)\$71.44}$

A. \$3.86 **C.** \$3.71
B. \$3.76 **D.** \$3.50

6. 2,407 ÷ 52 = ▇

F. 46 R15
G. 46 R5
H. 46
J. 40

7. 270,000 ÷ 90 = ▇

A. 30,000 **C.** 300
B. 3,000 **D.** 30

8. Which is the best estimate?

$77\overline{)485}$

F. 70 **H.** 8
G. 60 **J.** 6

9. $39\overline{)3{,}276}$

A. 84 R30 **C.** 80
B. 84 **D.** 80 R30

10. Which is the best estimate?

3,018 ÷ 58

F. 60 **H.** 6
G. 50 **J.** 5

11. Which is the best estimate?

245 ÷ 52

A. 50 **C.** 5
B. 40 **D.** 4

12. 609 ÷ 63 = ▇

F. 92 R16 **H.** 9 R62
G. 10 R6 **J.** 9 R42

GO ON

Name ____________________

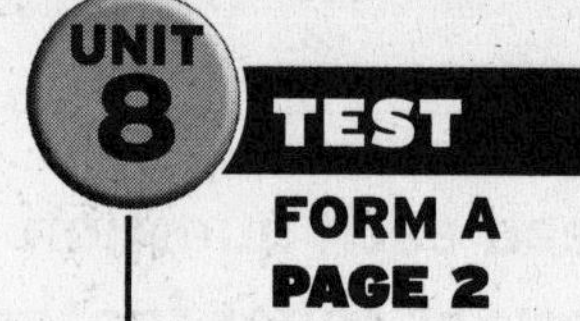

Use order of operations to simplify.

13. (7 × 5 + 4) ÷ 3 = ▢

A. 39 **C.** 21
B. 36 **D.** 13

---

14. (3 + 5) × 6 + 4 = ▢

F. 80 **H.** 37
G. 52 **J.** 34

---

15. 24 ÷ (4 + 2) × 5 = ▢

A. 90 **C.** 20
B. 40 **D.** 16

---

16. (8 + 2) × (3 + 5) = ▢

F. 80 **H.** 24
G. 35 **J.** 19

Solve.

17. The Washingtons have a garden that measures 72 feet by 24 feet. They are building a fence around the garden. The fence comes in 8-foot sections. How many sections are needed around the garden?

A. 30 sections
B. 24 sections
C. 18 sections
D. 12 sections

18. A town decorates the shoreline of the lake with lights. A light is placed every 12 feet along the 168-yard shoreline of the town park. How many lights are needed?

F. 492 lights
G. 42 lights
H. 14 lights
J. 12 lights

---

19. Students brought in 768 soda cans to recycle. They packed the cans in boxes of 24. How many boxes did they fill?

A. 40 boxes
B. 36 boxes
C. 32 boxes
D. 30 boxes

---

20. Landscapers spent $1,667.25 for 39 shrubs to plant around the new bank. About how much did each shrub cost?

F. $40
G. $30
H. $4
J. $3

21. 35,000 ÷ 50 = ■

A. 7,000 **C.** 70
B. 700 **D.** 7

22. 1,800 ÷ 30 = ■

F. 60,000
G. 6,000
H. 600
J. 60

23. Which is the best estimate?

1,487 ÷ 46

A. 40 **C.** 4
B. 30 **D.** 3

24. 60)54,000

F. 9,000 **H.** 90
G. 900 **J.** 9

25. 31)$132.99

A. $4.29 **C.** $4.00
B. $4.03 **D.** $1.06

26. 804 ÷ 43 = ■

F. 18 R30
G. 18
H. 15
J. 2

27. 32,000 ÷ 80 = ■

A. 4,000 **C.** 40
B. 400 **D.** 4

28. Which is the best estimate?

51)248

F. 50 **H.** 5
G. 40 **J.** 4

29. 73)4,088

A. 60 **C.** 56
B. 58 R64 **D.** 6 R50

30. Which is the best estimate?

5,396 ÷ 93

F. 60 **H.** 6
G. 50 **J.** 5

31. Which is the best estimate?

638 ÷ 77

A. 90 **C.** 9
B. 80 **D.** 8

32. 3,219 ÷ 68 = ■

F. 53 R35 **H.** 47 R23
G. 50 **J.** 47 R13

GO ON

Name ____________________

Use order of operations to simplify.

33. $2 \times (3 + 4) = \blacksquare$

A. 25 **C.** 17
B. 21 **D.** 14

34. $36 \div (3 + 6) \times 2 = \blacksquare$

F. 36 **H.** 8
G. 24 **J.** 2

35. $(3 \times 4) \times (4 + 2) = \blacksquare$

A. 72 **C.** 27
B. 50 **D.** 21

36. $(7 + 2) \times 3 + 6 = \blacksquare$

F. 81 **H.** 25
G. 33 **J.** 19

Solve.

37. A playground measures 200 feet by 160 feet. The fence comes in 8-foot sections. How many sections are needed for the playground fence?

A. 90 sections
B. 50 sections
C. 45 sections
D. 40 sections

38. An office wall is 90 yards long. The electrician installed wall outlets every 6 feet along the wall. How many outlets were needed?

F. 54 outlets
G. 45 outlets
H. 15 outlets
J. 6 outlets

39. A fast-food restaurant ordered 672 toys for their children's meals. The toys came in boxes of 48 toys. How many boxes did the toys come in?

A. 18 boxes
B. 16 boxes
C. 14 boxes
D. 13 boxes

40. A company spent $2,542 on 32 office chairs. About how much did each chair cost?

F. $80
G. $70
H. $8
J. $7

STOP

Name ______________________

Read each question carefully. Fill in the correct answer in the space provided.

1. 63,000 ÷ 90 = ________

2. 2,400 ÷ 30 = ________

3. Estimate.

912 ÷ 27

____

4. $30\overline{)18,000}$

____

5. $16\overline{)\$44.16}$

____

6. 2,225 ÷ 46 = ________

7. 560,000 ÷ 80 = ________

8. Estimate.

$83\overline{)479}$

____

9. $37\overline{)3,071}$

____

10. Estimate.

2,997 ÷ 63

____

GO ON

Name ____________________

UNIT 8 TEST
FORM B
PAGE 2

11. Estimate.

253 ÷ 47

____

12. 501 ÷ 61 = ____________

Use order of operations to simplify.

13. (5 × 4 + 8) ÷ 7 = ____________

14. (4 × 6) × 3 + 2 = ____________

15. 36 ÷ (4 + 2) × 7 = ____________

16. (9 + 2) × (6 + 3) = ____________

Solve.

17. The Blackshires have a garden that measures 60 feet by 18 feet. They are building a fence around the garden. If the fence comes in 6-foot sections, how many sections are needed?

____

18. A town decorates the shoreline of the lake with lights. A light is placed every 14 feet along the 168-yard shoreline. How many lights are needed?

____

19. Students brought in 864 soda cans to recycle. They packed the cans in boxes of 24. How many boxes did they fill?

____

20. Landscapers spent $1,589.75 for 42 trees to plant around the new school. About how much did each tree cost?

____

GO ON

Name ____________________

UNIT 8 TEST
FORM B
PAGE 3

21. $75{,}000 \div 50 =$ ________

22. $2{,}700 \div 90 =$ ________

23. Estimate.

$1521 \div 54$

____

24. $60\overline{)48{,}000}$

____

25. $29\overline{)\$116.87}$

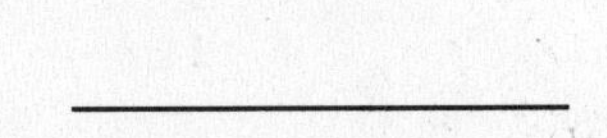

26. $726 \div 42 =$ ________

27. $48{,}000 \div 60 =$ ________

28. Estimate.

$62\overline{)357}$

____

29. $57\overline{)4161}$

____

30. Estimate.

$5{,}431 \div 88$

____

GO ON

Name ____________________

UNIT 8 TEST
FORM B
PAGE 4

31. Estimate.

645 ÷ 81

____

32. 2,539 ÷ 37 = ____________

Use order of operations to simplify.

33. 4 × (6 + 9) = ____________

34. 36 ÷ (4 + 2) × 5 = ____________

35. (2 × 8) × (2 + 8) = ____________

36. (9 − 2) × 3 + 5 = ____________

Solve.

37. A rectangular playground measures 360 feet by 240 feet. A fence is being built around the playground. If the fence comes in 8-foot sections, how many sections are needed?

____

38. A garage wall is 30 yards long. The electrician installed wall outlets every 6 yards along the wall. How many outlets were needed?

____

39. A fast-food restaurant ordered 832 toys for their children's meals. The toys came in boxes of 16. How many boxes did the toys come in?

____

40. A company spent $2730 on 32 office chairs. About how much did each chair cost?

____

STOP

Chapter 17 – Teacher Interview

Core Concept: ***Customary Units***

Student Activity: The student demonstrates an understanding of customary units for measuring length, weight, and capacity.

Teacher Question 1:

- What is the correct order of the following units from least to greatest: pint, cup, fluid ounce, gallon, quart?

Understanding Student Response	Practice and Improvement
Students who say the units in an incorrect order.	Review lesson 3 to help students understand the size of each unit.

Teacher Question 2:

- What is the correct order of the following units from shortest to longest: yard, inch, foot, mile?

Understanding Student Response	Practice and Improvement
Students who say the units in an incorrect order.	Review lesson 2 to help students understand the size of each unit.

Teacher Question 3:

- Which unit best describes your weight: ounce, pound, ton?

Understanding Student Response	Practice and Improvement
Students who say ounce.	Review lesson 3 to help students review that 16 ounces = 1 pound.
Students who say ton.	Review lesson 3 to help students review that 2,000 pounds = 1 ton.

Chapter 17 – Journal Writing

Encourage students to generate their own journal entries related to math ideas in general or to concepts in this chapter. For students requiring guidance, present the following journal prompt:

- When you are converting from one unit of measurement to another, what do you have to remember? Which are the two operations that you might use when converting?

  (Responses should include references that a table might have to be used to perform the conversions. Multiplication and division are the two operations useful in conversions.)

JOURNAL WRITING/PROBLEM SOLVING

Kristen was to buy 36 inches of lace trim for a dress she is making. The trim is sold by the foot. How many feet of lace trim should Kristen buy?

Read

Have students find the answer to the problem. Then ask them to write a few sentences telling—

- what information they needed to make the conversion
- which operation they used to make the conversion

Have students make up another problem with different information for which they would have to follow the same procedure. Then have students solve the problem and supply the correct response.

Plan

Students must know or be able to find out that there are 12 inches in one foot, use the appropriate operation, and compute correctly.

Solve

The correct response to the assigned problem is 3 feet. Students had to know how many inches were in one foot, use multiplication, and compute correctly.

Look Back

A correct response demonstrates the ability to find the conversion factor for the given problem, choose the appropriate operation, and solve the problem. (See scoring rubric on page 7.)

Chapter 17 – Monitoring Student Progress

☐ **Form A** ☐ **Form B**

Name ______________________ Date ______________

Directions: For each item that is answered incorrectly, cross out the item number. Then record the number of correct responses in the appropriate Student Score column. If the student has not met the Criterion Score for an objective, circle the student's score. Recommended assignments are listed in the Prescription Table on the next page.

Objective	Item Numbers	Criterion Score	Student Score
A. Estimate and measure with nonstandard units.	1	1/1	/1
B. Explore customary length to $\frac{1}{4}$ inch.	2, 3, 4, 5, 6, 7, 8	6/7	/7
C. Estimate and measure customary capacity and weight.	9, 10, 11, 12	3/4	/4
D. Convert customary units.	13, 14, 15, 16	3/4	/4
E. Use skills and strategies to solve problems.	17, 18, 19, 20	3/4	/4
Total Test Score		16/20	/20
Total Percent Correct			%

Chapter 17 – Prescription Table

The following chart correlates the tested objectives for this chapter to supplementary materials that meet the individual needs of the students. The Reteach and Practice pages are designed for students who need further instruction in the math concepts taught in this chapter. The Enrich pages are designed for students who need advanced challenges.

Objective	Reteach	Practice	Enrich
A. Estimate and measure with nonstandard units.	292	293	294
B. Explore customary length to $\frac{1}{4}$ inch.	295	296	297
C. Estimate and measure customary capacity and weight.	298	299	300
D. Convert customary units.	301	302	303
E. Use skills and strategies to solve problems.	304	305	306

Name ____________________

CHAPTER 17 TEST
FORM A
PAGE 1

Read each question carefully. Darken the circle on your answer sheet for the correct answer.

1. Choose the appropriate nonstandard unit to measure the following:

the length of a desk

A. a penny **C.** a broom
B. a pen **D.** a chair

2. Estimate and then measure.

F. 2 cm **H.** 4 cm
G. $7\frac{3}{4}$ cm **J.** $1\frac{1}{2}$ cm

Choose the best estimate for exercises 3–12.

3. length of a bed

A. 6 in. **C.** 6 yd
B. 6 mi **D.** 6 ft

4. height of a flagpole

F. 10 yd **H.** 10 mi
G. 10 lb **J.** 10 in.

5. distance between home and school

A. 3 yd **C.** 3 ft
B. 3 mi **D.** 3 in.

6. length of a book

F. 12 ft **H.** 12 yd
G. 12 mi **J.** 12 in.

7. height of a student

A. 50 in. **C.** 50 yd
B. 50 ft **D.** 50 mi

8. distance between two opposite walls in a room

F. 20 yd **H.** 20 ft
G. 20 in. **J.** 20 mi

9. capacity of a juice pitcher

A. 2 in. **C.** 2 qt
B. 2 fl oz **D.** 2 gal

10. weight of a guitar

F. 8 lb **H.** 8 T
G. 8 oz **J.** 80 lb

GO ON

Name ______________________________

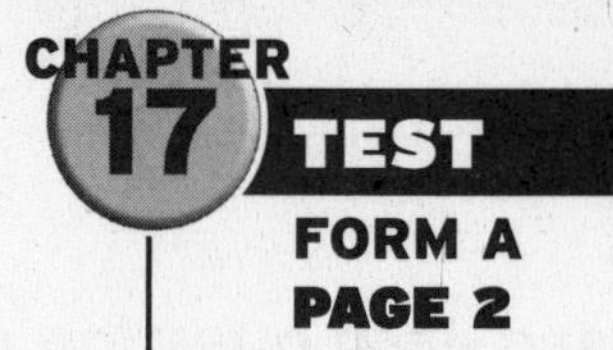

11. capacity of a soup pot

A. 1 fl oz
B. 1 c
C. 1 pt
D. 1 gal

---

12. weight of a tractor

F. 3 oz
G. 3 T
H. 3 lb
J. 3,000 oz

---

13. 8 lb = ■ oz

A. 128 oz
B. 120 oz
C. 80 oz
D. 24 oz

---

14. 12 ft = ■ in.

F. 24 in.
G. 120 in.
H. 144 in.
J. 240 in.

---

15. 27 ft = ■ yd

A. 24 yd
B. 18 yd
C. 12 yd
D. 9 yd

---

16. 20 pt = ■ qt

F. 40 qt
G. 20 qt
H. 10 qt
J. 5 qt

---

17. Mirabelle is making dinner for her family, which has four members. She decides to buy 40 pounds of fresh fish to cook. Is this reasonable? Explain why or why not.

A. yes; each person will get to eat 10 lb of fish
B. no; 10 lb of fish for each person is too much
C. no; each person will need more than 10 lb of fish
D. yes; she can feed the leftovers to the dog

---

18. Gwen poured 3 gallons of apple juice into glasses. She poured 12 oz of juice into each cup. How many glasses did she use?

F. 64 glasses
G. 48 glasses
H. 32 glasses
J. 24 glasses

---

19. Vivian needs 3 pounds of chocolate squares to make a cake. Which package of chocolate squares should she buy?

A. 48 oz
B. 32 oz
C. 24 oz
D. 16 oz

---

20. Frank pours 3 quarts of milk into glasses. He poured 6 oz of milk into each glass. How many glasses did he use?

F. 8 glasses
G. 16 glasses
H. 24 glasses
J. 32 glasses

STOP

Name ____________________

CHAPTER 17 TEST
FORM B
PAGE 1

Read each question carefully. Fill in the correct answer in the space provided.

1. Which of the following would be a more appropriate nonstandard unit to use to measure the length of your backyard: a ski pole or a toothpick?

   ____

2. Estimate in inches and then measure.

   ____

For exercises 3–8, choose from the following list and fill in the blank.

miles, yards, feet, inches

3. length of a couch = 8 __________

4. height of a door = 2 __________

5. length of the United States = 2,500 __________

6. length of a bicycle = 57 __________

7. height of a mountain = 12,000 __________

8. distance between two classrooms at school = 10 __________

For exercises 9–10, choose from the following list and fill in the blank.

cups, pints, quarts, gallons

9. capacity of a bathtub = 16 __________

10. capacity of a large bottle of soda = 2 __________

GO ON

Name ______________________________

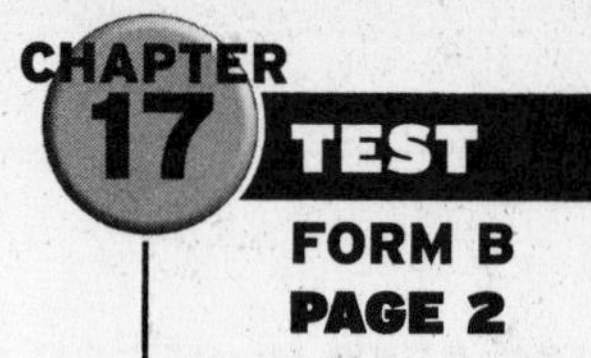

For exercises 11–12, choose from the following list and fill in the blank.

tons, pounds, ounces

11. weight of a cereal bowl = 20 ________

12. weight of a truck = 5 ________

13. 20 lb = ________ oz

14. 7 ft = ________ in.

15. 33 ft = ________ yd

16. 16 pt = ________ qt

17. Sally said that she lives 1 yard from school. Is this reasonable? Explain.

____

____

____

18. Chris poured 8 quarts of water into glasses. He poured 8 oz of water into each glass. How many glasses did he use?

____

19. Mario weighed 9 lb 4 oz when he was born. How many ounces did he weigh?

____

20. Betty filled a 3-gallon container with water. Then she poured water from the container into pint containers. How many pint containers did she fill?

____

STOP

Chapter 18 – Teacher Interview

Core Concept: ***Metric Units***

Student Activity: Students demonstrate an understanding of metric units for measuring length, mass, and capacity, and know the difference between degrees Celsius and Fahrenheit.

Teacher Question 1:

- What is the correct order of the following units from shortest to longest: meter, millimeter, kilometer, centimeter?

Understanding Student Response	Practice and Improvement
Students who say the units in an incorrect order.	Review lesson 1 to help students understand the size of each unit.

Teacher Question 2:

- Using the Fahrenheit scale, what is the freezing point of water?

Understanding Student Response	Practice and Improvement
Students who say 0 degrees.	Review lesson 5 to help students learn the freezing points for both temperature scales.
Students who say 212 degrees or 100 degrees.	Review lesson 5 to help students understand freezing and boiling points on both temperature scales.

Teacher Question 3:

- How many grams are in 1 kilogram?

Understanding Student Response	Practice and Improvement
Students who give an incorrect response.	Review lesson 3 to help students learn how to convert metric units.

Chapter 18 – Journal Writing

Encourage students to generate their own journal entries related to math ideas in general or to concepts in this chapter. For students requiring guidance, present the following journal prompt:

- How do you use the number 10 to convert between metric units?

  (Responses should describe multiplying by 10 to convert to smaller units and dividing by 10 to convert to larger units.)

JOURNAL WRITING/PROBLEM SOLVING

Neil and his family are traveling in Canada. They pass a sign that reads "Montreal 250 km." How many meters is that?

Read

Have students find the answer to the problem. Then ask them to write a few sentences telling—

- the relationship between a meter and a kilometer
- how they found the distance in meters

Have students make up another problem for which they would have to follow the same procedure, but with different information. Students should also supply the correct response.

Plan

Students must know how to convert from kilometers to meters.

Solve

The correct response to the assigned problem is 250,000 meters. Students had to know that 1 kilometer is equal to 1,000 meters. Students had to correctly convert 250 kilometers by multiplying by 1,000.

Look Back

A correct response demonstrates an ability to convert metric units. (See scoring rubric on page 7.)

Chapter 18 – Monitoring Student Progress

☐ **Form A** ☐ **Form B**

Name ______________________ Date ______________

Directions: For each item that is answered incorrectly, cross out the item number. Then record the number of correct responses in the appropriate Student Score column. If the student has not met the Criterion Score for an objective, circle the student's score. Recommended assignments are listed in the Prescription Table on the next page.

Objective	Item Numbers	Criterion Score	Student Score
A. Estimate and measure metric length.	1, 2, 3, 4	3/4	/4
B. Estimate and measure metric capacity and mass.	5, 6, 7, 8, 9, 10	5/6	/6
C. Convert metric units.	13, 14, 15, 16	3/4	/4
D. Estimate and measure temperature.	11, 12	1/2	/2
E. Use skills and strategies to solve problems.	17, 18, 19, 20	3/4	/4
Total Test Score		15/20	/20
Total Percent Correct			%

Chapter 18 – Prescription Table

The following chart correlates the tested objectives for this chapter to supplementary materials that meet the individual needs of the students. The Reteach and Practice pages are designed for students who need further instruction in the math concepts taught in this chapter. The Enrich pages are designed for students who need advanced challenges.

Objective	Reteach	Practice	Enrich
A. Estimate and measure metric length.	307	308	309
B. Estimate and measure metric capacity and mass.	310	311	312
C. Convert metric units.	313	314	315
D. Estimate and measure temperature.	319	320	321
E. Use skills and strategies to solve problems.	316, 317	318	

Name ______________________________

CHAPTER 18 TEST
FORM A
PAGE 1

Read each question carefully. Darken the circle on your answer sheet for the correct answer.

Choose the best estimate for exercises 1–12.

1. height of a bookshelf

A. 2 mm **C.** 2 m
B. 2 cm **D.** 2 km

2. length of a book

F. 24 mm
G. 24 cm
H. 24 m
J. 4 km

3. distance between school and store

A. 3 mm **C.** 3 m
B. 3 cm **D.** 3 km

4. length of an eraser

F. 36 mm **H.** 36 m
G. 36 cm **J.** 36 km

5. the capacity of a water bottle

A. 1 mL **C.** 1 L
B. 10 mL **D.** 10 L

6. capacity of an eye dropper

F. 2 mL **H.** 2 L
G. 200 mL **J.** 200 L

7. capacity of a washing machine

A. 10 mL
B. 1,000 mL
C. 10 L
D. 100 L

8. mass of a teacup

F. 2 g **H.** 2 kg
G. 100 g **J.** 100 kg

9. mass of a book bag when filled

A. 8 g **C.** 8 kg
B. 80 g **D.** 80 kg

10. mass of a truck

F. 5,000 kg
G. 500 kg
H. 5000 g
J. 500 g

GO ON

Name ________________________________

11. temperature of hot chocolate

A. 180°C **C.** 18°C
B. 180°F **D.** 18°F

---

12. temperature of a snowball

F. 20°C **H.** 50°C
G. 20°F **J.** 50°F

Write the number that makes each sentence true for exercises 13–16.

13. 8 m = ▢ mm

A. 8 **C.** 800
B. 80 **D.** 8,000

---

14. 33,000 g = ▢ kg

F. 3,300 **H.** 33
G. 330 **J.** 3

---

15. 12 L = ▢ mL

A. 120 **C.** 12,000
B. 1,200 **D.** 120,000

---

16. 40 kg = ▢ g

F. 400,000 **H.** 4,000
G. 40,000 **J.** 400

17. Mary is 3 inches taller than Joe. George is 2 inches shorter than Matt. Matt is 4 inches taller than Mary. Who is the shortest?

A. Mary **C.** George
B. Joe **D.** Matt

---

18. Harry measures 8 meters around a mattress. How many centimeters is that?

F. 8 **H.** 800
G. 80 **J.** 8,000

---

19. Jill has three times as many marbles as Paul. Paul has four times as many as Lisa. Jason has 8 fewer marbles than Lisa. If Jason has 2 marbles, how many does Jill have?

A. 10 marbles
B. 20 marbles
C. 40 marbles
D. 120 marbles

---

20. Melissa buys a 3-liter bottle of water. She pours the water into glasses. Each glass holds 500 mL of water. How many glasses does she use?

F. 6 glasses
G. 12 glasses
H. 60 glasses
J. 120 glasses

STOP

Name ____________________

CHAPTER 18 TEST
FORM B
PAGE 1

Read each question carefully. Fill in the correct answer in the space provided.

For exercises 1–4, choose from the following list and fill in the blank:

millimeters, centimeters, meters, kilometers

1. height of a table = 80

____

2. length of a laptop computer = 300

____

3. distance from one side of a street to the other = 10

____

4. distance between home and summer camp = 40

____

For exercises 5–10, choose from the following list and fill in the blank:

milliliters, liters, grams, kilograms

5. capacity of a bucket = 8

____

6. capacity of a teaspoon = 20

____

7. capacity of a mug = 500

____

8. mass of a large boulder = 40

____

9. mass of a feather = 4

____

10. mass of a bag of ice = 8

____

GO ON

Name ____________________

CHAPTER 18 TEST
FORM B
PAGE 2

For exercises 11–12, choose Fahrenheit or Celsius.

11. temperature of a swimming pool = 30°

____

12. temperature of an ice cube in a glass of water = 30°

____

Write the number that makes each sentence true for exercises 13–16.

13. 10 m = ________ mm

14. 21,000 g = ________ kg

15. 25 L = ________ mL

16. 7 kg = ________ g

17. Linda is 6 inches shorter than Don. Elise is 4 inches taller than Hector. Hector is 5 inches taller than Linda. Who is the tallest?

____

18. Harry measures 18 meters around a room. How many centimeters is that?

____

19. Trisha has four times as many stamps as Rick. David has twice as many stamps as Carol. Carol has 7 fewer stamps than Trisha. If David has 26 stamps, how many does Rick have?

____

20. Tessa buys three 2-liter bottles of juice. She pours all of the juice into cups. Each cup holds 500 mL of juice. How many cups does she use?

____

STOP

Unit 9 Performance Assessment

Measurement Concentration

- ***Target Skill:*** Convert customary units.
- ***Additional Skills:*** Convert metric units.

Task Description: This task requires students to play a concentration game involving five customary conversions and five metric conversions. Students will make 20 cards with 10 conversions and place them face down. Then they will match the equivalent measurements.

Preparing: Students should work in pairs or small groups. Discuss with students the types of measurements they can use for the activity. The activity can also be used entirely in one system or the other.

Materials	Group Size	Time on Task
Index cards	2 to 3 students	1–2 days

Guiding: Remind students that conversions will be in the same system, so if they pick a card with a metric unit and a customary unit, they can automatically know they don't have a match.

Observing/ Monitoring: As you move among the students, pose the following questions:

How did you write your conversions?

How do you know that you have a match?

Unit 9 Performance Assessment Scoring Rubric

Measurement Concentration

Score	Explanation
3	Students demonstrate an efficient strategy and a thorough approach that enables them to solve the problem completely. A satisfactory answer: • has five correct customary conversions; • has five correct metric conversions. Students are able to complete the problem quickly and have all of the above correct solutions.
2	Students demonstrate a strategy that enables them to solve most of the problem correctly. The strategy is somewhat disorganized, making it less efficient. A solution is found, but errors are contained. Students may: • have mostly correct conversions in either unit; • have correct conversions on the cards, but do not put them together during the activity. Students may have some difficulty determining all solutions correctly, but demonstrate an understanding of general concepts.
1	Students demonstrate a confused strategy, which leads to difficulty solving the problem. Most answers are incorrect, but students demonstrate knowledge of at least one concept being assessed, such as converting customary or metric units.

Name ________________________________

Unit 9 Performance Assessment Student Activity

Measurement Concentration

You will need
- Index cards

Work with a partner. Write 5 customary measurements on index cards. Then write 5 equal measurements in a different customary unit on 5 index cards.

Write 5 metric measurements on index cards. Then write 5 equal measurements in a different metric unit on 5 index cards.

Mix up the cards and place them face down in four rows of five. Pick two cards and put them face up in their same positions. If the measurements do not match, your turn is over. Turn the cards face down. If the measurements are equal, keep the cards and continue your turn.

If the measurements are equal, write them below.

	=	
	=	
	=	
	=	
	=	
	=	
	=	
	=	
	=	
	=	

The player with more cards at the end wins!

Unit 9 – Monitoring Student Progress

☐ Form A ☐ Form B

Name ______________________ Date ______________

Directions: This test targets selected objectives. For each item that is answered incorrectly, cross out the item number. Then record the number of correct responses in the column labeled **Number of Correct Responses.** Add to find the **Total Number of Correct Responses** and record the total. Use this total to determine the **Total Test Score** and the **Total Percent Correct.**

Strand • Objective(s)	Item Numbers	Number of Correct Responses
Measurement • Estimate and measure with nonstandard units. • Explore customary length to 1/4 inch. • Estimate and measure customary capacity and weight. • Convert customary units. • Estimate and measure metric length. • Estimate and measure metric capacity and mass. • Convert metric units. • Estimate and measure temperature. • Use skills and strategies to solve problems.	1, 2, 3, 4, 5, 6, 7, 8, 9, 10, 11, 12, 13, 14, 15, 16, 17, 18, 19, 20, 21, 22, 23, 24, 25, 26, 27, 28, 29, 30, 31, 32, 33, 34, 35, 36, 37, 38, 39, 40	/40
Total Number of Correct Responses		
Total Test Score		/40
Total Percent Correct		%

Name ______________________________

Reach each question carefully. Darken the circle on your answer sheet for the correct answer.

Choose the best estimate for exercises 1–12.

1. length of a couch

A. 6 mi **C.** 6 ft
B. 6 yd **D.** 6 in.

2. height of a fence

F. 3 km **H.** 3 cm
G. 3 m **J.** 3 mm

3. length of a house

A. 30 mi **C.** 30 ft
B. 30 yd **D.** 30 in.

4. distance between two towns

F. 5 km **H.** 5 cm
G. 5 m **J.** 5 mm

5. capacity of a small glass of water

A. 1 gal **C.** 1 pt
B. 1 qt **D.** 1 c

6. mass of a large turkey

F. 10 kg **H.** 10 g
G. 1 kg **J.** 1 g

7. weight of a car

A. 2 T **C.** 2 lb
B. 2,000 oz **D.** 2 oz

8. capacity of a sports bottle

F. 10 L **H.** 10 mL
G. 1 L **J.** 1 mL

9. temperature in a freezer

A. 32°F **C.** 0°F
B. 32°C **D.** 0°C

10. temperature on a day when you can swim in a lake

F. 50°F **H.** 27°F
G. 50°C **J.** 27°C

11. temperature of a hot tub

A. 105°F **C.** 20°F
B. 105°C **D.** 20°C

12. temperature of a heated room

F. 68°F **H.** 5°F
G. 68°C **J.** 5°C

GO ON

Name ____________________

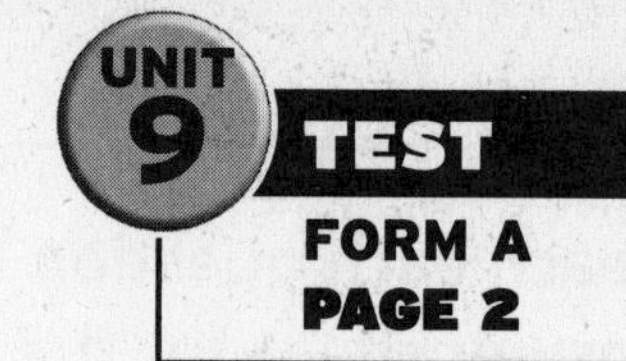

13. 6 L = ■ mL

A. 60,000 **C.** 600
B. 6,000 **D.** 60

14. 300 mm = ■ cm

F. 3,000 **H.** 30
G. 300 **J.** 3

15. 6 ft = ■ in.

A. 72
B. 18
C. 2
D. 0

16. 48 oz = ■ lb

F. 6 **H.** 3
G. 4 **J.** 2

Solve.

17. Steve is 5 inches shorter than Dave. Mark is 1 inch taller than Jim. Jim is 2 inches taller than Steve. Who is the tallest?

A. Steve
B. Dave
C. Mark
D. Jim

18. Joy has twice as many trading cards as Megan. Sara has 3 more than Joy. April has 2 fewer than Megan. If April has 4 cards, how many does Sara have?

F. 15 cards
G. 12 cards
H. 6 cards
J. 2 cards

19. Carol poured 6 liters of orange juice into glasses. She poured 400 mL of juice into each glass. How many glasses did she use?

A. 150 glasses
B. 24 glasses
C. 15 glasses
D. 5 glasses

20. Jerry needs 1 pound of chocolate chips to make cookies. Which package of chocolate chips should he buy?

F. 24 oz
G. 16 oz
H. 8 oz
J. 6 oz

GO ON

Name ______________________________________

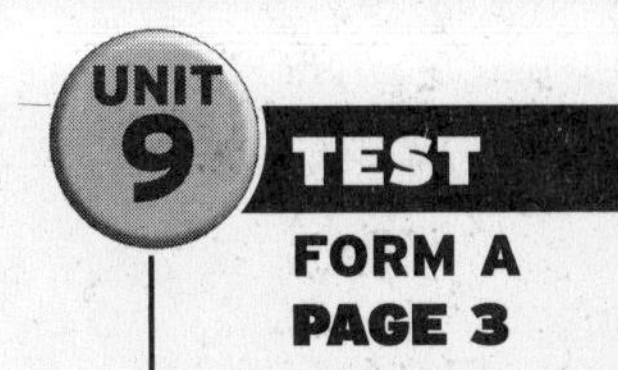

21. width of a car

A. 2 km **C.** 2 dm
B. 2 m **D.** 2 mm

22. capacity of a medium-sized pot

F. 6 gal **H.** 6 pt
G. 6 qt **J.** 6 c

23. mass of a chicken

A. 200 kg **C.** 2 kg
B. 200 g **D.** 2 g

24. temperature of a cup of coffee

F. 150°F **H.** 32°F
G. 150°C **J.** 32°C

25. width of a sheet of paper

A. 8 mi **C.** 8 ft
B. 8 yd **D.** 8 in.

26. mass of a large dog

F. 80 T **H.** 80 lb
G. 8 T **J.** 80 oz

27. temperature on a day when you can go skiing

A. 70°F **C.** 32°F
B. 70°C **D.** 32°C

28. length of a paper clip

F. 3 km **H.** 3 cm
G. 3 m **J.** 3 mm

29. weight of a pencil

A. 500 kg **C.** 5 kg
B. 500 g **D.** 5 g

30. temperature of a shower

F. 212°F **H.** 32°F
G. 212°C **J.** 32°C

31. distance between two cities

A. 100 mi **C.** 100 ft
B. 100 yd **D.** 100 in.

32. temperature of water from a hose

F. 69°F **H.** 0°F
G. 69°C **J.** 0°C

Name ______________________________

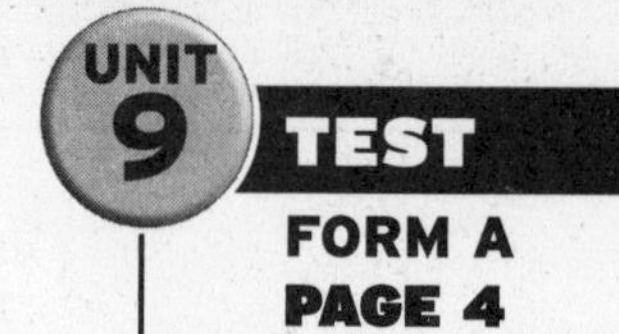

33. 2 gal = ▢ pt

A. 16 **C.** 8
B. 12 **D.** Not Here

---

34. 1,400 cm = ▢ m

F. 14,000 **H.** 140
G. 1,400 **J.** 14

---

35. 9 yd = ▢ ft

A. 108 **C.** 4
B. 27 **D.** 3

---

36. 5 kg = ▢ g

F. 5,000
G. 500
H. 50
J. 5

Solve.

37. Tracie is 2 years younger than Rosa. Amy is 4 years older than Tracie. Michelle is 1 year younger than Tracie. Who is the youngest?

A. Tracie
B. Rosa
C. Amy
D. Michelle

38. Mark read twice as many books as Nick. Sam read 5 fewer than Mark. Roberto read 7 more than Nick. Mark read 12 books. How many books did Roberto read?

F. 13 books
G. 12 books
H. 7 books
J. 6 books

---

39. At camp, there was a 5-gallon pail of water. Sherry poured the water into quart containers for groups to use for crafts. How many quart containers did she fill?

A. 80 containers
B. 40 containers
C. 20 containers
D. 10 containers

---

40. Jean weighed 8 lb when she was born. How many ounces did she weigh?

F. 128 oz
G. 112 oz
H. 108 oz
J. 12 oz

STOP

Name ___

Read each question carefully. Fill in the correct answer in the space provided.

Write the best estimate for exercises 1–12.

1. length of a table

8 mi	8 ft
8 yd	8 in.

___

2. distance between two towns

4 km	4 cm
4 m	4 mm

___

3. length of a truck

25 mi	25 ft
25 yd	25 in.

___

4. height of an action figure

10 km	10 cm
10 m	10 mm

___

5. capacity of a small glass of orange juice

1 gal	1 pt
1 qt	1 c

___

6. mass of a can of soda

40 kg	400 g
4 kg	40 g

___

7. weight of a truck

3 T	3 lb
3,000 oz	3 oz

___

8. capacity of a bath tub

50 gal	50 pt
50 qt	50 c

___

9. temperature of a bath

100°C	50°C
30°C	0°C

___

10. temperature inside a classroom

212°F	100°F
65°F	32°F

___

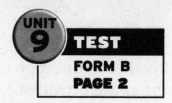

11. temperature of water you would swim in

60°F 30°F
60°C 30°C

____

12. temperature on a day when you go to the beach

55°F 25°F
55°C 25°C

____

Fill in the correct answer in the space provided.

13. 4,000 mL = ________ L

14. 500 mm = ________ cm

15. 72 in. = ________ ft

16. 16 oz = ________ lb

17. Justin is 6 inches shorter than Pete. Mark is 2 inches taller than Ron. Ron is 5 inches taller than Justin. Who is the tallest?

____

18. Lindsey has twice as many quarters as Stacey. Sharon has 4 more than Lindsey. Joanna has 3 less than Stacey. If Joanna has 5 quarters, how many does Sharon have?

____

19. Theresa has a 4-liter bucket of water. She poured the bucket into 500 mL bottles for the team to drink out of. How many bottles did she fill?

____

20. Jenny needs 4 pounds of cement for a project. If the cement is sold in 16 oz. packages, how many packages should she buy?

____

Name ____________________

Write the best estimate for exercises 21–32.

21. height of a car

4 mi 4 ft
4 yd 4 in.

____

22. weight of a potato

1,000 lb 100 lb
10 lb 1 lb

____

23. mass of a paper clip

20 kg 2 kg
20 g 2 g

____

24. mass of a cat

300 kg 30 kg
3 kg 300 g

____

25. temperature of lemonade

25°F 5°F
25°C 5°C

____

26. length of a bicycle

5 mi 5 yd
5 ft 5 in.

____

27. capacity of a large cooler

5 gal 5 pt
5 qt 5 c

____

28. temperature of warm soup

200°F 100°F
200°C 100°C

____

29. Height of a basketball net—3 m or 180 in.

____

30. capacity of a swimming pool

5,000 gal 5,000 pt
5,000 qt 5,000 c

____

GO ON

Name ____________________

31. temperature inside a freezer

40°F   20°F
40°C   20°C

____

32. weight of a large dog

50 T   50 lb
5 T   5 lb

____

Fill in the correct answer in the space provided.

33. 1 gallon = ________ c

34. 15,000 mm = ________ m

35. 72 in. = ________ yd

36. 4 kg = ________ g

37. Janice is 3 years older than Patricia. April is 2 years younger than Janice. Michelle is 1 year older than Patricia. Who is the youngest?

____

38. Scott ran twice as many laps as Joe. Isaiah ran 7 more than Joe. Roberto ran 4 less than Scott. Roberto ran 6 laps. How many laps did Isaiah run?

____

39. Jim poured one and a half gallons of milk into glasses. He poured 12 oz of milk into each glass. How many glasses did he use?

____

40. Renee weighed 7 lb when she was born. How many ounces did she weigh?

____

STOP

Chapter 19 – Teacher Interview

Core Concept: *Space and Plane Figures*

Student Activity: Students demonstrate an understanding of 2-dimensional shapes and 3-dimensional figures.

Teacher Question 1:

- What are two differences between triangles and quadrilaterals?

Understanding Student Response	Practice and Improvement
Students can only name one difference.	Review lesson 2 to help students differentiate between 2-dimensional shapes.

Teacher Question 2:

- Which of the following are 3-dimensional figures: sphere, square, cube, cone, and pentagon?

Understanding Student Response	Practice and Improvement
Students do not name all of the 3-dimensional figures.	Review lesson 1 to help students visualize various 3-dimensional figures.
Students name a mixture of 2-dimensional shapes and 3-dimensional figures.	Review lessons 1 and 2 to help students conceptualize the differences between 2-dimensional shapes and 3-dimensional figures.

Teacher Question 3:

- How are triangles classified?

Understanding Student Response	Practice and Improvement
Students cannot explain how triangles are classified.	Review lesson 4 to reinforce the different types of triangles.

Chapter 19 – Journal Writing

Encourage students to generate their own journal entries related to math ideas in general or to concepts in this chapter. For students requiring guidance, present the following journal prompt:

- Think about trying to make a flat map from a globe, which shows the map of the world (the globe is a sphere). Do you think it is possible to create a net for a 3-dimensional figure that has faces that aren't flat or straight? If yes, how do you think you could do it? If no, what problems would prevent you from doing it?
  (Responses may explore the idea of perhaps 'unzipping' a sphere, but should note that it couldn't lie flat without being cut or stretched.)

JOURNAL WRITING/PROBLEM SOLVING

What are all of the polygons that make up the faces of a triangular prism? How many of each can you find?

Read

Have students find the answer to the problem. Then ask them to write a few sentences telling—

- how they found the number of faces on a triangular prism
- how they unfolded the triangular prism to see all of the faces
- how they split up the net to find the polygons

Have students make up another problem with different information for which they would have to follow the same procedure. Then have students solve the problem and supply the correct response.

Plan

Students must be able to identify a triangular prism, be able to count its faces, be able to create a net for it, and be able to identify the polygons that comprise the net.

Solve

The correct response to the assigned problem is that the five faces of a triangular prism consist of two triangles and three rectangles or squares.

Look Back

A correct response demonstrates that students can identify 3-dimensional figures, can unfold them using nets, and can identify the polygons that make up the faces of 3-dimensional figures. (See scoring rubric on page 7.)

Chapter 19 – Monitoring Student Progress

☐ Form A ☐ Form B

Name ______________________ Date ______________

Directions: For each item that is answered incorrectly, cross out the item number. Then record the number of correct responses in the appropriate Student Score column. If the student has not met the Criterion Score for an objective, circle the student's score. Recommended assignments are listed in the Prescription Table on the next page.

Objective	Item Numbers	Criterion Score	Student Score
A. Identify, describe, and classify 3-dimensional figures.	1, 6, 11	2/3	/3
B. Identify, describe, and classify 2-dimensional shapes.	2, 7, 12	2/3	/3
C. Identify, describe, and classify lines, line segments, rays, triangles, and quadrilaterals.	3, 8, 13, 16	3/4	/4
D. Identify, describe, classify, and draw angles.	4, 9, 14	2/3	/3
E. Identify and describe circles.	5, 10, 15	2/3	/3
F. Use skills and strategies to solve problems.	17, 18, 19, 20	3/4	/4
Total Test Score		14/20	/20
Total Percent Correct			%

Chapter 19 – Prescription Table

The following chart correlates the tested objectives for this chapter to supplementary materials that meet the individual needs of the students. The Reteach and Practice pages are designed for students who need further instruction in the math concepts taught in this chapter. The Enrich pages are designed for students who need advanced challenges.

Objective	Reteach	Practice	Enrich
A. Identify, describe, and classify 3-dimensional figures.	324	325	326
B. Identify, describe, and classify 2-dimensional shapes.	327	328	329
C. Identify, describe, and classify lines, line segments, rays, triangles, and quadrilaterals.	330	331	332
D. Identify, describe, classify, and draw angles.	333, 336	334, 337	335, 338
E. Identify and describe circles.	342	343	344
F. Use skills and strategies to solve problems.	339	340	341

Name ____________________

Read each question carefully. Darken the circle on your answer sheet for the correct answer.

1. Identify the 3-dimensional figure.

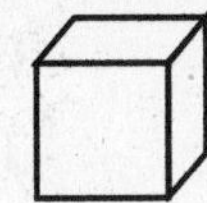

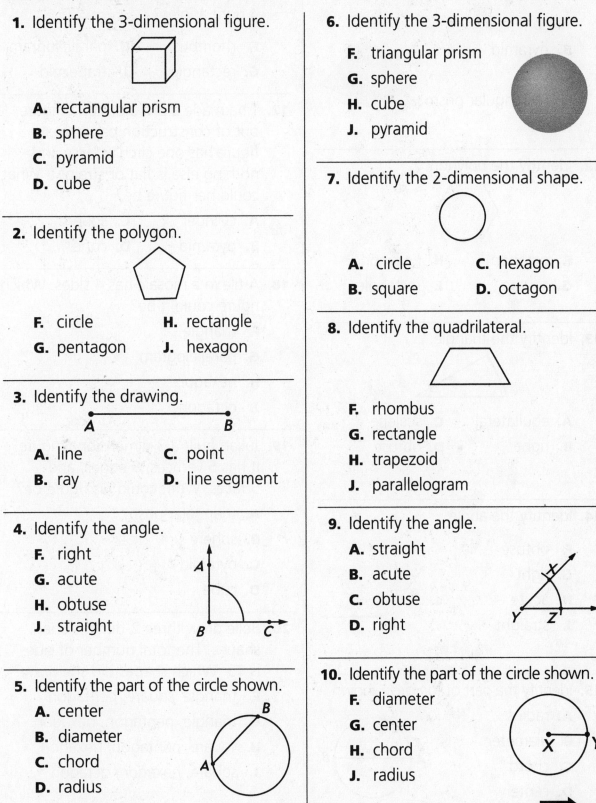

A. rectangular prism
B. sphere
C. pyramid
D. cube

2. Identify the polygon.

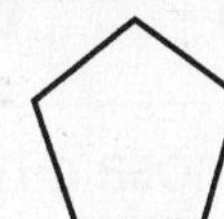

F. circle
G. pentagon
H. rectangle
J. hexagon

3. Identify the drawing.

A. line
B. ray
C. point
D. line segment

4. Identify the angle.

F. right
G. acute
H. obtuse
J. straight

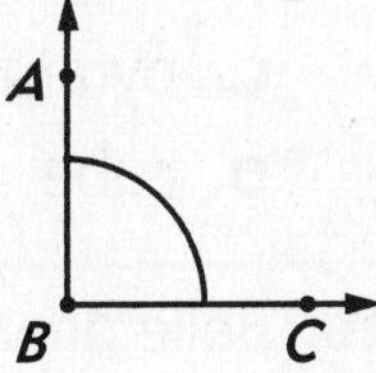

5. Identify the part of the circle shown.

A. center
B. diameter
C. chord
D. radius

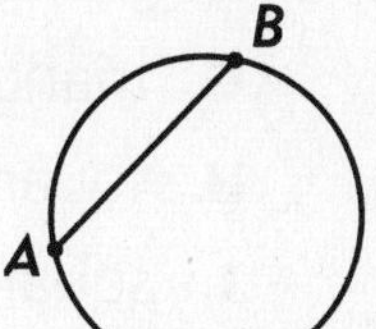

6. Identify the 3-dimensional figure.

F. triangular prism
G. sphere
H. cube
J. pyramid

7. Identify the 2-dimensional shape.

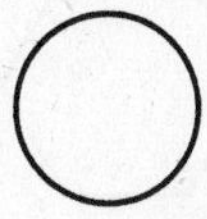

A. circle
B. square
C. hexagon
D. octagon

8. Identify the quadrilateral.

F. rhombus
G. rectangle
H. trapezoid
J. parallelogram

9. Identify the angle.

A. straight
B. acute
C. obtuse
D. right

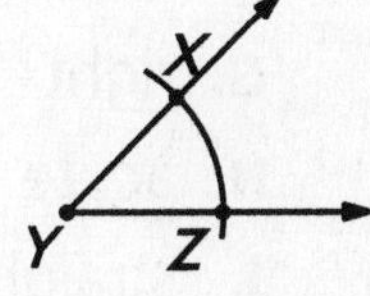

10. Identify the part of the circle shown.

F. diameter
G. center
H. chord
J. radius

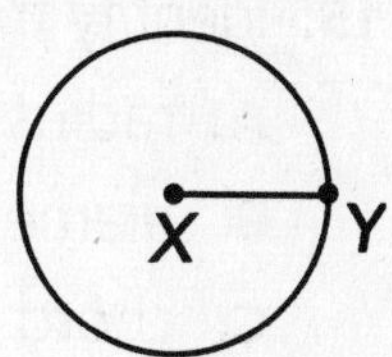

Name ________________________________

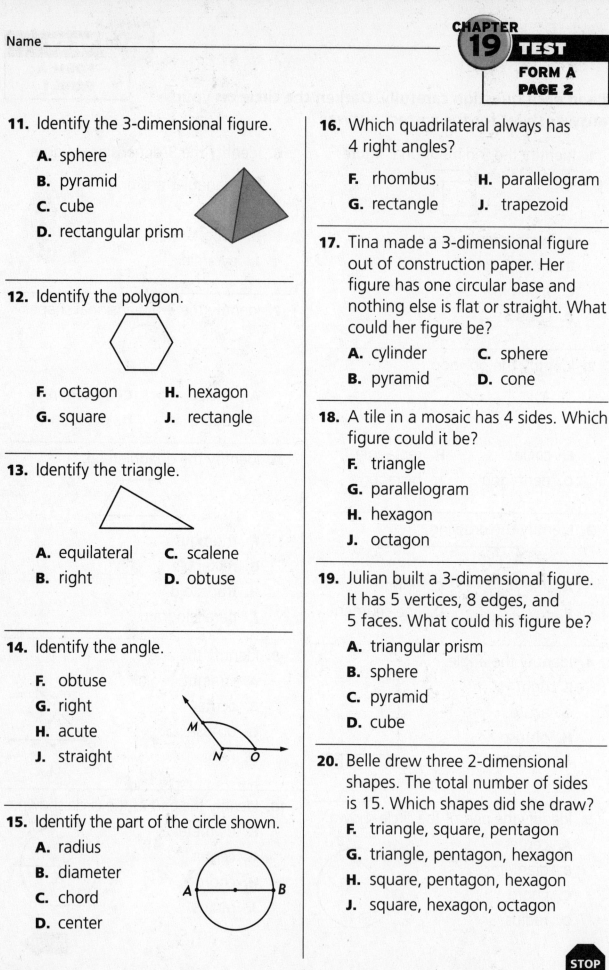

11. Identify the 3-dimensional figure.

A. sphere
B. pyramid
C. cube
D. rectangular prism

12. Identify the polygon.

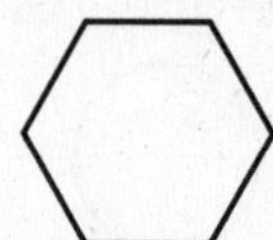

F. octagon **H.** hexagon
G. square **J.** rectangle

13. Identify the triangle.

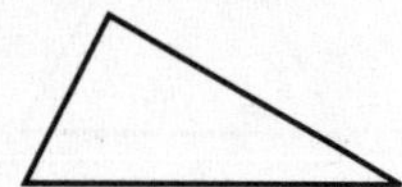

A. equilateral **C.** scalene
B. right **D.** obtuse

14. Identify the angle.

F. obtuse
G. right
H. acute
J. straight

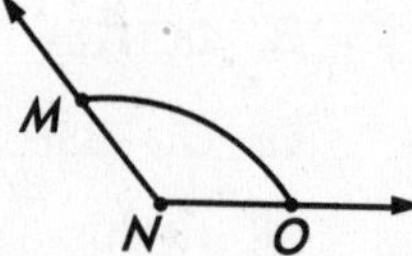

15. Identify the part of the circle shown.

A. radius
B. diameter
C. chord
D. center

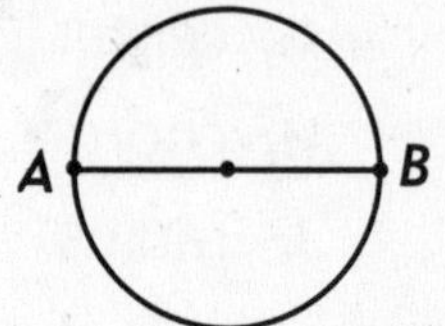

16. Which quadrilateral always has 4 right angles?

F. rhombus **H.** parallelogram
G. rectangle **J.** trapezoid

17. Tina made a 3-dimensional figure out of construction paper. Her figure has one circular base and nothing else is flat or straight. What could her figure be?

A. cylinder **C.** sphere
B. pyramid **D.** cone

18. A tile in a mosaic has 4 sides. Which figure could it be?

F. triangle
G. parallelogram
H. hexagon
J. octagon

19. Julian built a 3-dimensional figure. It has 5 vertices, 8 edges, and 5 faces. What could his figure be?

A. triangular prism
B. sphere
C. pyramid
D. cube

20. Belle drew three 2-dimensional shapes. The total number of sides is 15. Which shapes did she draw?

F. triangle, square, pentagon
G. triangle, pentagon, hexagon
H. square, pentagon, hexagon
J. square, hexagon, octagon

STOP

Name ______________________________

CHAPTER 19 TEST
FORM B
PAGE 1

Read each question carefully. Fill in the correct answer in the space provided.

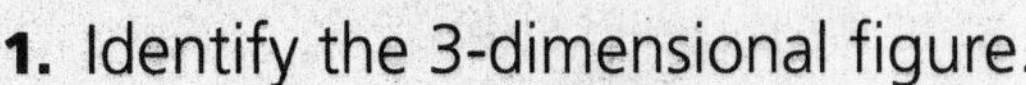

1. Identify the 3-dimensional figure.

____

2. Identify the polygon.

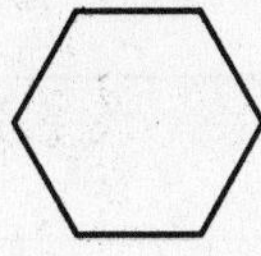

____

3. Identify the drawing.

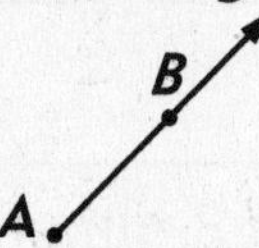

____

4. Name and identify the angle as *acute*, *right*, or *obtuse*.

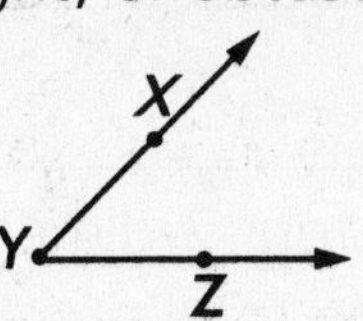

____

5. Identify the part of the circle shown.

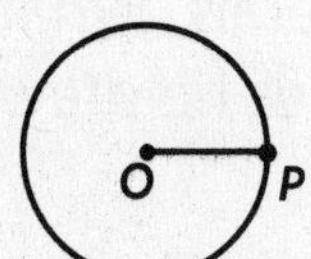

____

6. Identify the 3-dimensional figure.

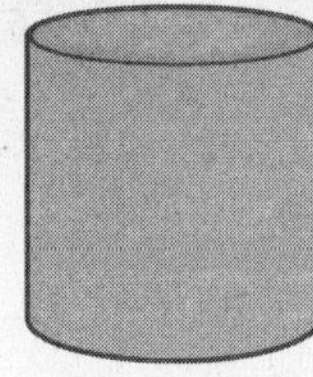

____

7. Identify the polygon.

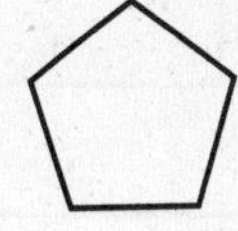

____

8. Identify the quadrilateral.

____

9. Name and identify the angle as *acute*, *right*, or *obtuse*.

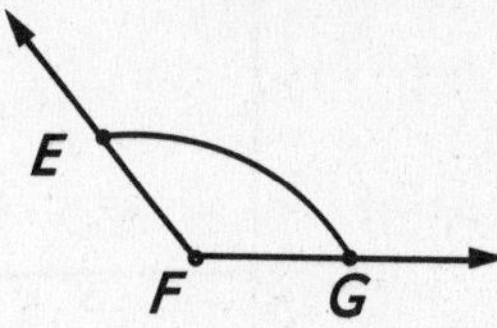

____

10. Identify the part of the circle shown.

____

GO ON

Name ___________________________________

11. Identify the 3-dimensional figure.

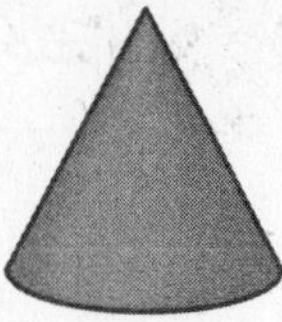

____

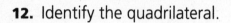

12. Identify the quadrilateral.

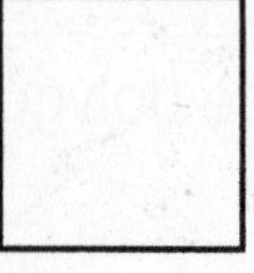

____

13. Identify the triangle.

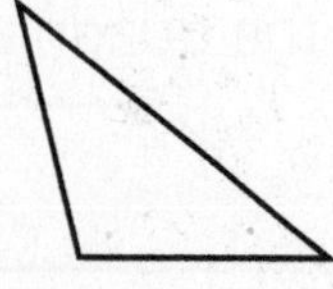

____

14. Name and identify the angle as *acute*, *right*, or *obtuse*.

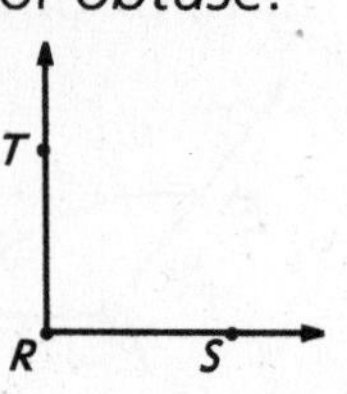

____

15. Identify the part of the circle shown.

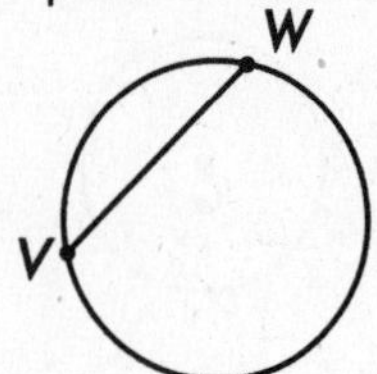

____

16. Which quadrilateral has exactly one pair of parallel sides?

____

17. Joshua made a 3-dimensional figure out of construction paper. His figure has four equilateral triangular faces. What could his figure be?

____

18. A street sign has 3 sides. What 2-dimensional shape could it be?

____

19. Tony built a 3-dimensional figure. His figure has 6 vertices, 9 edges, and 5 faces. What could his figure be?

____

20. Billy drew four 2-dimensional shapes. The total number of sides for all three shapes is 17 sides. Two of the shapes were quadrilaterals. The rest of the shapes were not quadrilaterals. What were the other two shapes he drew?

____

STOP

Chapter 20 – Teacher Interview

Core Concept: ***Perimeter, Circumference, and Area***

Student Activity: Students demonstrate an understanding of finding the perimeter and area of a rectangle and the circumference of a circle.

Teacher Question 1:

- What is the perimeter of a rectangle with a length of 10 inches and a width of 6 inches?

Understanding Student Response	Practice and Improvement
Students who say 16 inches did not multiply each of the sides by 2.	Review lesson 4 to help reinforce that the formula for finding the perimeter of a rectangle is $2l + 2w$.
Students who multiply the sides are confusing perimeter with area.	Review lesson 4 to help students review that perimeter is the distance around a figure.

Teacher Question 2:

- What is the area of the same rectangle?

Understanding Student Response	Practice and Improvement
Students who say 16 inches added the sides instead of multiplying them.	Review lesson 6 to help students learn the formula for the area of a rectangle which is the length times the width.
Students who say 60 inches did not use the proper notation for area.	Review lesson 6 to help students learn that the notation for area is square units, or in this case square inches.

Teacher Question 3:

- How can you estimate the circumference of a circle without using string?

Understanding Student Response	Practice and Improvement
Students who fail to mention multiplying the diameter by 3 do not understand the concept of circumference.	Review lesson 5 to help students learn that an estimate for circumference is to multiply the diameter by 3.

Chapter 20 – Journal Writing

Encourage students to generate their own journal entries related to math ideas in general or to concepts in this chapter. For students requiring guidance, present the following journal prompt:

- You know how to find the perimeter of simple polygons and how to use this to find the area of more complex figures. You also know how to find the volume of rectangular prisms. Explain how you could use this knowledge to find the volume of more complex 3-dimensional figures.

  (Responses should include the idea of breaking down the more complex 3-dimensional figure into rectangular prisms, if possible, then finding the volume of those figures and adding them together – an analogous process to the one they know for area.)

JOURNAL WRITING/PROBLEM SOLVING

A Stop sign is an octagon. The Stop sign at the entrance to the Berkeley School has a perimeter of 24 decimeters. Draw three other polygons with perimeters of 24 decimeters and label the lengths of each side.

Read

Have students find the answer to the problem. Then ask them to write a few sentences telling—

- why they selected the polygons that they used
- how they found the lengths of the sides of the polygons they chose

Have students make up another problem with different information for which they would have to follow the same procedure. Then have students solve the problem and supply the correct response.

Plan

Students need to understand perimeter and how to compute it, for a number of polygons.

Solve

The correct response to the assigned problem will vary, but will probably include a triangle, a square, and another quadrilateral. The polygons do not need to be equilateral. Students must find the perimeter of the figures they have drawn by either adding the lengths of the sides, or, for equilateral figures, multiplying the length of a side by the number of sides.

Look Back

A correct solution demonstrates the ability to calculate perimeter and also shows knowledge of polygons. (See scoring rubric on page 7.)

Chapter 20 – Monitoring Student Progress

☐ Form A ☐ Form B

Name ______________________ Date ______________

Directions: For each item that is answered incorrectly, cross out the item number. Then record the number of correct responses in the appropriate Student Score column. If the student has not met the Criterion Score for an objective, circle the student's score. Recommended assignments are listed in the Prescription Table on the next page.

Objective	Item Numbers	Criterion Score	Student Score
A. Identify congruent and similar 2-dimensional figures.	1, 6, 11	2/3	/3
B. Identify translations, reflections, and rotations.	2, 7, 12	2/3	/3
C. Identify and draw symmetrical objects.	3, 8, 13	2/3	/3
D. Estimate and determine perimeter, circumference, area, and volume.	4, 5, 9, 10, 14, 15, 16	6/7	/7
E. Use skills and strategies to solve problems.	17, 18, 19, 20	3/4	/4
Total Test Score		15/20	/20
Total Percent Correct			%

Chapter 20 – Prescription Table

The following chart correlates the tested objectives for this chapter to supplementary materials that meet the individual needs of the students. The Reteach and Practice pages are designed for students who need further instruction in the math concepts taught in this chapter. The Enrich pages are designed for students who need advanced challenges.

Objective	Reteach	Practice	Enrich
A. Identify congruent and similar 2-dimensional figures.	345	346	347
B. Identify translations, reflections, and rotations.	348	349	350
C. Identify and draw symmetrical objects.	348	349	350
D. Estimate and determine perimeter, circumference, area, and volume.	354, 357, 360, 363	355, 358, 361, 364	356, 359, 362, 365
E. Use skills and strategies to solve problems.	351, 352	353	

Name ______________________________

Read each question carefully. Darken the circle on your answer sheet for the correct answer.

1. Which set of figures is congruent?

A. 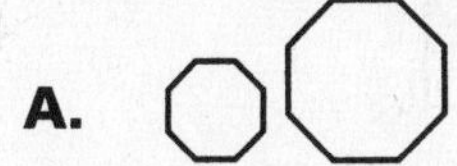

C. 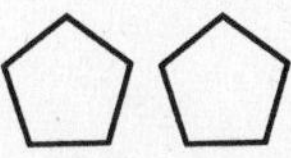

B. 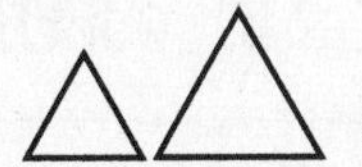

D. 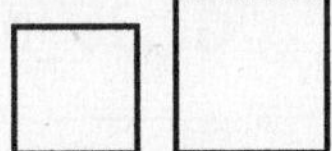

2. Which describes how the figure was moved?

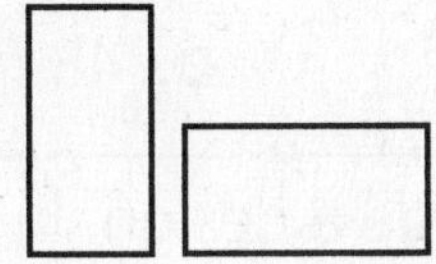

F. rotation
G. reflection
H. translation
J. symmetry

3. Which figure has rotational symmetry?

A. 

C. 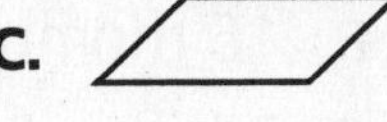

B. 

D. 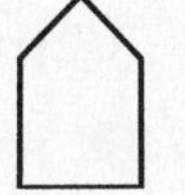

4. Find the perimeter.

F. 8 in.
G. 12 in.
H. 32 in.
J. 64 in.

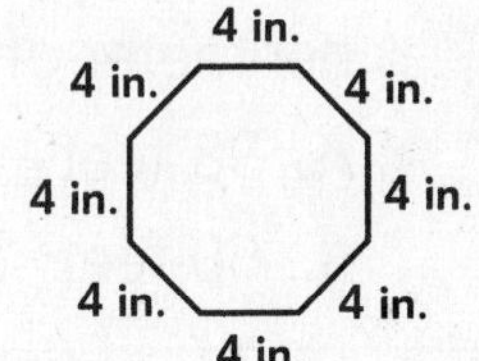

5. Find the volume.

A. 13 cubic units
B. 18 cubic units
C. 36 cubic units
D. 72 cubic units.

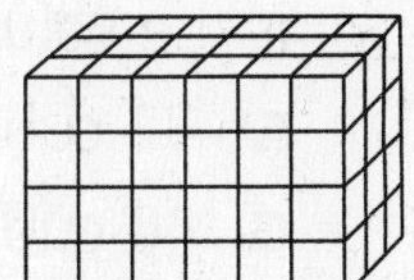

6. Which set of figures is congruent?

F.

H.

G.

J.

7. Which describes how the figure was moved?

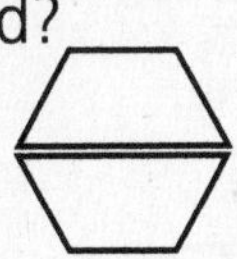

A. rotation
B. reflection
C. translation
D. symmetry

8. Which letter has bilateral symmetry?

F. Z

H. N

G. Q

J. Y

9. Estimate the circumference.

A. 45 ft
B. 90 ft
C. 675 ft
D. 900 ft

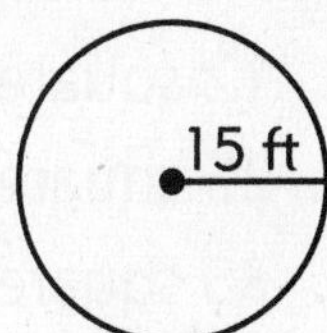

10. Find the area.

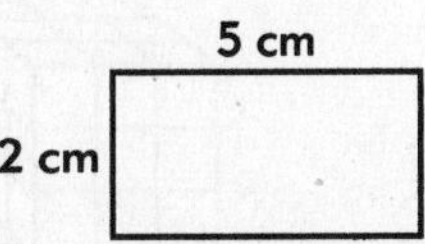

F. 7 square centimeters
G. 10 square centimeters
H. 14 square centimeters
J. 20 square centimeters

GO ON

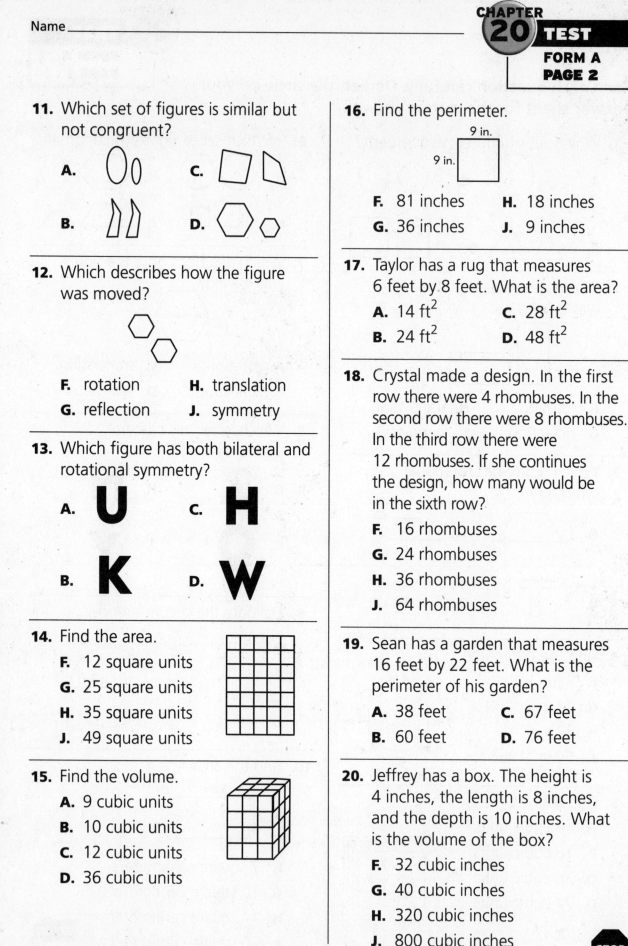

Name ____________________

11. Which set of figures is similar but not congruent?

A.

B.

C.

D.

12. Which describes how the figure was moved?

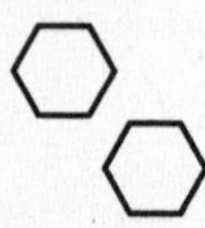

F. rotation **H.** translation
G. reflection **J.** symmetry

13. Which figure has both bilateral and rotational symmetry?

A. U **C.** H
B. K **D.** W

14. Find the area.

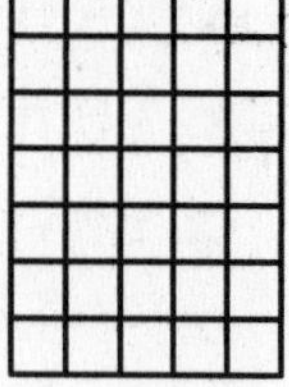

F. 12 square units
G. 25 square units
H. 35 square units
J. 49 square units

15. Find the volume.

A. 9 cubic units
B. 10 cubic units
C. 12 cubic units
D. 36 cubic units

16. Find the perimeter.

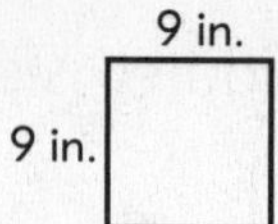

F. 81 inches **H.** 18 inches
G. 36 inches **J.** 9 inches

17. Taylor has a rug that measures 6 feet by 8 feet. What is the area?

A. 14 ft^2 **C.** 28 ft^2
B. 24 ft^2 **D.** 48 ft^2

18. Crystal made a design. In the first row there were 4 rhombuses. In the second row there were 8 rhombuses. In the third row there were 12 rhombuses. If she continues the design, how many would be in the sixth row?

F. 16 rhombuses
G. 24 rhombuses
H. 36 rhombuses
J. 64 rhombuses

19. Sean has a garden that measures 16 feet by 22 feet. What is the perimeter of his garden?

A. 38 feet **C.** 67 feet
B. 60 feet **D.** 76 feet

20. Jeffrey has a box. The height is 4 inches, the length is 8 inches, and the depth is 10 inches. What is the volume of the box?

F. 32 cubic inches
G. 40 cubic inches
H. 320 cubic inches
J. 800 cubic inches

STOP

Name ________________________________

CHAPTER 20 TEST
FORM B
PAGE 1

Read each question carefully. Fill in the correct answer in the space provided.

1. Are the figures congruent, similar, or neither?

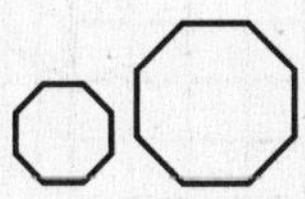

____

2. Write *translation*, *reflection*, or *rotation* to tell how the figure was moved.

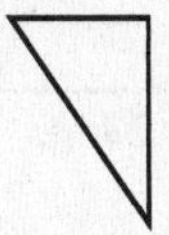

____

3. Does the figure have rotational symmetry?

____

4. Find the perimeter.

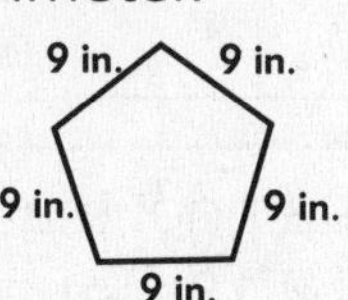

____

5. Find the volume.

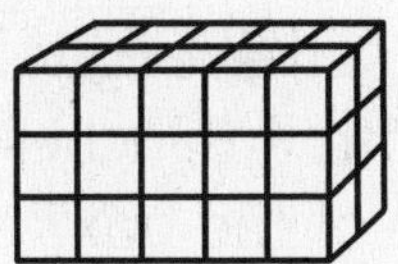

____

6. Are the figures congruent, similar, or neither?

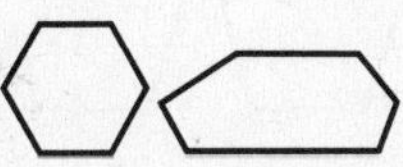

____

7. Write *translation*, *reflection*, or *rotation* to tell how the figure was moved.

____

8. Which letter in the word below has bilateral symmetry?

SPELL

____

9. Estimate the circumference.

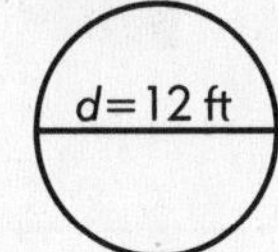

____

10. Find the area.

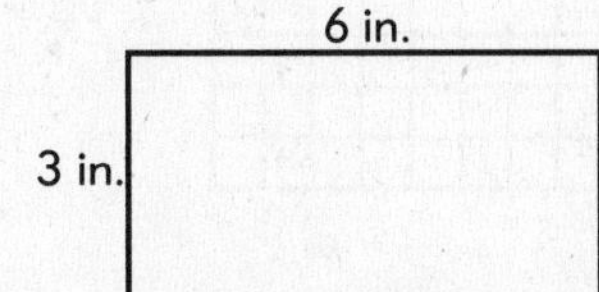

____

GO ON

Name ____________________

11. Are the figures congruent, similar, or neither?

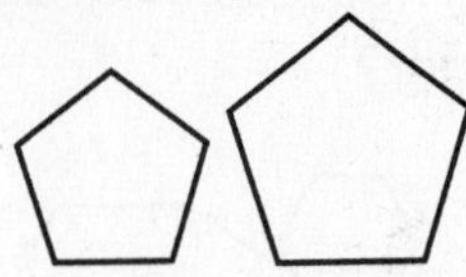

____

12. Write *translation*, *reflection*, or *rotation* to tell how the figure was moved.

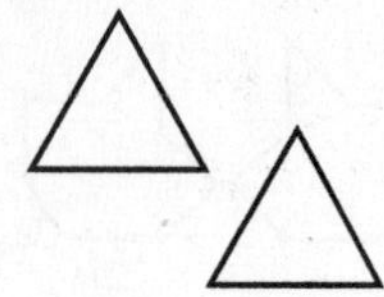

____

13. Does the figure have bilateral symmetry, rotational symmetry, both, or neither?

____

14. Find the area.

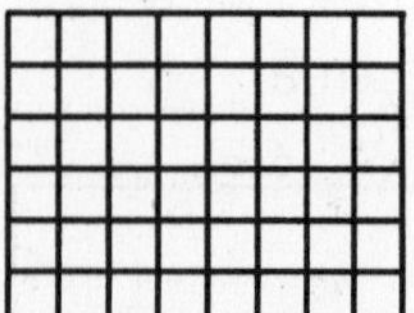

____

15. Find the volume.

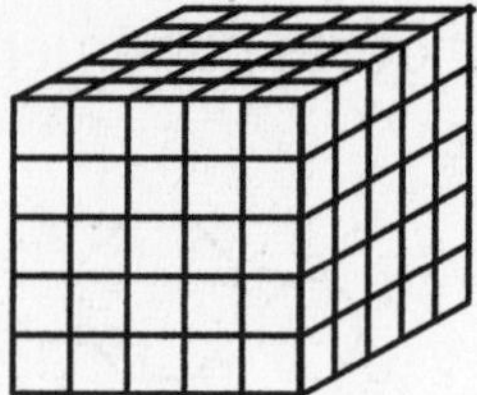

____

16. Find the perimeter.

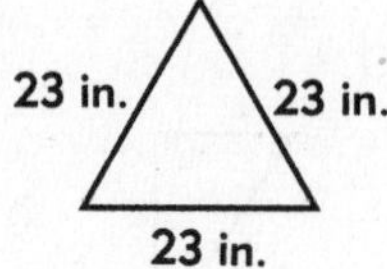

____

17. Wendell has a rug that measures 9 feet by 6 feet. What is the area?

____

18. Deirdre made a design. In the first row there were 6 ovals. In the second row there were 11 ovals. In the third row there were 16 ovals. If she continues the design, how many would be in the seventh row?

____

19. Jake has a pool that measures 24 feet by 18 feet. What is the perimeter of his pool?

____

20. Lucy has a box. The height is 7 inches, the length is 9 inches, and the depth is 8 inches. What is the volume of the box?

____

STOP

Unit 10 Performance Assessment

The Park

- ***Target Skill:*** Estimate and determine the perimeter and area.
- ***Additional Skills:*** Identify, describe, and classify 2-dimensional shapes.

Task Description: This task requires students to design a park with rectangles for three different areas on graph paper and then exchange papers with a classmate to find the perimeter and area of the rectangles.

Preparing: You may wish to discuss with students the various uses for parks and the size of parks before the students begin their designs.

Materials	Group Size	Time on Task
Graph paper	1 to 2 students	1–2 days

Guiding: Remind students that perimeter is the distance around a shape.

Remind students that area is the amount of space inside a shape.

Remind students that a square is a special type of rectangle.

Observing/ Monitoring: As you move among the students, pose the following questions:

How did you design your parks?

How do you find the perimeter of a rectangle?

How do you find the area of a rectangle?

Unit 10 Performance Assessment Scoring Rubric

The Park

Score	Explanation
3	Students demonstrate an efficient strategy and a thorough approach that enables them to solve the problem completely. A satisfactory answer: • correctly writes the dimensions of the park; • finds the perimeter and area of the park and each of the three student-drawn sections; • has rectangles or squares for the student-drawn sections. Students are able to complete the problem quickly and have all of the above correct solutions.
2	Students demonstrate a strategy that enables them to solve most of the problem correctly. The strategy is somewhat disorganized, making it less efficient. A solution is found, but errors are contained. Students may: • draw rectangles on the grid paper; • correctly find most of the perimeters and the areas. Students may have some difficulty determining all solutions correctly, but demonstrate an understanding of general concepts.
1	Students demonstrate a confused strategy, which leads to difficulty solving the problem. Most answers are incorrect, but students demonstrate knowledge of at least one concept being assessed. Students may: • draw rectangles; OR • correctly find some of the perimeters; OR • correctly find some of the areas.

Name ______________________________

Unit 10 Performance Assessment Student Activity

The Park

You will need
- Graph paper

Your town is building a new park. The grid below shows the shape and size of the park.

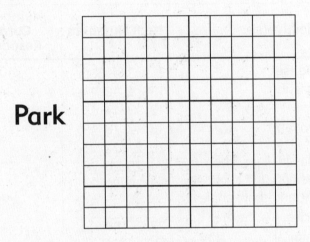

You have a chance to help design the park. Choose three sections shaped like rectangles where playgrounds will be built. Draw your rectangles on the grid and exchange papers with a partner.

1. Find the perimeter and area of the entire park.

____

2. What are the dimensions of each of the three playgrounds?

____

3. Find the perimeter of each of the three playgrounds of the park.

____

4. Find the area of each of the three playgrounds of the park.

____

Unit 10 – Monitoring Student Progress

☐ Form A ☐ Form B

Name ______________________ Date ______________

Directions: This test targets selected objectives. For each item that is answered incorrectly, cross out the item number. Then record the number of correct responses in the column labeled **Number of Correct Responses.** Add to find the **Total Number of Correct Responses** and record the total. Use this total to determine the **Total Test Score** and the **Total Percent Correct.**

Strand • Objective(s)	Item Numbers	Number of Correct Responses
Geometry and Spatial Sense • Identify, describe, and classify 3-dimensional figures. • Identify, describe, and classify 2-dimensional shapes. • Identify, describe, and classify lines, line segments, rays, triangles, and quadrilaterals. • Identify, describe, classify, and draw angles. • Identify and describe circles. • Identify congruent and similar 2-dimensional shapes. • Identify translations, reflections, and rotations. • Identify and draw symmetrical objects. • Estimate and determine perimeter, circumference, area, and volume. • Use skills and strategies to solve problems.	1, 2, 3, 4, 5, 6, 7, 8, 9, 10, 11, 12, 13, 14, 15, 16, 17, 18, 19, 20, 21, 22, 23, 24, 25, 26, 27, 28, 29, 30, 31, 32, 33, 34, 35, 36, 37, 38, 39, 40	/40
Total Number of Correct Responses		
Total Test Score		/40
Total Percent Correct		%

Name ____________________

Read each question carefully. Darken the circle on your answer sheet for the correct answer.

1.

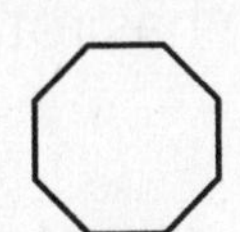

A. pentagon **C.** trapezoid
B. rectangle **D.** octagon

2.

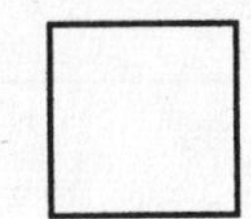

F. circle **H.** pentagon
G. square **J.** rectangle

3.

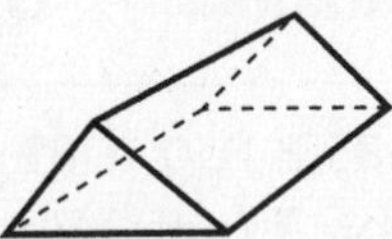

A. rectangular prism
B. cube
C. sphere
D. triangular prism

4. Find the volume.
length: 10 m
width: 8 m height: 2 m

F. 160 m^3 **H.** 40 m^3
G. 80 m^3 **J.** 20 m^3

5. How many triangles are there?

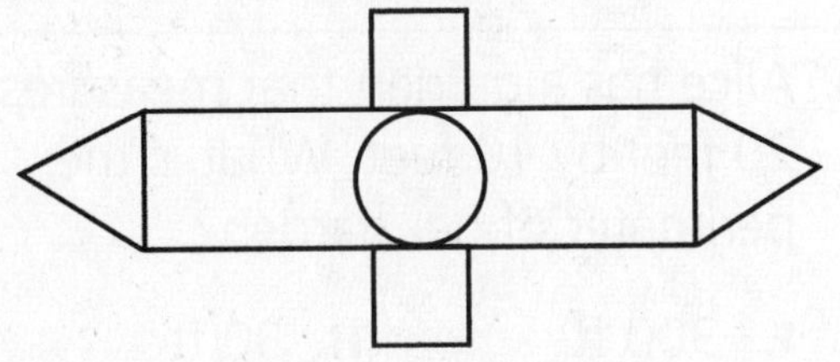

A. 4 **B.** 3 **C.** 2 **D.** 1

6. Which 3-dimensional figure will this net make?

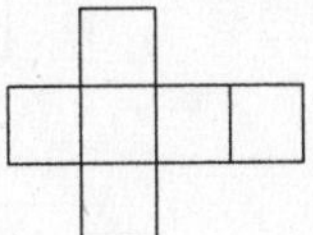

F. cylinder
G. cube
H. triangular prism
J. sphere

7.

A. right triangle
B. equilateral triangle
C. acute triangle
D. obtuse triangle

8. How many angles does a quadrilateral have?

F. 5 **G.** 4 **H.** 3 **J.** 2

9. Which set of figures is congruent?

A.

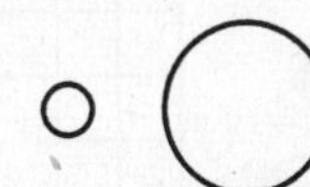

C.

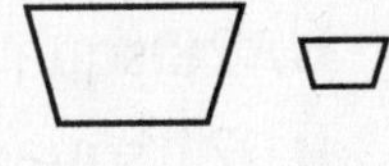

B.

D.

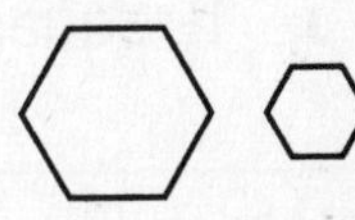

10. Which quadrilateral has only one pair of parallel sides?

F. rhombus **H.** rectangle
G. square **J.** trapezoid

Name ____________________

UNIT 10 TEST
FORM A
PAGE 2

11. Find the perimeter.

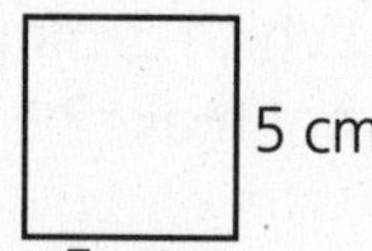

A. 25 cm
B. 20 cm
C. 15 cm
D. 10 cm

12. Which set of shapes is congruent?

F.  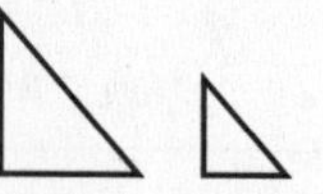

H. 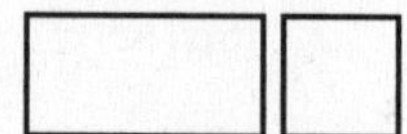

G. 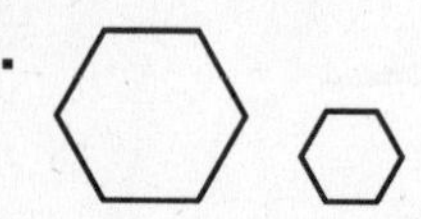

J. 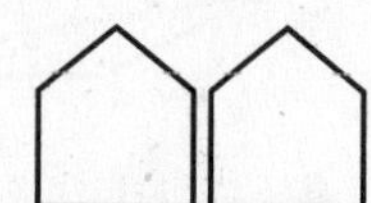

13. Find the perimeter.

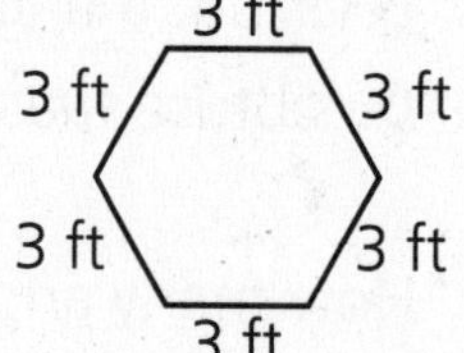

A. 18 ft
B. 12 ft
C. 9 ft
D. 6 ft

14. Find the area.

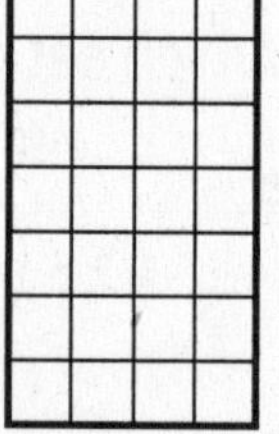

F. 36 square units
G. 28 square units
H. 21 square units
J. 19 square units

15. Which letter has bilateral symmetry?

A. J  **B.** P **C.** M 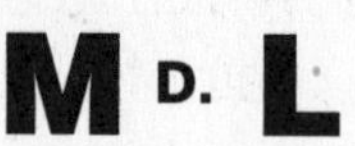 **D.** L

16. Which shape has rotational symmetry?

F. 

H. 

G. 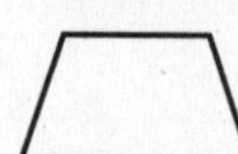

J. 

Solve.

17. A tile on a bathroom floor has 8 sides. Which shape is it?

A. octagon
B. pentagon
C. trapezoid
D. hexagon

18. Tyler has a rug that measures 8 feet by 3 feet. What is the area?

F. 24 ft^2
G. 22 ft^2
H. 11 ft^2
J. 8 ft^2

19. Tony made a design. In the first row there were 7 trapezoids. In the second row, there were 10. There were 13 in the third row. If he continues the design, how many would be in the fifth row?

A. 25 trapezoids
B. 21 trapezoids
C. 19 trapezoids
D. 14 trapezoids

20. Alice has a garden that measures 20 feet by 10 feet. What is the perimeter of her garden?

F. 300 ft
G. 60 ft
H. 30 ft
J. 20 ft

GO ON

21.

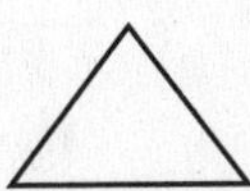

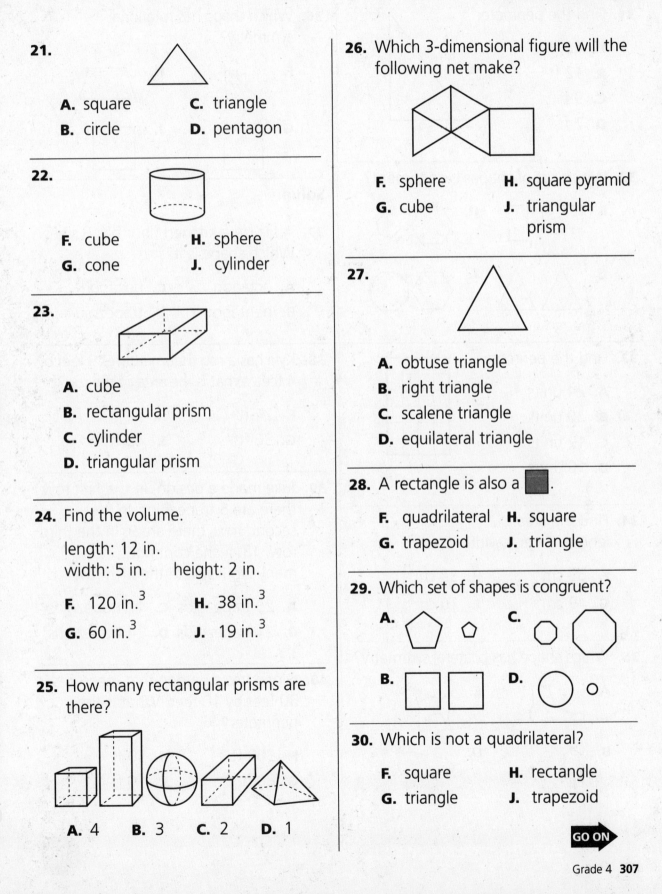

A. square
B. circle
C. triangle
D. pentagon

22.

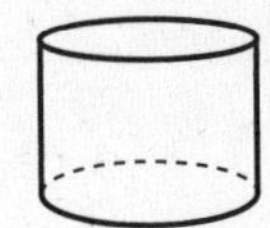

F. cube
G. cone
H. sphere
J. cylinder

23.

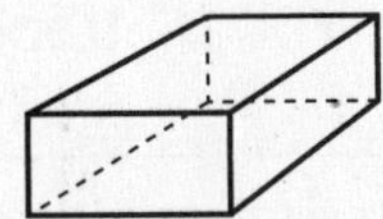

A. cube
B. rectangular prism
C. cylinder
D. triangular prism

24. Find the volume.

length: 12 in.
width: 5 in. height: 2 in.

F. 120 in.^{3}
G. 60 in.^{3}
H. 38 in.^{3}
J. 19 in.^{3}

25. How many rectangular prisms are there?

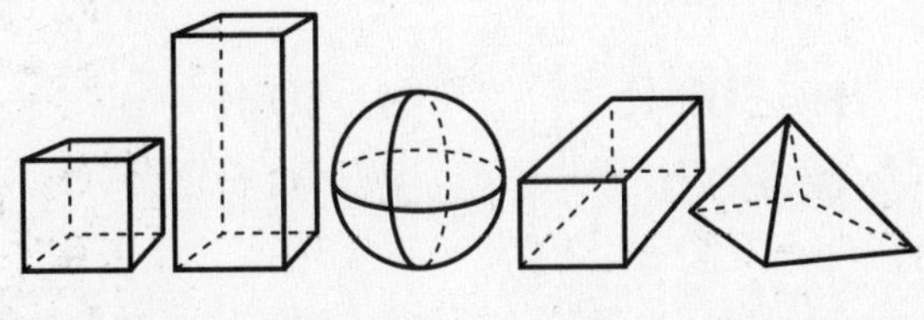

A. 4 **B.** 3 **C.** 2 **D.** 1

26. Which 3-dimensional figure will the following net make?

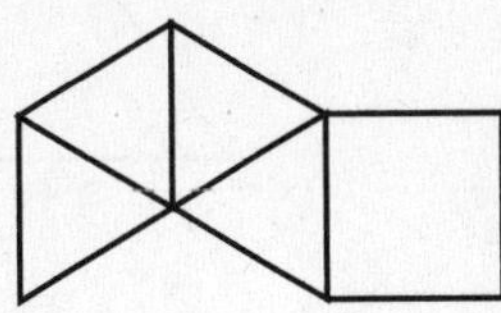

F. sphere
G. cube
H. square pyramid
J. triangular prism

27.

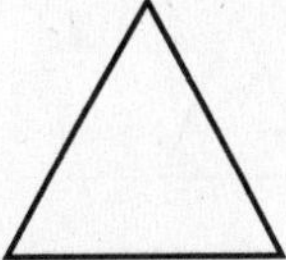

A. obtuse triangle
B. right triangle
C. scalene triangle
D. equilateral triangle

28. A rectangle is also a .

F. quadrilateral
G. trapezoid
H. square
J. triangle

29. Which set of shapes is congruent?

A. 

C. 

B. 

D. 

30. Which is not a quadrilateral?

F. square
G. triangle
H. rectangle
J. trapezoid

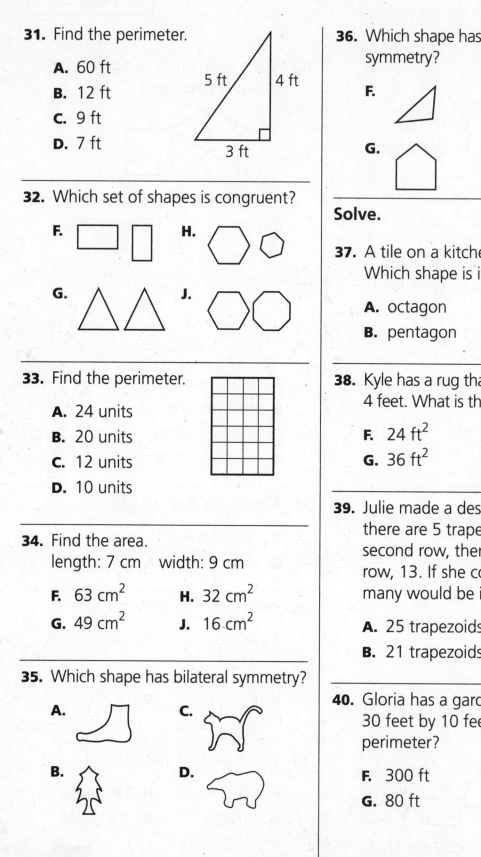

Name ____________________

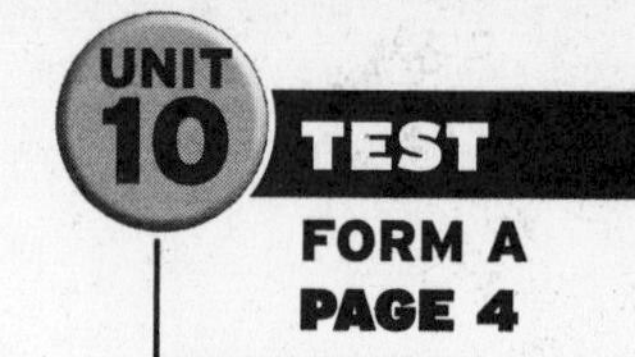

31. Find the perimeter.

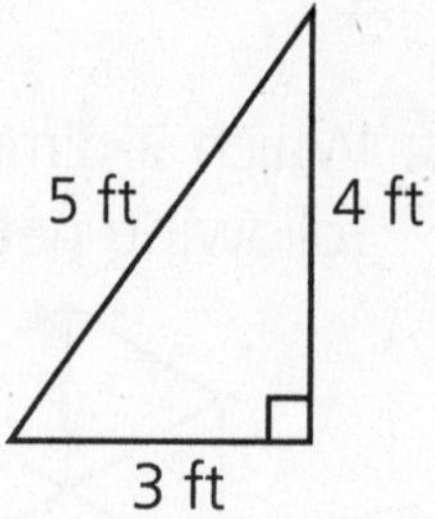

A. 60 ft
B. 12 ft
C. 9 ft
D. 7 ft

---

32. Which set of shapes is congruent?

F. 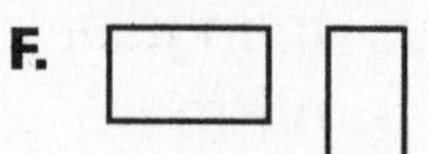

H. 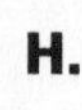 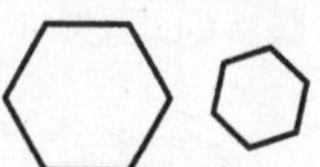

G. 

J. 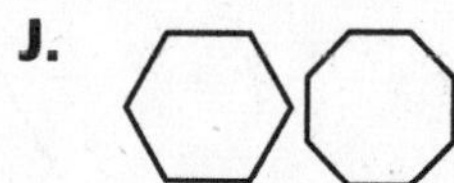

---

33. Find the perimeter.

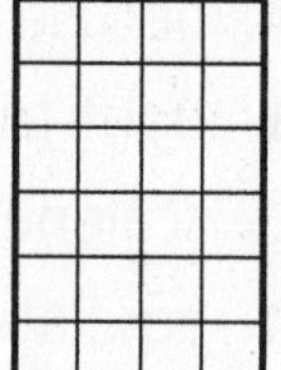

A. 24 units
B. 20 units
C. 12 units
D. 10 units

---

34. Find the area.
length: 7 cm   width: 9 cm

F. 63 cm^2 **H.** 32 cm^2
G. 49 cm^2 **J.** 16 cm^2

---

35. Which shape has bilateral symmetry?

A. 

C. 

B. 

D. 

---

36. Which shape has rotational symmetry?

F. 

H. 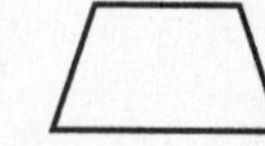

G. 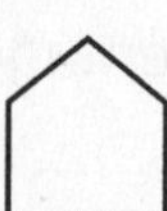

J.

Solve.

37. A tile on a kitchen floor has 6 sides. Which shape is it?

A. octagon   **C.** hexagon
B. pentagon   **D.** trapezoid

---

38. Kyle has a rug that measures 9 feet by 4 feet. What is the area of the rug?

F. 24 ft^2 **H.** 42 ft^2
G. 36 ft^2 **J.** 45 ft^2

---

39. Julie made a design. In the first row, there are 5 trapezoids. In the second row, there are 9. In the third row, 13. If she continues, how many would be in the fifth row?

A. 25 trapezoids   **C.** 17 trapezoids
B. 21 trapezoids   **D.** 14 trapezoids

---

40. Gloria has a garden that measures 30 feet by 10 feet. What is the perimeter?

F. 300 ft   **H.** 30 ft
G. 80 ft   **J.** 10 ft

STOP

Name ______________________

UNIT 10 **TEST**
FORM B
PAGE 1

Read each question carefully. Fill in the correct answer in the space provided.

1. Identify.

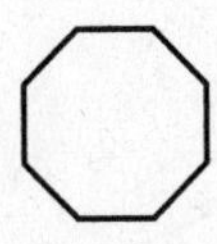

____

2. Identify.

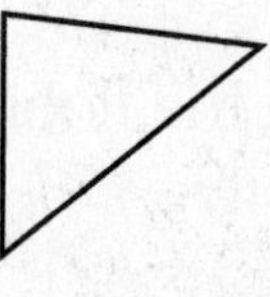

____

3. Identify.

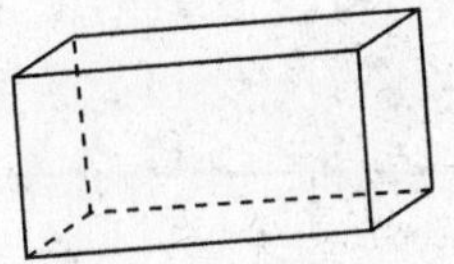

____

4. Find the volume.

Length: 5 m
Width: 10 m
Height: 3 m

____

5. How many triangles are there:

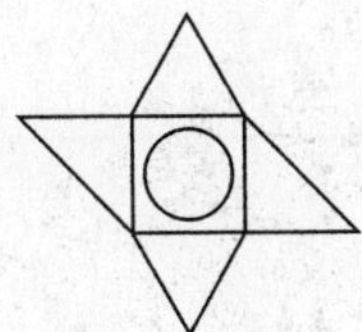

____

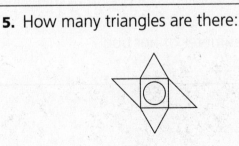

6. What 3-dimensional figure will this net make?

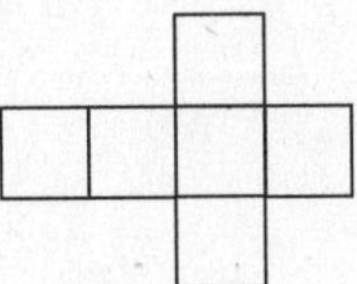

____

7. Identify the type of triangle:

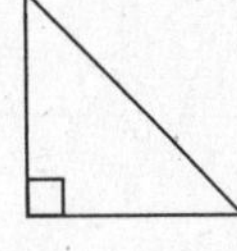

____

8. How many angles does a quadrilateral have?

____

9. Are these shapes congruent?

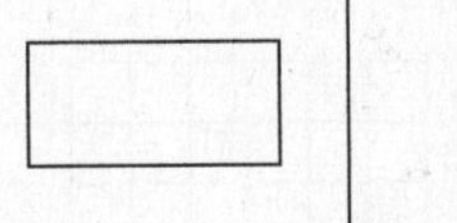

____

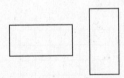

10. Name a quadrilateral with two pairs of parallel sides but no right angles.

____

GO ON

Name ____________________

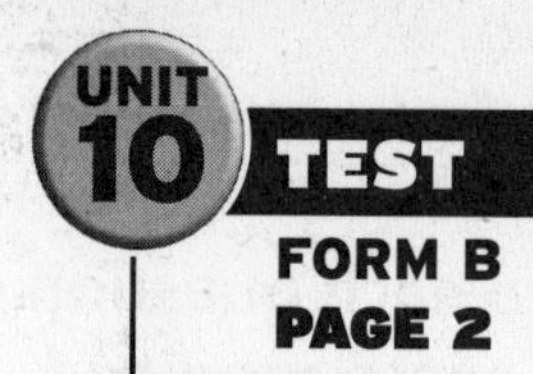

11. Find the perimeter:

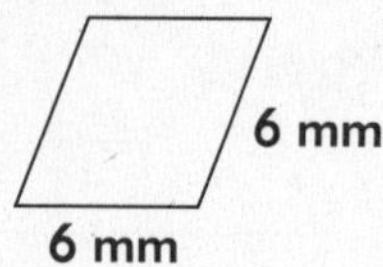

____

12. Are these shapes congruent?

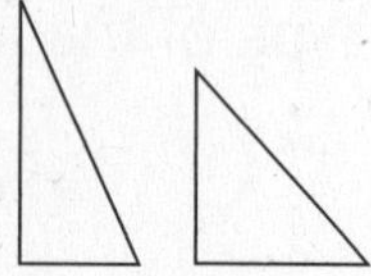

____

13. Find the perimeter.

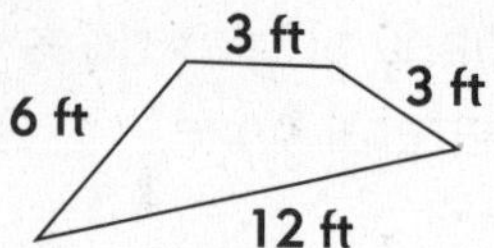

____

14. Find the area.

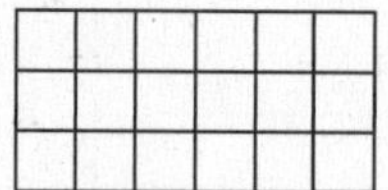

____

15. Circle the letter with bilateral symmetry.

16. Circle the shape with rotational symmetry.

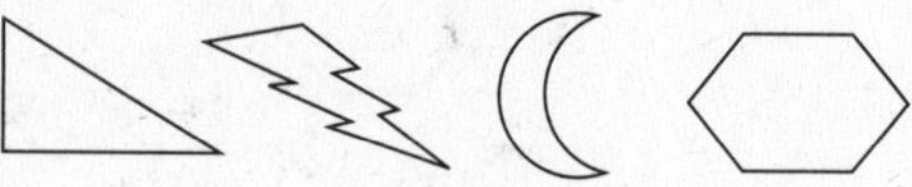

____

Solve.

17. A tile on the floor has 6 sides. What shape is it?

____

18. Jerome has a rectangular towel that measures 5 feet by 4 feet. What is the area?

____

19. Nelson drew a design. In the first row there were 8 squares. In the second row, there were 12 squares. There were 16 squares in the third row. If he continues the design, how many squares would be in the fourth row?

____

20. Annabelle has a pool that measures 30 m by 10 m. What is the perimeter of her pool?

____

Name ______________________________

21. Identify.

____

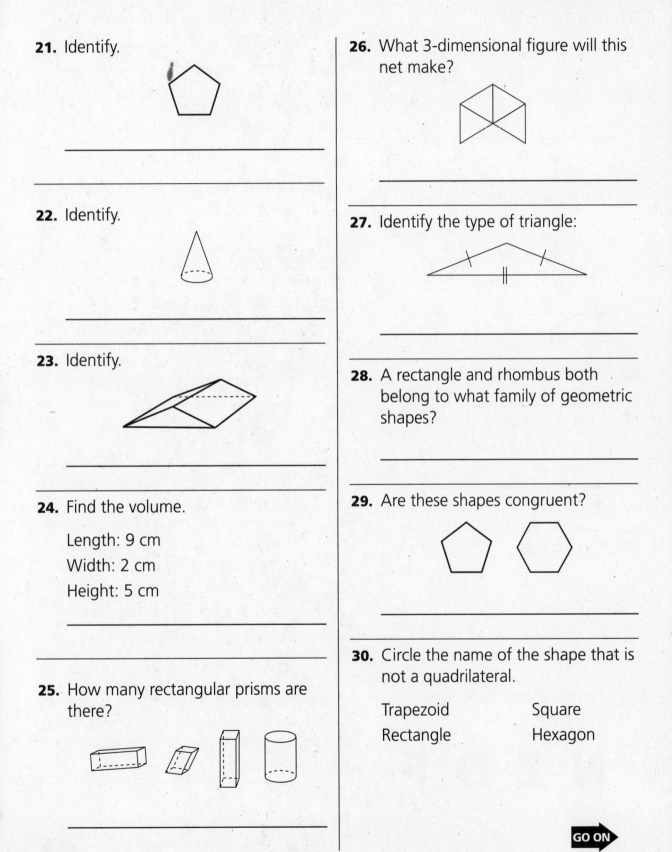

22. Identify.

____

23. Identify.

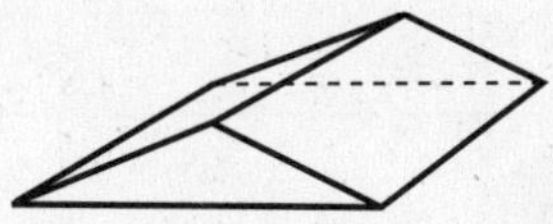

____

24. Find the volume.

Length: 9 cm
Width: 2 cm
Height: 5 cm

____

25. How many rectangular prisms are there?

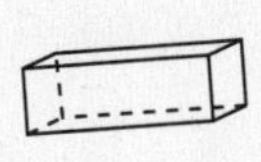  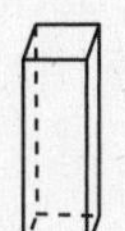 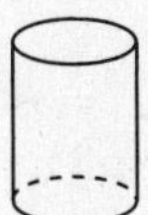

____

26. What 3-dimensional figure will this net make?

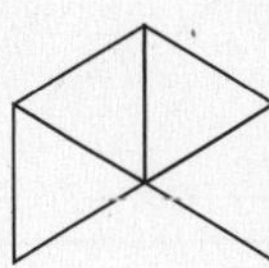

____

27. Identify the type of triangle:

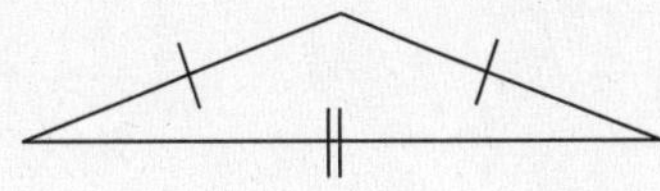

____

28. A rectangle and rhombus both belong to what family of geometric shapes?

____

29. Are these shapes congruent?

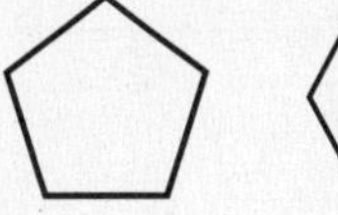

____

30. Circle the name of the shape that is not a quadrilateral.

Trapezoid   Square
Rectangle   Hexagon

GO ON

Name ____________________

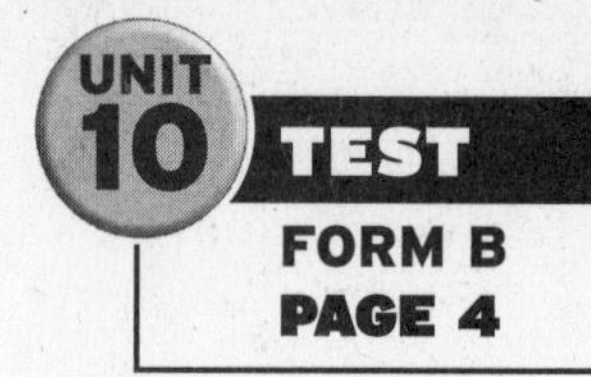

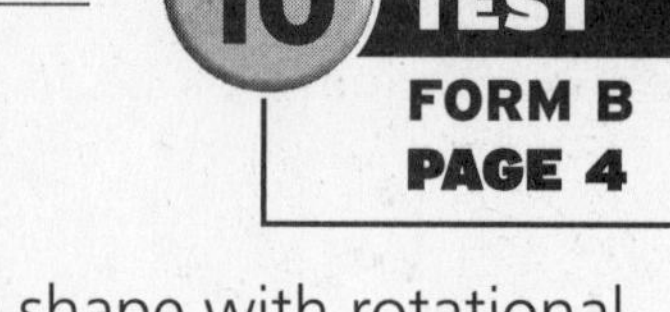

31. Find the perimeter.

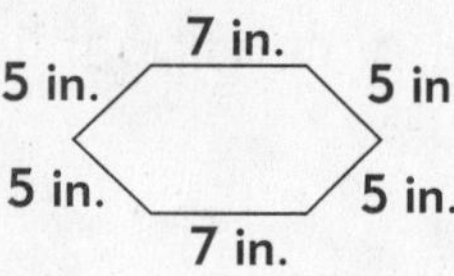

____

32. Are these shapes congruent?

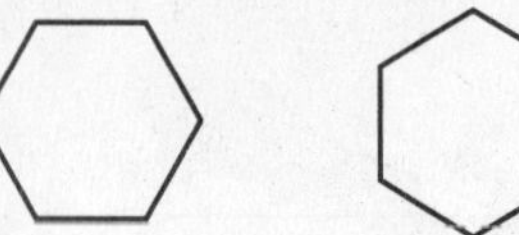

____

33. Find the perimeter.

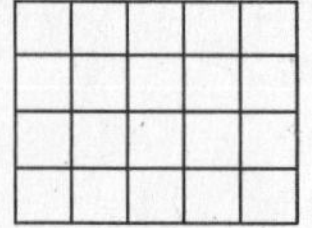

____

34. Find the area.

Length: 8 in.

Width: 9 in.

____

35. Circle the letter with bilateral symmetry.

N Z D F

36. Circle the shape with rotational symmetry.

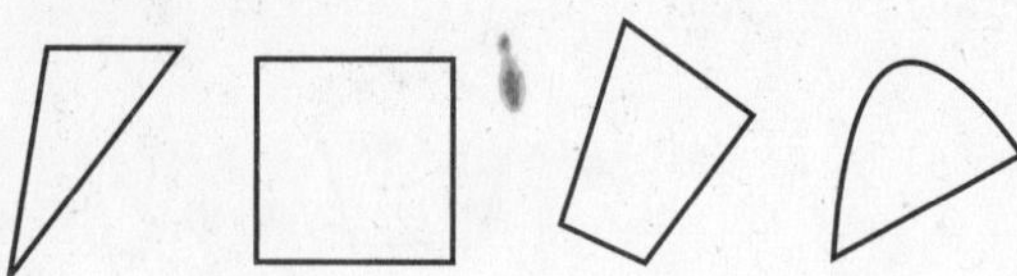

37. A tile on the floor has 8 sides. What shape is it?

____

38. Sharon has a poster that measures 8 feet by 4 feet. What is the area of the poster?

____

39. Vicki was stacking cans on a shelf. In the first row she placed 9 cans. In the second she placed 7. In the third she placed 5. If she continues the pattern, how many cans will be in the fifth row?

____

40. Hermes has a rectangular garden that measures 13 ft by 9 feet. What is the perimeter of his garden.

____

STOP

Chapter 21 – Teacher Interview

Core Concept: ***Fractions***

Student Activity: Students demonstrate an understanding of fractions when asked to work with a common fraction.

Teacher Question 1:

- How would you represent a circle that is $\frac{2}{4}$ shaded?

Understanding Student Response	Practice and Improvement
Students draw a circle divided into anything but fourths.	Review lesson 1 to help students practice writing fractions.
Students shade more or less than $\frac{2}{4}$ of the circle.	Review lesson 1 to help students practice identifying fractions.

Teacher Question 2:

- What is an equivalent fraction for $\frac{2}{4}$?

Understanding Student Response	Practice and Improvement
Students answer other than $\frac{1}{2}$.	Review lesson 3 to help students explore the concept of equivalent fractions.

Teacher Question 3:

- Is $\frac{2}{4}$ greater than or less than $\frac{3}{4}$?

Understanding Student Response	Practice and Improvement
Students answer greater than.	Review lesson 4 to help students compare fractions.

Chapter 21 – Journal Writing

Encourage students to generate their own journal entries related to math ideas in general or to concepts in this chapter. For students requiring guidance, present the following journal prompt:

- Is it always possible to order two fractions on the number line? Why?

  (Responses should include the idea that you can always find equivalent fractions for each fraction that have the same denominator. Applying the Commutative Property of Multiplication lets us see that the first denominator times the second is the same as the second times the first.)

JOURNAL WRITING/PROBLEM SOLVING

The end of the school year is coming, and Jana wants to plan her time. She will spend 5 days working on science, 3 days working on English, and 2 days working on social studies. How many weeks is that?

Read

Have students find the answer to the problem. Then ask them to write a few sentences telling—

- how they write the number of days as number of weeks
- whether they expressed the number as a mixed number or an improper fraction, and why

Have students make up another problem with different information for which they would have to follow the same procedure. Then have students solve the problem and supply the correct response.

Plan

Students must be able to represent parts of a whole as fractions and write the improper fraction or the equivalent mixed number.

Solve

The correct response to the assigned problem is $\frac{10}{7}$, or $1\frac{3}{7}$. Students must recognize that there are 7 days in a week and that Jana is planning 10 days of work.

Look Back

A correct solution demonstrates an understanding of expressing parts of a whole as a fraction and the ability to convert an improper fraction to a mixed number. (See scoring rubric on page 7.)

Chapter 21 – Monitoring Student Progress

☐ **Form A** ☐ **Form B**

Name ______________________________ Date ____________________

Directions: For each item that is answered incorrectly, cross out the item number. Then record the number of correct responses in the appropriate Student Score column. If the student has not met the Criterion Score for an objective, circle the student's score. Recommended assignments are listed in the Prescription Table on the next page.

Objective	Item Numbers	Criterion Score	Student Score
A. Identify, read, and write fractions and mixed numbers.	1, 2, 3, 4	3/4	/4
B. Compare, order, and find equivalent and simpler fractions.	5, 6, 7, 8, 9, 10, 11, 12, 13, 14, 15, 16	11/12	/12
C. Use skills and strategies to solve problems.	17, 18, 19, 20	3/4	/4
Total Test Score		17/20	/20
Total Percent Correct			%

Chapter 21 – Prescription Table

The following chart correlates the tested objectives for this chapter to supplementary materials that meet the individual needs of the students. The Reteach and Practice pages are designed for students who need further instruction in the math concepts taught in this chapter. The Enrich pages are designed for students who need advanced challenges.

Objective	Reteach	Practice	Enrich
A. Identify, read, and write fractions and mixed numbers.	367, 370, 382, 385	368, 371, 383, 386	369, 372 384, 387
B. Compare, order, and find equivalent and simpler fractions.	373, 376	374, 377	375, 378
C. Use skills and strategies to solve problems.	379	380	381

Name ________________________________

CHAPTER 21 TEST
FORM A
PAGE 1

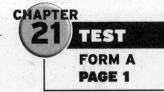

Read each question carefully. Darken the circle on your answer sheet for the correct answer.

For exercises 1–4, match the model with the fraction that correctly represents the shaded part of the model.

1.

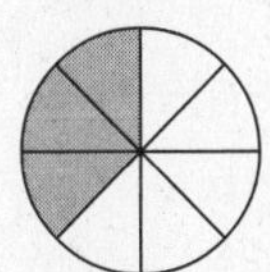

A. $\frac{8}{3}$ **B.** $\frac{1}{3}$ **C.** $\frac{3}{8}$ **D.** $\frac{5}{8}$

2.

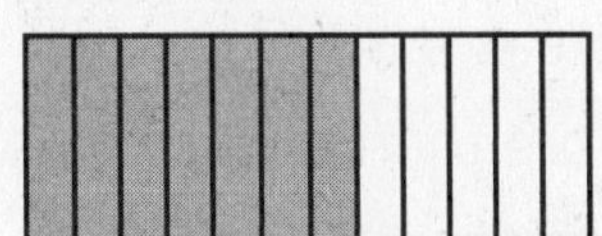

F. $\frac{1}{7}$ **G.** $\frac{12}{7}$ **H.** $\frac{5}{12}$ **J.** $\frac{7}{12}$

3.

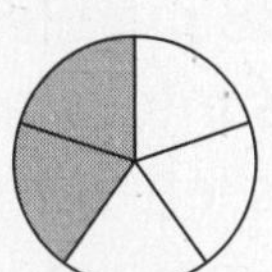

A. $\frac{2}{5}$ **B.** $\frac{5}{2}$ **C.** $\frac{3}{5}$ **D.** $\frac{1}{5}$

4.

F. $\frac{10}{8}$ **G.** $\frac{8}{10}$ **H.** $\frac{2}{8}$ **J.** $\frac{2}{10}$

5. Which has the greatest value?

$\frac{3}{12}$ $\frac{1}{5}$ $\frac{2}{6}$ $\frac{3}{8}$

A. $\frac{3}{12}$ **B.** $\frac{1}{5}$ **C.** $\frac{2}{6}$ **D.** $\frac{3}{8}$

6. Order from least to greatest.

$\frac{2}{4}$ $\frac{3}{8}$ $\frac{7}{12}$

F. $\frac{3}{8}, \frac{7}{12}, \frac{2}{4}$ **H.** $\frac{7}{12}, \frac{3}{8}, \frac{2}{4}$

G. $\frac{2}{4}, \frac{3}{8}, \frac{7}{12}$ **J.** $\frac{3}{8}, \frac{2}{4}, \frac{7}{12}$

7. Write $\frac{27}{36}$ in simplest form.

A. $\frac{9}{4}$ **B.** $\frac{4}{9}$ **C.** $\frac{3}{4}$ **D.** $\frac{3}{9}$

8. Rename $\frac{19}{3}$ as a mixed number in simplest form.

F. $6\frac{3}{19}$ **H.** $\frac{6}{3}$

G. $6\frac{1}{3}$ **J.** $\frac{6}{19}$

9. Which has the least value?

$\frac{2}{10}$ $\frac{3}{5}$ $\frac{1}{4}$ $\frac{3}{20}$

A. $\frac{2}{10}$ **B.** $\frac{3}{5}$ **C.** $\frac{1}{4}$ **D.** $\frac{3}{20}$

10. Order from greatest to least.

$\frac{2}{8}$ $\frac{5}{16}$ $\frac{1}{2}$

F. $\frac{1}{2}, \frac{5}{16}, \frac{2}{8}$ **H.** $\frac{2}{8}, \frac{5}{16}, \frac{1}{2}$

G. $\frac{5}{16}, \frac{1}{2}, \frac{2}{8}$ **J.** $\frac{1}{2}, \frac{2}{8}, \frac{5}{16}$

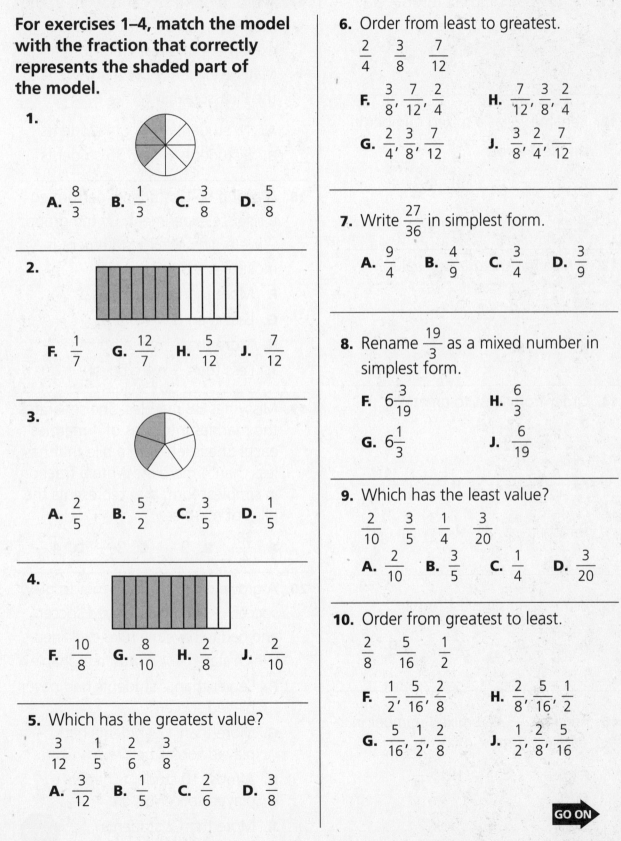

GO ON

Name ____________________

CHAPTER 21 TEST
FORM A
PAGE 2

11. Write $\frac{7}{21}$ in simplest form.

A. $\frac{7}{14}$ **B.** $\frac{1}{7}$ **C.** $\frac{1}{3}$ **D.** $\frac{3}{21}$

---

12. Rename $\frac{35}{8}$ as a mixed number in simplest form.

F. $8\frac{3}{8}$ **H.** $4\frac{8}{35}$

G. $4\frac{3}{8}$ **J.** $3\frac{4}{35}$

---

13. Which has the greatest value?

$\frac{2}{3}$ $\frac{5}{6}$ $\frac{7}{9}$ $\frac{3}{4}$

A. $\frac{2}{3}$ **B.** $\frac{5}{6}$ **C.** $\frac{7}{9}$ **D.** $\frac{3}{4}$

---

14. Order from least to greatest.

$\frac{7}{8}$ $\frac{3}{4}$ $\frac{8}{12}$

F. $\frac{8}{12}, \frac{3}{4}, \frac{7}{8}$ **H.** $\frac{3}{4}, \frac{7}{8}, \frac{8}{12}$

G. $\frac{8}{12}, \frac{7}{8}, \frac{3}{4}$ **J.** $\frac{3}{4}, \frac{8}{12}, \frac{7}{8}$

---

15. Write $\frac{12}{20}$ in simplest form.

A. $\frac{4}{5}$ **B.** $\frac{3}{4}$ **C.** $\frac{3}{5}$ **D.** $\frac{6}{10}$

---

16. Rename $\frac{26}{5}$ as a mixed number in simplest form.

F. $5\frac{6}{5}$ **H.** $5\frac{1}{26}$

G. $\frac{5}{26}$ **J.** $5\frac{1}{5}$

17. A group of 40 students went to the museum. $\frac{3}{5}$ went to the Picasso exhibit and the rest went to the Matisse exhibit. How many went to the Picasso exhibit?

A. 15 students **C.** 24 students

B. 8 students **D.** 35 students

---

18. A group of 12 students performed a science experiment. Of the group, $\frac{2}{3}$ were girls. Which statement is most reasonable?

F. More than 9 were girls.

G. Less than 8 were girls.

H. More than $\frac{1}{4}$ were boys.

J. Less than $\frac{1}{3}$ were boys.

---

19. Missy has 38 marbles. She separates the marbles into piles of 4 marbles each. She is left with a pile that has less than 4 marbles. Write a fraction in simplest form that represents the piles of marbles.

A. $\frac{38}{4}$ **B.** $9\frac{1}{2}$ **C.** $9\frac{4}{38}$ **D.** $4\frac{9}{4}$

---

20. A group of 16 students met to play soccer. $\frac{1}{8}$ had never played soccer and had to have the rules explained. Which statement is most reasonable?

F. Fewer than 2 students had never played soccer.

G. More than 12 students had played soccer before.

H. Almost 10 students had played soccer before.

J. More than 2 students had never played soccer.

STOP

Name ______________________________

CHAPTER 21 TEST
FORM B
PAGE 1

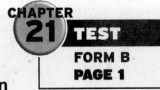

Read each question carefully. Fill in the correct answer in the space provided.

For exercises 1–4, write the fraction that correctly represents the shaded part of the model.

1.

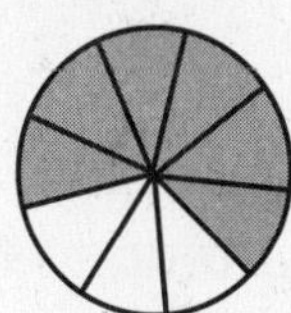

______

2.

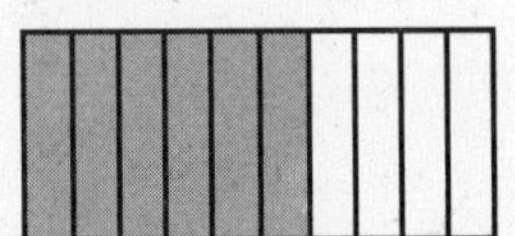

______

3.

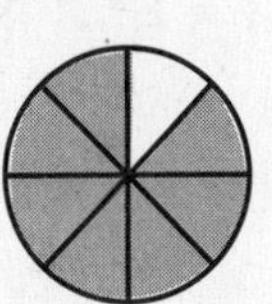

______

4.

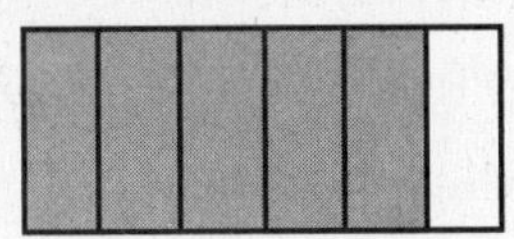

______

5. Which has the greatest value?

$\frac{4}{5}$ $\frac{3}{4}$ $\frac{4}{10}$ $\frac{12}{20}$

______

6. Order from least to greatest.

$\frac{3}{5}$ $\frac{4}{10}$ $\frac{5}{15}$

______

7. Write $\frac{18}{27}$ in simplest form.

______

8. Rename $\frac{17}{6}$ as a mixed number in simplest form.

______

9. Which has the least value?

$\frac{1}{5}$ $\frac{3}{10}$ $\frac{5}{20}$ $\frac{10}{40}$

______

10. Order from greatest to least.

$\frac{5}{6}$ $\frac{7}{9}$ $\frac{13}{18}$

______

GO ON

Name ______________________________

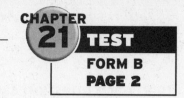

11. Write $\frac{15}{25}$ in simplest form.

______

12. Rename $\frac{29}{7}$ as a mixed number in simplest form.

______

13. Which has the greatest value?

$\frac{7}{10}$ $\frac{3}{5}$ $\frac{10}{15}$ $\frac{22}{30}$

______

14. Order from least to greatest.

$\frac{6}{9}$ $\frac{3}{6}$ $\frac{3}{4}$

______

15. Write $\frac{24}{36}$ in simplest form.

______

16. Rename $\frac{32}{6}$ as a mixed number in simplest form.

______

17. A group of 30 students went to a ballet. $\frac{5}{6}$ had never seen a ballet performance before. How many had never seen a ballet?

______

18. 25 students attended the science fair. $\frac{3}{5}$ entered their projects into the competition. Is it reasonable to say that fewer than 12 students entered the competition? Write yes or no and explain your answer.

______

19. Joseph has 47 coins. He separates them into piles of 8. He is left with a pile that has fewer than 8 coins. Write a fraction in simplest form that represents the piles of coins.

______

20. 18 students met to rehearse for a school play. $\frac{1}{2}$ of the students had never been in a play before. Is it reasonable to say that fewer than 10 students had never been in a play? Write *yes* or *no* and explain your answer.

______

______

STOP

Chapter 22 – Teacher Interview

Core Concept: *Probability*

Student Activity: Students demonstrate an understanding of determining the likeliness of events, and can write the theoretical probability of an event. Assign a problem such as finding the probability of a spinner landing on red if red is one of four equal sections

Teacher Question 1:

- Describe a spinner that has two colors that are equally likely.

Understanding Student Response	Practice and Improvement
Students do not have two sections with the same probability.	Review lesson 1 to reinforce the concept of equally likely events.

Teacher Question 2:

- A spinner has 4 equal sections. If one of those sections is red, is the probability of spinning red likely, unlikely, certain, or impossible?

Understanding Student Response	Practice and Improvement
Students answer certain.	Review lesson 1 to help students understand the concept of certain.
Students answer impossible.	Review lesson 1 to help students understand the concept of impossible.
Students answer likely.	Review lesson 1 to help students understand the concepts of likely and unlikely.

Teacher Question 3:

- What fraction represents the red part of that spinner?

Understanding Student Response	Practice and Improvement
Students who answer $\frac{3}{4}$ answered the part that was not red.	Review lesson 2 to help students learn that probability is expressed as the fraction of favorable outcomes over the number of possible outcomes.
Students answer any other incorrect answer.	Review lesson 2 to help students learn that probability is expressed as the fraction of favorable outcomes over the number of possible outcomes.

Chapter 22 – Journal Writing

Encourage students to generate their own journal entries related to math ideas in general or to concepts in this chapter. For students requiring guidance, present the following journal prompt:

- Give an example of two equally likely events that are unlikely. Give an example of two equally likely events that are impossible. Give an example of two equally likely events that are certain.

  (Responses will vary. For instance, if a bag has 98 red marbles, one green marble and one blue marble, it's equally likely, and unlikely, that the first marble pulled out will be blue or green. It's equally likely, and impossible, that the sun will rise in the west tomorrow and that you can toss a number cube with three yellow faces and three red faces and have it turn up white. It's equally likely, and certain, that you will spin purple on a spinner with four sections, all purple, as it is that you will toss a 1 through 6 number cube and get a number less than 7.)

JOURNAL WRITING/PROBLEM SOLVING

Carlos and his family live outside of Newtown. They are planning a trip into town for an activity. There are two ways of getting into town, Lowe Road and Scenic Route. They have time for one activity: eating at the Sundae Shoppe, shopping at Toy Bazaar, or touring On a String, the balloon factory. What are all the possible combinations of the route they can take and the activity they can do?

Read

Have students find the answer to the problem. Then ask them to write a few sentences telling—

- how they organized the information
- how they found all of the possible combinations

Have students make up another problem with different information for which they would have to follow the same procedure. Then have students solve the problem and supply the correct response.

Plan

Students must know how to use a decision tree to lay out combinations of two decisions.

Solve

The correct response to the assigned problem is six combinations.

Look Back

A correct response demonstrates an ability to use decision trees to determine possible combinations of events. (See scoring rubric on page 7.)

Chapter 22 – Monitoring Student Progress

☐ **Form A** ☐ **Form B**

Name ______________________ Date ______________

Directions: For each item that is answered incorrectly, cross out the item number. Then record the number of correct responses in the appropriate Student Score column. If the student has not met the Criterion Score for an objective, circle the student's score. Recommended assignments are listed in the Prescription Table on the next page.

Objective	Item Numbers	Criterion Score	Student Score
A. Identify the likeliness of events.	1, 2, 3, 8, 13	4/5	/5
B. Find and explore probability.	4, 5, 9, 10, 11, 12, 16	6/7	/7
C. Predict the outcome in an experiment.	6, 15, 19, 20	3/4	/4
D. Use skills and strategies to solve problems.	7, 14, 17, 18	3/4	/4
Total Test Score		16/20	/20
Total Percent Correct			%

Chapter 22 – Prescription Table

The following chart correlates the tested objectives for this chapter to supplementary materials that meet the individual needs of the students. The Reteach and Practice pages are designed for students who need further instruction in the math concepts taught in this chapter. The Enrich pages are designed for students who need advanced challenges.

Objective	Reteach	Practice	Enrich
A. Identify the likeliness of events.	388	389	390
B. Find and explore probability.	391	392	393
C. Predict the outcome in an experiment.	397	398	399
D. Use skills and strategies to solve problems.	394, 395	396	

Name ______________________________

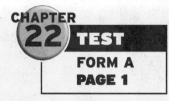

Read each question carefully. Darken the circle on your answer sheet for the correct answer.

For exercises 1–3, use the spinner shown below. Choose the word that best describes the probability of the spinner landing on the given color.

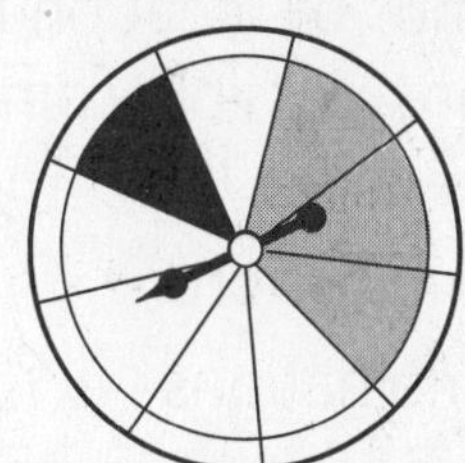

1. White
   - **A.** certain
   - **B.** unlikely
   - **C.** likely
   - **D.** impossible

2. Black
   - **F.** likely
   - **G.** certain
   - **H.** impossible
   - **J.** unlikely

3. Orange
   - **A.** certain
   - **B.** impossible
   - **C.** unlikely
   - **D.** likely

4. How many possible outcomes are there when tossing a number cube?
   F. 1 **G.** 3 **H.** 6 **J.** 8

5. What is the probability of spinning a 4?

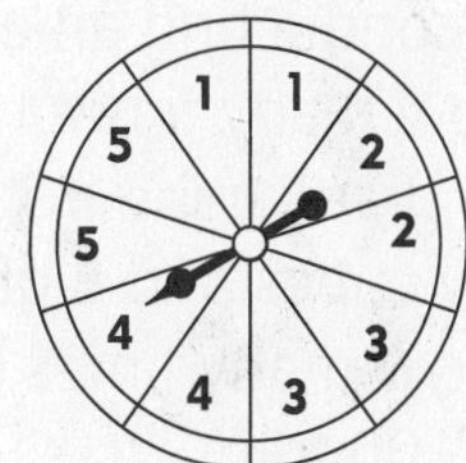

A. $\frac{1}{10}$ **B.** $\frac{1}{4}$ **C.** $\frac{2}{5}$ **D.** $\frac{1}{5}$

6. If you take one card without looking, how many possible outcomes are there?

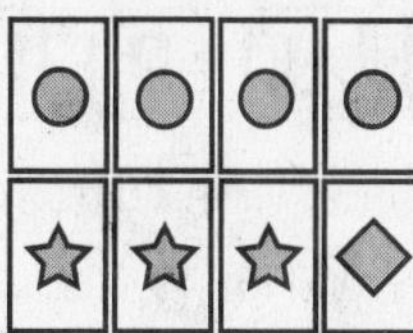

F. 1 **G.** 3 **H.** 4 **J.** 8

7. Nathan tossed a coin and spun a spinner numbered 1–4. How many possible outcomes were there?
   A. 2 **B.** 4 **C.** 8 **D.** 16

For exercises 8–10, use the cards shown below.

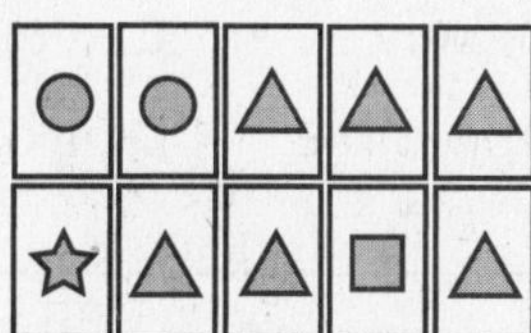

8. Describe the probability of picking a triangle.
   - **F.** likely
   - **G.** certain
   - **H.** impossible
   - **J.** unlikely

9. What is the probability of picking a circle?
   A. $\frac{1}{10}$ **B.** $\frac{1}{5}$ **C.** $\frac{3}{5}$ **D.** $\frac{6}{10}$

10. If you take one card without looking, how many possible outcomes are there?
    F. 10 **G.** 6 **H.** 4 **J.** 1

GO ON

Name ____

For exercises 11–13, use the numbered buttons shown below.

 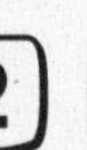 

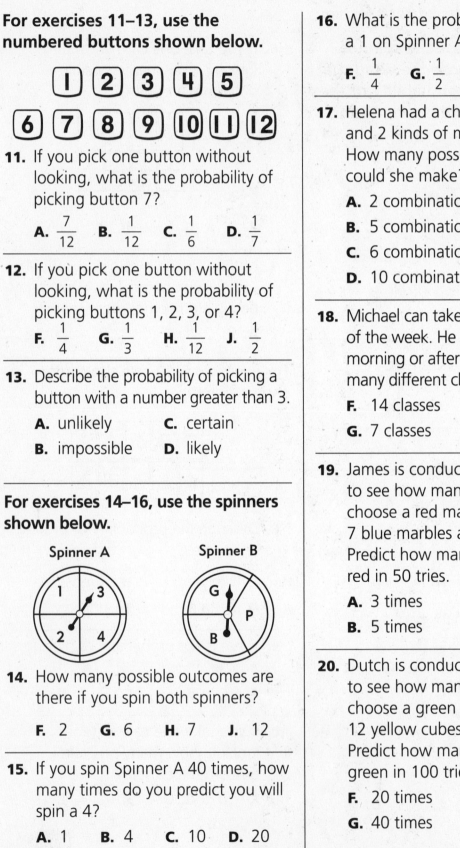

11. If you pick one button without looking, what is the probability of picking button 7?

A. $\frac{7}{12}$ **B.** $\frac{1}{12}$ **C.** $\frac{1}{6}$ **D.** $\frac{1}{7}$

---

12. If you pick one button without looking, what is the probability of picking buttons 1, 2, 3, or 4?

F. $\frac{1}{4}$ **G.** $\frac{1}{3}$ **H.** $\frac{1}{12}$ **J.** $\frac{1}{2}$

---

13. Describe the probability of picking a button with a number greater than 3.

A. unlikely **C.** certain

B. impossible **D.** likely

For exercises 14–16, use the spinners shown below.

Spinner A

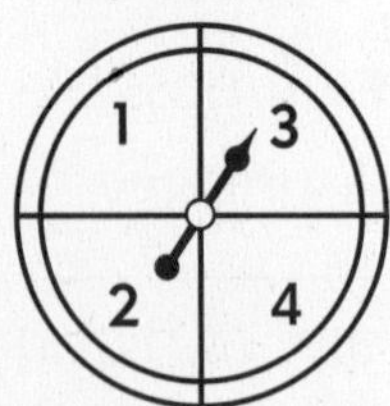

Spinner B

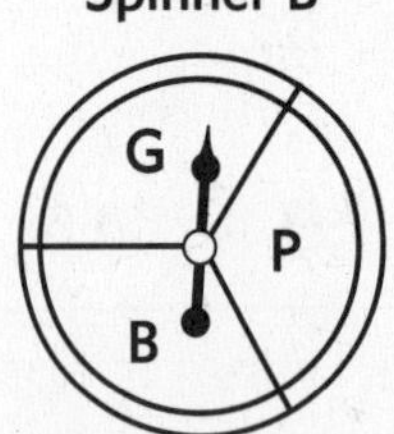

14. How many possible outcomes are there if you spin both spinners?

F. 2 **G.** 6 **H.** 7 **J.** 12

---

15. If you spin Spinner A 40 times, how many times do you predict you will spin a 4?

A. 1 **B.** 4 **C.** 10 **D.** 20

16. What is the probability of spinning a 1 on Spinner A?

F. $\frac{1}{4}$ **G.** $\frac{1}{2}$ **H.** $\frac{1}{3}$ **J.** 1

---

17. Helena had a choice of 5 vegetables and 2 kinds of meat on her pizza. How many possible combinations could she make?

A. 2 combinations

B. 5 combinations

C. 6 combinations

D. 10 combinations

---

18. Michael can take a yoga class any day of the week. He also has a choice of morning or afternoon classes. How many different classes could he take?

F. 14 classes **H.** 4 classes

G. 7 classes **J.** 2 classes

---

19. James is conducting an experiment to see how many times he would choose a red marble from a bag of 7 blue marbles and 3 red marbles. Predict how many times he will pick red in 50 tries.

A. 3 times **C.** 7 times

B. 5 times **D.** 15 times

---

20. Dutch is conducting an experiment to see how many times he would choose a green cube from a bag of 12 yellow cubes and 8 green cubes. Predict how many times he will pick green in 100 tries.

F. 20 times **H.** 80 times

G. 40 times **J.** 100 times

STOP

Name ____________________

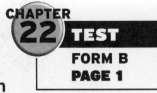

Read each question carefully. Fill in the correct answer in the space provided.

For exercises 1–3, use the spinner shown below. Write the words likely, certain, unlikely, or impossible to best describe the probability of the spinner landing on the given color.

1. White

____

2. Black

____

3. Gray

____

4. How many possible outcomes are there when spinning a spinner like the one below?

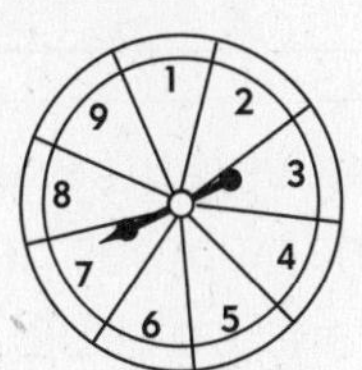

____

5. What is the probability of spinning a 1 or a 2?

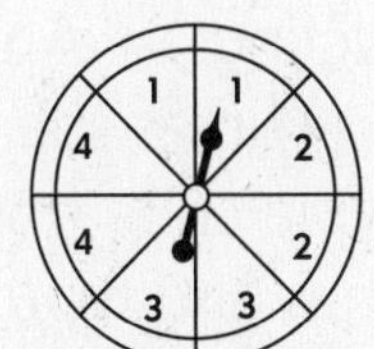

____

6. If you take one card without looking, how many possible outcomes are there?

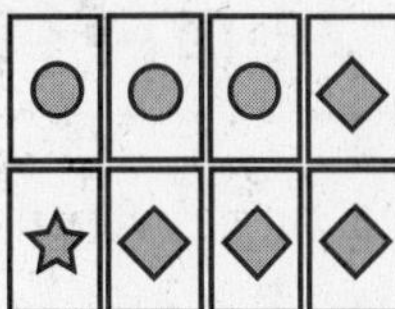

____

7. Nathan tossed a coin and spun a spinner numbered 1–6. How many possible outcomes were there?

____

For exercises 8–10, use the cards shown below.

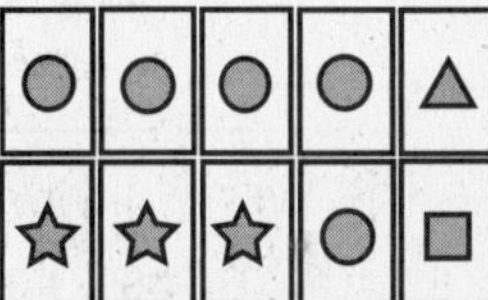

8. Write the words *likely*, *certain*, *unlikely*, or *impossible* to best describe the probability of picking a card with a heart on it.

____

9. What is the probability of picking a circle?

____

10. If you take one card without looking, how many possible outcomes are there?

____

GO ON

Name ____________________

For exercises 11–13, use the numbered buttons shown below.

11. If you pick one button without looking, what is the probability of picking button 2?

____

12. If you pick one button without looking, what is the probability of picking buttons 1, 4, 7, or 10?

____

13. Write the words likely, certain, unlikely, or impossible to best describe the probability of picking a button with a number greater than 4.

____

For exercises 14–16, use the spinners shown below.

Spinner A

Spinner B

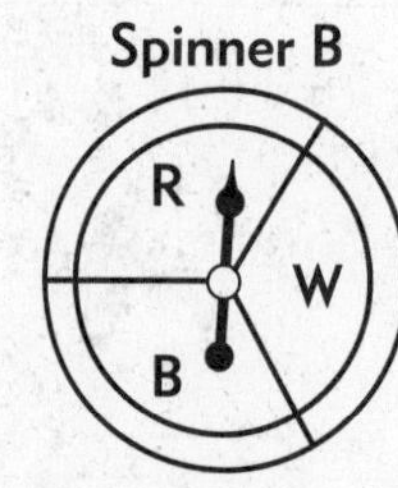

14. How many possible outcomes are there if you spin both spinners?

____

15. If you spin Spinner A 30 times, how many times do you predict you will spin a 2?

____

16. What is the probability of spinning a 1 on Spinner A?

____

17. Georgia had a choice of 4 colors and 2 sizes for a customized printed T-shirt. How many possible combinations could she make?

____

18. Amy had a choice of 5 different days of the week on which she could take a computer class. She also had a choice of afternoon or evening classes. How many different combinations of days and times of day could she make?

____

19. Linus is conducting an experiment to see how many times he would choose an orange marble from a bag of 5 blue marbles and 10 orange marbles. Predict how many times he will pick orange in 60 tries.

____

20. Lexi is conducting an experiment to see how many times she would choose a purple cube from a bag of 19 white cubes and 6 purple cubes. Predict how many times she will pick purple in 100 tries.

____

STOP

Unit 11 Performance Assessment

Spin the Spinner

- ***Target Skill:*** Predict the outcome in an experiment.
- ***Additional Skills:*** Find and explore probability; identify, read, and write fractions and mixed numbers; collect and organize data in tables and graphs.

Task Description: This task requires students to design a spinner with 8 equal sections. The spinner will be labeled with letters from A and at least one part of the spinner has to have a probability of $\frac{1}{4}$ or greater. Students will make predictions based on 30 and 60 spins, then using a tally table and the spinner, will carry out their experiments.

Preparing: You may wish to discuss with students the fractions associated with an 8-part spinner. Review with students that the fractions can range from $\frac{1}{8}$ to $\frac{7}{8}$ in this experiment.

Materials	Group Size	Time on Task
Spinners	2 to 3 students	2 to 3 days

Guiding: Remind students that their predictions should be based on the probability that each number spun will be multiplied by the number of spins.

Remind students that the sections must be equal for the experiment to work.

Observing/ Monitoring: As you move among the students, pose the following questions:

How did you design your spinners?

How did you determine the probability of each letter?

How are you keeping your tally table?

Unit 11 Performance Assessment Scoring Rubric

Spin the Spinner

<table>
<tr><th>Score</th><th>Explanation</th></tr>
<tr><td>3</td><td>Students demonstrate an efficient strategy and a thorough approach that enables them to solve the problem completely. A satisfactory answer:
• gives each letter its proper probability;
• has predictions that are close to the actual results;
• has predictions for 60 spins that are double that of their predictions for 30 spins.
Students are able to complete the problem quickly and have all of the above correct solutions.</td></tr>
<tr><td>2</td><td>Students demonstrate a strategy that enables them to solve most of the problem correctly. The strategy is somewhat disorganized, making it less efficient. A solution is found, but errors are contained. Students may:
• find most of the correct probabilities;
• make predictions that are close to the actual results.
Students may have some difficulty determining all solutions correctly, but demonstrate an understanding of general concepts.</td></tr>
<tr><td>1</td><td>Students demonstrate a confused strategy, which leads to difficulty solving the problem. Most answers are incorrect, but students demonstrate knowledge of at least one concept being assessed such as finding the probability or identifying, reading, and writing fractions.</td></tr>
</table>

Name ____

Unit 11 Performance Assessment Student Activity

Spin the Spinner

You will need
- Graph paper

Make a spinner with 8 equal sections. Label each section with a letter. Use one letter at least twice to design your spinner.

Exchange spinners with a classmate.

- You are going to spin the spinner 30 times. Predict how many times each letter will be spun. Write your prediction in the table.
- Spin the spinner 30 times.
- Record each spin in the tally table.

Letter	Prediction	Spins

1. How did the actual results compare to your predictions of the spinner?

____

2. What fraction did you use to make your predictions for each letter?

____

3. What do you think would happen if you spun the spinner 60 more times?

____

Unit 11 – Monitoring Student Progress

☐ **Form A**   ☐ **Form B**

Name ______________________ Date ______________

Directions: This test targets selected objectives. For each item that is answered incorrectly, cross out the item number. Then record the number of correct responses in the column labeled **Number of Correct Responses.** Add to find the **Total Number of Correct Responses** and record the total. Use this total to determine the **Total Test Score** and the **Total Percent Correct.**

Strand • Objective(s)	Item Numbers	Number of Correct Responses
Number Sense, Concepts, and Operations • Identify, read, and write fractions and mixed numbers. • Compare, order, and find equivalent and simpler fractions. • Use skills and strategies to solve problems.	1, 2, 3, 4, 6, 7, 8, 10, 11, 13, 14, 17, 21, 22, 24, 25, 27, 28, 30, 31, 33, 34, 40	/23
Data Analysis and Probability • Identify the likeliness of events. • Find and explore probability. • Predict the outcome in an experiment. • Use skills and strategies to solve problems.	5, 9, 12, 15, 16, 18, 19, 20, 23, 26, 29, 32, 35, 36, 37, 38, 39	/17
Total Number of Correct Responses		
Total Test Score		/40
Total Percent Correct		%

Name ____________________

Read each question carefully. Darken the circle on your answer sheet for the correct answer.

1. What part is shaded?

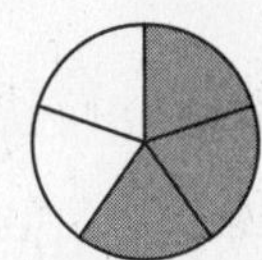

A. $\frac{5}{5}$ **B.** $\frac{4}{5}$ **C.** $\frac{3}{5}$ **D.** $\frac{1}{5}$

---

2. Which has the greatest value?

$\frac{4}{24}$ $\frac{5}{12}$ $\frac{3}{8}$ $\frac{2}{3}$

F. $\frac{2}{3}$ **G.** $\frac{5}{12}$ **H.** $\frac{4}{24}$ **J.** $\frac{3}{8}$

---

3. What is the number of possible outcomes when you are rolling a number cube?

A. 8 **B.** 6 **C.** 4 **D.** 2

---

4. What part is shaded?

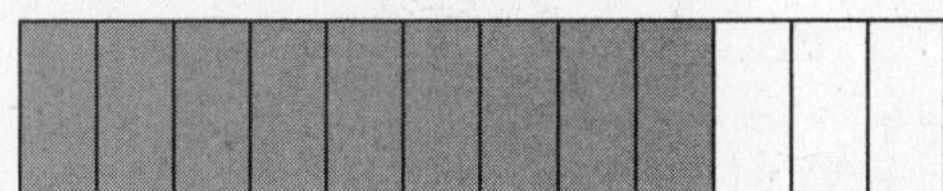

F. $\frac{12}{12}$ **G.** $\frac{11}{12}$ **H.** $\frac{10}{12}$ **J.** $\frac{9}{12}$

---

5. Order from least to greatest.

$\frac{2}{5}$ $\frac{1}{3}$ $\frac{3}{15}$

A. $\frac{2}{5}, \frac{1}{3}, \frac{3}{15}$ **C.** $\frac{1}{3}, \frac{3}{15}, \frac{2}{5}$

B. $\frac{1}{3}, \frac{2}{5}, \frac{3}{15}$ **D.** $\frac{3}{15}, \frac{1}{3}, \frac{2}{5}$

---

6. If you take one card without looking, how many possible outcomes are there?

F. 6 **G.** 5 **H.** 4 **J.** 3

---

7. What part is shaded?

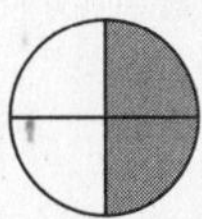

A. $\frac{5}{4}$ **B.** $\frac{3}{4}$ **C.** $\frac{2}{4}$ **D.** $\frac{1}{4}$

---

8. Order from greatest to least.

$\frac{7}{12}$ $\frac{3}{4}$ $\frac{1}{2}$

F. $\frac{7}{12}, \frac{3}{4}, \frac{1}{2}$ **H.** $\frac{1}{2}, \frac{7}{12}, \frac{3}{4}$

G. $\frac{3}{4}, \frac{7}{12}, \frac{1}{2}$ **J.** $\frac{3}{4}, \frac{1}{2}, \frac{7}{12}$

---

9. What is the probability of spinning a B?

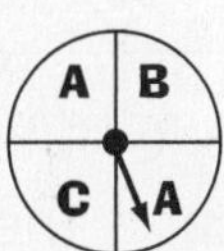

A. $\frac{3}{4}$ **B.** $\frac{1}{2}$ **C.** $\frac{1}{4}$ **D.** $\frac{4}{4}$

---

10. What part is shaded?

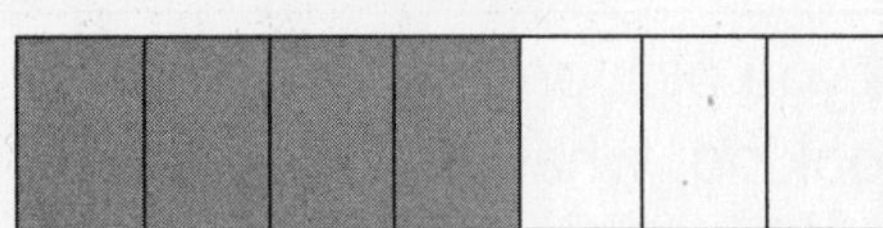

F. $\frac{6}{7}$ **G.** $\frac{5}{7}$ **H.** $\frac{4}{7}$ **J.** $\frac{2}{7}$

Name ______________________________

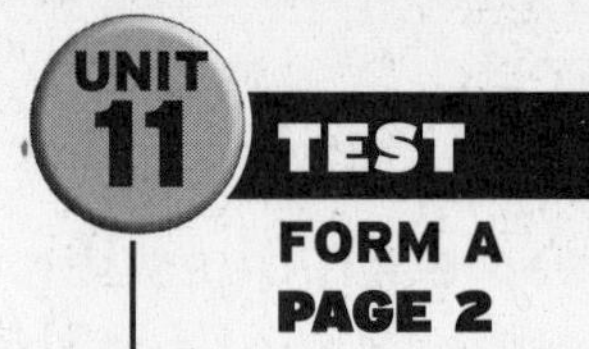

11. Write $\frac{4}{32}$ in simplest form.

A. $\frac{1}{8}$ **B.** $\frac{2}{16}$ **C.** $\frac{1}{9}$ **D.** $\frac{1}{28}$

---

12. Cheyenne tossed 2 coins. How many possible outcomes were there?

F. 8 **G.** 4 **H.** 3 **J.** 2

---

13. Rename $\frac{27}{4}$ as a fraction in simplest form.

A. $6\frac{3}{4}$ **B.** $4\frac{3}{6}$ **C.** $4\frac{3}{7}$ **D.** $4\frac{1}{8}$

---

14. Write $\frac{24}{27}$ in simplest form.

F. $\frac{8}{9}$ **G.** $\frac{6}{7}$ **H.** $\frac{3}{4}$ **J.** $\frac{1}{3}$

Use the numbered buttons for exercises 15–16.

15. If you pick one button without looking, what is the probability of picking button 6?

A. $\frac{1}{2}$ **B.** $\frac{1}{4}$ **C.** $\frac{1}{6}$ **D.** $\frac{1}{8}$

---

16. If you pick one button without looking, what is the probability of picking buttons 2, 4, or 8?

F. $\frac{1}{2}$ **G.** $\frac{3}{8}$ **H.** $\frac{1}{4}$ **J.** $\frac{1}{8}$

Solve.

17. A group of 36 campers went for a hike. Afterward, $\frac{1}{3}$ of the campers went swimming. How many went swimming?

A. 12 campers **C.** 6 campers
B. 9 campers **D.** 3 campers

Use the cards for problems 18–19.

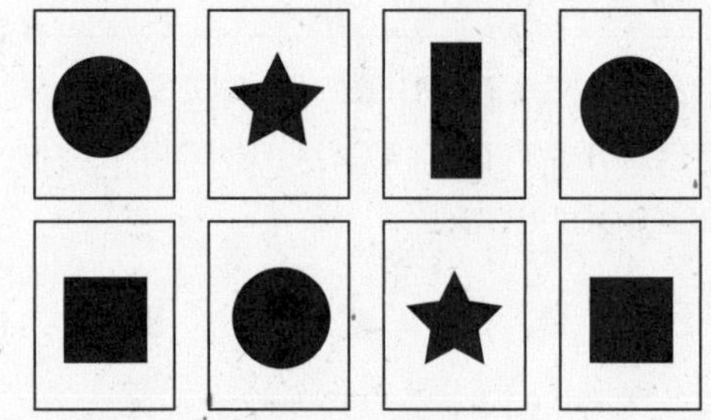

18. Describe the probability of picking a triangle.

F. certain **H.** likely
G. impossible **J.** unlikely

---

19. What is the probability of picking a star?

A. $\frac{1}{8}$ **B.** $\frac{1}{4}$ **C.** $\frac{3}{8}$ **D.** $\frac{7}{8}$

---

20. Mandy had a choice of 4 bats and 2 gloves in the sports store. How many possible combinations could she make?

F. 8 combinations
G. 6 combinations
H. 4 combinations
J. 2 combinations

GO ON

Name ____________________

21. What part is shaded?

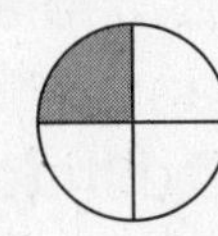

A. $\frac{1}{1}$ **B.** $\frac{1}{2}$ **C.** $\frac{1}{3}$ **D.** $\frac{1}{4}$

22. Which has the least value?

$\frac{2}{3}$ $\frac{2}{6}$ $\frac{3}{12}$ $\frac{3}{6}$

F. $\frac{2}{3}$ **G.** $\frac{3}{6}$ **H.** $\frac{3}{12}$ **J.** $\frac{2}{6}$

23. What are the number of possible outcomes when tossing a coin?

A. 4 **B.** 3 **C.** 2 **D.** 1

24. What part is shaded?

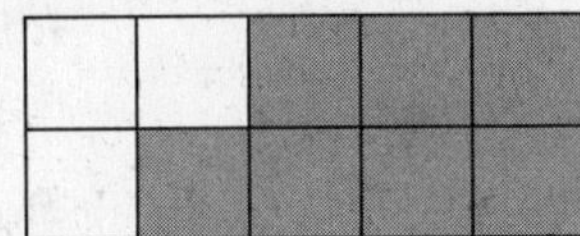

F. $\frac{10}{10}$ **G.** $\frac{7}{10}$ **H.** $\frac{5}{10}$ **J.** $\frac{4}{10}$

25. Order from greatest to least.

$\frac{1}{3}$ $\frac{2}{12}$ $\frac{4}{6}$

A. $\frac{4}{6}, \frac{1}{3}, \frac{2}{12}$ **C.** $\frac{2}{12}, \frac{1}{3}, \frac{4}{6}$

B. $\frac{2}{12}, \frac{4}{6}, \frac{1}{3}$ **D.** $\frac{4}{6}, \frac{2}{12}, \frac{1}{3}$

26. How many possible outcomes are there?

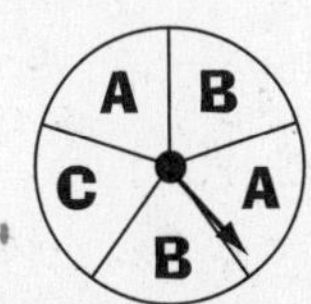

F. 4 **G.** 3 **H.** 2 **J.** 1

27. What part is shaded?

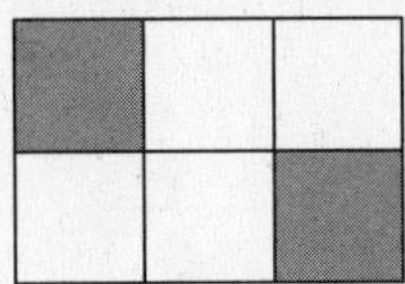

A. $\frac{4}{6}$ **B.** $\frac{3}{6}$ **C.** $\frac{2}{6}$ **D.** $\frac{1}{6}$

28. Order from least to greatest.

$\frac{7}{8}$ $\frac{1}{2}$ $\frac{3}{4}$

F. $\frac{1}{2}, \frac{7}{8}, \frac{3}{4}$ **H.** $\frac{7}{8}, \frac{3}{4}, \frac{1}{2}$

G. $\frac{1}{2}, \frac{3}{4}, \frac{7}{8}$ **J.** $\frac{7}{8}, \frac{1}{2}, \frac{3}{4}$

29. What is the probability of picking a card with a star?

 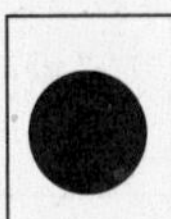 

A. 1 **B.** $\frac{2}{3}$ **C.** $\frac{1}{3}$ **D.** 0

30. What part is shaded?

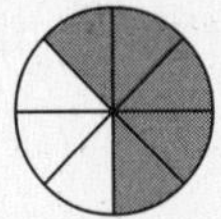

F. $\frac{6}{8}$ **G.** $\frac{5}{8}$ **H.** $\frac{4}{8}$ **J.** $\frac{2}{8}$

GO ON

Name ____________________

31. Write $\frac{12}{18}$ in simplest form.

A. $\frac{3}{4}$ **B.** $\frac{4}{6}$ **C.** $\frac{2}{3}$ **D.** $\frac{6}{9}$

32. Ron tosses a coin and then rolls a number cube. How many possible outcomes are there?

F. 12 **G.** 8 **H.** 6 **J.** 2

33. Rename $\frac{10}{7}$ as a mixed number.

A. $1\frac{4}{7}$ **B.** $1\frac{3}{7}$ **C.** $1\frac{2}{7}$ **D.** $1\frac{1}{7}$

34. Write $\frac{45}{50}$ in simplest form.

F. $\frac{9}{10}$ **G.** $\frac{4}{5}$ **H.** $\frac{20}{25}$ **J.** $\frac{1}{10}$

Use the spinner for exercises 35–36.

35. What is the probability of spinning a 4?

A. $\frac{2}{3}$ **B.** $\frac{1}{2}$ **C.** $\frac{1}{3}$ **D.** $\frac{1}{6}$

36. What is the probability of spinning a 1 or a 2?

F. $\frac{2}{3}$ **G.** $\frac{1}{2}$ **H.** $\frac{1}{3}$ **J.** $\frac{1}{6}$

37. At lunch, Bob had a choice of 3 different sandwiches. He also had a choice of 2 different salads. How many possible combinations of salad and sandwich could he make?

A. 6 combinations
B. 5 combinations
C. 3 combinations
D. 2 combinations

Use the spinner for problems 38–39.

38. Describe the probability of spinning a 1.

F. certain **H.** likely
G. impossible **J.** unlikely

39. What is the probability of spinning a 4?

A. $\frac{1}{3}$ **B.** $\frac{1}{4}$ **C.** $\frac{1}{5}$ **D.** $\frac{1}{8}$

40. A class of 24 students voted on their favorite school lunch. One fourth of the students voted for tacos. How many students voted for tacos?

F. 8 students
G. 6 students
H. 4 students
J. 3 students

STOP

Name ______________________________

Read each question carefully. Fill in the correct answer in the space provided.

1. What part is shaded?

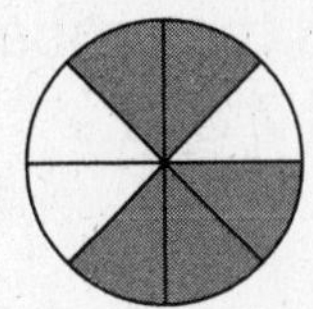

______

2. Which has the greatest value?

$\frac{3}{24}$ $\frac{1}{8}$ $\frac{4}{5}$ $\frac{3}{15}$

______

3. What is the number of possible outcomes when you are rolling a single number cube?

______

4. What part is shaded?

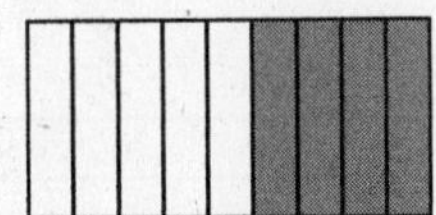

______

5. Order from least to greatest.

$\frac{4}{12}$ $\frac{2}{24}$ $\frac{1}{6}$

______

6. If you take one card without looking, how many possible outcomes are there?

______

7. What part is shaded?

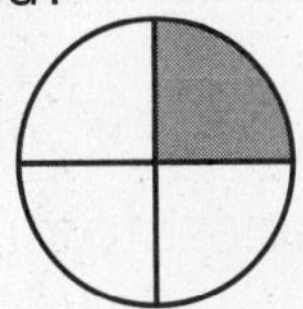

______

8. Order from greatest to least.

$\frac{1}{5}$ $\frac{3}{12}$ $\frac{1}{2}$

______

9. What is the probability of spinning an A?

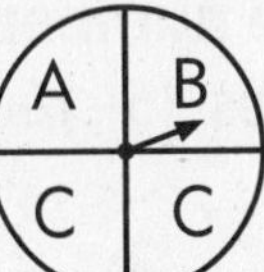

______

10. What part is shaded?

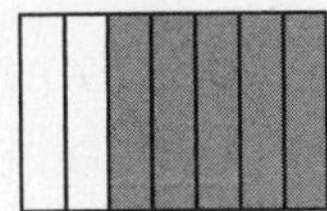

______

GO ON

Name ____________________

UNIT 11 TEST
FORM B
PAGE 2

11. Write $\frac{8}{32}$ in simplest form.

______

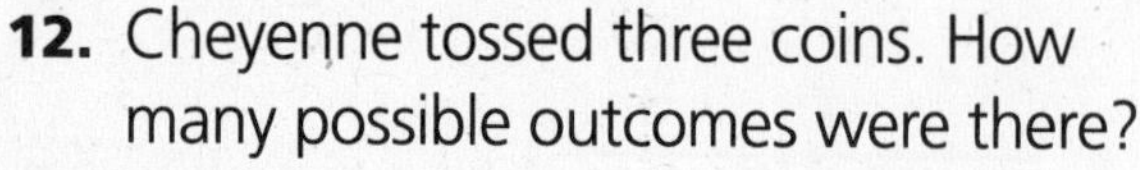

12. Cheyenne tossed three coins. How many possible outcomes were there?

______

13. Rename $\frac{25}{3}$ as a fraction in simplest form.

______

14. Write $\frac{35}{40}$ in simplest form.

______

Use the numbered buttons for exercises 15–16.

15. If you pick one button without looking, what is the probability of picking button 4?

______

16. If you pick one button without looking, what is the probability of picking buttons 2 or 5.

______

17. A group of 42 students went to the playground for recess. During recess, $\frac{1}{3}$ of the students played tag. How many students played tag?

______

Use the cards for problems 18–19.

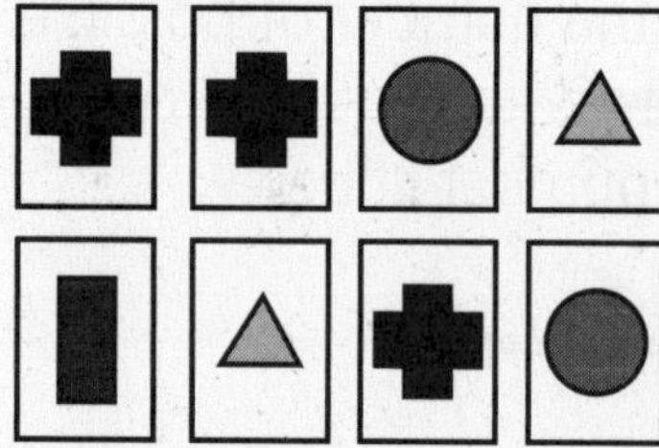

18. Is the probability of picking a heart certain, likely, or impossible?

______

19. What is the probability of picking a cross?

______

20. Mr. Tower has a choice of 3 shirts and 4 ties in his closet. How many possible combinations can he make?

______

GO ON

21. What part is shaded?

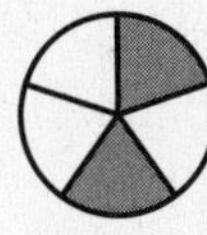

______

22. Which has the least value?

$\frac{3}{8}$ $\frac{2}{3}$ $\frac{3}{4}$ $\frac{4}{16}$

______

23. What is the number of possible outcomes when you toss two coins?

______

24. What part is shaded?

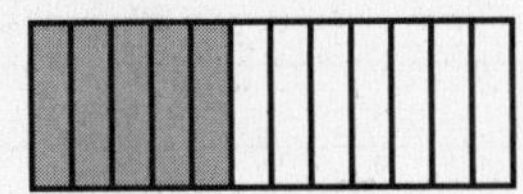

______

25. Order from greatest to least.

$\frac{6}{7}$ $\frac{6}{36}$ $\frac{8}{24}$

______

26. How many possible outcomes are there?

______

27. What part is shaded?

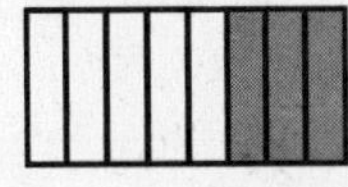

______

28. Order from least to greatest.

$\frac{3}{5}$ $\frac{1}{2}$ $\frac{7}{8}$

______

29. What is the probability of picking a card with a heart?

______

30. What part is shaded?

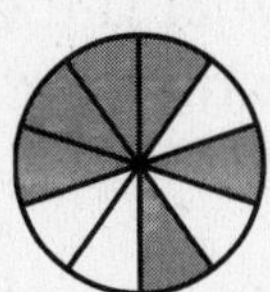

______

GO ON

Name ____________________

UNIT 11 TEST
FORM B
PAGE 4

31. Write $\frac{12}{40}$ in simplest form.

____

32. Lupe tossed a coin and then rolled a number cube. How many possible outcomes are there?

____

33. Rename $\frac{30}{7}$ as a mixed number.

____

34. Write $\frac{24}{40}$ in simplest form.

____

Use the spinner for exercises 35–36.

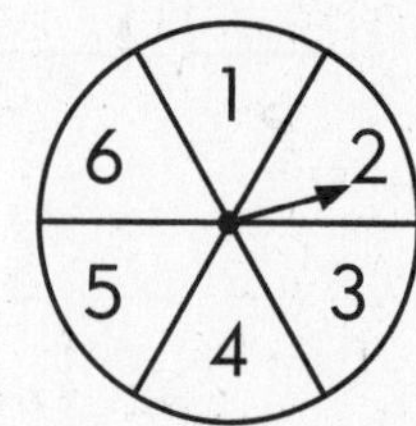

35. What is the probability of spinning a 2?

____

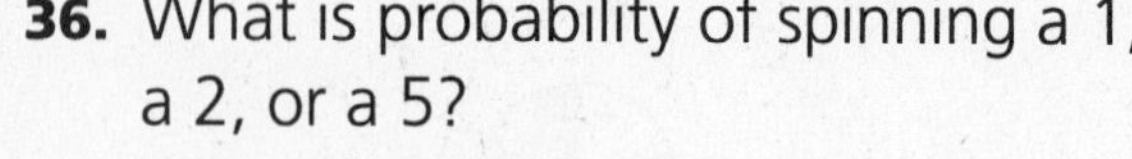

36. What is probability of spinning a 1, a 2, or a 5?

____

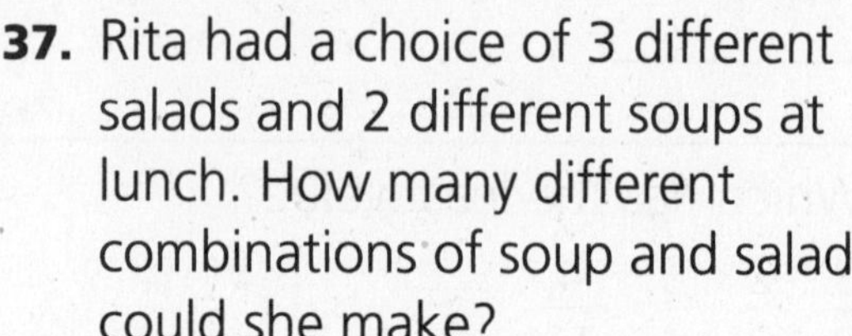

37. Rita had a choice of 3 different salads and 2 different soups at lunch. How many different combinations of soup and salad could she make?

____

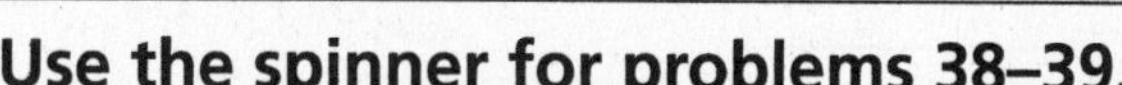

Use the spinner for problems 38–39.

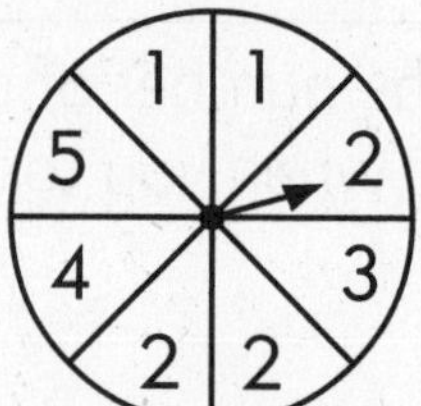

38. Is the probability of spinning a 2 certain, likely, or impossible?

____

39. What is the probability of spinning a 1?

____

40. A group of 32 teachers voted on their favorite color of pen. Of the teachers, $\frac{1}{4}$ voted for red. How many teachers voted for red?

____

STOP

Chapter 23 – Teacher Interview

Core Concept: *Add Fractions*

Student Activity: Students demonstrate an understanding of adding fractions with like and unlike denominators such as $\frac{2}{5} + \frac{1}{2}$.

Teacher Question 1:

- How do you find the sum of two fractions with like denominators?

Understanding Student Response	Practice and Improvement
Students say add the numerators and the denominators.	Review lesson 1 to help students understand that to add fractions it is only necessary to add the numerators.

Teacher Question 2:

- What equivalent fractions are needed to add $\frac{2}{5} + \frac{1}{2}$?

Understanding Student Response	Practice and Improvement
Students do not have a denominator of 10.	Review lesson 3 to help students use common denominators in order to add fractions with unlike denominators.
Students have a denominator of 10, but do not have $\frac{4}{10} + \frac{5}{10}$.	Review lesson 3 to help students learn how to write equivalent fractions when adding.

Teacher Question 3:

- What is the sum of $\frac{2}{5} + \frac{1}{2}$?

Understanding Student Response	Practice and Improvement
Students say $\frac{3}{7}$.	Review lesson 3 to help students use common denominators in order to add fractions with unlike denominators.
Students give an answer other than $\frac{9}{10}$.	Review lessons 2 and 3 to help students understand the process of adding fractions with unlike denominators.

Chapter 23 – Journal Writing

Encourage students to generate their own journal entries related to math ideas in general or to concepts in this chapter. For students requiring guidance, present the following journal prompt:

- When you add fractions to solve a word problem, what are the different ways you might need to interpret an answer that is a mixed number?

  (Responses should include the idea that a mixed number answer in a word problem can be part of the answer ($1\frac{1}{2}$ cups of flour in a recipe) or not part of the answer ($1\frac{1}{2}$ people per car).

JOURNAL WRITING/PROBLEM SOLVING

Alberto spends $\frac{3}{4}$ hour on his science project, $1\frac{1}{2}$ hours on his English essay, and $1\frac{1}{3}$ hours on his math problems. How much time has he spent doing homework?

Read

Have students find the answer to the problem. Then ask them to write a few sentences telling—

- how they found the common denominator
- how they wrote the answer in simplest form

Have students make up another problem with different information for which they would have to follow the same procedure. Then have students solve the problem and supply the correct response.

Plan

Students must know how to find a common denominator, how to get equivalent fractions, and how to properly add fractions. They must also know how to convert an improper fraction to a mixed number.

Solve

The correct response to the assigned problem is $3\frac{7}{12}$ hours (3:35). Students had to find the common denominator of 12, compute the equivalent fractions, add, and convert the improper fraction to simplest form of hours and fraction of an hour (or minutes).

Look Back

A successful answer demonstrates an ability to find common denominators, find equivalent fractions, and add fractions. It also shows facility with converting improper fractions to simplest form. (See scoring rubric on page 7.)

Chapter 23 – Monitoring Student Progress

☐ **Form A** ☐ **Form B**

Name ______________________________ Date __________________

Directions: For each item that is answered incorrectly, cross out the item number. Then record the number of correct responses in the appropriate Student Score column. If the student has not met the Criterion Score for an objective, circle the student's score. Recommended assignments are listed in the Prescription Table on the next page.

Objective	Item Numbers	Criterion Score	Student Score
A. Add fractions with like denominators.	1, 5, 9, 13, 14, 15	5/6	/6
B. Add fractions with unlike denominators.	2, 3, 4, 6, 7, 8, 10, 11 12, 16	9/10	/10
C. Use skills and strategies to solve problems.	17, 18, 19, 20	3/4	/4
Total Test Score		17/20	/20
Total Percent Correct			%

Chapter 23 – Prescription Table

The following chart correlates the tested objectives for this chapter to supplementary materials that meet the individual needs of the students. The Reteach and Practice pages are designed for students who need further instruction in the math concepts taught in this chapter. The Enrich pages are designed for students who need advanced challenges.

Objective	Reteach	Practice	Enrich
A. Add fractions with like denominators.	402	403	404
B. Add fractions with unlike denominators.	405, 408	406, 409	407, 410
C. Use skills and strategies to solve problems.	411	412	413

Name ____________________

CHAPTER 23 TEST
FORM A
PAGE 1

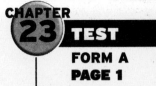

Read each question carefully. Darken the circle on your answer sheet for the correct answer. Put all answers in simplest form.

1. $\begin{array}{r} \frac{5}{9} \\ + \frac{3}{9} \\ \hline \end{array}$

A. $\frac{2}{9}$ **B.** $\frac{4}{9}$ **C.** $\frac{7}{9}$ **D.** $\frac{8}{9}$

2. $\frac{3}{8} + \frac{1}{4} = \blacksquare$

F. $\frac{1}{8}$ **G.** $\frac{2}{8}$ **H.** $\frac{1}{3}$ **J.** $\frac{5}{8}$

3. $\frac{3}{4} + \frac{7}{8} = \blacksquare$

A. $\frac{5}{6}$ **B.** $\frac{7}{8}$ **C.** $1\frac{3}{8}$ **D.** $1\frac{5}{8}$

4. $\frac{5}{7} + \frac{3}{7} + \frac{1}{5} = \blacksquare$

F. $1\frac{12}{35}$ **H.** $1\frac{13}{35}$

G. $1\frac{1}{3}$ **J.** $\frac{9}{19}$

5. $\frac{6}{7} + \frac{5}{7} = \blacksquare$

A. $1\frac{4}{7}$ **C.** $\frac{11}{14}$

B. $1\frac{4}{11}$ **D.** $\frac{7}{11}$

6. $\begin{array}{r} \frac{5}{6} \\ + \frac{3}{4} \\ \hline \end{array}$

F. $\frac{3}{4}$ **G.** $\frac{13}{16}$ **H.** $1\frac{7}{12}$ **J.** $\frac{4}{5}$

7. $\frac{2}{5} + \frac{8}{15} = \blacksquare$

A. $\frac{13}{15}$ **B.** $\frac{14}{15}$ **C.** 1 **D.** $1\frac{1}{15}$

8. $\frac{7}{8} + (\frac{3}{8} + \frac{3}{4}) = \blacksquare$

F. $1\frac{3}{8}$ **G.** $1\frac{3}{4}$ **H.** $1\frac{7}{8}$ **J.** 2

9. $\begin{array}{r} \frac{11}{24} \\ + \frac{7}{24} \\ \hline \end{array}$

A. $\frac{2}{3}$ **B.** $\frac{3}{8}$ **C.** $\frac{3}{4}$ **D.** $\frac{5}{6}$

10. $\begin{array}{r} \frac{1}{3} \\ + \frac{7}{9} \\ \hline \end{array}$

F. $1\frac{1}{9}$ **H.** $\frac{10}{12}$

G. $\frac{11}{9}$ **J.** $\frac{4}{9}$

GO ON

Name ______________________________

11. $\frac{1}{12} + \frac{5}{6} = \blacksquare$

A. $\frac{5}{6}$ **B.** $\frac{11}{12}$ **C.** 1 **D.** $1\frac{1}{12}$

---

12. $\frac{2}{5} + \frac{4}{5} + \frac{1}{8} = \blacksquare$

F. $1\frac{13}{40}$ **G.** $1\frac{3}{10}$ **H.** $1\frac{1}{4}$ **J.** $1\frac{3}{20}$

---

13. $\begin{array}{r} \frac{11}{15} \\ + \frac{8}{15} \\ \hline \end{array}$

A. $\frac{19}{30}$ **B.** $1\frac{4}{15}$ **C.** $1\frac{1}{5}$ **D.** $1\frac{1}{3}$

---

14. $\frac{4}{5} + \frac{4}{5} = \blacksquare$

F. $\frac{4}{5}$ **G.** $1\frac{3}{10}$ **H.** $\frac{12}{15}$ **J.** $1\frac{3}{5}$

---

15. $\frac{11}{16} + \frac{7}{16} = \blacksquare$

A. $\frac{1}{4}$ **B.** $\frac{9}{16}$ **C.** $1\frac{1}{8}$ **D.** $1\frac{1}{2}$

---

16. $\frac{5}{8} + \frac{2}{3} = \blacksquare$

F. $1\frac{1}{4}$ **G.** $1\frac{7}{24}$ **H.** $1\frac{1}{3}$ **J.** $\frac{7}{8}$

---

17. Gina ate $\frac{1}{4}$ of a sandwich and Brianna ate $\frac{2}{3}$ of the sandwich. How much of the sandwich did the girls eat?

A. $\frac{11}{12}$ sandwich **C.** $\frac{3}{7}$ sandwich

B. $\frac{5}{6}$ sandwich **D.** 1 sandwich

18. One fillet of fish weighs $\frac{2}{3}$ of a pound. Another fillet weighs $\frac{3}{4}$ pound. How many pounds do the fillets weigh in all?

F. $\frac{5}{7}$ pound **H.** $1\frac{1}{4}$ pounds

G. $1\frac{1}{8}$ pounds **J.** $1\frac{5}{12}$ pounds

---

19. A recipe calls for $\frac{7}{8}$ cup of white sugar and $\frac{1}{4}$ cup of brown sugar. How many cups of sugar are in the recipe?

A. $1\frac{7}{8}$ cups **C.** $1\frac{1}{4}$ cups

B. $1\frac{1}{8}$ cups **D.** $\frac{2}{3}$ cup

---

20. Alberto ate $\frac{1}{8}$ of the chocolates in a box. Katlyn ate $\frac{1}{3}$ of the chocolates in a box. How much of the chocolate in the box did they eat?

F. $\frac{2}{11}$ box **H.** $\frac{1}{2}$ box

G. $\frac{5}{12}$ box **J.** $\frac{11}{24}$ box

STOP

Name ____

CHAPTER 23 TEST
FORM B
PAGE 1

Read each question carefully. Fill in the correct answer in the space provided. Put all answers in simplest form.

1. $\begin{array}{r} \frac{2}{7} \\ + \frac{4}{7} \\ \hline \end{array}$

---

2. $\frac{5}{6} + \frac{1}{3} =$ ________

---

3. $\frac{2}{3} + \frac{5}{9} =$ ________

---

4. $\frac{1}{4} + \frac{4}{5} + \frac{3}{4} =$ ________

---

5. $\frac{8}{15} + \frac{4}{15} =$ ________

6. $\begin{array}{r} \frac{9}{10} \\ + \frac{4}{5} \\ \hline \end{array}$

---

7. $\frac{3}{4} + \frac{1}{5} =$ ________

---

8. $\frac{5}{12} + \frac{17}{20} + \frac{7}{12} =$ ________

---

9. $\begin{array}{r} \frac{15}{18} \\ + \frac{2}{18} \\ \hline \end{array}$

---

10. $\frac{1}{5} + \frac{3}{20} =$ ________

GO ON

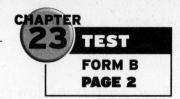

11. $\frac{3}{5} + \frac{8}{9} =$ ________

12. $\frac{4}{15} + \frac{2}{5} + \frac{3}{10} =$ ________

13. $\frac{9}{20}$
$+ \frac{6}{20}$

14. $\frac{1}{4} + \frac{2}{4} =$ ________

15. $\frac{7}{15} + \frac{4}{15} =$ ________

16. $\frac{9}{10} + \frac{7}{20} =$ ________

17. Alex ate $\frac{3}{8}$ of a candy bar and Julie ate $\frac{1}{2}$ of the candy bar. How much of the candy bar did the girls eat?

____

18. One apple weighs $\frac{1}{5}$ of a pound. Another apple weighs $\frac{3}{10}$ of a pound. How much do they weigh all together?

____

19. A recipe calls for $\frac{11}{16}$ cup of corn flour and $\frac{3}{4}$ cup of wheat flour. How many cups of flour are in the recipe?

____

20. Sarah ate $\frac{1}{3}$ of the cookies in a box. Penelope ate $\frac{1}{4}$ of the cookies in the box. How much of the box did they eat in all?

____

STOP

Chapter 24 – Teacher Interview

Core Concept: *Subtracting Fractions*

Student Activity: Students demonstrate an understanding of fraction operations by subtracting fractions with unlike denominators such as $\frac{7}{8} - \frac{5}{6}$.

Teacher Question 1:

- What is the denominator of the difference?

Understanding Student Response	Practice and Improvement
Students who answer 2, 6, or 8.	Review lesson 3 to help students understand how to subtract fractions with unlike denominators.

Teacher Question 2:

- What is the numerator of the difference?

Understanding Student Response	Practice and Improvement
Students who answer 2 or more.	Review lesson 3 to help students understand how to subtract fractions with unlike denominators.

Teacher Question 3:

- Is the difference expressed in simplest terms?

Understanding Student Response	Practice and Improvement
Students who say no.	Review Chapter 21 lesson 3 to help students review how to express a difference in simplest terms.

Chapter 24 – Journal Writing

Encourage students to generate their own journal entries related to math ideas in general or to concepts in this chapter. For students requiring guidance, present the following journal prompt:

- Is the difference of two fractions always a fraction?

  (Responses should indicate that while the answer can always be in fractional form, at times the answer in simplest form is a whole number.)

JOURNAL WRITING/PROBLEM SOLVING

Alain is planning to split the reading of his summer reading list over June, July, and August. If he reads $\frac{1}{4}$ of the list in June and $\frac{3}{8}$ in July, how much more must he read in August?

Read

Have students find the answer to the problem. Then ask them to write a few sentences telling—

- how they found the common denominator
- how they know their answer is in simplest form

Have students make up another problem with different information for which they would have to follow the same procedure. Then have students solve the problem and supply the correct response.

Plan

Students must know how to find the common denominator, compute equivalent fractions, subtract like fractions, and make sure the answer is in simplest form.

Solve

The correct response to the assigned problem is $\frac{3}{8}$ of the list. Students must find the common denominator of 8, compute the equivalent fractions, subtract, and recognize that the answer is already in simplest form, as the greatest common factor of 3 and 8 is 1.

Look Back

A correct response demonstrates that students can find the common denominator, compute equivalent fractions, subtract like fractions, and recognize greatest common factors. (See scoring rubric on page 7.)

Chapter 24 – Monitoring Student Progress

☐ **Form A** ☐ **Form B**

Name ______________________________ Date ____________________

Directions: For each item that is answered incorrectly, cross out the item number. Then record the number of correct responses in the appropriate Student Score column. If the student has not met the Criterion Score for an objective, circle the student's score. Recommended assignments are listed in the Prescription Table on the next page.

Objective	Item Numbers	Criterion Score	Student Score
A. Subtract fractions with like denominators.	1, 2, 3, 7, 9, 10, 11	6/7	/7
B. Subtract fractions with unlike denominators.	4, 5, 6, 8, 12	4/5	/5
C. Read and make circle graphs.	13, 14, 15, 16	3/4	/4
D. Use skills and strategies to solve problems.	17, 18, 19, 20	3/4	/4
Total Test Score		16/20	/20
Total Percent Correct			%

Chapter 24 – Prescription Table

The following chart correlates the tested objectives for this chapter to supplementary materials that meet the individual needs of the students. The Reteach and Practice pages are designed for students who need further instruction in the math concepts taught in this chapter. The Enrich pages are designed for students who need advanced challenges.

Objective	Reteach	Practice	Enrich
A. Subtract fractions with like denominators.	414	415	416
B. Subtract fractions with unlike denominators.	417, 420	418, 421	419, 422
C. Read and make circle graphs.	426	427	428
D. Use skills and strategies to solve problems.	423, 424	425	

Name ____________________

Read each question carefully. Darken the circle on your answer sheet for the correct answer. Put all answers in simplest form.

1. $\frac{7}{9} - \frac{2}{9} = \blacksquare$

A. $\frac{2}{9}$ **B.** $\frac{5}{9}$ **C.** $\frac{7}{9}$ **D.** 1

2. $\frac{7}{10} - \frac{3}{5}$

F. $\frac{1}{5}$ **G.** $\frac{4}{5}$ **H.** $\frac{1}{10}$ **J.** $\frac{4}{10}$

3. $\frac{5}{6} - \frac{1}{6} = \blacksquare$

A. $\frac{2}{3}$ **B.** $\frac{1}{2}$ **C.** $\frac{1}{3}$ **D.** $\frac{1}{6}$

4. $\frac{4}{5} - \frac{7}{15}$

F. $\frac{5}{7}$ **G.** $\frac{5}{12}$ **H.** $\frac{1}{3}$ **J.** $\frac{1}{5}$

5. $\frac{8}{9} - \frac{2}{3} = \blacksquare$

A. $\frac{2}{3}$ **B.** $\frac{4}{9}$ **C.** $\frac{1}{3}$ **D.** $\frac{2}{9}$

6. $\frac{19}{20} - \frac{9}{10} = \blacksquare$

F. $\frac{1}{20}$ **G.** $\frac{1}{10}$ **H.** $\frac{1}{2}$ **J.** 1

7. $\frac{8}{12} - \frac{5}{12}$

A. $1\frac{1}{12}$ **B.** $\frac{3}{5}$ **C.** $\frac{1}{8}$ **D.** $\frac{1}{4}$

8. $\frac{3}{4} - \frac{5}{8} = \blacksquare$

F. $\frac{1}{2}$ **G.** $\frac{1}{8}$ **H.** $\frac{1}{4}$ **J.** 1

9. $\frac{14}{15} - \frac{5}{15} = \blacksquare$

A. $\frac{3}{5}$ **B.** $\frac{4}{5}$ **C.** $\frac{2}{3}$ **D.** $\frac{11}{15}$

10. $\frac{3}{4} - \blacksquare = \frac{3}{4}$

F. 1 **G.** $\frac{3}{4}$ **H.** $\frac{3}{8}$ **J.** 0

GO ON

11. $\frac{7}{9} - \square = 0$

A. $\frac{1}{3}$ B. $\frac{1}{9}$ C. $\frac{4}{9}$ D. $\frac{7}{9}$

12. $\frac{14}{20} - \frac{3}{5} = \square$

F. $\frac{1}{20}$ G. $\frac{1}{10}$ H. $\frac{1}{5}$ J. $\frac{11}{20}$

For Problems 13–16, use the circle graph below. The graph shows the results of a poll of 50 students who were asked what their favorite color was.

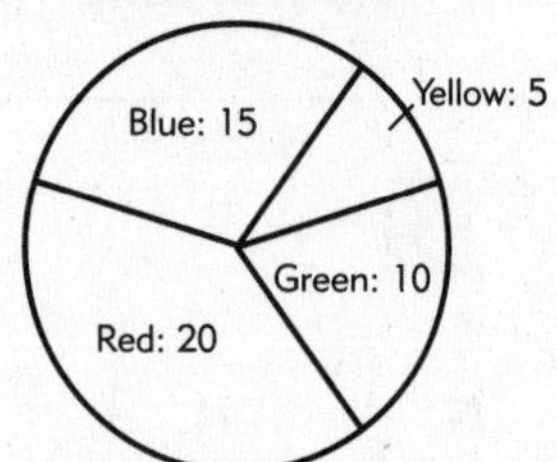

13. What fraction of the students polled choose red as their favorite color?

A. $\frac{1}{5}$ B. $\frac{2}{5}$ C. $\frac{1}{2}$ D. $\frac{1}{3}$

14. What fraction of the students polled choose green as their favorite color?

F. $\frac{1}{15}$ G. $\frac{1}{5}$ H. $\frac{1}{4}$ J. $\frac{1}{3}$

15. How many more students choose red than yellow? What is the fraction of the students polled?

A. $\frac{7}{20}$ B. $\frac{3}{10}$ C. $\frac{2}{15}$ D. $\frac{1}{10}$

16. What fraction of the total students did not choose blue?

F. $\frac{3}{10}$ G. $\frac{3}{5}$ H. $\frac{7}{10}$ J. $\frac{4}{5}$

17. Eric drank $\frac{3}{8}$ pint of juice. Mary drank $\frac{1}{4}$ pint of juice. How much more juice did Eric drink?

A. $\frac{1}{4}$ pint C. $\frac{1}{6}$ pint

B. $\frac{1}{8}$ pint D. $\frac{1}{12}$ pint

18. Penny had $\frac{3}{4}$ of a stick of butter. She used $\frac{1}{2}$ of the butter for a cookie recipe. How much of a stick of butter was left?

F. $\frac{1}{4}$ stick H. $\frac{1}{12}$ stick

G. $\frac{1}{2}$ stick J. $\frac{8}{12}$ stick

19. Lars drank $\frac{1}{8}$ of a quart of milk. David drank $\frac{1}{4}$ of the quart of milk. How much more did David drink than Lars?

A. $\frac{1}{8}$ quart C. $\frac{1}{6}$ quart

B. $\frac{1}{4}$ quart D. $\frac{3}{8}$ quart

20. Orin made $\frac{3}{4}$ cup of raspberry sauce. He used $\frac{1}{8}$ cup for a layer in a chocolate cake and the rest for the cake topping. How many cups of sauce did he use for the topping?

F. $\frac{3}{8}$ cup H. $\frac{5}{8}$ cup

G. $\frac{7}{8}$ cup J. $\frac{5}{4}$ cup

STOP

Name ____________________

CHAPTER 24 TEST
FORM B
PAGE 1

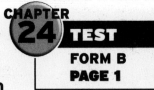

Read each question carefully. Fill in the correct answer in the space provided. Put all answers in simplest form.

1. $\frac{11}{20} - \frac{7}{20}$

2. $\frac{3}{4} - \frac{5}{12}$

3. $\frac{8}{11} - \frac{3}{11} =$ ________

4. $\frac{1}{2} - \frac{3}{8}$

5. $\frac{4}{5} - \frac{2}{15} =$ ________

6. $\frac{3}{4} - \frac{1}{8} =$ ________

7. $\frac{11}{12} - \frac{7}{12}$

8. $\frac{8}{15} - \frac{1}{5} =$ ________

9. $\frac{13}{20} - \frac{9}{20} =$ ________

10. $\frac{5}{6} -$ ________ $= \frac{5}{6}$

11. $\frac{1}{3} -$ ________ $= 0$

12. $\frac{9}{10} - \frac{1}{5} =$ ________

GO ON

Name ____________________

For problems 13–16, use the circle graph below. The graph shows the results of a poll of 48 students who were asked what their favorite sport was.

Favorite Sports

Track: 8
Soccer: 8
Baseball: 4
Basketball: 16
Volleyball: 12

13. What fraction of the students polled choose volleyball as their favorite sport?

____

14. What fraction of the students polled choose soccer as their favorite sport?

____

15. How many more students choose basketball than baseball? What fraction of the students polled is this?

____

16. What fraction of the total students did not choose soccer?

____

17. Elliot drank $\frac{9}{16}$ cup of juice. Laura drank $\frac{3}{8}$ cup of juice. How much more did Elliot drink?

____

18. Roger had $\frac{7}{8}$ of a tube of paint. He used $\frac{5}{6}$ of the tube for a painting. How much of the tube of paint was left?

____

19. Daryl drank $\frac{3}{16}$ of a pint of apple juice. Tessa drank $\frac{5}{8}$ of the pint of apple juice. How many more pints did Tessa drink than Daryl?

____

20. Billy mixed paints together to make $\frac{3}{5}$ of a gallon of green paint. He used $\frac{1}{4}$ of the gallon for one wall and the rest for the ceiling. How many gallons of paint did he use for the ceiling?

____

STOP

Unit 12 Performance Assessment

Shrimp and Vegetables

- ***Target Skill:*** Add fractions with like and unlike denominators.
- ***Additional Skills:*** Subtract fractions with like and unlike denominators.

Task Description: This task requires students to answer questions about the ingredients involving fractions in a shrimp and vegetable dish. The students will be asked to double all of the ingredients, as well as add and subtract fractions.

Preparing: You may wish to have students write about times when their family has needed to make more than the amount given in a recipe. Have them discuss what they would do to make sure a larger amount of the recipe would taste the same.

Materials	Group Size	Time on Task
Pencil Paper	2 to 3 students	1 day

Guiding: Tell students that they should find common denominators for those problems with unlike denominators.

Observing/ Monitoring: As you move among the students, pose the following questions:

How do you add and subtract fractions with like denominators?

How do you add and subtract fractions with unlike denominators?

How do you double a recipe?

Unit 12 Performance Assessment Scoring Rubric

Shrimp and Vegetables

Score	Explanation
3	Students demonstrate an efficient strategy and a thorough approach that enables them to solve the problem completely. A satisfactory answer: • adds and subtracts to find the amount of teaspoons; • correctly doubles each of the ingredients and writes the sums in simplest form; • shows all work. Students are able to complete the problem quickly and have all of the correct solutions.
2	Students demonstrate a strategy that enables them to solve most of the problem correctly. The strategy is somewhat disorganized, making it less efficient. A solution is found, but errors are contained. Students may: • add and subtract properly; • double most of the ingredients correctly. Students may have some difficulty determining all solutions correctly, but demonstrate an understanding of general concepts.
1	Students demonstrate a confused strategy, which leads to difficulty solving the problem. Most answers are incorrect, but students demonstrate knowledge of at least one concept being assessed, such as adding or subtracting fractions.

Name ______________________________

Unit 12 Performance Assessment Student Activity

Shrimp and Vegetables

You will need

- Pencil
- Paper

You are having 7 friends over for dinner. You have a recipe for shrimp and vegetables that feeds 4. The following are some of the ingredients that are needed:

Ingredient	Amount (in teaspoons)
Sugar	$\frac{1}{4}$
Minced fresh ginger	$\frac{1}{2}$
Pepper	$\frac{1}{8}$
Salt	$\frac{3}{8}$

1. How many more teaspoons of sugar are there than pepper? Show your work.

____

2. How many teaspoons of salt and pepper are needed to make the recipe for 4 people? Show your work.

____

3. How many more teaspoons of minced fresh ginger are there than salt? Show your work.

____

4. To make the dish for 8, you have to double the recipe. How many teaspoons of each ingredient do you need? Show your work.

____

Unit 12 – Monitoring Student Progress

☐ Form A ☐ Form B

Name ______________________ Date ____________

Directions: This test targets selected objectives. For each item that is answered incorrectly, cross out the item number. Then record the number of correct responses in the column labeled **Number of Correct Responses.** Add to find the **Total Number of Correct Responses** and record the total. Use this total to determine the **Total Test Score** and the **Total Percent Correct.**

Strand • Objective(s)	Item Numbers	Number of Correct Responses
Number Sense, Concepts, and Operations • Add fractions with like and unlike denominators. • Subtract fractions with like and unlike denominators. • Use skills and strategies to solve problems.	1, 2, 3, 4, 5, 6, 7, 8, 9, 10, 11, 12, 13, 14, 15, 16, 17, 18, 19, 20, 21, 22, 23, 24, 25, 26, 27, 31, 32, 33, 34, 35, 36, 37, 38, 39, 40	/37
Data Analysis and Probability • Read and make circle graphs.	28, 29, 30	/3
Total Number of Correct Responses		
Total Test Score		/40
Total Percent Correct		%

Name ______________________________

TEST
FORM A
PAGE 1

Read each question carefully. Darken the circle on your answer sheet for the correct answer.

1. $\begin{array}{r} \frac{2}{7} \\ + \frac{3}{7} \\ \hline \end{array}$

A. $\frac{6}{7}$ **B.** $\frac{5}{7}$ **C.** $\frac{4}{7}$ **D.** $\frac{5}{14}$

2. $\frac{10}{12} - \frac{6}{12} = \blacksquare$

F. $1\frac{1}{4}$ **H.** $\frac{1}{6}$

G. $\frac{1}{3}$ **J.** $\frac{1}{8}$

3. $\frac{4}{5} - \frac{2}{5} = \blacksquare$

A. $\frac{2}{10}$ **B.** $\frac{2}{5}$ **C.** $\frac{6}{10}$ **D.** $\frac{6}{5}$

4. $\begin{array}{r} \frac{4}{9} \\ + \frac{2}{3} \\ \hline \end{array}$

F. $1\frac{5}{9}$ **G.** $1\frac{1}{9}$ **H.** $\frac{2}{3}$ **J.** $\frac{1}{2}$

5. $\begin{array}{r} \frac{5}{7} \\ - \frac{1}{2} \\ \hline \end{array}$

A. $\frac{13}{14}$ **B.** $\frac{4}{5}$ **C.** $\frac{4}{14}$ **D.** $\frac{3}{14}$

6. $\frac{3}{8} + \frac{5}{6} = \blacksquare$

F. $\frac{1}{3}$ **G.** $\frac{8}{14}$ **H.** 1 **J.** $1\frac{5}{24}$

7. $\begin{array}{r} \frac{3}{4} \\ + \frac{2}{4} \\ \hline \end{array}$

A. $1\frac{1}{2}$ **B.** $1\frac{1}{4}$ **C.** 1 **D.** $\frac{5}{8}$

8. $\begin{array}{r} \frac{4}{5} \\ - \frac{3}{10} \\ \hline \end{array}$

F. $1\frac{4}{5}$ **G.** $\frac{1}{2}$ **H.** $\frac{1}{5}$ **J.** $\frac{1}{10}$

9. $\frac{5}{8} + \frac{3}{8} = \blacksquare$

A. $\frac{1}{8}$ **B.** $\frac{1}{4}$ **C.** $\frac{1}{2}$ **D.** 1

10. $\frac{7}{11} + \frac{8}{11} = \blacksquare$

F. $1\frac{4}{11}$ **G.** $1\frac{3}{11}$ **H.** $\frac{11}{15}$ **J.** $\frac{15}{22}$

GO ON

Name ______________________________

11. $\frac{7}{8} - \frac{1}{4} = \blacksquare$

A. $1\frac{1}{2}$ **B.** $1\frac{1}{8}$ **C.** $\frac{3}{4}$ **D.** $\frac{5}{8}$

---

12. $\frac{5}{8} - \frac{3}{8} = \blacksquare$

F. $\frac{1}{8}$ **G.** $\frac{1}{4}$ **H.** $\frac{1}{2}$ **J.** 1

---

13. $\frac{2}{3} + \frac{5}{6}$

A. $1\frac{1}{2}$ **B.** $1\frac{1}{3}$ **C.** $\frac{7}{9}$ **D.** $\frac{3}{4}$

---

14. $\frac{8}{9} - \frac{1}{9} = \blacksquare$

F. $1\frac{1}{9}$ **G.** 1 **H.** $\frac{7}{9}$ **J.** $\frac{2}{3}$

---

15. $\frac{3}{5} + \frac{1}{2} = \blacksquare$

A. $1\frac{1}{10}$ **B.** $\frac{4}{7}$ **C.** $\frac{11}{20}$ **D.** $\frac{2}{5}$

---

16. $\frac{5}{6} - \frac{1}{2}$

F. $\frac{2}{3}$ **G.** $\frac{1}{2}$ **H.** $\frac{1}{3}$ **J.** $\frac{1}{6}$

---

17. Roberto ate $\frac{1}{3}$ of a pizza and Aaron ate $\frac{1}{4}$ of the pizza. How much of the pizza did the boys eat?

A. $\frac{3}{4}$ pizza **C.** $\frac{1}{2}$ pizza

B. $\frac{7}{12}$ pizza **D.** $\frac{2}{7}$ pizza

---

18. Marcie drank $\frac{3}{4}$ cup of juice. Yolanda drank $\frac{1}{2}$ cup of juice. How much more juice did Marcie drink?

F. $1\frac{1}{4}$ cups **H.** $\frac{1}{2}$ cup

G. $\frac{3}{4}$ cup **J.** $\frac{1}{4}$ cup

---

19. A recipe calls for $\frac{3}{4}$ cup of granulated sugar and $\frac{2}{3}$ cup of powdered sugar. How much sugar is in the recipe?

A. $1\frac{5}{12}$ cups **C.** $\frac{5}{12}$ cup

B. $\frac{5}{7}$ cup **D.** $\frac{1}{12}$ cup

---

20. Brandon had $\frac{1}{2}$ gallon of windshield washer fluid. He poured $\frac{1}{3}$ gallon into his car. How much was left?

F. $\frac{5}{6}$ gallon **H.** $\frac{1}{6}$ gallon

G. $\frac{1}{3}$ gallon **J.** $\frac{1}{8}$ gallon

GO ON

Name ____________________

UNIT 12 TEST FORM A PAGE 3

21. $\frac{9}{11} + \frac{9}{11}$

A. $1\frac{8}{11}$ C. $\frac{9}{11}$

B. $1\frac{7}{11}$ D. $\frac{1}{11}$

22. $\frac{4}{7} - \frac{1}{7} = \blacksquare$

F. $\frac{5}{7}$ G. $\frac{4}{7}$ H. $\frac{3}{7}$ J. $\frac{2}{7}$

23. $\frac{7}{11} - \frac{5}{11} = \blacksquare$

A. $\frac{2}{11}$ B. $\frac{7}{11}$ C. $\frac{12}{22}$ D. $1\frac{1}{11}$

24. $\frac{5}{10} + \frac{3}{10}$

F. $1\frac{1}{2}$ G. 1 H. $\frac{4}{5}$ J. $\frac{2}{5}$

25. $\frac{7}{12} + \frac{2}{3}$

A. $3\frac{3}{4}$ B. $1\frac{3}{4}$ C. $1\frac{1}{2}$ D. $1\frac{1}{4}$

26. $\frac{1}{4} + \frac{2}{3} = \blacksquare$

F. $\frac{3}{7}$ H. $\frac{11}{12}$

G. $\frac{3}{4}$ J. $1\frac{1}{12}$

27. $\frac{5}{6} - \frac{1}{2}$

A. $1\frac{1}{3}$ B. 1 C. $\frac{1}{3}$ D. $\frac{1}{6}$

Use the circle graph for questions 28–30.

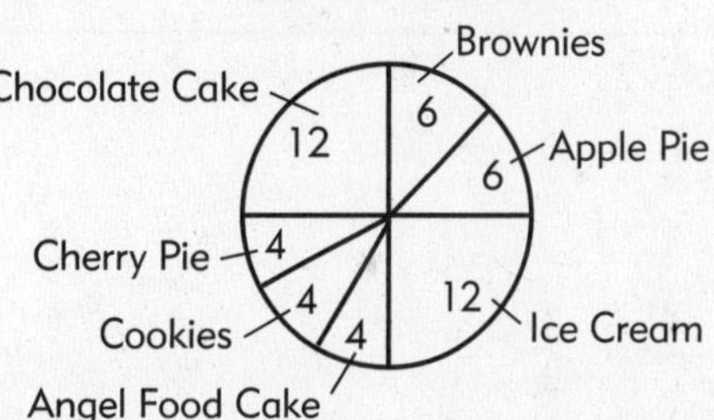

28. How many more people liked apple pie than cherry pie?

F. 0 G. 2 H. 4 J. 6

29. How many people liked ice cream or brownies?

A. 6 B. 12 C. 16 D. 18

30. How many people were surveyed?

F. 40 G. 44 H. 48 J. 32

Name ______________________________

31. $\frac{9}{10} - \frac{1}{3} = \blacksquare$

A. $1\frac{1}{7}$ **B.** $\frac{17}{30}$ **C.** $\frac{4}{15}$ **D.** $\frac{7}{30}$

32. $\frac{3}{7} + \frac{5}{14} = \blacksquare$

F. $\frac{3}{14}$ **G.** $\frac{4}{7}$ **H.** $\frac{11}{14}$ **J.** $1\frac{4}{7}$

33. $\frac{1}{2} + \frac{5}{8}$

A. $1\frac{3}{4}$ **B.** $1\frac{1}{4}$ **C.** $1\frac{1}{8}$ **D.** $\frac{3}{5}$

34. $\frac{7}{8} - \frac{1}{4}$

F. $1\frac{1}{12}$ **G.** $\frac{3}{4}$ **H.** $\frac{5}{8}$ **J.** $\frac{1}{2}$

35. $\frac{3}{4} + \frac{2}{9}$

A. $\frac{35}{36}$ **B.** $\frac{29}{36}$ **C.** $\frac{5}{13}$ **D.** $\frac{5}{36}$

36. $\frac{9}{11} - \frac{6}{11} = \blacksquare$

F. $1\frac{4}{11}$ **G.** $\frac{3}{11}$ **H.** $\frac{2}{11}$ **J.** $\frac{1}{11}$

37. Katie ate $\frac{1}{6}$ of a cheesecake and Lauren ate $\frac{1}{12}$ of the cake. How much did they eat in all?

A. $\frac{1}{3}$ **B.** $\frac{1}{4}$ **C.** $\frac{1}{6}$ **D.** $\frac{1}{9}$

38. Al made a mixture of $\frac{3}{4}$ cup of orange juice and $\frac{2}{3}$ cup of pineapple juice. How much more orange juice was there than pineapple juice?

F. $1\frac{5}{12}$ cups **H.** $\frac{1}{12}$ cup

G. $\frac{1}{3}$ cup **J.** $\frac{1}{6}$ cup

39. Tony used $\frac{7}{8}$ cup of chocolate chips and $\frac{3}{4}$ cup of butterscotch chips. How many cups of chips did he use altogether?

A. $1\frac{5}{8}$ cups **C.** $\frac{1}{2}$ cup

B. $1\frac{1}{8}$ cups **D.** $\frac{1}{8}$ cup

40. Meghan had $\frac{1}{2}$ cup of taco sauce. She used $\frac{1}{4}$ cup for the taco filling and the rest for the topping. How much sauce did she use for the topping?

F. $\frac{3}{4}$ cup **H.** $\frac{1}{4}$ cup

G. $\frac{3}{8}$ cup **J.** $\frac{1}{8}$ cup

STOP

Name ______________________

TEST
FORM B
PAGE 1

Read each question carefully. Fill in the correct answer in the space provided.

Write all fraction answers in *simplest form*.

1. $\begin{array}{r} \frac{3}{5} \\ + \frac{1}{5} \\ \hline \end{array}$

2. $\frac{4}{7} - \frac{1}{7} =$ ________

3. $\frac{7}{8} - \frac{1}{8} =$ ________

4. $\begin{array}{r} \frac{5}{9} \\ + \frac{2}{3} \\ \hline \end{array}$

5. $\begin{array}{r} \frac{4}{5} \\ - \frac{1}{2} \\ \hline \end{array}$

6. $\frac{3}{5} + \frac{1}{15} =$ ________

7. $\begin{array}{r} \frac{2}{3} \\ + \frac{2}{3} \\ \hline \end{array}$

8. $\begin{array}{r} \frac{5}{6} \\ - \frac{7}{12} \\ \hline \end{array}$

9. $\frac{2}{3} + \frac{4}{5} =$ ________

10. $\frac{4}{11} + \frac{10}{11} =$ ________

GO ON

Name ______________________________

11. $\frac{5}{9} - \frac{1}{3} =$ ________

12. $\frac{5}{6} - \frac{1}{6} =$ ________

13. $\begin{array}{r} \frac{7}{8} \\ + \frac{1}{4} \\ \hline \end{array}$

14. $\frac{5}{7} - \frac{1}{7} =$ ________

15. $\frac{5}{7} + \frac{1}{2} =$ ________

16. $\begin{array}{r} \frac{3}{4} \\ - \frac{1}{2} \\ \hline \end{array}$

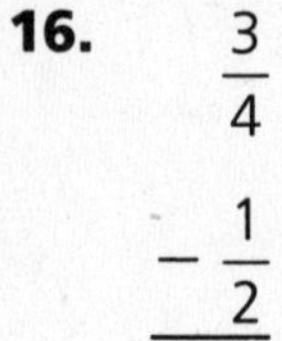

17. Jake ate $\frac{1}{4}$ of the pizza and Aaron ate $\frac{1}{2}$ of the pizza. How much of the pizza did the boys eat?

____

18. Peggy swam $\frac{5}{6}$ of a lap under water and Pete swam $\frac{1}{2}$ of a lap underwater. How much more did Peggy swim?

____

19. Lenora added $\frac{3}{4}$ cup of juice to a glass and $\frac{3}{4}$ cup water. How much liquid is in the glass?

____

20. Laurie had $\frac{1}{2}$ gallon of milk. She drank $\frac{1}{7}$ gallon today. How much does she have left?

____

Name ____________________

21. $\begin{array}{r} \frac{7}{12} \\ + \frac{7}{12} \\ \hline \end{array}$

22. $\frac{11}{15} - \frac{8}{15} =$ ________

23. $\frac{4}{7} - \frac{2}{7} =$ ________

24. $\begin{array}{r} \frac{3}{8} \\ + \frac{1}{8} \\ \hline \end{array}$

25. $\begin{array}{r} \frac{5}{12} \\ + \frac{2}{3} \\ \hline \end{array}$

26. $\frac{4}{9} + \frac{2}{3} =$ ________

27. $\begin{array}{r} \frac{2}{3} \\ - \frac{1}{2} \\ \hline \end{array}$

Use this circle graph for questions 28–30.

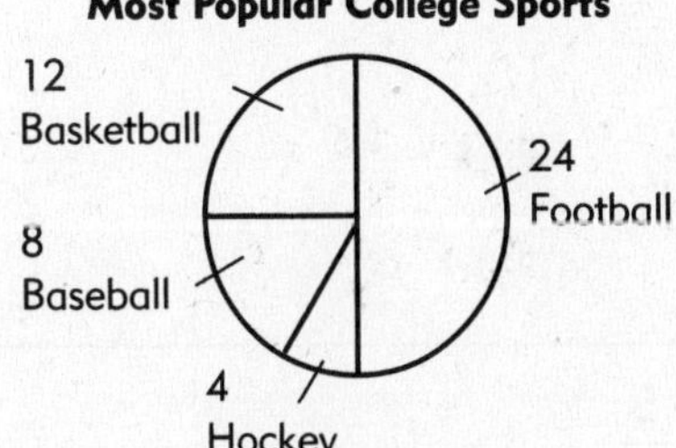

28. How many more people like basketball than hockey?

____

29. How many people like football or baseball?

____

30. How many people were surveyed?

____

GO ON

Name ____________________

UNIT 12 TEST
FORM B
PAGE 4

31. $\frac{7}{10} - \frac{1}{3} =$ ________

32. $\frac{7}{8} + \frac{1}{5} =$ ________

33. $\begin{array}{r} \frac{1}{2} \\ + \frac{5}{9} \\ \hline \end{array}$

34. $\begin{array}{r} \frac{5}{8} \\ - \frac{1}{4} \\ \hline \end{array}$

35. $\begin{array}{r} \frac{1}{4} \\ + \frac{5}{9} \\ \hline \end{array}$

36. $\frac{7}{13} - \frac{3}{13} =$ ________

37. Elise ate $\frac{1}{3}$ of the pie and Samantha ate $\frac{5}{12}$ of the pie. How much of the pie did they eat in all?

____

38. Horatio made a mixture of $\frac{2}{3}$ cup apple juice and $\frac{4}{5}$ cup grape juice. How much more grape juice was there than apple juice?

____

39. Tia used $\frac{2}{3}$ lb of peanuts and $\frac{5}{6}$ lb of walnuts in her recipe. How many pounds of nuts did she use altogether?

____

40. Jaoquin had $\frac{1}{2}$ cup of ranch dressing. He used $\frac{1}{3}$ cup on his salad and the rest on his sandwich. How much dressing did he use on the sandwich?

____

STOP

Chapter 25 – Teacher Interview

Core Concept: ***Fractions and Decimals***

Student Activity: Students demonstrate an understanding of decimals and the relationship between fractions and decimals.

Teacher Question 1:

- What is $\frac{4}{10}$ expressed as a decimal?

Understanding Student Response	Practice and Improvement
Students say 0.04.	Review lesson 2 to help students write decimals.
Students say 0.004.	Review lesson 2 to help students write decimals.

Teacher Question 2:

- What is 0.4 expressed as a fraction in simplest terms?

Understanding Student Response	Practice and Improvement
Students say $\frac{4}{10}$.	Review Chapter 21 lesson 3 to help students recognize fractions in simplest form.
Students say $\frac{2}{50}$ or $\frac{1}{25}$.	Review lesson 2 to help students understand how to write decimals.

Teacher Question 3:

- What is 0.004 expressed as a fraction in simplest terms?

Understanding Student Response	Practice and Improvement
Students say $\frac{4}{100}$.	Review lesson 4 to help students understand the thousandths place.
Students say $\frac{4}{1,000}$.	Review lesson 4 to help students understand the thousandths place.

Chapter 25 – Journal Writing

Encourage students to generate their own journal entries related to math ideas in general or to concepts in this chapter. For students requiring guidance, present the following journal prompt:

- How can it be easier to express fractions as decimals? When can it be easier to express decimals as fractions?

  (Responses should indicate that it is easier to compare unlike fractions by expressing them as decimals, and that it can be easier to understand how much a decimal is by expressing it as a fraction in simplest form.)

JOURNAL WRITING/PROBLEM SOLVING

Etta worked on her Spanish lesson for $\frac{3}{4}$ of an hour. Then she spent $\frac{1}{2}$ hour practicing flute. After that, she practiced foul shots for $\frac{3}{5}$ of an hour. Express the amount of time she spent on each activity as a decimal part of an hour. On which activity did she spend the most time?

Read

Have students find the answer to the problem. Then ask them to write a few sentences telling—

- how they expressed each fraction as a decimal
- how they found the activity on which Etta spent the most time

Have students make up another problem with different information for which they would have to follow the same procedure. Then have students solve the problem and supply the correct response.

Plan

Students must find the equivalent fractions with a denominator of 100, express the fractions as decimals, then compare the values of the decimals taking place value into account.

Solve

The correct response to the assigned problem is her Spanish lesson. She spends 0.75 hours on Spanish, 0.50 hours on flute, and 0.60 hours on foul shooting.

Look Back

A correct response demonstrates that students can find the equivalent fraction needed to express fractions as decimals. It also demonstrates that they can compare decimals, taking place value into account. (See scoring rubric on page 7.)

Chapter 25 – Monitoring Student Progress

☐ Form A ☐ Form B

Name ______________________ Date ______________

Directions: For each item that is answered incorrectly, cross out the item number. Then record the number of correct responses in the appropriate Student Score column. If the student has not met the Criterion Score for an objective, circle the student's score. Recommended assignments are listed in the Prescription Table on the next page.

Objective	Item Numbers	Criterion Score	Student Score
A. Identify fraction and decimal equivalents.	1, 2, 3, 6, 7, 8, 11, 12, 13, 14, 15, 16	11/12	/12
B. Read and write decimals to the tenths, hundredths, and thousandths.	4, 5, 9, 10	3/4	/4
C. Use skills and strategies to solve problems.	17, 18, 19, 20	3/4	/4
Total Test Score		17/20	/20
Total Percent Correct			%

Chapter 25 – Prescription Table

The following chart correlates the tested objectives for this chapter to supplementary materials that meet the individual needs of the students. The Reteach and Practice pages are designed for students who need further instruction in the math concepts taught in this chapter. The Enrich pages are designed for students who need advanced challenges.

Objective	Reteach	Practice	Enrich
A. Identify fractions and decimal equivalents.	430	431	432
B. Read and write decimals to the tenths, hundredths, and thousandths.	433, 439	434, 440	435, 441
C. Use skills and strategies to solve problems.	436	437	438

Name ____________________

CHAPTER 25 TEST
FORM A
PAGE 1

Read each question carefully. Darken the circle on your answer sheet for the correct answer. Put all answers in simplest form.

1. Write $\frac{4}{10}$ as a decimal.

A. 4.000 **C.** 0.04
B. 0.4 **D.** 0.0004

2. Write an equivalent decimal.

0.8

F. 8.0 **H.** 0.080
G. 0.008 **J.** 0.80

3. Write $\frac{13}{100}$ as a decimal.

A. 13.00 **C.** 0.13
B. 0.013 **D.** 1.3

Use the model for problems 4–5.

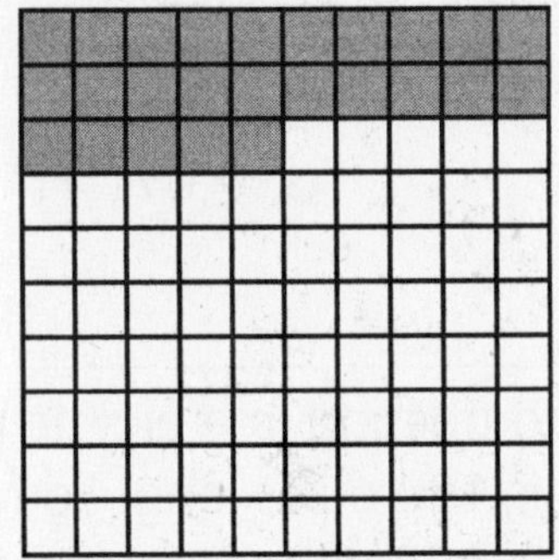

4. Which decimal matches the model?

F. 0.025 **H.** 0.25
G. 2.5000 **J.** 25.00

5. Which fraction matches the model?

A. $\frac{1}{4}$ **B.** $\frac{1}{2}$ **C.** $\frac{3}{4}$ **D.** $\frac{4}{5}$

6. Write 0.009 as a fraction in simplest form.

F. $\frac{9}{10}$ **H.** $\frac{9}{1,000}$
G. $\frac{9}{100}$ **J.** $\frac{9}{1}$

7. Write $\frac{44}{100}$ as a decimal.

A. 0.44 **C.** 0.404
B. 0.044 **D.** 0.0044

8. Write $\frac{373}{1,000}$ as a decimal.

F. 373.000 **H.** 3.73
G. 37.3 **J.** 0.373

Use the model for problems 9–10.

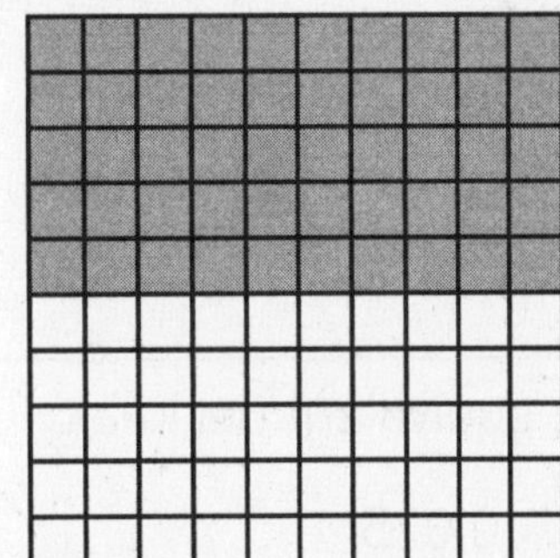

9. Which decimal matches the model?

A. 0.5 **C.** 0.005
B. 0.05 **D.** 5.00

10. Which fraction matches the model?

F. $\frac{1}{4}$ **G.** $\frac{1}{2}$ **H.** $\frac{2}{3}$ **J.** $\frac{3}{4}$

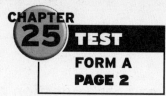

11. Write an equivalent decimal.

0.5

A. 0.50 **C.** 0.005
B. 0.050 **D.** 0.0050

---

12. Write $\frac{12}{100}$ as a decimal.

F. 1.2 **H.** 0.012
G. 0.12 **J.** 0.0012

---

13. Write an equivalent decimal.

0.47

A. 4.700 **C.** 0.470
B. 0.047 **D.** 0.0047

---

14. Write $\frac{33}{100}$ as a decimal.

F. 0.33 **H.** 0.0033
G. 0.033 **J.** 3.003

---

15. Write an equivalent decimal.

0.025

A. 0.0025 **C.** 0.250
B. 0.0250 **D.** 0.2500

---

16. Write $\frac{558}{1,000}$ as a decimal.

F. 5.580 **H.** 0.0558
G. 0.558 **J.** 0.00558

---

17. Rachel starts painting on a canvas and covers $\frac{1}{4}$ of the canvas with paint. Express this as a decimal.

A. 0.75 **C.** 0.25
B. 0.025 **D.** 2.5

---

18. David is buying furniture for his home office. His desk takes up $\frac{1}{10}$ of the area of the room. Express this as a decimal.

F. 1.0 **H.** 0.01
G. 0.1 **J.** 0.001

---

19. Maika polled 100 students about their favorite ice cream. Vanilla was chosen by 27 of the students. Express this as a decimal.

A. 0.27 **C.** 0.0027
B. 0.027 **D.** 2.07

---

20. Blake is competing in a bicycle race. The race is 100 miles long. So far he has bicycled 88 miles. How much of the race has he completed?

F. 88 **H.** 0.88
G. 8.8 **J.** 0.088

STOP

Name ____________________

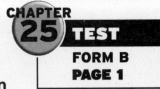

Read each question carefully. Fill in the correct answer in the space provided.

Put all answers in simplest form.

1. Write $\frac{7}{10}$ as a decimal.

____

2. Write an equivalent decimal.

0.2

____

3. Write $\frac{67}{100}$ as a decimal.

____

Use the model for problems 4–5.

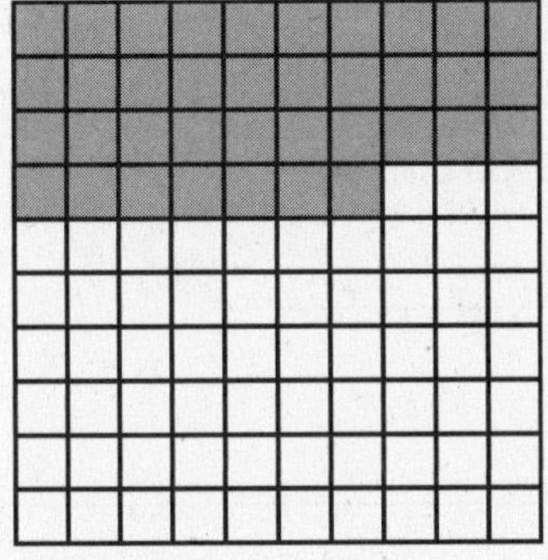

4. What decimal matches the model?

____

5. What fraction matches the model? Express in simplest form.

____

6. Write 0.003 as a fraction in simplest form.

____

7. Write $\frac{41}{100}$ as a decimal.

____

8. Write $\frac{519}{1,000}$ as a decimal.

____

Use the model for problems 9–10.

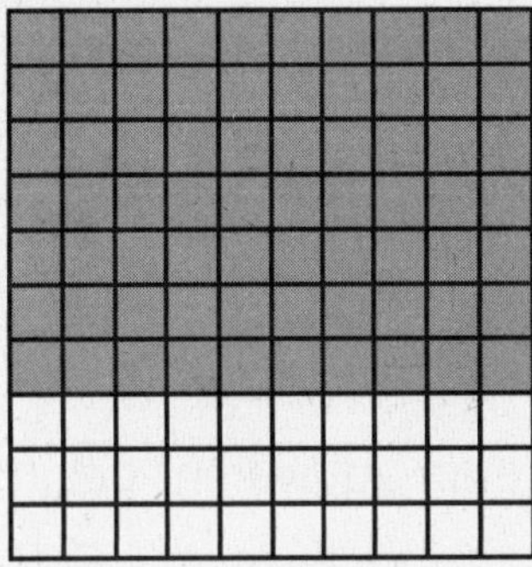

9. What decimal matches the model?

____

10. What fraction matches the model? Express in simplest form.

____

GO ON

Name ____

CHAPTER 25 TEST
FORM B
PAGE 2

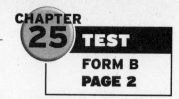

11. Write an equivalent decimal.

0.4

____

12. Write $\frac{83}{100}$ as a decimal.

____

13. Write an equivalent decimal.

0.91

____

14. Write $\frac{23}{100}$ as a decimal.

____

15. Write an equivalent decimal.

0.099

____

16. Write $\frac{817}{1,000}$ as a decimal.

____

17. Terry eats $\frac{2}{5}$ of a pizza. Express this as a decimal.

____

18. Richard is building a darkroom for developing photographs. The sinks in the room take up $\frac{3}{10}$ of the area of the room. Express this as a decimal.

____

19. Ellen polled 100 students about their favorite sports. Basketball was chosen by 34 of them. Express this as a decimal.

____

20. Amy has 100 sheets of photographic paper. She prints 74 photos using a sheet of paper for each photo. Express this as a decimal.

____

STOP

Chapter 26 – Teacher Interview

Core Concept: ***Compare and Order Decimals and Round Decimals***

Student Activity: Students demonstrate an understanding of comparing and ordering three decimals and can also round decimals to the nearest tenth and whole number.

Teacher Question 1:

- Order 2.85, 2.92, and 2.9 from least to greatest.

Understanding Student Response	Practice and Improvement
Students say 2.9 is the least number.	Review lesson 2 to help students understand that a number with more decimal places is not necessarily greater than a number with fewer decimal places.
Students make any other error in ordering the decimals.	Review lesson 2 to reinforce the concept of looking at the greatest place and going to each successive place until the digits differ.

Teacher Question 2:

- Round 4.547 to the nearest whole number.

Understanding Student Response	Practice and Improvement
Students give a decimal answer.	Review lesson 4 to help students learn how to round to the nearest whole number.
Students say 4.	Review lesson 4 to reinforce how to round to a given place.

Teacher Question 3:

- Round 4.547 to the nearest tenth.

Understanding Student Response	Practice and Improvement
Students give a whole number answer.	Review lesson 4 to help students learn how to round to the nearest tenth.
Students give an answer of 4.6.	Review lesson 4 to help students learn to look one place to the right of the place they are rounding.

Chapter 26 – Journal Writing

Encourage students to generate their own journal entries related to math ideas in general or to concepts in this chapter. For students requiring guidance, present the following journal prompt:

- When you are rounding decimals, why is it important to know the place value of the decimals? What do you have to remember when you are rounding?

  (Responses should include that you must know the location of the place to which a number has to be rounded and the steps to be followed when rounding.)

JOURNAL WRITING/PROBLEM SOLVING

Louis is cooking hamburgers for lunch. He has 0.829 ounces of meat. Round the amount of meat Louis will cook to the nearest hundredth.

Read

Have students find the answer to the problem. Then ask them to write a few sentences telling—

- what place they needed to round the number to
- how they decided it was necessary to round up

Have students make up another problem with different information for which they would have to follow the same procedure. Then have students solve the problem and supply the correct response.

Plan

Students must know the place values of a decimal, and be able to follow the procedure for rounding.

Solve

The correct response to the assigned problem is 0.83. Students had to know the place values of a given decimal and follow the sequence for rounding to a given place.

Look Back

A correct response demonstrates the ability to know the locations of the places in a decimal, and use the steps for rounding to a specific place. (See scoring rubric on Page 7.)

Chapter 26 – Monitoring Student Progress

☐ **Form A** ☐ **Form B**

Name ______________________ Date ______________

Directions: For each item that is answered incorrectly, cross out the item number. Then record the number of correct responses in the appropriate Student Score column. If the student has not met the Criterion Score for an objective, circle the student's score. Recommended assignments are listed in the Prescription Table on the next page.

Objective	Item Numbers	Criterion Score	Student Score
A. Compare and order decimals.	5, 6, 7, 8, 13, 14, 15	6/7	/7
B. Round decimals.	9, 10, 11, 12, 16	4/5	/5
C. Write decimals greater than one.	1, 2, 3, 4	3/4	/4
D. Use skills and strategies to solve problems.	17, 18, 19, 20	3/4	/4
Total Test Score		16/20	/20
Total Percent Correct			%

Chapter 26 – Prescription Table

The following chart correlates the tested objectives for this chapter to supplementary materials that meet the individual needs of the students. The Reteach and Practice pages are designed for students who need further instruction in the math concepts taught in this chapter. The Enrich pages are designed for students who need advanced challenges.

Objective	Reteach	Practice	Enrich
A. Compare and order decimals.	445	446	447
B. Round decimals.	451	452	453
C. Write decimals greater than one.	442	443	444
D. Use skills and strategies to solve problems.	448, 449	450	

Name ______________________________

Read each question carefully. Darken the circle on your answer sheet for the correct answer. Put all answers in simplest form.

1. Write $22\frac{34}{100}$ as a decimal.

A. 22.34 **C.** 22.304
B. 22.034 **D.** 22.0034

2. Write $9\frac{12}{100}$ as a decimal.

F. 91.2 **H.** 9.012
G. 9.12 **J.** 9.0012

3.

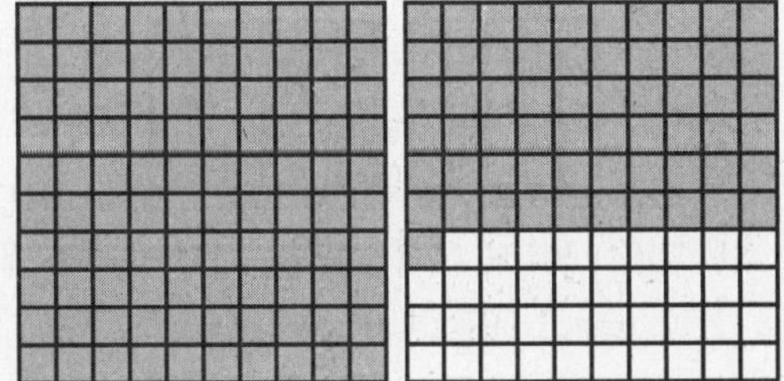

Write as a decimal to tell how much is shaded.

A. 0.00161 **C.** 0.161
B. 16.1 **D.** 1.61

4.

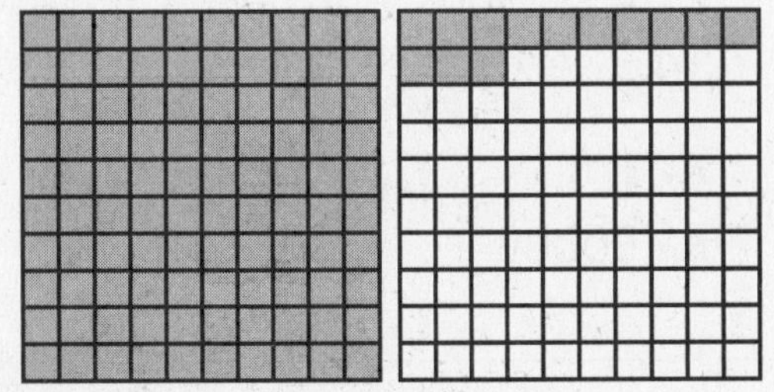

Write as a decimal to tell how much is shaded.

F. 1.13 **H.** 1.0013
G. 1.013 **J.** 13.1

5. Order from least to greatest.

0.830, 0.803, 0.083

A. 0.830, 0.803, 0.083
B. 0.803, 0.830, 0.083
C. 0.083, 0.803, 0.830
D. 0.083, 0.830, 0.803

6. Which has the least value?

1.818 1.118 1.801 1.181

F. 1.818 **H.** 1.801
G. 1.118 **J.** 1.181

7. Which has the greatest value?

A. 39.07 **C.** 39.17
B. 39.7 **D.** 39.107

8. Order from greatest to least.

0.053, 0.503, 0.530

F. 0.503, 0.530, 0.053
G. 0.530, 0.053, 0.503
H. 0.530, 0.503, 0.053
J. 0.053, 0.530, 0.503

9. Round 0.428 to the nearest tenth.

A. 0.43 **B.** 0.4 **C.** 0.5 **D.** 0.42

10. Round 0.872 to the nearest hundredth.

F. 0.9 **G.** 0.88 **H.** 0.87 **J.** 0.8

GO ON

Name ____

11. Round 4.345 to the nearest hundredth.

A. 4.4 **C.** 4.35
B. 4.34 **D.** 4.5

---

12. Round 7.085 to the nearest hundredth.

F. 7.09 **H.** 7.08
G. 7.1 **J.** 7.9

---

13. Which has the least value?

A. 2.040 **C.** 2.404
B. 2.044 **D.** 2.440

---

14. Which has the greatest value?

F. 13.9 **H.** 13.109
G. 13.09 **J.** 13.91

---

15. Order from least to greatest.

0.450, 0.405, 0.045

A. 0.045, 0.405, 0.450
B. 0.045, 0.450, 0.405
C. 0.405, 0.045, 0.450
D. 0.450, 0.405, 0.045

---

16. Round 4.707 to the nearest hundredth.

F. 4.70 **H.** 4.708
G. 4.71 **J.** 4.7

---

17. The distance from Harry's house to school is 3.7 km. The distance from his house to the park is 3.4 km. The distance from his house to the record store is 3.9 km. From the library to his house is 3.8 km. Which is closest to Harry's house?

A. school **C.** record store
B. park **D.** library

---

18. In 2001, a computer company made $32.48 million and in 2002 it made $32.4 million. In 2003, the company made $34.2 million and in 2004 it made $34.48 million. In which year did the company make the least amount of money?

F. 2001 **H.** 2003
G. 2002 **J.** 2004

---

19. In the 100-meter race, Jim had a time of 11.8 seconds. Bobby's time was 12.2 seconds, Ramon's was 11.4 seconds, and Leah's time was 14.3 seconds. Who won the race?

A. Jim **C.** Ramon
B. Bobby **D.** Leah

---

20. Lacy rides 7.8 km to school. George rides 7.83 km, Kelly rides 7.03 km, and Larry rides 7.08 km. Who has the longest ride to school?

F. Lacy **H.** Kelly
G. George **J.** Larry

STOP

Name ______________________________

Read each question carefully. Fill in the correct answer in the space provided. Put all answers in simplest form.

1. Write $22\frac{3}{100}$ as a decimal.

____

2. Write $9\frac{17}{100}$ as a decimal.

____

3. 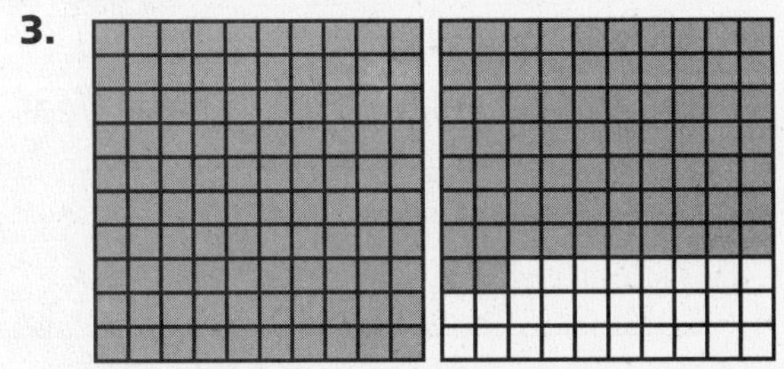

Write as a decimal to tell how much is shaded.

____

4. 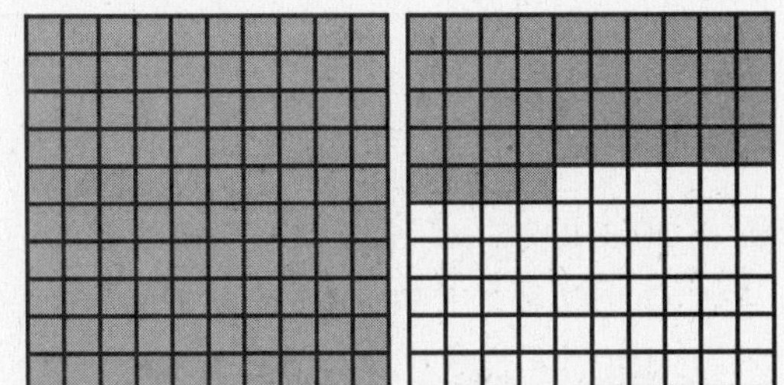

Write as a decimal to tell how much is shaded.

____

5. Order from least to greatest.

0.640, 0.643, 0.064

____

6. Which has the least value?

1.471 1.174 1.714 1.147

____

7. Which has the greatest value?

52.13 52.31 52.4 52.09

____

8. Order from greatest to least.

0.702, 0.072, 2.070

____

9. Round 0.467 to the nearest tenth.

____

10. Round 0.653 to the nearest hundredth.

____

GO ON

Name ______________________________

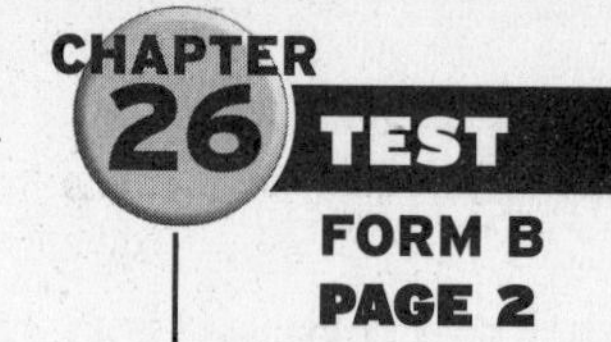

11. Round 3.781 to the nearest hundredth.

____

12. Round 6.479 to the nearest hundredth.

____

13. Which has the least value?

3.05 3.055 3.505 3.55

____

14. Which has the greatest value?

16.2 16.29 16.209 16.19

____

15. Order from least to greatest.

0.670, 0.607, 0.067

____

16. Round 5.254 to the nearest hundredth.

____

17. The distance from Lenny's house to school is 4.2 mi. The distance from his house to the movies is 4.7 km. The distance from his house to the gym is 4.7 km. From the library to his house is 4.4 km. Which building is closest to Lenny's house?

____

18. In 2001, a pet food company made $2.68 million and in 2002 it made $2.4 million. In 2003, the company made $2.25 million and in 2004 it made $2.82 million. In what year did the company make the least money?

____

19. In the 200-meter race, Jamal had a time of 27.3 seconds. Eddie's time was 26.8 seconds, Malcolm's was 26.9 seconds, and Juan's was 27.5 seconds. Who won the race?

____

20. Rosie jogged 8 km yesterday. Danny jogged 8.2 km yesterday, Mickey jogged 8.1 km, and Suzie jogged 8.8 km. Who jogged the least yesterday?

____

STOP

Unit 13 Performance Assessment

Basketball Records

- ***Target Skill:*** Compare and order decimals.
- ***Additional Skills:*** Write decimals greater than one; read and write decimals to the tenths, hundredths, and thousandths.

Task Description: This task requires students to compare and order decimals less than 1 and greater than 1 by matching a basketball record with its decimal.

Preparing: You may wish to have students talk about their favorite teams and players. Field goal percentage is the number of field goals (shots not counting free throws) made divided by the number of field goals attempted.

Materials	Group Size	Time on Task
Pencil Paper	1 to 2 students	1 day

Guiding: Remind students that a decimal with 1 place to the right of the decimal point can be greater than a decimal point with 3 places to the right of the decimal point.

Remind students to align the decimal point when comparing decimals.

Observing/ Monitoring: As you move among the students, pose the following questions:

Did you remember to align the decimals?

Which place value should you start with when comparing and ordering decimals?

Unit 13 Performance Assessment Scoring Rubric

Basketball Records

Score	Explanation
3	Students demonstrate an efficient strategy and a thorough approach that enables them to solve the problem completely. A satisfactory answer: • matches the records to the categories; • correctly orders the records from greatest to least; • selects decimals that are greater than and less than each of the middle three records. Students are able to complete the problem quickly and have all of the above correct solutions.
2	Students demonstrate a strategy that enables them to solve most of the problem correctly. The strategy is somewhat disorganized, making it less efficient. A solution is found, but errors are contained. Students may: • match most of the records; • order the records from greatest to least; • write one decimal that is between the middle three records. Students may have some difficulty determining all solutions correctly, but demonstrate an understanding of general concepts.
1	Students demonstrate a confused strategy, which leads to difficulty solving the problem. Most answers are incorrect, but students demonstrate knowledge of at least one concept being assessed. Students may: • match some of the records; OR • show an order of the decimals, but not from greatest to least.

Name ____________________

Unit 13 Performance Assessment Student Activity

Basketball Records

You will need

- Pencil
- Paper

Compare and order decimals to find some records that are held in basketball. Use the descriptions to match the record with its category.

0.727	Best winning percentage in an NBA season
50.4	Highest field goal percentage in an NBA season
23.1	Highest scoring average in a WNBA season
0.878	Highest scoring average in an NBA season
22.9	Highest rebound average in an NBA career

1. The greatest number is the highest scoring average in an NBA season.

____

2. The least number is the highest field goal percentage in an NBA season.

____

3. Of the remaining three records the least decimal is the highest winning percentage in an NBA season and the greatest decimal is the highest scoring average in a WNBA season.

____

4. Order the decimals by record from greatest to least.

A. ____________ **D.** ____________

B. ____________ **E.** ____________

C. ____________

5. Write a decimal that would go between each of the records.

____

____

Unit 13 – Monitoring Student Progress

☐ **Form A** ☐ **Form B**

Name ______________________ Date ______________

Directions: This test targets selected objectives. For each item that is answered incorrectly, cross out the item number. Then record the number of correct responses in the column labeled **Number of Correct Responses.** Add to find the **Total Number of Correct Responses** and record the total. Use this total to determine the **Total Test Score** and the **Total Percent Correct.**

Strand • Objective(s)	Item Numbers	Number of Correct Responses
Number Sense, Concepts, and Operations • Identify fraction and decimal equivalents. • Read and write decimals to the tenths, hundredths, and thousandths. • Compare and order decimals. • Round decimals. • Write decimals greater than one. • Use skills and strategies to solve problems.	1, 2, 3, 4, 5, 6, 7, 8, 9, 10, 11, 12, 13, 14, 15, 16, 17, 18, 19, 20, 21, 22, 23, 24, 25, 26, 27, 28, 29, 30, 31, 32, 33, 34, 35, 36, 37, 38, 39, 40	/40
Total Number of Correct Responses		
Total Test Score		/40
Total Percent Correct		%

Name ____________________

UNIT 13 **TEST** FORM A PAGE 1

Read each question carefully. Darken the circle on your answer sheet for the correct answer.

1. Write $\frac{2}{10}$ as a decimal.

A. 20.000 **C.** 0.02
B. 0.2 **D.** 0.0002

2. Order from least to greatest.

3.19, 0.319, 0.139

F. 3.19, 0.139, 0.319
G. 3.19, 0.319, 0.139
H. 0.319, 0.139, 3.19
J. 0.139, 0.319, 3.19

3. Write an equivalent decimal.

0.6

A. 6.0 **C.** 0.06
B. 0.600 **D.** 0.006

4. Write $6\frac{34}{100}$ as a decimal.

F. 634.000 **H.** 6.034
G. 6.34 **J.** 0.634

5. Order from least to greatest.

0.702, 0.720, 0.072

A. 0.720, 0.702, 0.072
B. 0.702, 0.720, 0.072
C. 0.072, 0.702, 0.720
D. 0.072, 0.720, 0.702

6. Write an equivalent decimal.

0.39

F. 3.90 **H.** 0.039
G. 0.390 **J.** 0.0039

7. Write $\frac{8}{100}$ as a decimal.

A. 800.00 **C.** 0.08
B. 0.8 **D.** 0.008

8. Which has the least value?

1.155 1.150 1.105 1.501

F. 1.501 **H.** 1.150
G. 1.105 **J.** 1.155

9. Write an equivalent decimal.

0.5

A. 0.005 **C.** 0.050
B. 0.05 **D.** 0.0500

10. Write $\frac{30}{1,000}$ as a decimal.

F. 30.00 **H.** 0.030
G. 0.30 **J.** 0.003

GO ON

11. Which has the greatest value?

71.6 71.06 71.16 71.106

A. 71.16 **C.** 71.6
B. 71.106 **D.** 71.06

12. Write an equivalent decimal.

0.007

F. 0.0070 **H.** 0.70
G. 0.070 **J.** 7.0

13. Write $35\frac{15}{100}$ as a decimal.

A. 35.15 **C.** 35.015
B. 35.105 **D.** 35.0015

14. Round 0.751 to the nearest tenth.

F. 1.0 **H.** 0.7
G. 0.8 **J.** 0.75

15. Write $\frac{789}{1,000}$ as a decimal.

A. 789.00 **C.** 7.89
B. 78.9 **D.** 0.789

16. Round 3.406 to the nearest hundredth.

F. 3.5 **H.** 3.41
G. 3.0 **J.** 3.40

17. The distance from Nikki's house to school is 2.4 km. The distance from her house to the post office is $2\frac{9}{10}$ km. From the bakery to Nikki's house is $2\frac{1}{10}$ km and from the grocery store to her house is 3.1 km. Which is closest to Nikki's house?

A. school **C.** bakery
B. post office **D.** grocery store

18. In 1995, a jewelry company made $78.9 million and in 1996 it made $80.23 million. In 1997, the company made $77.65 million and in 1998 it made $80.03 million. In what year did the company make the least money?

F. 1995 **H.** 1997
G. 1996 **J.** 1998

19. A movie theater will take up $\frac{3}{4}$ of the available space at a mall. Express this as a decimal.

A. 0.75 **C.** 0.075
B. 0.34 **D.** 0.034

20. There are 4 floors in an apartment building. Erica lives on the floor between Wen and Alice. Mark lives on the bottom floor. Wen lives on the floor above Erica. Who lives on the second floor?

F. Erica **H.** Alice
G. Wen **J.** Mark

GO ON

21. Write $\frac{9}{10}$ as a decimal.

A. 9.00 **C.** 0.09
B. 0.9 **D.** 0.009

22. Order from greatest to least.

0.100, 0.001, 0.010

F. 0.100, 0.010, 0.001
G. 0.100, 0.001, 0.010
H. 0.001, 0.010, 0.100
J. 0.001, 0.100, 0.010

23. Write an equivalent decimal.

0.61

A. 6.1 **C.** 0.061
B. 0.610 **D.** 0.0061

24. Write $\frac{3}{100}$ as a decimal.

F. 300.00 **H.** 0.03
G. 0.3 **J.** 0.0003

25. Order from greatest to least.

2.47, 2.74, 2.40

A. 2.74, 2.47, 2.40
B. 2.74, 2.40, 2.47
C. 2.40, 2.74, 2.47
D. 2.40, 2.47, 2.74

26. Write an equivalent decimal.

0.8

F. 8.0 **H.** 0.080
G. 0.800 **J.** 0.008

27. Write $4\frac{86}{100}$ as a decimal.

A. 486.00 **C.** 4.086
B. 4.86 **D.** 0.486

28. Which has the least value?

4.13 4.31 4.30 4.10

F. 4.31 **H.** 4.13
G. 4.30 **J.** 4.10

29. Write an equivalent decimal.

0.25

A. 0.0025 **C.** 0.250
B. 0.025 **D.** 0.205

30. Write $\frac{60}{1,000}$ as a decimal.

F. 60.00 **H.** 0.060
G. 0.60 **J.** 0.006

31. Which has the greatest value?

0.942 0.904 0.924 0.920

A. 0.920 **C.** 0.942
B. 0.924 **D.** 0.904

Name ____________________

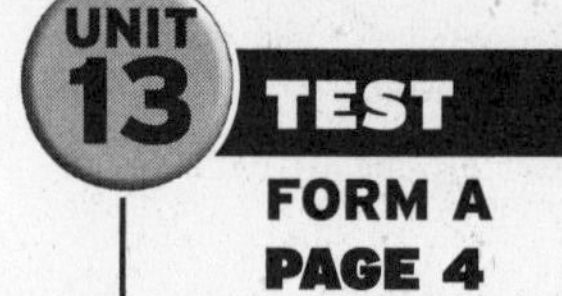

32. Write an equivalent decimal.

0.003

F. 30.0 **H.** 0.030
G. 3.0 **J.** 0.0030

33. Write $\frac{231}{1,000}$ as a decimal.

A. 231.000 **C.** 20.31
B. 23.10 **D.** 0.231

34. Round 45.64 to the nearest tenth.

F. 50.00 **H.** 45.6
G. 45.7 **J.** 40.00

35. Write $79\frac{45}{100}$ as a decimal.

A. 79.45 **C.** 79.045
B. 79.405 **D.** 79.0045

36. Round 5.951 to the nearest hundredth.

F. 6.0 **H.** 5.95
G. 5.96 **J.** 5.90

37. At field day, Team A carried an egg on a spoon for 29.5 m. Team B carried it for 29.85 m. Team C carried it for 29.13 m, while Team D carried it for 29.2 m. Which team carried the egg the longest distance?

A. Team A **C.** Team C
B. Team B **D.** Team D

38. In the election, 1.35 million voted for Candidate W and 1.14 million voted for Candidate X. Candidate Y received 1.08 million votes, while Candidate Z received 1.2 million votes. Which candidate received the least amount of votes?

F. W **G.** X **H.** Y **J.** Z

39. Mr. and Mrs. Ho built a new house. The kitchen takes up $\frac{1}{5}$ of the area of the house. Express this as a decimal.

A. 0.5 **C.** 0.005
B. 0.2 **D.** 0.002

40. There are 4 rose bushes planted in a line at the school. The red bush is in between the white one and the pink one. The yellow bush is the farthest left. The white bush is an end bush. Which bush is second in line?

F. red **H.** pink
G. white **J.** yellow

STOP

Name ______________________________

UNIT 13 TEST
FORM B
PAGE 1

Read each question carefully. Fill in the correct answer in the space provided.

1. Write $\frac{3}{10}$ as a decimal.

____

2. Order from least to greatest.

4.29, 0.429, 0.249

____

3. Write an equivalent decimal.

0.8

____

4. Write $3\frac{56}{100}$ as a decimal.

____

5. Order from least to greatest.

0.204, 0.240, 0.042

____

6. Write an equivalent decimal.

0.77

____

7. Write $\frac{5}{100}$ as a decimal.

____

8. Which has the least value?

3.244	3.240
3.204	3.424

____

9. Write an equivalent decimal.

0.25

____

10. Write $\frac{20}{1,000}$ as a decimal.

____

GO ON

11. Which has the greatest value?

17.5 17.05 17.15 17.105

____

12. Write an equivalent decimal.

0.003

____

13. Write $65\frac{14}{100}$ as a decimal.

____

14. Round 0.654 to the nearest tenth.

____

15. Write $\frac{493}{1,000}$ as a decimal.

____

16. Round 8.308 to the nearest hundredth.

____

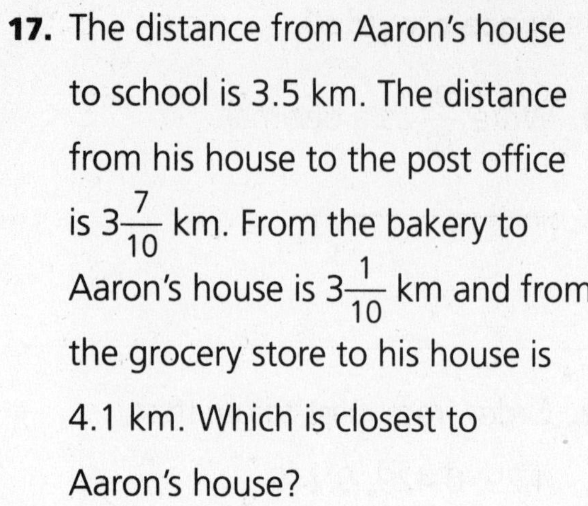

17. The distance from Aaron's house to school is 3.5 km. The distance from his house to the post office is $3\frac{7}{10}$ km. From the bakery to Aaron's house is $3\frac{1}{10}$ km and from the grocery store to his house is 4.1 km. Which is closest to Aaron's house?

____

18. In 1992, a video game company made $47.9 million, and in 1993, it made $50.12 million. In 1994, the company made $46.83 million, and in 1995 it made $50.06 million. In what year did the company make the least money?

____

19. A car dealer uses $\frac{3}{5}$ of its parking lot for new cars. Express this as a decimal.

____

20. There are 4 floors in an apartment building. Adam lives on the floor between Carla and James. Nicole lives on the bottom floor. Carla lives on the floor above Adam. Who lives on the second floor?

____

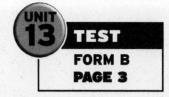

21. Write $\frac{4}{10}$ as a decimal.

____

22. Order from greatest to least.

0.300, 0.003, 0.030

____

23. Write an equivalent decimal.

0.57

____

24. Write $\frac{6}{100}$ as a decimal.

____

25. Order from greatest to least.

9.36, 9.63, 9.30

____

26. Write an equivalent decimal.

0.4

____

27. Write $5\frac{93}{100}$ as a decimal.

____

28. Which has the least value?

2.28   2.82   2.80   2.20

____

29. Write an equivalent decimal.

0.5

____

30. Write $\frac{20}{1,000}$ as a decimal.

____

GO ON

Name ________________________________

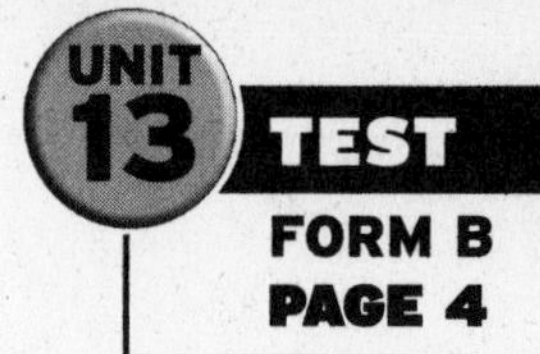

31. Which has the greatest value?

0.741 0.704 0.714 0.710

____

32. Write an equivalent decimal.

0.009

____

33. Write $\frac{549}{1{,}000}$ as a decimal.

____

34. Round 86.62 to the nearest tenth.

____

35. Write $24\frac{18}{100}$ as a decimal.

____

36. Round 4.263 to the nearest hundredth.

____

37. At field day, Team A carries an egg on a spoon for 38.6 m. Team B carries it for $38\frac{18}{20}$ m. Team C carries it for $38\frac{11}{100}$ m while Team D carries it for 38.3 m. Which team carries the egg the longest distance?

____

38. In the election, 2.37 million voted for Candidate W and 2.19 voted for Candidate X. Candidate Y received 2.05 million votes, while Candidate Z received 2.2 million votes. Which candidate received the fewest votes?

____

39. Corrine calculates that her bed takes up $\frac{2}{5}$ of her bedroom. Express this as a decimal.

____

40. There are 4 cars lined up in a parking lot. The blue car is in between the black car and the gray car. The brown car is the farthest left. The black car is an end car. Which car is second from the left?

____

STOP

Chapter 27 – Teacher Interview

Core Concept: ***Decimal Operations***

Student Activity: Students demonstrate an understanding of decimal operations by adding decimals such as 2.145 + 0.79.

Teacher Question 1:

- How would you set up this addition problem?

Understanding Student Response	Practice and Improvement
Students who set up the problem shown at right. 2.145 + .079	Review lesson 2 to help students align decimals according to place value.
Students who set up the problem shown at right. 2.145 +0. 79	Review lesson 2 to help students align decimals according to place value.

Teacher Question 2:

- What is the sum of 2.145 + 0.079.

Understanding Student Response	Practice and Improvement
Students who say 2.965.	Review lesson 2 to help students align decimals according to place value.
Students who give any other incorrect answer.	Review lesson 2. Assign problems and allow students to practice adding decimals.

Teacher Question 3:

- Estimate. Round to the nearest whole number.
  2.145 + 0.079

Understanding Student Response	Practice and Improvement
Students who say 4 rounded both up.	Review lesson 4 to help students recognize the nearest whole number of each addend.
Students who say 3 rounded 0.079 to 1.	Review lesson 4 to help students recognize the nearest whole number of each addend. Point out that 0.079 should be rounded down to 0.

Chapter 27 – Journal Writing

Encourage students to generate their own journal entries related to math ideas in general or to concepts in this chapter. For students requiring guidance, present the following journal prompt:

- Why is it possible to regroup across the decimal point when adding decimal numbers?

  (Responses should mention that the decimal point indicates the separation between whole numbers and the decimal part, and that $10 \times \frac{1}{10}$ equals 1—just as 10 ones equals ten.)

JOURNAL WRITING/PROBLEM SOLVING

Matt and Kenyon enter the Little Falls Fishing Derby. Matt catches fish weighing 3.405 kg, 1.73 kg, and 11.2 kg. Kenyon catches fish weighing 7.834 kg and 9.013 kg. Whose fish weigh more? If the judges decide the winner based on the weights rounded to the nearest tenth of a kg, who wins?

Read

Have students find the answer to the problem. Then ask them to write a few sentences telling—

- how they aligned the numbers for each child's catch
- how they rounded the numbers to decide the winner

Have students make up another problem with different information for which they would have to follow the same procedure. Then have students solve the problem and supply the correct response.

Plan

Students must align the decimal points for both sums, perform the addition, compare the totals, round each total, and compare them again.

Solve

The correct responses to the assigned problems are that Kenyon's fish weigh more, 16.847 kg to 16.835 for Matt, but that to the nearest tenth of a kg, the contest is a tie.

Look Back

A correct response demonstrates that students can perform decimal addition and round decimals properly. (See scoring rubric on page 7.)

Chapter 27 – Monitoring Student Progress

☐ Form A ☐ Form B

Name ______________________ Date ______________

Directions: For each item that is answered incorrectly, cross out the item number. Then record the number of correct responses in the appropriate Student Score column. If the student has not met the Criterion Score for an objective, circle the student's score. Recommended assignments are listed in the Prescription Table on the next page.

Objective	Item Numbers	Criterion Score	Student Score
A. Add decimals to thousandths.	1, 2, 4, 5, 6, 7, 8, 10, 11, 13, 14, 16	11/12	/12
B. Estimate decimal sums.	3, 9, 12, 15	3/4	/4
C. Use skills and strategies to solve problems.	17, 18, 19, 20	3/4	/4
Total Test Score		17/20	/20
Total Percent Correct			%

Chapter 27 – Prescription Table

The following chart correlates the tested objectives for this chapter to supplementary materials that meet the individual needs of the students. The Reteach and Practice pages are designed for students who need further instruction in the math concepts taught in this chapter. The Enrich pages are designed for students who need advanced challenges.

Objective	Reteach	Practice	Enrich
A. Add decimals to thousandths.	456, 459, 468	457, 460, 469	458, 461, 470
B. Estimate decimal sums.	465	466	467
C. Use skills and strategies to solve problems.	462	463	464

Name ____________________

CHAPTER 27 TEST
FORM A
PAGE 1

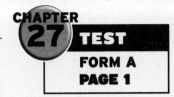

Read each question carefully. Darken the circle on your answer sheet for the correct answer.

Put all answers in simplest form.

1. $\begin{array}{r} 0.73 \\ +\ 0.48 \\ \hline \end{array}$

A. 1.12 **C.** 1.21
B. 1.121 **D.** 1.211

2. $r + 3.87 = 3.87$

F. 3.87 **H.** 1
G. 0 **J.** 0.13

3. Which is the best estimate?

0.8 + 13.3

A. 12 **C.** 14
B. 13 **D.** 15

4. $\begin{array}{r} 9.042 \\ +\ 4.872 \\ \hline \end{array}$

F. 13.014 **H.** 14.014
G. 13.914 **J.** 14.914

5. 3.172 + 0.05 = ▢

A. 3.322 **C.** 3.22
B. 3.222 **D.** 3.022

6. $7.0 + k = 8.7$

F. 0 **H.** 2.4
G. 1.7 **J.** 4.6

7. 72.481 + 6.27 = ▢

A. 72.751 **C.** 78.571
B. 79.751 **D.** 78.751

8. $9.5 + y = 13.6$

F. 4.5 **H.** 4.1
G. 9.1 **J.** 9.5

9. Which is the best estimate?

24.7 + 4.9

A. 29 **C.** 31
B. 30 **D.** 32

10. $\begin{array}{r} 8.842 \\ +\ 3.084 \\ \hline \end{array}$

F. 11.296 **H.** 12.926
G. 12.296 **J.** 11.926

GO ON

Name ________________________________

11. $4.218 + v = 4.218$

A. 0 **C.** 0.782
B. 4.218 **D.** 1

12. Which is the best estimate?

41.3 + 8.6

F. 49 **H.** 51
G. 50 **J.** 52

13. 11.074 + 8.451 = ■

A. 18.252 **C.** 19.252
B. 18.525 **D.** 19.525

14. $107.99 = z + 24.81$

F. 24.81 **H.** 0
G. 83.18 **J.** 1

15. Which is the best estimate?

67.8 + 22.9

A. 88 **C.** 90
B. 89 **D.** 91

16. 7.152 + 0.045 = ■

F. 7.187 **H.** 7.207
G. 7.197 **J.** 7.797

17. Linda bicycled 4.8 miles on Monday, 3.9 miles on Wednesday, and 5.2 miles on Friday. How many miles did she bicycle all together?

A. 12.1 miles **C.** 13.9 miles
B. 14 miles **D.** 14.1 miles

18. Nellie bought lunch for $6.37 and an apple to go for $0.39. She also bought a magazine for $3.89. How much did she spend in all?

F. $10.65 **H.** $11.65
G. $10.75 **J.** $12.05

19. In the first week of May, Vera bought 14.2 gallons of gas. The next week she bought 8.3 gallons. The following week she bought 11.5 gallons. How many gallons of gas did she buy all together?

A. 35.8 gallons
B. 34.2 gallons
C. 33.7 gallons
D. 34.0 gallons

20. A bus travels 2.4 miles to the first stop, 3.7 miles to the second stop, and 5.2 miles to the third stop. How many miles does the bus travel all together?

F. 11.3 miles **H.** 10.3 miles
G. 10.7 miles **J.** 9.7 miles

STOP

Name ______________________________

CHAPTER 27 TEST
FORM B
PAGE 1

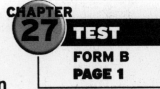

Read each question carefully. Fill in the correct answer in the space provided.

Put all answers in simplest form.

1. $\begin{array}{r} 0.29 \\ +\ 0.84 \\ \hline \end{array}$

2. $d + 1.08 = 1.08$

______

3. Estimate.

0.4 + 8.9

______

4. $\begin{array}{r} 2.708 \\ +\ 6.451 \\ \hline \end{array}$

5. 7.132 + 0.09 = ____________

6. 8.0 + k = 10.4

____

7. 18.437 + 8.43 = ____________

8. 8.2 + y = 15.7

____

9. Estimate.

15.4 + 8.2

____

10. $\begin{array}{r} 6.715 \\ +\ 5.809 \\ \hline \end{array}$

GO ON

Name ______________________________

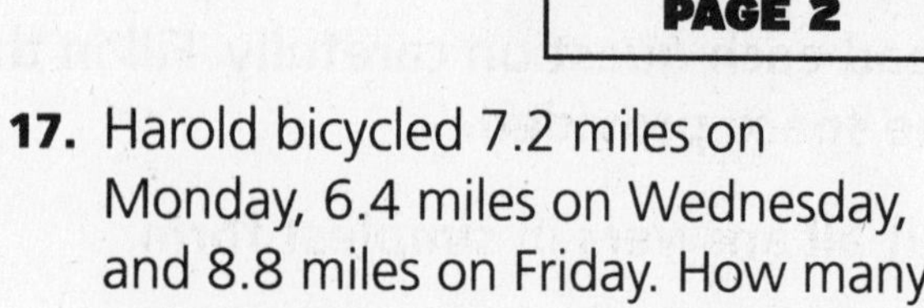

11. $5.427 + v = 5.427$

______

12. Estimate.

39.7 + 4.8

______

13. $21.708 + 5.567 =$ ______

14. $97.55 = z + 34.84$

______

15. Estimate.

36.2 + 48.5

______

16. $6.234 + 0.078 =$ ______

17. Harold bicycled 7.2 miles on Monday, 6.4 miles on Wednesday, and 8.8 miles on Friday. How many miles did he bicycle all together?

______

18. Delia bought dinner for $9.78 and a cookie for $1.39. She also rented a movie for $2.79. How much did she spend in all?

______

19. In the first week of December, Sam bought 8.7 gallons of gas. The next week he bought 11.4 gallons. The following week he bought 10.3 gallons. How many gallons of gas did he buy all together?

______

20. A train travels 5.7 kilometers to the first stop, 6.8 kilometers to the second stop, and 0.7 kilometers to the third stop. How many kilometers does the train travel all together?

______

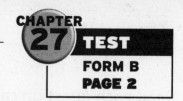

STOP

Chapter 28 – Teacher Interview

Core Concept: *Subtracting Decimals*

Student Activity: Students demonstrate an understanding of subtracting decimals and estimating differences.

Teacher Question 1:

- Subtract 3.47 − 2.62.

Understanding Student Response	Practice and Improvement
Students who say 1.85.	Review lesson 2 to help students learn how to regroup when subtracting decimals.
Students who give any other incorrect answer.	Review lesson 1 to help students understand how to subtract decimals.

Teacher Question 2:

- Estimate 16.2 − 9.8 to the nearest whole number.

Understanding Student Response	Practice and Improvement
Students who say 10.	Review lesson 4 to help students understand how to estimate a difference to the nearest whole number.
Students who say 6.4.	Review lesson 4 to help students learn how to find the estimated difference of two decimals.
Students who give any answer other than those above.	Review lesson 4 to help students learn how to estimate differences.

Teacher Question 3:

- How does adding one or more zeros at the end of a decimal affect the difference?

Understanding Student Response	Practice and Improvement
Students who say it does affect the difference.	Review lesson 2 to help students learn how to add zeros to a decimal to make subtracting easier.

Chapter 28 – Journal Writing

Encourage students to generate their own journal entries related to math ideas in general or to concepts in this chapter. For students requiring guidance, present the following journal prompt:

- When you are estimating decimal differences, why is it important to know how to round decimals? To which place would you round decimals?

  (Responses should include that rounding decimals would make it easier to subtract numbers. For ease, decimals could be rounded to whole numbers.)

JOURNAL WRITING/PROBLEM SOLVING

The average number of incorrect answers on Mr. Johnson's Social Studies weekly test was 8.9 for the month of April. During the month of May, the average number of incorrect answers on this test dropped to 3.7. Estimate the difference.

Read

Have students find the answer to the problem. Then ask them to write a few sentences telling—

- what place value they rounded to
- how they did the rounding

Have students make up another problem with different information for which they would have to follow the same procedure. Then have students solve the problem and supply the correct response.

Plan

Students must know that decimals should be rounded to whole numbers when estimating, must be able to complete this process, and solve correctly.

Solve

The correct response to the assigned problem is 5. Students had to be able to round decimals to whole numbers and subtract correctly.

Look Back

A correct response demonstrates the ability to understand that decimals can be rounded to whole numbers for estimation purposes, and to perform the operation correctly. (See scoring rubric on page 7.)

Chapter 28 – Monitoring Student Progress

☐ **Form A** ☐ **Form B**

Name ______________________________ Date ____________________

Directions: For each item that is answered incorrectly, cross out the item number. Then record the number of correct responses in the appropriate Student Score column. If the student has not met the Criterion Score for an objective, circle the student's score. Recommended assignments are listed in the Prescription Table on the next page.

Objective	Item Numbers	Criterion Score	Student Score
A. Subtract decimals to thousandths.	1, 2, 4, 5, 6, 7, 8, 10, 11, 13, 14, 16	11/12	/12
B. Estimate decimal differences.	3, 9, 12, 15	3/4	/4
C. Use skills and strategies to solve problems.	17, 18, 19, 20	3/4	/4
Total Test Score		17/20	/20
Total Percent Correct			%

Chapter 28 – Prescription Table

The following chart correlates the tested objectives for this chapter to supplementary materials that meet the individual needs of the students. The Reteach and Practice pages are designed for students who need further instruction in the math concepts taught in this chapter. The Enrich pages are designed for students who need advanced challenges.

Objective	Reteach	Practice	Enrich
A. Subtract decimals to thousandths.	471, 474, 483	472, 475, 484	473, 476, 485
B. Estimate decimal differences.	480	481	482
C. Use skills and strategies to solve problems.	477, 478	479	

Name ______________________________

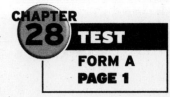

Read each question carefully. Darken the circle on your answer sheet for the correct answer.

Put all answers in simplest form.

1. $\begin{array}{r} 6.7 \\ -\ 0.9 \\ \hline \end{array}$

A. 5.2 **C.** 6.6
B. 5.8 **D.** 6.8

2. $4.28 + 0.4 - 0.4 = x$

F. 4.28 **H.** 0
G. 0.4 **J.** 1

3. Which is the best estimate?

15.62 − 7.83

A. 6 **C.** 8
B. 7 **D.** 9

4. $\begin{array}{r} 8.2 \\ -\ 0.47 \\ \hline \end{array}$

F. 6.37 **H.** 7.73
G. 6.73 **J.** 7.83

5. $\begin{array}{r} 11.084 \\ -\ 9.2 \\ \hline \end{array}$

A. 1.488 **C.** 1.984
B. 1.884 **D.** 2.884

6. $6.2 + 11.4 - 6.2 = h$

F. 0 **H.** 11.4
G. 6.2 **J.** 5.2

7. 7.49 − 3.85 = ■

A. 2.46 **C.** 3.46
B. 2.64 **D.** 3.64

8. 3.287 − 0.68 = ■

F. 1.607 **H.** 2.607
G. 1.707 **J.** 2.707

9. Which is the best estimate?

21.8 − 8.3

A. 13 **C.** 15
B. 14 **D.** 16

10. $\begin{array}{r} 16.32 \\ -\ 4.085 \\ \hline \end{array}$

F. 12.235 **H.** 12.523
G. 12.325 **J.** 12.532

GO ON

Name ____

11. 21.8 − 4.271 = ■

A. 17.259 **C.** 17.592
B. 17.529 **D.** 18.529

---

12. Which is the best estimate?

52.8 − 18.2

F. 32 **H.** 34
G. 33 **J.** 35

13.

$$\begin{array}{r} 23.46 \\ -\ 9.07 \\ \hline \end{array}$$

A. 13.39 **C.** 14.49
B. 14.39 **D.** 14.59

---

14. 6.2 − *t* = 5.38

F. 5.38 **H.** 0
G. 0.82 **J.** 1

---

15. Which is the best estimate?

27.88 − 18.19

A. 11 **C.** 9
B. 10 **D.** 8

---

16. 6.074 − 3.548 = ■

F. 3.526 **H.** 2.526
G. 2.626 **J.** 2.426

---

17. The Wurtzel family's patio was 8.3 meters long. They extended it so that it measured 12.9 meters long. By how many meters did they extend their patio?

A. 3.6 **C.** 4.8
B. 4.6 **D.** 5.2

---

18. Jason had a water cooler with 14.2 liters of water. He poured out 5.7 liters of water. How much was left in the cooler?

F. 5.7 **H.** 8.4
G. 7.5 **J.** 8.5

---

19. Carrie has $64.83 in her savings account. She withdraws $38.45. How much does she have left in her savings account?

A. $27.38 **C.** $26.38
B. $26.83 **D.** 26.37

---

20. David bought a CD for $14.39 and a magazine for $6.72. How much more did he spend on the CD?

F. $6.67 **H.** $7.67
G. $7.57 **J.** $7.77

STOP

Name ____________________

CHAPTER 28 TEST
FORM B
PAGE 1

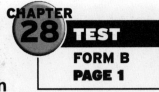

Read each question carefully. Fill in the correct answer in the space provided.

Put all answers in simplest form.

1. $\begin{array}{r} 5.4 \\ -\ 2.7 \\ \hline \end{array}$

2. 3.08 + 2.7 − 2.7 = ________

3. Estimate.

12.79 − 5.42

____

4. $\begin{array}{r} 7.5 \\ -\ 0.88 \\ \hline \end{array}$

5. $\begin{array}{r} 18.478 \\ -\ 6.7 \\ \hline \end{array}$

6. 8.5 + 13.1 − 8.5 = ________

7. 11.78 − 8.49 = ________

8. 10.107 − 8.4 = ________

9. Estimate.

23.8 − 17.5

____

10. $\begin{array}{r} 8.461 \\ -\ 5.048 \\ \hline \end{array}$

GO ON

Name ____________________

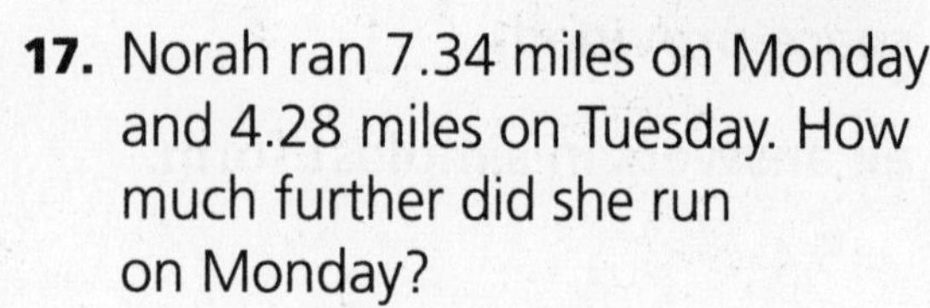

11. 17.57 − 8.042 = __________

12. Estimate.

44.1 − 26.8

____

13. 53.8
− 11.9

14. 8.0 − *t* = 6.22

____

15. Estimate.

25.74 − 13.48

____

16. 7.184 − 4.89 = __________

17. Norah ran 7.34 miles on Monday and 4.28 miles on Tuesday. How much further did she run on Monday?

____

18. Missy measured out exactly 1 liter of water into a beaker as part of a science experiment. She poured out 0.284 liters. How much water was left in the beaker?

____

19. Allen has $78.24 in his savings account. He withdraws $22.78. How much does he have left in his savings account?

____

20. Georgia bought a set of paints for $10.39 and a brush for $7.27. How much more did she spend on the paints?

____

STOP

Unit 14 Performance Assessment

Spin for Fun

- ***Target Skill:*** Add and subtract decimals properly.
- ***Additional Skills:*** Select operations correctly and follow a set of rules.

Task Description: This task requires students to add and subtract different combinations of 2-digit decimals. The students will be asked to select a set of eight decimals and fill in the spinner, then toss the number cube to select the required operation, perform the calculation correctly, and add all of their results.

Preparing: You may wish to have students discuss how they will cooperate to select the decimals, and how they will check each other's work.

Materials	Group Size	Time on Task
Spinner with eight sections Number cube	2 students	2 hours

Guiding: Tell students that they will use a game to get practice adding and subtracting 2-digit decimals.

Observing/ Monitoring: As you move among the students, pose the following questions:

How do you add and subtract 2-digit decimals?

What happens if you spin the same decimal with both of your spins, and have to subtract?

What is the highest and the lowest score you can get on one turn?

Unit 14 Performance Assessment Scoring Rubric

Spin for Fun

Score	Explanation
3	Students demonstrate an efficient strategy and a thorough approach that enables them to solve the problem completely. A satisfactory answer: • adds and subtracts decimals correctly; • selects the correct operation; • shows all work and follows the game rules. Students are able to complete the problem quickly and have all of the above correct solutions.
2	Students demonstrate a strategy that enables them to solve most of the problem correctly. The strategy is somewhat disorganized, making it less efficient. A solution is found, but errors are contained. Students may: • add and subtract decimals properly; • select the correct operation. Students may have some difficulty determining all solutions correctly, but demonstrate an understanding of general concepts.
1	Students demonstrate a confused strategy, which leads to difficulty solving the problem. Most answers are incorrect, but students demonstrate knowledge of at least one concept being assessed, such as adding or subtracting decimals.

Name ____________________

Unit 14 Performance Assessment Student Activity

Spin for Fun

You will need
- Spinner with eight sections
- Number cube

Play with a partner and pick eight 2-digit decimals. Fill in each section of the spinner with one of the decimals.

- Taking turns, players spin the spinner twice and write down the two decimals.
- Players then toss the number cube. If the number is even, add the two decimals. If the number is odd, subtract the smaller decimal from the larger one.
- The result is the score for that turn. If players calculate the decimal incorrectly, they score 0 for that turn.
- Add the score for each turn.

Whoever has the higher score after five turns wins the game!

First Spin	Second Spin	Total
		Game total:

Unit 14 – Monitoring Student Progress

☐ **Form A** ☐ **Form B**

Name ______________________ Date ______________

Directions: This test targets selected objectives. For each item that is answered incorrectly, cross out the item number. Then record the number of correct responses in the column labeled **Number of Correct Responses.** Add to find the **Total Number of Correct Responses** and record the total. Use this total to determine the **Total Test Score** and the **Total Percent Correct.**

Strand • Objective(s)	Item Numbers	Number of Correct Responses
Number Sense, Concepts, and Operations • Add decimals to thousandths. • Estimate decimal sums. • Subtract decimals to thousandths. • Estimate decimal differences. • Use skills and strategies to solve problems.	1, 2, 3, 4, 5, 6, 7, 8, 9, 10, 11, 12, 13, 14, 15, 16, 17, 18, 19, 20, 21, 22, 23, 24, 25, 26, 27, 28, 29, 30, 31, 32, 33, 34, 35, 36, 37, 38, 39, 40	/40
Total Number of Correct Responses		
Total Test Score		/40
Total Percent Correct		%

Name ____________________

UNIT 14 **TEST** FORM A PAGE 1

Read each question carefully. Darken the circle on your answer sheet for the correct answer.

1. $\begin{array}{r} 0.95 \\ +\ 0.68 \\ \hline \end{array}$

A. 1.63 C. 0.163
B. 1.53 D. 0.153

2. $\begin{array}{r} 4.2 \\ -\ 0.8 \\ \hline \end{array}$

F. 5.0 H. 4.4
G. 4.6 J. 3.4

3. $s + 7.16 = 7.16$

A. 7.16 C. 0.84
B. 1 D. 0

4. Which is the best estimate?

0.6 + 15.8

F. 18 H. 16
G. 17 J. 15

5. $\begin{array}{r} 7.046 \\ +\ 6.974 \\ \hline \end{array}$

A. 14.020
B. 13.910
C. 13.1020
D. 0.072

6. $\begin{array}{r} 7.4 \\ -\ 0.39 \\ \hline \end{array}$

F. 7.79 H. 7.19
G. 7.35 J. 7.01

7. $5.23 + 0.6 - 0.6 = t$

A. 5.23 C. 0.6
B. 1 D. 0

8. Which is the best estimate?

8.2 + 4.7

F. 15 H. 13
G. 14 J. 12

9. 2.356 + 0.07 = ■

A. 3.1056 C. 2.426
B. 3.056 D. 2.363

10. 8.09 − 3.58 = ■

F. 5.51 H. 5.32
G. 5.49 J. 4.51

GO ON

Name ____________________

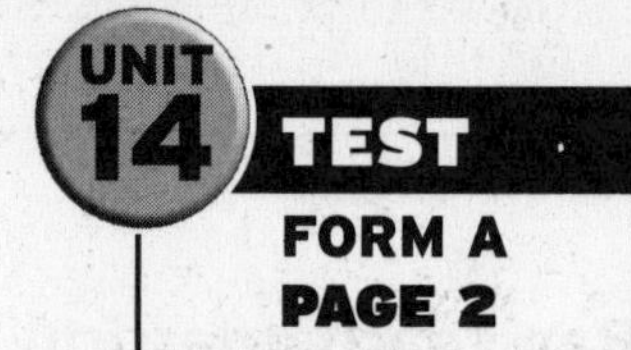

11. $7.0 + r = 9.4$

A. 5.3 **C.** 1.7
B. 2.4 **D.** 0

12. Which is the best estimate?

9.4 − 6.5

F. 5 **H.** 3
G. 4 **J.** 2

13. 34.507 + 8.32 = ■

A. 42.827 **C.** 42.539
B. 42.809 **D.** 43.539

14. 11.013 − 6.2 = ■

F. 5.213 **H.** 4.813
G. 5.011 **J.** 4.013

15. $12.3 + d = 16.2$

A. 12.3 **C.** 1
B. 3.9 **D.** 0

16. Which is the best estimate?

18.35 − 2.71

F. 16 **H.** 14
G. 15 **J.** 13

17. Mr. Adler bought breakfast for $4.65 and a muffin to go for $0.89. He also bought a paper for $0.75. How much did he spend in all?

A. $6.39 **C.** $5.29
B. $6.29 **D.** $5.19

18. The Young family's garden was 22.9 meters long. They extended it so that it measured 40.3 meters long. By how many meters did they extend their garden?

F. 63.2 meters **H.** 18.4 meters
G. 18.6 meters **J.** 17.4 meters

19. In the first week of February, Jane bought 9.3 gallons of gas. The next week she bought 11.4 gallons. The following week she bought 8.9 gallons. How many gallons of gas did she buy all together?

A. 29.6 gallons **C.** 28.16 gallons
B. 28.6 gallons **D.** 18.6 gallons

20. Tim had a cooler with 9.5 liters of sports drink. How much does he drink if he wants to leave behind 6.25 liters of sports drink?

F. 3.25 liters **H.** 2.25 liters
G. 2.8 liters **J.** 1.50 liters

GO ON

Name ____________________

21. $\begin{array}{r} 0.63 \\ +\ 0.49 \\ \hline \end{array}$

A. 1.12 **C.** 0.112
B. 1.02 **D.** 0.102

22. $\begin{array}{r} 5.1 \\ -\ 0.7 \\ \hline \end{array}$

F. 5.8 **H.** 5.4
G. 5.6 **J.** 4.4

23. $5.9 + b = 6.7$

A. 6.7 **C.** 2.4
B. 3.5 **D.** 0.8

24. Which is the best estimate?

13.64 + 0.3

F. 16 **H.** 14
G. 15 **J.** 13

25. $\begin{array}{r} 13.139 \\ +\ 2.086 \\ \hline \end{array}$

A. 15.225
B. 15.215
C. 15.125
D. 15.115

26. $\begin{array}{r} 0.081 \\ -\ 0.003 \\ \hline \end{array}$

F. 0.78 **H.** 0.078
G. 0.51 **J.** 0.051

27. $5.6 + 0.3 - 0.3 = m$

A. 5.6 **C.** 0.3
B. 1 **D.** 0

28. Which is the best estimate?

7.8 − 5.1

F. 4 **H.** 2
G. 3 **J.** 1

29. 4.033 + 0.09 = ■

A. 5.23 **C.** 4.123
B. 4.42 **D.** 4.042

30. 7.17 − 3.59 = ■

F. 4.68 **H.** 4.42
G. 4.58 **J.** 3.58

31. $10.23 = 0.7 + t$

A. 9.60 **C.** 0.7
B. 9.53 **D.** 0

GO ON

Name ____________________

UNIT 14 **TEST** FORM A PAGE 4

32. Which is the best estimate?

14.02 + 8.19

F. 25 **H.** 23
G. 24 **J.** 22

33. 17.809 + 6.13 = ■

A. 24.02 **C.** 23.822
B. 23.939 **D.** 23.102

34. 10.063 − 3.2 = ■

F. 7.263 **H.** 7.043
G. 7.061 **J.** 6.863

35. $8.14 - d = 8.14$

A. 8.14 **C.** 1
B. 0.5 **D.** 0

36. Which is the best estimate?

15.65 − 8.70

F. 7 **H.** 5
G. 6 **J.** 4

37. Maryann has $50.35 in her savings account. She withdraws $9.67. How much does she have left in her savings account?

A. $41.68 **C.** $40.68
B. $41.32 **D.** $40.70

38. Alex rode his bike 6.78 kilometers on Monday. On Tuesday he rode 4.93 kilometers. On Wednesday he rode 5.5 kilometers. How many kilometers did he ride in all?

F. 18 km **H.** 16.76 km
G. 17.21 km **J.** 16.221 km

39. Yesterday, Jan swam for 0.5 hours in the morning, 1.25 hours in the afternoon, and 0.4 hours in the evening. How long did she swim yesterday?

A. 2.15 hours **C.** 1.24 hours
B. 1.34 hours **D.** 1.115 hours

40. A train travels 3.5 miles to the first stop, 2.8 miles to the second stop, and 6.3 miles to the third stop. Which stop should Olga get off at if she does not want to travel more than 12 miles?

F. first stop **H.** third stop
G. second stop

STOP

Name ______________________________

UNIT 14 TEST
FORM B
PAGE 1

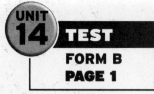

Read each question carefully. Fill in the correct answer in the space provided.

1. $\begin{array}{r} 0.45 \\ +\ 0.62 \\ \hline \end{array}$

2. $\begin{array}{r} 0.72 \\ -\ 0.09 \\ \hline \end{array}$

3. Solve the equation for *b*.

$b + 5.37 = 5.37$

____

4. Estimate the sum.

$0.7 + 12.1$

____

5. $\begin{array}{r} 8.391 \\ +\ 4.850 \\ \hline \end{array}$

6. $\begin{array}{r} 3.7 \\ -\ 0.81 \\ \hline \end{array}$

7. Solve the equation for *g*.

$6.41 + 8.2 - 8.2 = g$

____

8. Estimate the sum.

$9.3 + 5.6$

____

9. $3.297 + 0.28 =$ ______________

10. $6.32 - 5.21 =$ ______________

GO ON

Name ____________________

UNIT 14 TEST
FORM B
PAGE 2

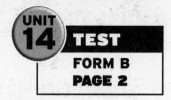

11. Solve the equation for *s*.

$5.0 + s = 7.4$

____

12. Estimate the difference.

$8.5 - 2.4$

____

13. $84.518 + 9.04 =$ ________

14. $31.607 - 8.5 =$ ________

15. Solve the equation for *q*.

$3.8 + q = 8.3$

____

16. Estimate the difference.

$19.28 - 5.67$

____

17. Gary bought an apple for $0.69, a newspaper for $0.50 and a sandwich for $3.75. How much money did Gary spend?

____

18. Marty bought 19.5 ounces of ground beef for hamburgers. He used 6.8 ounces for dinner and stored the rest. How much ground beef did Marty have left to store?

____

19. Karen went fishing and caught a 1.8-pound fish, a 4.3-pound fish and a 3.5-pound fish. How much did her fish weigh all together?

____

20. Lenny has 1.38 gallons of milk in his refrigerator. If he uses 0.87 gallon at a dinner party, how much milk does he have left?

____

GO ON

Name ______________________________

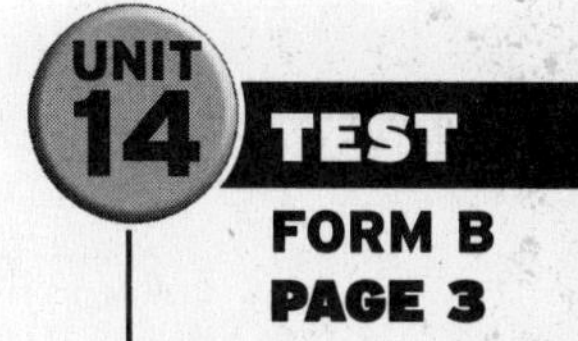

21.
$$\begin{array}{r} 0.58 \\ +\ 0.29 \\ \hline \end{array}$$

22.
$$\begin{array}{r} 6.3 \\ -\ 0.8 \\ \hline \end{array}$$

23. Solve the equation for *r*.

$7.8 + r = 9.6$

____

24. Estimate the sum.

$15.51 + 0.28$

____

25.
$$\begin{array}{r} 18.983 \\ +\ 3.097 \\ \hline \end{array}$$

26.
$$\begin{array}{r} 0.131 \\ +\ 0.092 \\ \hline \end{array}$$

27. Solve the equation for *p*.

$8.2 + 0.9 - 0.9 = p$

____

28. Estimate the difference.

$9.2 - 0.6$

____

29. $2.81 + 0.84 =$ ______________

30. $6.51 - 3.96 =$ ______________

GO ON

31. Solve the equation for *f*.

$12.91 = 9.5 + f$

______

32. Estimate the sum.

$5.08 + 12.3$

______

33. $28.403 + 3.58 =$ ______

34. $21.08 - 2.1 =$ ______

35. Solve the equation for *t*.

$4.23 - t = 4.23$

______

36. Estimate the difference.

$18.38 - 4.61$

______

37. Tera cashes a check for $83.50 and spends $29.84. How much money does she have left?

______

38. Barry long jumped 14.8 feet in his first attempt, 12.9 feet in his second attempt, and 15.3 feet in his final attempt. What is the total of his 3 jumps?

______

39. Sarah exercised for 32.4 minutes on Monday, 68.0 minutes on Tuesday, and 43.8 minutes on Wednesday. How many minutes did she exercise all together?

______

40. Mike is driving to work. There are 3 gas stations along the way. Station A is 14.8 miles from his house. Station B is 9 miles after A and station C is 12.4 miles after the station B. If Mike's car will run out of gas after 30 miles, what is the last gas station he could stop at?

______

STOP

Final Test – Monitoring Student Progress

☐ **Form A** ☐ **Form B**

Name ______________________ Date ______________

Directions: This test targets selected objectives. For each item that is answered incorrectly, cross out the item number. Then record the number of correct responses for each strand in the column labeled **Number of Correct Responses.** Add to find the **Total Number of Correct Responses** and record the total. Use this total to determine the **Total Test Score** and the **Total Percent Correct.**

Strand • Objective(s)	Item Numbers	Number of Correct Responses
Number Sense • Read and write whole numbers in millions. Compare, order, and round whole numbers and money. • Add whole numbers and money. • Subtract whole numbers and money. • Multiply facts through 12. • Estimate products, including money. • Divide by 2-digit numbers. • Multiply by multiples of 10, 100, and 1,000. • Multiply multi-digit numbers. • Multiply by 2-digit numbers. • Estimate products. • Divide multi-digit numbers by 1-digit numbers. • Estimate quotients. • Find the better buy. • Divide multiples of 10 and multidigit numbers by 2-digit numbers. • Identify, read, and write fractions and mixed numbers. • Add fractions with like and unlike denominators.• Round decimals. • Subtract fractions with like and unlike denominators. • Identify fraction and decimal equivalents. • Read and write decimals to tenths, hundredths, and thousandths. • Add decimals to thousandths. • Subtract decimals to thousandths.	1, 2, 3, 6, 7, 8, 9, 10, 12, 13, 14, 15, 17, 18, 21, 23, 24, 25, 27, 29, 30, 31, 32, 33, 37, 40	/26
Algebra & Functions • Use properties of multiplication. • Convert customary units. • Evaluate expressions. • Estimate and determine perimeter, circumference, area, and volume.	5, 16, 20, 26	/4
Measurement and Geometry • Identify, describe, and classify 3-dimensional figures. • Tell time and find elapsed time. • Identify and describe circles. • Identify translations, reflections, and rotations.	22, 34, 38, 39	/4
Statistics, Data, and Probability • Read and interpret data. • Find range, median, and mode. • Find and explore probability.	4, 11, 35	/3
Mathematical Reasoning • Use skills and strategies to solve problems.	19, 28, 36	/3
Total Number of Correct Responses		
Total Test Score		/40
Total Percent Correct		%

Name ____________________

FINAL TEST
FORM A PAGE 1

Read each question carefully. Darken the circle on your answer sheet for the correct answer.

1. What is the standard form of three million, twenty-one thousand, ninety?

A. 3,210,900 **C.** 3,021,900
B. 3,210,090 **D.** 3,021,090

2. $\begin{array}{r} 53,432 \\ -\ 25,674 \\ \hline \end{array}$

F. 79,106 **H.** 32,242
G. 38,868 **J.** 27,758

3. Jan's lunch bill is $5.74. She pays with a $10 bill. How much change does she receive?

A. $5.74 **C.** $4.74
B. $5.26 **D.** $4.26

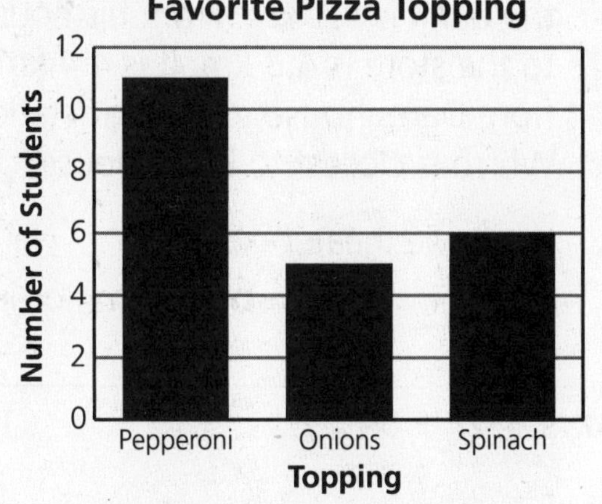

4. How many more students liked pepperoni than spinach?

F. 5 students **H.** 3 students
G. 4 students **J.** 2 students

5. $6 \times 0 = \blacksquare$

A. 6 **C.** $\frac{1}{6}$
B. 1 **D.** 0

6. Which is the best estimate?

208×76

F. 30,000 **H.** 16,000
G. 28,000 **J.** 10,000

7. $96 \div 8 = \blacksquare$

A. 9 **C.** 11
B. 10 **D.** 12

8. $54,218 + 2,896 = \blacksquare$

F 83,178 **H.** 56,004
G. 57,114 **J.** 51,322

9. $\blacksquare \times 8 = 56$

A. 9 **C.** 7
B. 8 **D.** 6

10. $4\overline{)\$170.24}$

F. $42.56 **H.** $42.06
G. $42.51 **J.** $42.01

Name ____________________

FINAL TEST
FORM A PAGE 2

11. Jenna had the following mini-golf scores: 65, 75, 63, and 66.

What was the median?

A. 68 **C.** 65
B. 66 **D.** 65.5

---

12. $48\overline{)1{,}490}$

F. 31 R2 **H.** 30 R5
G. 31 **J.** 30

---

13. $60 \times 4{,}000 = \blacksquare$

A. 240,000 **C.** 2,400
B. 24,000 **D.** 240

---

14. $34 \times 2{,}803 = \blacksquare$

F. 95,392 **H.** 90,000
G. 95,302 **J.** 19,702

---

15. Which is the best estimate?

$7{,}839 \div 91$

A. 900 **C.** 90
B. 700 **D.** 70

---

16. $20 \text{ qt} = \blacksquare \text{ pt}$

F. 40 **H.** 5
G. 10 **J.** 2

---

17. Write a fraction for the shaded part.

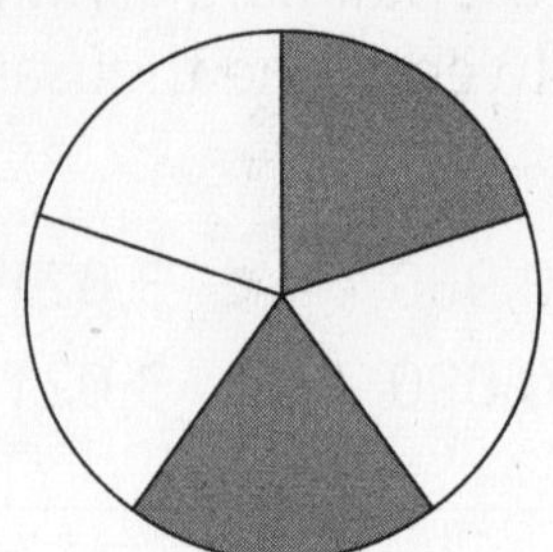

A. $\frac{4}{5}$ **C.** $\frac{2}{5}$
B. $\frac{3}{5}$ **D.** $\frac{1}{5}$

---

18. $\frac{3}{4} - \frac{2}{3} = \blacksquare$

F. $1\frac{5}{12}$ **H.** $\frac{5}{12}$
G. $\frac{7}{12}$ **J.** $\frac{1}{12}$

---

19. From Dan's house to the movie theater is 4.6 km. From his house to the bank is 5.1 km. From his house to the store is 4.3 km. It is 4.4 km from Dan's house to the gas station. Which is closest to Dan's house?

A. movie theater **C.** store
B. bank **D.** gas station

---

20. $s = 2t + 5$

$t = 3$

$s = \blacksquare$

F. 16 **H.** 8
G. 11 **J.** 6

GO ON

Name ____________________

21. Which is the best estimate?

512×86

A. 50,000
B. 45,000
C. 36,000
D. 32,000

22. Identify the figure.

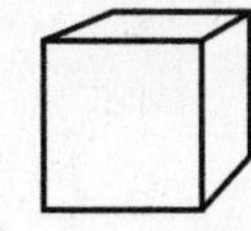

F. cone
G. cylinder
H. sphere
J. cube

23. $\frac{1}{4} + \frac{7}{8} = \blacksquare$

A. $1\frac{1}{4}$
B. $1\frac{1}{8}$
C. 1
D. $\frac{2}{3}$

24. Round 6.239 to the nearest tenth.

F. 6.3
G. 6.24
H. 6.23
J. 6.2

25. $\$31.90 \times 7$

A. $223.30
B. $217.30
C. $133.30
D. $22.33

26. Heather has a rectangular rug in her room that measures 5 feet by 8 feet. What is the area of the rug?

F. 40 ft^2
G. 26 ft^2
H. 20 ft^2
J. 13 ft^2

27. $5.498 + 0.03 = \blacksquare$

A. 5.798
B. 5.528
C. 5.501
D. 5.428

28. How many possible combinations of a soup and a sandwich are there when there is a choice of 3 sandwiches and 3 soups?

F. 12 combinations
G. 9 combinations
H. 6 combinations
J. 3 combinations

29. Write $\frac{13}{1,000}$ as a decimal.

A. 1.3
B. 0.13
C. 0.013
D. 0.0013

30. $(8 \times 4) \times 5 = \blacksquare$

F. 320
G. 160
H. 32
J. 17

GO ON

Name ______________________________

FINAL TEST
FORM A PAGE 4

31. 1.385 − 0.667 = ■

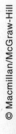

A. 2.052 **C.** 0.718
B. 1.722 **D.** 0.628

32. Write $5\frac{9}{1,000}$ as a decimal.

F. 5.9 **H.** 0.59
G. 5.009 **J.** 0.45

33. Round $149.49 to the nearest dollar.

A. $198 **C.** $149
B. $150 **D.** $100

34. If a test starts at 11:45 A.M. and ends at 1:55 P.M., how long do you have to do the test?

F. 9 hours, 50 minutes
G. 2 hours, 10 minutes
H. 1 hour, 50 minutes
J. 40 minutes

35. If your bag of marbles has 5 cats-eyes and 7 aggies, what is the chance of pulling out an aggie on your first try?

A. $\frac{7}{5}$ **C.** $\frac{7}{12}$
B. $\frac{5}{7}$ **D.** $\frac{1}{12}$

36. Noam is 12 pounds heavier than Said. Ron is 4 pounds lighter than Alroy. Alroy is 5 pounds heavier than Said. Who is the heaviest?

F. Ron **H.** Said
G. Alroy **J.** Noam

37. 7 × $28.92 = ■

A. $196.00 **C.** $198.00
B. $196.44 **D.** $202.44

38. A triangle with three sides of different lengths is always ■.

F. equilateral **H.** scalene
G. obtuse **J.** acute

39. A regular pentagon has exactly how many lines of symmetry?

A. 1 line of symmetry
B. 2 lines of symmetry
C. 3 lines of symmetry
D. 4 lines of symmetry

40. Melba is offered 9 pencils for $2.52, or 5 pencils for $1.60. How much less would she pay for each pencil if she buys 9 instead of 5?

F. $1.00 **H.** 4¢
G. 25¢ **J.** 3¢

STOP

Name ______________________________

FINAL TEST
FORM B
PAGE 1

Read each question carefully. Fill in the correct answer in the space provided.

1. What is the standard form of four million, one hundred five thousand, seventeen?

____

2. $$\begin{array}{r} 41{,}731 \\ -\ 25{,}899 \\ \hline \end{array}$$

3. Rocco's lunch bill is $14.49. He pays with a $20 bill. How much change does he receive?

____

4. How many more students liked vanilla than rocky road?

____

5. 11 × 1 = ______

6. Estimate.

304 × 47

____

7. 84 ÷ 7 = ______

8. 64,928 + 7,185 = __________

9. ______ × 9 = 63

10. $6\overline{)\$270.24}$

____

GO ON

Name ______________________________

11. Gini had the following bowling scores: 71, 85, 63, and 73.

What is the median?

____

12. 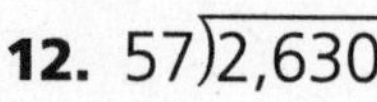
57)2,630

____

13. $50 \times 7{,}500 =$ ________

14. $41 \times 1{,}981 =$ ________

15. Estimate.

$8{,}109 \div 91$

____

16. 12 yd = ______ in.

17. Write a fraction for the shaded part.

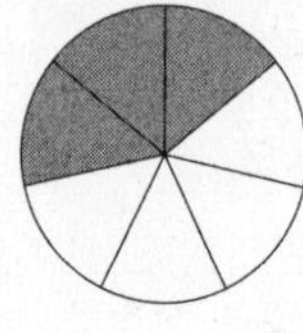

____

18. $\frac{7}{8} - \frac{1}{3} =$ ________

19. From Chang-shah's house to the mall is 2.4 mi. From his house to the supermarket is 3.1 mi. From his house to the zoo is 4.3 mi. It is 2.7 mi from Chang-shah's house to the cinema. Which is closest to his house?

____

20. $m = 3v - 4$

$v = 3$

$m =$ ______

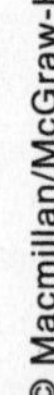

GO ON

Name ______________________________

21. Estimate.

694 × 72

____

22. Identify the figure.

____

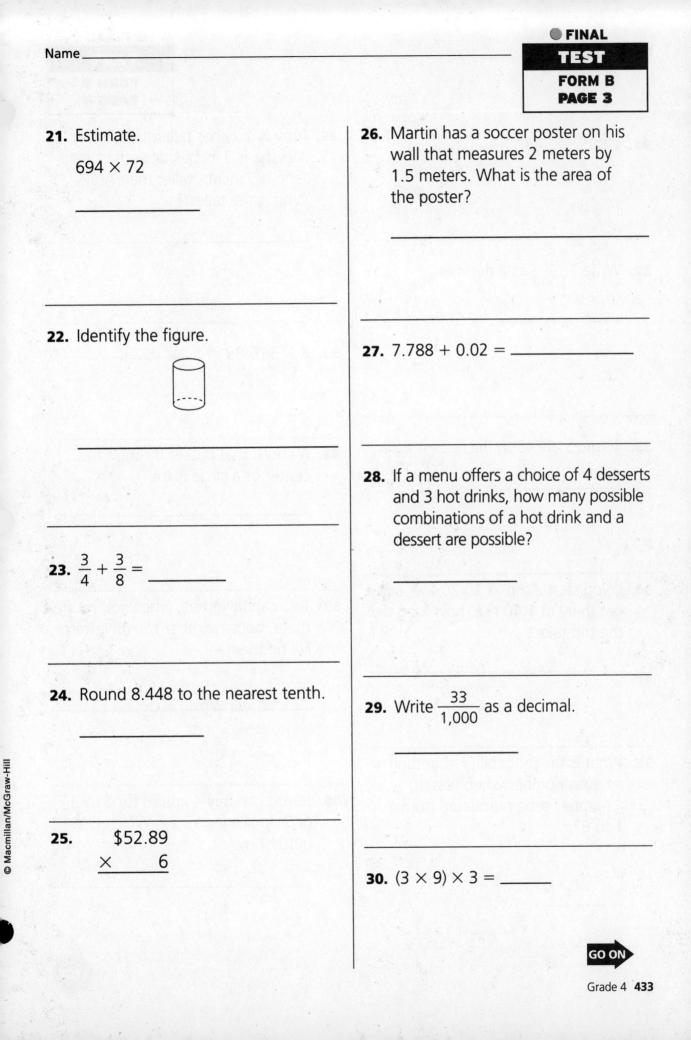

23. $\frac{3}{4} + \frac{3}{8} =$ ______

24. Round 8.448 to the nearest tenth.

____

25. $52.89 × 6

26. Martin has a soccer poster on his wall that measures 2 meters by 1.5 meters. What is the area of the poster?

____

27. 7.788 + 0.02 = ______________

28. If a menu offers a choice of 4 desserts and 3 hot drinks, how many possible combinations of a hot drink and a dessert are possible?

____

29. Write $\frac{33}{1,000}$ as a decimal.

____

30. (3 × 9) × 3 = ______

GO ON

Name ____________________

31. 6.095 − 0.487 = ________

32. Write $7\frac{87}{1000}$ as a decimal.

____

33. Round $199.45 to the nearest dollar.

____

34. If you start a trip at 10:20 A.M. and get there at 1:40 P.M., how long did the trip take?

____

35. What is the probability of getting an even number when tossing a number cube numbered from 1 to 6?

____

36. Amy is 4 inches taller than Penny. Aleysha is 3 inches taller than Jane. Jane is 5 inches taller than Amy. Who is the tallest?

____

37. 8 × $16.89 = ________

38. A chord that passes through the center of a circle is the

____

39. Two capital letters, when you rotate them, become other capital letters. Name them.

____

40. Jerrod can buy 4 apples for $1.99, or 7 apples for $3.29. Which is the better buy?

____

STOP

Inventory

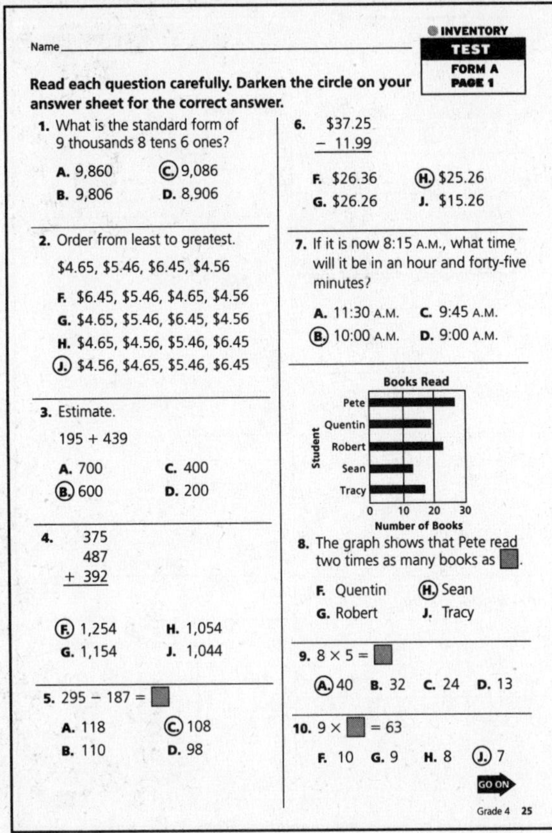

Name____________________

INVENTORY
TEST
FORM A
PAGE 1

Read each question carefully. Darken the circle on your answer sheet for the correct answer.

1. What is the standard form of 9 thousands 8 tens 6 ones?

   A. 9,860 C. 9,086
   B. 9,806 D. 8,906

2. Order from least to greatest.

   \$4.65, \$5.46, \$6.45, \$4.56

   F. \$6.45, \$5.46, \$4.65, \$4.56
   G. \$4.65, \$5.46, \$6.45, \$4.56
   H. \$4.65, \$4.56, \$5.46, \$6.45
   J. \$4.56, \$4.65, \$5.46, \$6.45

3. Estimate.

   195 + 439

   A. 700 C. 400
   B. 600 D. 200

4. 375 + 487 + 392

   F. 1,254 H. 1,054
   G. 1,154 J. 1,044

5. 295 − 187 = ■

   A. 118 C. 108
   B. 110 D. 98

6. \$37.25 − 11.99

   F. \$26.36 H. \$25.26
   G. \$26.26 J. \$15.26

7. If it is now 8:15 A.M., what time will it be in an hour and forty-five minutes?

   A. 11:30 A.M. C. 9:45 A.M.
   B. 10:00 A.M. D. 9:00 A.M.

8. The graph shows that Pete read two times as many books as ■.

   F. Quentin H. Sean
   G. Robert J. Tracy

9. 8 × 5 = ■

   A. 40 B. 32 C. 24 D. 13

10. 9 × ■ = 63

    F. 10 G. 9 H. 8 J. 7

GO ON

Grade 4 25

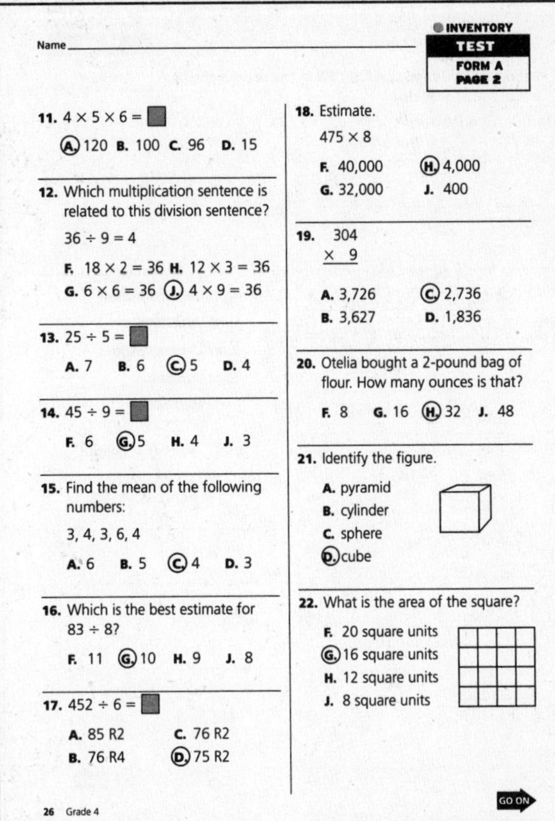

Name____________________

INVENTORY
TEST
FORM A
PAGE 2

11. 4 × 5 × 6 = ■

    A. 120 B. 100 C. 96 D. 15

12. Which multiplication sentence is related to this division sentence?

    36 ÷ 9 = 4

    F. 18 × 2 = 36 H. 12 × 3 = 36
    G. 6 × 6 = 36 J. 4 × 9 = 36

13. 25 ÷ 5 = ■

    A. 7 B. 6 C. 5 D. 4

14. 45 ÷ 9 = ■

    F. 6 G. 5 H. 4 J. 3

15. Find the mean of the following numbers:

    3, 4, 3, 6, 4

    A. 6 B. 5 C. 4 D. 3

16. Which is the best estimate for 83 ÷ 8?

    F. 11 G. 10 H. 9 J. 8

17. 452 ÷ 6 = ■

    A. 85 R2 C. 76 R2
    B. 76 R4 D. 75 R2

18. Estimate.

    475 × 8

    F. 40,000 H. 4,000
    G. 32,000 J. 400

19. 304 × 9

    A. 3,726 C. 2,736
    B. 3,627 D. 1,836

20. Otelia bought a 2-pound bag of flour. How many ounces is that?

    F. 8 G. 16 H. 32 J. 48

21. Identify the figure.

    A. pyramid
    B. cylinder
    C. sphere
    D. cube

22. What is the area of the square?

    F. 20 square units
    G. 16 square units
    H. 12 square units
    J. 8 square units

26 Grade 4

GO ON

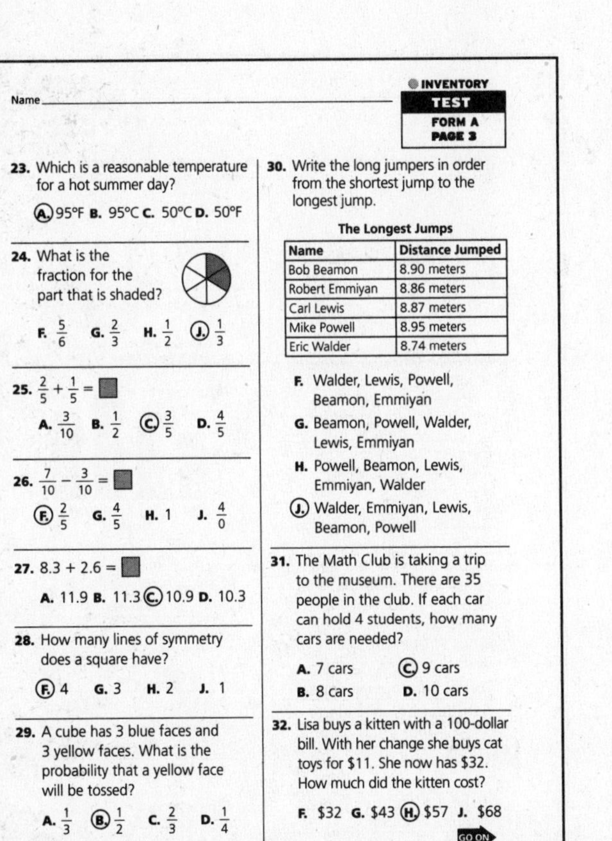

Name____________________

INVENTORY
TEST
FORM A
PAGE 3

23. Which is a reasonable temperature for a hot summer day?

    A. 95°F B. 95°C C. 50°C D. 50°F

24. What is the fraction for the part that is shaded?

    F. $\frac{5}{6}$ G. $\frac{2}{3}$ H. $\frac{1}{2}$ J. $\frac{1}{3}$

25. $\frac{2}{5} + \frac{1}{5} =$ ■

    A. $\frac{3}{10}$ B. $\frac{1}{2}$ C. $\frac{3}{5}$ D. $\frac{4}{5}$

26. $\frac{7}{10} - \frac{3}{10} =$ ■

    F. $\frac{2}{5}$ G. $\frac{4}{5}$ H. 1 J. $\frac{4}{0}$

27. 8.3 + 2.6 = ■

    A. 11.9 B. 11.3 C. 10.9 D. 10.3

28. How many lines of symmetry does a square have?

    F. 4 G. 3 H. 2 J. 1

29. A cube has 3 blue faces and 3 yellow faces. What is the probability that a yellow face will be tossed?

    A. $\frac{1}{3}$ B. $\frac{1}{2}$ C. $\frac{2}{3}$ D. $\frac{1}{4}$

30. Write the long jumpers in order from the shortest jump to the longest jump.

    The Longest Jumps

Name	Distance Jumped
Bob Beamon	8.90 meters
Robert Emmiyan	8.86 meters
Carl Lewis	8.87 meters
Mike Powell	8.95 meters
Eric Walder	8.74 meters

    F. Walder, Lewis, Powell, Beamon, Emmiyan
    G. Beamon, Powell, Walder, Lewis, Emmiyan
    H. Powell, Beamon, Lewis, Emmiyan, Walder
    J. Walder, Emmiyan, Lewis, Beamon, Powell

31. The Math Club is taking a trip to the museum. There are 35 people in the club. If each car can hold 4 students, how many cars are needed?

    A. 7 cars C. 9 cars
    B. 8 cars D. 10 cars

32. Lisa buys a kitten with a 100-dollar bill. With her change she buys cat toys for \$11. She now has \$32. How much did the kitten cost?

    F. \$32 G. \$43 H. \$57 J. \$68

GO ON

Grade 4 27

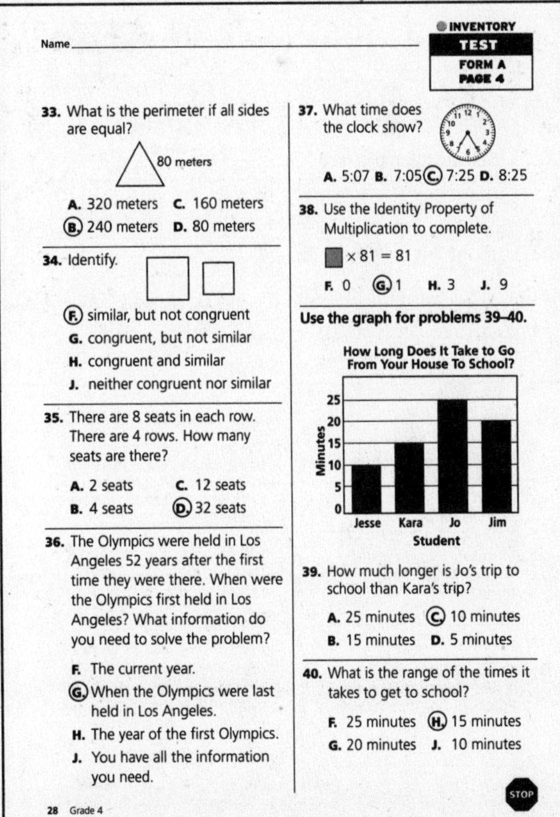

Name____________________

INVENTORY
TEST
FORM A
PAGE 4

33. What is the perimeter if all sides are equal?

    80 meters

    A. 320 meters C. 160 meters
    B. 240 meters D. 80 meters

34. Identify.

    F. similar, but not congruent
    G. congruent, but not similar
    H. congruent and similar
    J. neither congruent nor similar

35. There are 8 seats in each row. There are 4 rows. How many seats are there?

    A. 2 seats C. 12 seats
    B. 4 seats D. 32 seats

36. The Olympics were held in Los Angeles 52 years after the first time they were there. When were the Olympics first held in Los Angeles? What information do you need to solve the problem?

    F. The current year.
    G. When the Olympics were last held in Los Angeles.
    H. The year of the first Olympics.
    J. You have all the information you need.

37. What time does the clock show?

    A. 5:07 B. 7:05 C. 7:25 D. 8:25

38. Use the Identity Property of Multiplication to complete.

    ■ × 81 = 81

    F. 0 G. 1 H. 3 J. 9

Use the graph for problems 39–40.

39. How much longer is Jo's trip to school than Kara's trip?

    A. 25 minutes C. 10 minutes
    B. 15 minutes D. 5 minutes

40. What is the range of the times it takes to get to school?

    F. 25 minutes H. 15 minutes
    G. 20 minutes J. 10 minutes

STOP

28 Grade 4

Inventory

Name________________________

INVENTORY TEST FORM B PAGE 1

Read each question carefully. Fill in the correct answer in the space provided.

1. What is the standard form of 8 thousands 6 tens 4 ones?

8,064

2. Write in order from least to greatest.

\$5.25, \$4.46, \$6.54, \$4.65

\$4.46, \$4.65, \$5.25, \$6.54

3. Estimate.

185 + 429

Accept 600 or 620.

4. 352 + 435 + 533 = 1,320

5. 286 − 177 = 109

6. \$56.35 − 24.99 = \$31.36

7. If it is now 7:15 A.M., what time will it be in an hour and thirty-five minutes?

8:50 A.M.

Books Read

Student	Number of Books
Paul	
Steve	
Ricky	
Scott	
Tia	

Number of Books: 0, 10, 20, 30

8. The graph shows that Paul read two times as many books as ___.

Scott

9. 6 × 5 = 30

10. 7 × 9 = 63

GO ON

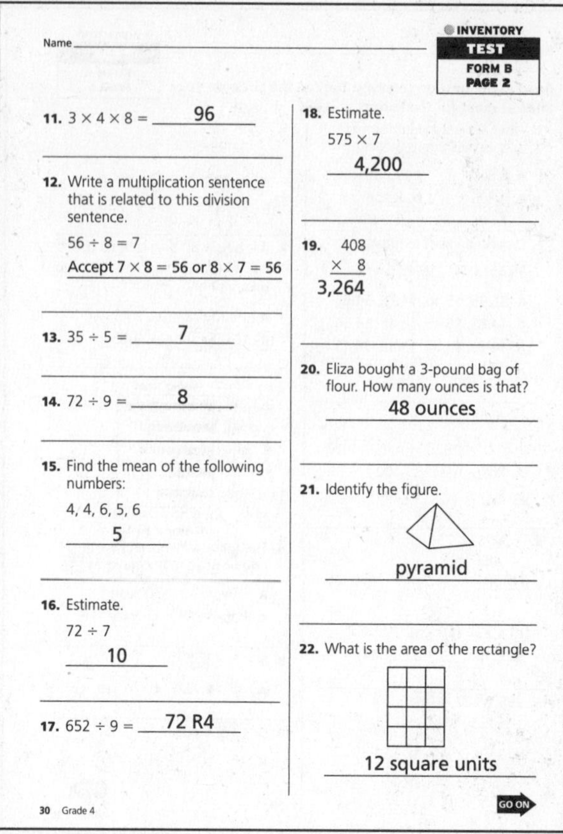

Name________________________

INVENTORY TEST FORM B PAGE 2

11. 3 × 4 × 8 = 96

12. Write a multiplication sentence that is related to this division sentence.

56 ÷ 8 = 7

Accept 7 × 8 = 56 or 8 × 7 = 56

13. 35 ÷ 5 = 7

14. 72 ÷ 9 = 8

15. Find the mean of the following numbers:

4, 4, 6, 5, 6

5

16. Estimate.

72 ÷ 7

10

17. 652 ÷ 9 = 72 R4

18. Estimate.

575 × 7

4,200

19. 408 × 8 = 3,264

20. Eliza bought a 3-pound bag of flour. How many ounces is that?

48 ounces

21. Identify the figure.

pyramid

22. What is the area of the rectangle?

12 square units

GO ON

30 Grade 4

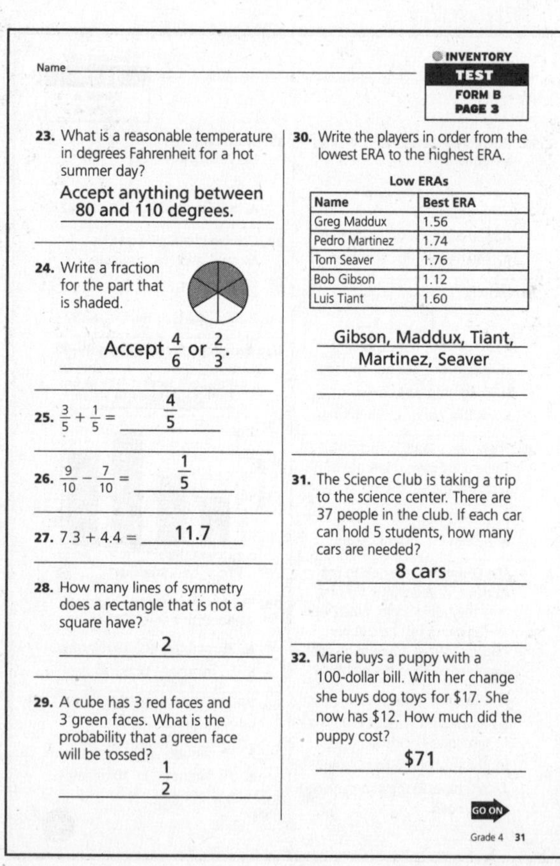

Name________________________

INVENTORY TEST FORM B PAGE 3

23. What is a reasonable temperature in degrees Fahrenheit for a hot summer day?

Accept anything between 80 and 110 degrees.

24. Write a fraction for the part that is shaded.

Accept $\frac{4}{6}$ or $\frac{2}{3}$.

25. $\frac{3}{5} + \frac{1}{5} = \frac{4}{5}$

26. $\frac{9}{10} - \frac{7}{10} = \frac{1}{5}$

27. 7.3 + 4.4 = 11.7

28. How many lines of symmetry does a rectangle that is not a square have?

2

29. A cube has 3 red faces and 3 green faces. What is the probability that a green face will be tossed?

$\frac{1}{2}$

30. Write the players in order from the lowest ERA to the highest ERA.

Low ERAs

Name	Best ERA
Greg Maddux	1.56
Pedro Martinez	1.74
Tom Seaver	1.76
Bob Gibson	1.12
Luis Tiant	1.60

Gibson, Maddux, Tiant, Martinez, Seaver

31. The Science Club is taking a trip to the science center. There are 37 people in the club. If each car can hold 5 students, how many cars are needed?

8 cars

32. Marie buys a puppy with a 100-dollar bill. With her change she buys dog toys for \$17. She now has \$12. How much did the puppy cost?

\$71

GO ON

Grade 4 31

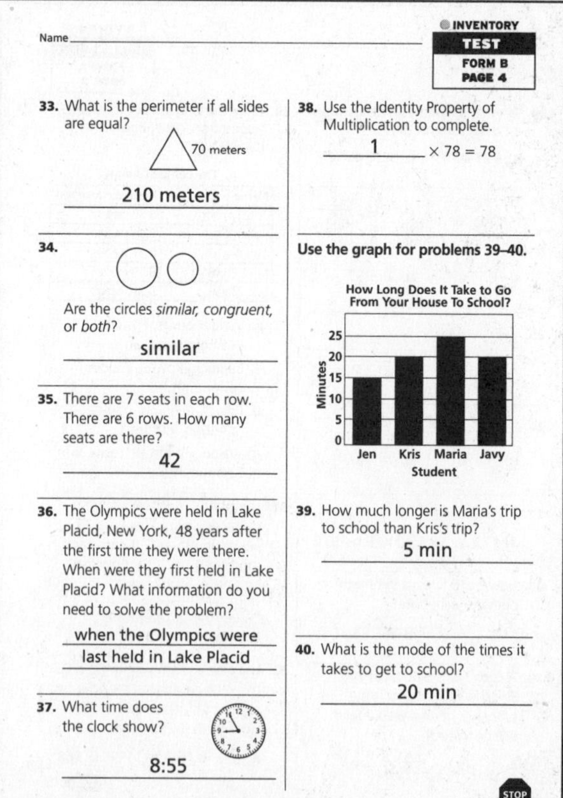

Name________________________

INVENTORY TEST FORM B PAGE 4

33. What is the perimeter if all sides are equal?

70 meters

210 meters

34. Are the circles *similar*, *congruent*, or *both*?

similar

35. There are 7 seats in each row. There are 6 rows. How many seats are there?

42

36. The Olympics were held in Lake Placid, New York, 48 years after the first time they were there. When were they first held in Lake Placid? What information do you need to solve the problem?

when the Olympics were last held in Lake Placid

37. What time does the clock show?

8:55

38. Use the Identity Property of Multiplication to complete.

1 × 78 = 78

Use the graph for problems 39–40.

How Long Does It Take to Go From Your House To School?

39. How much longer is Maria's trip to school than Kris's trip?

5 min

40. What is the mode of the times it takes to get to school?

20 min

STOP

32 Grade 4

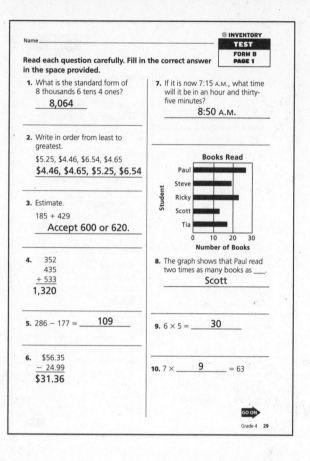

Chapter 1

Name___

CHAPTER 1 TEST FORM A PAGE 1

Read each question carefully. Darken the circle on your answer sheet for the correct answer.

1. Use a benchmark number to help you decide the number of stars on the right.

50 Stars

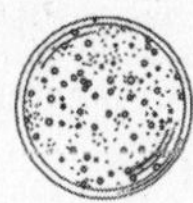

A. 50 (B.) 200 C. 500 D. 2,000

2. What is the standard form of eight million, three hundred fifteen thousand, forty-three?

(F.) 8,315,043 H. 80,315,043
G. 8,315,403 J. 803,015,043

3. Order from greatest to least.

31,114; 31,600; 30,533

A. 30,533; 31,114; 31,600
B. 31,600; 30,533; 31,114
(C.) 31,600; 31,114; 30,533
D. 31,114; 31,600; 30,533

4. What is the standard form of fifty-six million, thirty-three thousand?

(F.) 56,033,000 H. 56,303,000
G. 56,300,000 J. 56,330,000

5. What is the standard form of 900,000 + 600 + 80 + 2?

A. 9,682 C. 906,082
(B.) 900,682 D. 900,000,682

6. Order from least to greatest.

11,679; 10,850; 12,039

F. 11,679; 12,039; 10,850
G. 10,850; 12,039; 11,679
H. 12,039; 10,850; 11,679
(J.) 10,850; 11,679; 12,039

7. What is the name for 2,046,701?

A. two million, four hundred-six thousand, seven hundred one
B. two million, forty-six thousand, seventy-one
(C.) two million, forty-six thousand, seven hundred one
D. two million, forty-six thousand, seven hundred ten

8. What is the expanded form of 73,011?

F. 70,000 + 3,000 + 100 + 1
(G.) 70,000 + 3,000 + 10 + 1
H. 700,000 + 3,000 + 10 + 1
J. 70,000 + 3,000 + 100 + 10

9. Which digit makes the sentence true?

4,518 < 4, ■ 18

A. 3 B. 4 C. 5 (D.) 6

Name___

CHAPTER 1 TEST FORM A PAGE 2

10. What is the standard form of 300,000,000 + 40,000,000 + 800,000 + 200 + 30 + 6?

F. 348,236 H. 3,408,236
G. 3,048,236 (J.) 340,800,236

11. What is the standard form of twenty million, six hundred thousand, four hundred thirty-nine?

A. 26,439 (C.) 20,600,439
B. 2,600,439 D. 20,604,039

12. What is the standard form of 90,000,000 + 700,000 + 30,000 + 1,000 + 600 + 5?

F. 973,165 H. 90,731,065
G. 9,731,605 (J.) 90,731,605

13. Which digit makes the sentence true?

8,375 = 8,3 ■ 5

A. 8 (B.) 7 C. 5 D. 3

14. Order from greatest to least.

389,042; 389,402; 398,042

(F.) 398,042; 389,402; 389,042
G. 389,402; 389,042; 398,042
H. 398,042; 389,042; 389,402
J. 389,042; 389,402; 398,042

15. Order from least to greatest.

24, 421; 24, 412; 42, 241

A. 42, 241; 24, 412; 24, 421
B. 42, 241; 24, 421; 24, 412
C. 24, 421; 24, 412; 42, 241
(D.) 24, 412; 24, 421; 42, 241

16. Use a benchmark number to help you decide which is the more reasonable number of marbles.

F. 400 G. 200 (H.) 40 J. 20

17. Jen's book has 619 pages and Matt's book has 594 pages. Carl's book has 835 pages and Terry's book has 1,023 pages. Whose book has the least number of pages?

A. Jen (B.) Matt C. Carl D. Terry

18. The distance between the Earth and the Sun is about 93,000,000 miles. What is this distance written as a short word name?

F. 93 trillion (H.) 93 million
G. 93 billion J. 93 thousand

19. Maria went on four plane trips last year. The spring trip was 738 miles long and the summer trip was 593 miles long. The fall trip was 1,058 miles long and the winter trip was 783 miles long. Which season's trip was the longest?

A. spring (C.) fall
B. summer D. winter

20. Amy sells cookies. She sold 136 boxes in May, 179 in June, 139 in July, and 152 in August. In which month did she sell the least?

(F.) May H. July
G. June J. August

Name___

CHAPTER 1 TEST FORM B PAGE 1

Read each question carefully. Fill in the correct answer in the space provided.

1. Use a benchmark number to help you decide which is the more reasonable number. 1,500 Grapes or 150 Grapes?

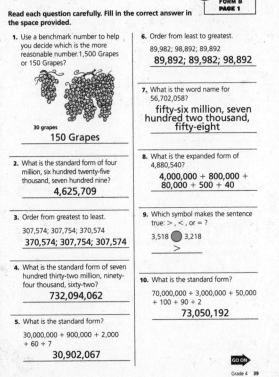

30 grapes

150 Grapes

2. What is the standard form of four million, six hundred twenty-five thousand, seven hundred nine?

4,625,709

3. Order from greatest to least.

307,574; 307,754; 370,574

370,574; 307,754; 307,574

4. What is the standard form of seven hundred thirty-two million, ninety-four thousand, sixty-two?

732,094,062

5. What is the standard form?

30,000,000 + 900,000 + 2,000 + 60 + 7

30,902,067

6. Order from least to greatest.

89,982; 98,892; 89,892

89,892; 89,982; 98,892

7. What is the word name for 56,702,058?

fifty-six million, seven hundred two thousand, fifty-eight

8. What is the expanded form of 4,880,540?

4,000,000 + 800,000 + 80,000 + 500 + 40

9. Which symbol makes the sentence true: >, <, or = ?

3,518 ● 3,218

>

10. What is the standard form?

70,000,000 + 3,000,000 + 50,000 + 100 + 90 + 2

73,050,192

Name___

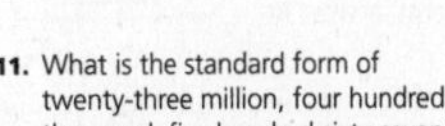

CHAPTER 1 TEST FORM B PAGE 2

11. What is the standard form of twenty-three million, four hundred thousand, five hundred sixty-seven?

23,400,567

12. What is the standard form?

30,000,000 + 800,000 + 10,000 + 4,000 + 60 + 2

30,814,062

13. Which symbol makes the sentence true: >, <, or = ?

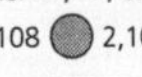

2,108 ● 2,108

=

14. Order from greatest to least.

542,180; 524,180; 542,018

542,180; 542,018; 524,180

15. Order from least to greatest.

37,380,092; 37,380,091; 37,380,910

37,380,091; 37,380,092; 37,380,910

16. Use a benchmark number to help you decide which is the more reasonable number 240 pennies or 2,400 pennies?

240 pennies

17. Heightstown Middle School has 874 students. Sparta Middle School has 947 students. East Orange Middle School has 1,293 students. Middleneck Middle School has 849 students. Which school has the greatest number of students?

East Orange Middle School

18. The distance between the Sun and the planet Saturn is about 886,000,000 miles. What is this distance written as a short word name?

886 million

19. Georgia read four magazine articles about art. The first article had 1,428 words and the second had 1,782 words. The third article had 1,274 words and the fourth had 1,872 words. Which article had the least number of words?

the third article

20. Exit 9 clothing store sold 734 pairs of jeans last year. They also sold 437 t-shirts, 873 pairs of socks, and 783 hats. Which kind of clothing did Exit 9 sell the greatest number of last year?

socks

Chapter 2

Name______________________

CHAPTER 2 TEST FORM A PAGE 1

Read each question carefully. Darken the circle on your answer sheet for the correct answer.

1. Find the amount of change.
   Price: $2.68
   Amount given: $5.00
   (A.) $2.32 C. $2.68
   B. $2.38 D. $3.32

2. Round to the nearest hundred thousand.
   8,361,319
   F. 8,300,000 H. 8,361,300
   G. 8,361,000 (J.) 8,400,000

3. Find the amount of change.
   Price: $0.79
   Amount given: $1.00
   (A.) $0.21 C. $1.21
   B. $0.31 D. $1.79

4. Round $172.52 to the nearest dollar.
   F. $170.00 (H.) $173.00
   G. $172.00 J. $180.00

5. Find the amount of change.
   Price: $3.24
   Amount given: $10.00
   (A.) $6.76 C. $7.86
   B. $7.76 D. $13.24

6. How much money is shown?
   F. $2.35 H. $6.30
   (G.) $6.35 J. $10.35

7. Find the amount of change.
   Price: $3.39
   Amount given: $5.00
   A. $0.61 (C.) $1.61
   B. $0.71 D. $1.71

8. Round to the nearest million.
   80,830,485
   F. 79,000,000 (H.) 81,000,000
   G. 80,000,000 J. 90,000,000

9. Which digit makes the sentence true?
   $43,273.48 > $43,2 ■ 3.48
   A. 9 B. 8 C. 7 (D.) 6

10. Find the amount of change.
    Price: $4.03
    Amount given: $10.00
    (F.) $5.97 H. $6.07
    G. $6.03 J. $6.97

GO ON

Name______________________

CHAPTER 2 TEST FORM A PAGE 2

11. Round $19.38 to the nearest ten cents.
    A. $19.30 C. $20.38
    (B.) $19.40 D. $20.40

12. Find the amount of change.
    Price: $0.68
    Amount given: $1.00
    (F.) $0.32 H. $1.32
    G. $0.42 J. $1.42

13. Which digit makes the sentence true?
    $23,581.27 = $23,5 ■ 1.27
    A. 9 (B.) 8 C. 7 D. 6

14. How much money is shown?

    F. $3.35 (H.) $7.35
    G. $3.40 J. $7.40

15. Round $3,089.56 to the nearest dollar.
    A. $3,089.00 (C.) $3,090.00
    B. $3,089.60 D. $3,090.60

16. Which digit makes the sentence true?
    $68,84 ■ .38 < $68,842.38
    F. 4 G. 3 H. 2 (J.) 1

17. Kai bought a DVD for $12.75. She paid with a $20.00 bill. How much change will she receive?
    (A.) $7.25 C. $8.25
    B. $7.35 D. $8.35

18. Rusty, David, Arnold, and Jules each play a different musical instrument; either drums, bass, keyboards, or guitar. Rusty plays drums. Jules doesn't play drums or bass. David plays guitar. What instrument does Arnold play?
    F. drums H. keyboards
    (G.) bass J. guitar

19. Jody buys a breakfast meal for $4.72. She pays with a $10.00 bill. How much change does she receive?
    (A.) $5.28 C. $5.38
    B. $6.38 D. $6.72

20. Kelly buys a package of guitar strings for $5.95. Lester pays $6.05 in a second store. Marian pays $4.25 in a third store. Wendell pays $5.45 in a fourth store. Who paid the least?
    F. Kelly (H.) Marian
    G. Lester J. Wendell

Name______________________

CHAPTER 2 TEST FORM B PAGE 1

Read each question carefully. Fill in the correct answer in the space provided.

1. Find the amount of change.
   Price: $7.63
   Amount given: $10.00
   $2.37

2. Round to the nearest hundred thousand.
   9,513,572
   9,500,000

3. Find the amount of change.
   Price: $0.71
   Amount given: $1.00
   $0.29

4. Round $381.25 to the nearest dollar.
   $381.00

5. Find the amount of change.
   Price: $3.44
   Amount given: $20.00
   $16.56

6. How much money is shown?

   $16.65

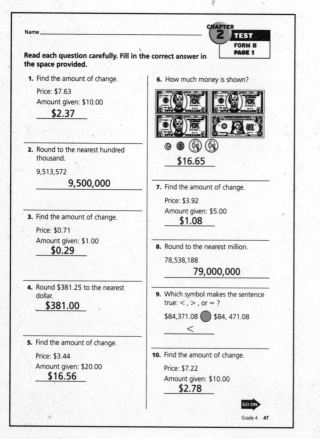

7. Find the amount of change.
   Price: $3.92
   Amount given: $5.00
   $1.08

8. Round to the nearest million.
   78,538,188
   79,000,000

9. Which symbol makes the sentence true: < , > , or = ?
   $84,371.08 ● $84, 471.08
   <

10. Find the amount of change.
    Price: $7.22
    Amount given: $10.00
    $2.78

Name______________________

CHAPTER 2 TEST FORM B PAGE 2

11. Round $53.28 to the nearest ten cents.
    $53.30

12. Find the amount of change.
    Price: $0.39
    Amount given: $1.00
    $0.61

13. Which symbol makes the sentence true: < , > , or = ?
    $58,150.79 ● $58,150.79
    =

14. How much money is shown?

    $11.30

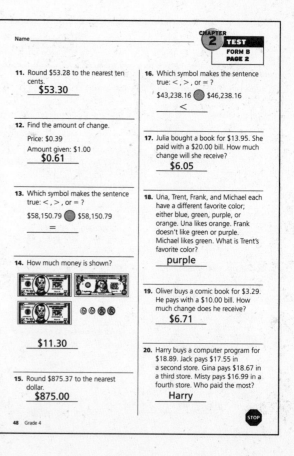

15. Round $875.37 to the nearest dollar.
    $875.00

16. Which symbol makes the sentence true: < , > , or = ?
    $43,238.16 ● $46,238.16
    <

17. Julia bought a book for $13.95. She paid with a $20.00 bill. How much change will she receive?
    $6.05

18. Una, Trent, Frank, and Michael each have a different favorite color; either blue, green, purple, or orange. Una likes orange. Frank doesn't like green or purple. Michael likes green. What is Trent's favorite color?
    purple

19. Oliver buys a comic book for $3.29. He pays with a $10.00 bill. How much change does he receive?
    $6.71

20. Harry buys a computer program for $18.89. Jack pays $17.55 in a second store. Gina pays $18.67 in a third store. Misty pays $16.99 in a fourth store. Who paid the most?
    Harry

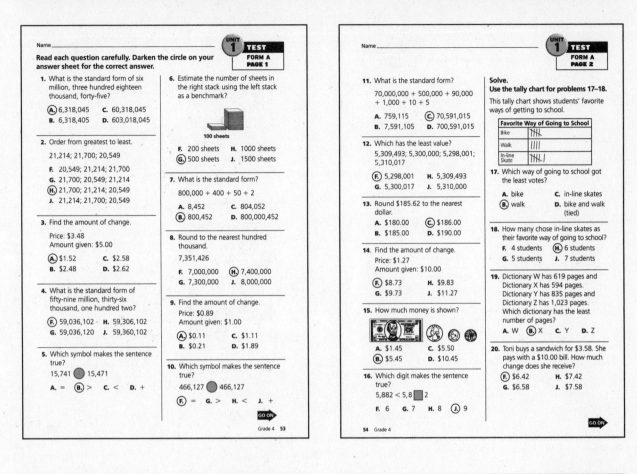

Name ______________________

UNIT 1 TEST FORM A PAGE 1

Read each question carefully. Darken the circle on your answer sheet for the correct answer.

1. What is the standard form of six million, three hundred eighteen thousand, forty-five?
   (A) 6,318,045 C. 60,318,045
   B. 6,318,405 D. 603,018,045

2. Order from greatest to least.
   21,214; 21,700; 20,549
   F. 20,549; 21,214; 21,700
   G. 21,700; 20,549; 21,214
   (H) 21,700; 21,214; 20,549
   J. 21,214; 21,700; 20,549

3. Find the amount of change.
   Price: $3.48
   Amount given: $5.00
   (A) $1.52 C. $2.58
   B. $2.48 D. $2.62

4. What is the standard form of fifty-nine million, thirty-six thousand, one hundred two?
   (F) 59,036,102 H. 59,306,102
   G. 59,036,120 J. 59,360,102

5. Which symbol makes the sentence true?
   15,741 ● 15,471
   A. = (B) > C. < D. +

6. Estimate the number of sheets in the right stack using the left stack as a benchmark?

100 sheets

   F. 200 sheets H. 1000 sheets
   (G) 500 sheets J. 1500 sheets

7. What is the standard form?
   800,000 + 400 + 50 + 2
   A. 8,452 C. 804,052
   (B) 800,452 D. 800,000,452

8. Round to the nearest hundred thousand.
   7,351,426
   F. 7,000,000 (H) 7,400,000
   G. 7,300,000 J. 8,000,000

9. Find the amount of change.
   Price: $0.89
   Amount given: $1.00
   (A) $0.11 C. $1.11
   B. $0.21 D. $1.89

10. Which symbol makes the sentence true?
    466,127 ● 466,127
    (F) = G. > H. < J. +

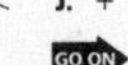

GO ON

Name ______________________

UNIT 1 TEST FORM A PAGE 2

11. What is the standard form?
    70,000,000 + 500,000 + 90,000 + 1,000 + 10 + 5
    A. 759,115 (C) 70,591,015
    B. 7,591,105 D. 700,591,015

12. Which has the least value?
    5,309,493; 5,300,000; 5,298,001; 5,310,017
    (F) 5,298,001 H. 5,309,493
    G. 5,300,017 J. 5,310,000

13. Round $185.62 to the nearest dollar.
    A. $180.00 (C) $186.00
    B. $185.00 D. $190.00

14. Find the amount of change.
    Price: $1.27
    Amount given: $10.00
    (F) $8.73 H. $9.83
    G. $9.73 J. $11.27

15. How much money is shown?

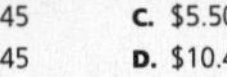

    A. $1.45 C. $5.50
    (B) $5.45 D. $10.45

16. Which digit makes the sentence true?
    5,882 < 5,8■2
    F. 6 G. 7 H. 8 (J) 9

Solve.
Use the tally chart for problems 17–18.

This tally chart shows students' favorite ways of getting to school.

Favorite Way of Going to School	
Bike	𝍸
Walk	||||
In-line Skate	𝍸 |

17. Which way of going to school got the least votes?
    A. bike C. in-line skates
    (B) walk D. bike and walk (tied)

18. How many chose in-line skates as their favorite way of going to school?
    F. 4 students (H) 6 students
    G. 5 students J. 7 students

19. Dictionary W has 619 pages and Dictionary X has 594 pages. Dictionary Y has 835 pages and Dictionary Z has 1,023 pages. Which dictionary has the least number of pages?
    A. W (B) X C. Y D. Z

20. Toni buys a sandwich for $3.58. She pays with a $10.00 bill. How much change does she receive?
    (F) $6.42 H. $7.42
    G. $6.58 J. $7.58

GO ON

Name ______________________

UNIT 1 TEST FORM A PAGE 3

21. What is the standard form of two million, forty-six thousand, seven hundred one?
    A. 2,046,071 C. 2,460,710
    (B) 2,046,701 D. 246,000,701

22. Order from least to greatest.
    $116.79; $108.50; $120.39
    (F) $108.50; $116.79; $120.39
    G. $108.50; $120.39; $116.79
    H. $120.39; $108.50; $116.79
    J. $116.79; $120.39; $108.50

23. Find the amount of change.
    Price: $4.59
    Amount given: $5.00
    (A) $0.41 C. $1.41
    B. $0.51 D. $1.51

24. What is the standard form of eighty million, five hundred thousand, one hundred thirty-nine?
    F. 85,139 (H) 80,500,139
    G. 8,500,139 J. 80,501,039

25. Round to the nearest dollar.
    $61.63
    A. $62.60 C. $61.60
    (B) $62.00 D. $61.00

26. What is the standard form of 3,000,000 + 70,000 + 3,000 + 10 + 1?
    F. 37,311 (H) 3,073,011
    G. 301,311 J. 3,073,101

27. Round to the nearest million.
    20,720,685
    A. 19,000,000 (C) 21,000,000
    B. 20,000,000 D. 30,000,000

28. Find the amount of change.
    Price: $6.03
    Amount given: $10.00
    (F) $3.97 H. $4.07
    G. $4.03 J. $4.97

29. Which symbol makes the sentence true?
    8,422,611 ● 8,471,906
    A. = (B) < C. > D. +

30. What is the standard form of 400,000,000 + 90,000,000 + 800,000 + 700 + 50 + 6?
    F. 498,756 H. 4,908,756
    G. 4,098,756 (J) 490,800,756

31. Which has the least value?
    $55.00; $54.99; $54.51; $54.12
    A. $54.99 (C) $54.12
    B. $55.00 D. $54.51

GO ON

Name ______________________

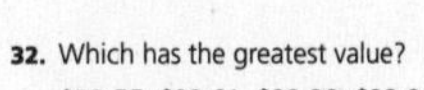

UNIT 1 TEST FORM A PAGE 4

32. Which has the greatest value?
    $23.55; $23.61; $22.29; $23.00
    F. $23.55 (H) $23.61
    G. $23.00 J. $22.29

33. Round $49.17 to the nearest ten cents.
    A. $49.10 (C) $49.20
    B. $50.17 D. $50.20

34. Find the amount of change.
    Price: $0.42
    Amount given: $1.00
    F. $0.48 H. $1.42
    (G) $0.58 J. $1.58

35. How much money is shown?

    A. $ 3.35 C. $12.40
    (B) $12.35 D. $30.35

36. Which symbol makes the sentence true?
    $512.35 ● $511.55
    F. = G. < (H) > J. +

Solve.
Use the tally chart for problems 37–38.

This tally chart shows students' pets.

Pets Students Own	
Cat	||||
Dog	𝍸
Fish	|||
Bird	||

37. Which pet is owned by the least number of students?
    A. cat B. dog C. fish (D) bird

38. How many students own a dog?
    F. 2 students H. 4 students
    G. 3 students (J) 5 students

39. Maria saw a CD on sale in 4 stores. The prices of the CD were: $12.69 at Acme; $11.39 at Ben's; $11.91 at CD Heaven; and $12.05 at Downtown. What store charged the least amount for the CD?
    A. Acme C. CD Heaven
    (B) Ben's D. Downtown

40. Casey bought a book for $15.65. He paid with a $20.00 bill. How much change will he receive?
    (F) $4.35 H. $5.35
    G. $4.45 J. $5.45

STOP

Unit 1

Name

Read each question carefully. Fill in the correct answer in the space provided.

UNIT 1 TEST
FORM B
PAGE 1

1. What is the standard form of three million, four hundred twelve thousand, and fifty-four?
   3,412,054

2. Order from greatest to least.
   34,440; 25,440; 34,611
   25,440; 34,611; 34,440

3. Find the amount of change.
   Price: $8.67
   Amount given: $10.00
   $1.33

4. What is the standard form of forty-two million, fifty-seven thousand, three hundred six?
   42,057,306

5. Which symbol makes the sentence true?
   24,506 ◯ 24,506
   =

Use the diagram for item 6.

2 Cups

6. Estimate the amount of water in the right glass using the left glass as a benchmark.
   6 cups

7. What is the standard form of 700,000 + 4000 + 300 + 5?
   704,305

8. Round to the nearest thousand.
   16,543,788
   16,544,000

9. Find the amount of change.
   Price: $2.14
   Amount given: $5.00
   $2.86

10. Which symbol makes the sentence true?
    322,989 ◯ 321,899
    >

GO ON

Grade 4 57

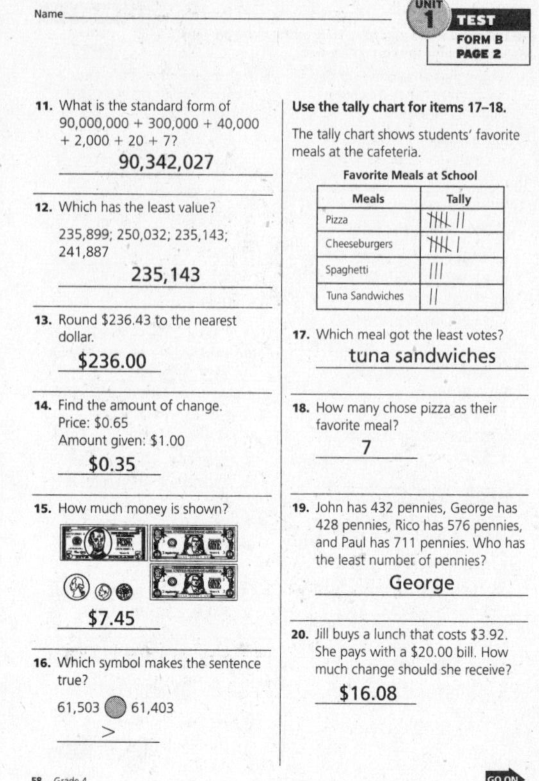

Name

UNIT 1 TEST
FORM B
PAGE 2

11. What is the standard form of 90,000,000 + 300,000 + 40,000 + 2,000 + 20 + 7?
    90,342,027

12. Which has the least value?
    235,899; 250,032; 235,143; 241,887
    235,143

13. Round $236.43 to the nearest dollar.
    $236.00

14. Find the amount of change.
    Price: $0.65
    Amount given: $1.00
    $0.35

15. How much money is shown?
    $7.45

16. Which symbol makes the sentence true?
    61,503 ◯ 61,403
    >

Use the tally chart for items 17–18.

The tally chart shows students' favorite meals at the cafeteria.

Favorite Meals at School

Meals	Tally
Pizza	卌 ||
Cheeseburgers	卌 |
Spaghetti	|||
Tuna Sandwiches	||

17. Which meal got the least votes?
    tuna sandwiches

18. How many chose pizza as their favorite meal?
    7

19. John has 432 pennies, George has 428 pennies, Rico has 576 pennies, and Paul has 711 pennies. Who has the least number of pennies?
    George

20. Jill buys a lunch that costs $3.92. She pays with a $20.00 bill. How much change should she receive?
    $16.08

58 Grade 4

GO ON

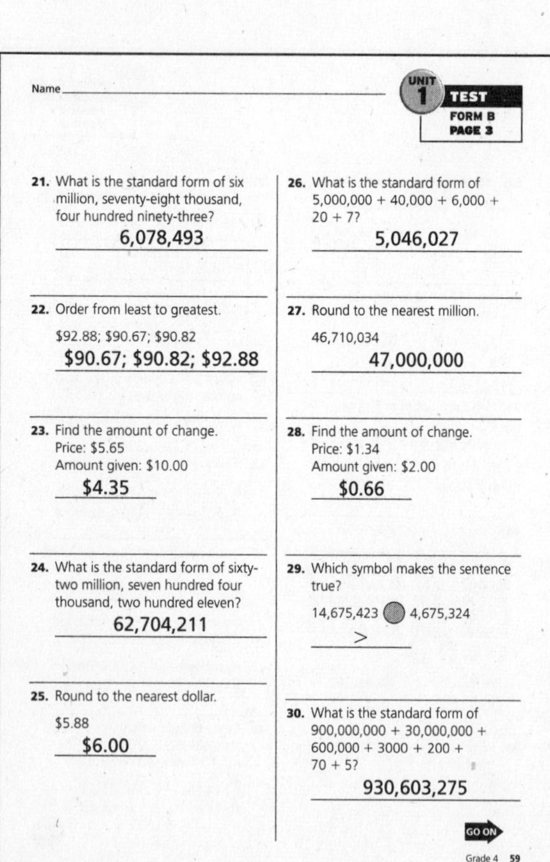

Name

UNIT 1 TEST
FORM B
PAGE 3

21. What is the standard form of six million, seventy-eight thousand, four hundred ninety-three?
    6,078,493

22. Order from least to greatest.
    $92.88; $90.67; $90.82
    $90.67; $90.82; $92.88

23. Find the amount of change.
    Price: $5.65
    Amount given: $10.00
    $4.35

24. What is the standard form of sixty-two million, seven hundred four thousand, two hundred eleven?
    62,704,211

25. Round to the nearest dollar.
    $5.88
    $6.00

26. What is the standard form of 5,000,000 + 40,000 + 6,000 + 20 + 7?
    5,046,027

27. Round to the nearest million.
    46,710,034
    47,000,000

28. Find the amount of change.
    Price: $1.34
    Amount given: $2.00
    $0.66

29. Which symbol makes the sentence true?
    14,675,423 ◯ 4,675,324
    >

30. What is the standard form of 900,000,000 + 30,000,000 + 600,000 + 3000 + 200 + 70 + 5?
    930,603,275

GO ON

Grade 4 59

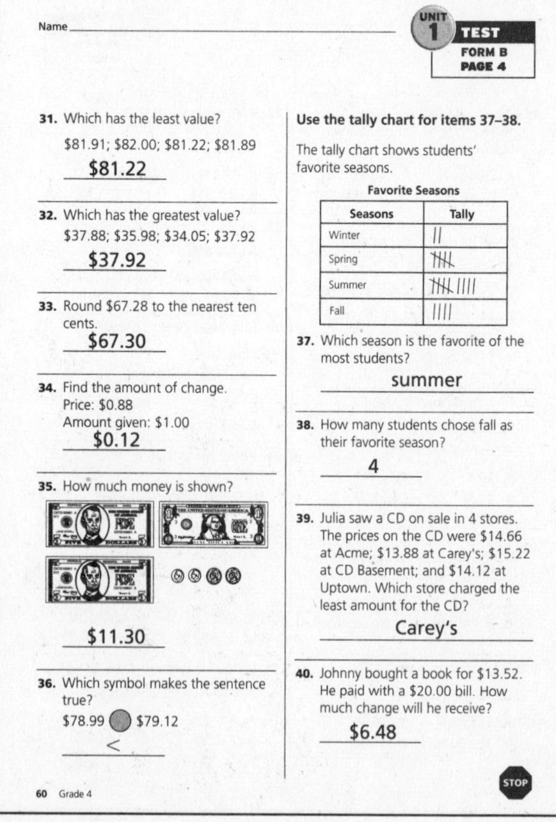

Name

UNIT 1 TEST
FORM B
PAGE 4

31. Which has the least value?
    $81.91; $82.00; $81.22; $81.89
    $81.22

32. Which has the greatest value?
    $37.88; $35.98; $34.05; $37.92
    $37.92

33. Round $67.28 to the nearest ten cents.
    $67.30

34. Find the amount of change.
    Price: $0.88
    Amount given: $1.00
    $0.12

35. How much money is shown?
    $11.30

36. Which symbol makes the sentence true?
    $78.99 ◯ $79.12
    <

Use the tally chart for items 37–38.

The tally chart shows students' favorite seasons.

Favorite Seasons

Seasons	Tally
Winter	||
Spring	卌
Summer	卌 ||||
Fall	||||

37. Which season is the favorite of the most students?
    summer

38. How many students chose fall as their favorite season?
    4

39. Julia saw a CD on sale in 4 stores. The prices on the CD were $14.66 at Acme; $13.88 at Carey's; $15.22 at CD Basement; and $14.12 at Uptown. Which store charged the least amount for the CD?
    Carey's

40. Johnny bought a book for $13.52. He paid with a $20.00 bill. How much change will he receive?
    $6.48

STOP

60 Grade 4

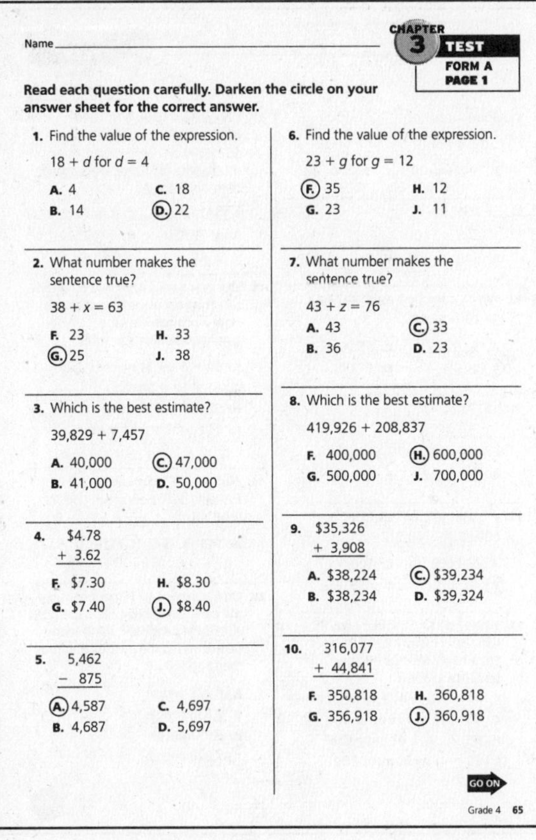

Name____________________

CHAPTER 3 TEST FORM A PAGE 1

Read each question carefully. Darken the circle on your answer sheet for the correct answer.

1. Find the value of the expression.
   $18 + d$ for $d = 4$
   A. 4 B. 14 C. 18 **D. 22**

2. What number makes the sentence true?
   $38 + x = 63$
   F. 23 **G. 25** H. 33 J. 38

3. Which is the best estimate?
   39,829 + 7,457
   A. 40,000 B. 41,000 **C. 47,000** D. 50,000

4. $4.78 + 3.62
   F. $7.30 G. $7.40 H. $8.30 **J. $8.40**

5. 5,462 − 875
   A. 4,587 B. 4,687 C. 4,697 D. 5,697

6. Find the value of the expression.
   $23 + g$ for $g = 12$
   F. 35 G. 23 H. 12 J. 11

7. What number makes the sentence true?
   $43 + z = 76$
   A. 43 B. 36 **C. 33** D. 23

8. Which is the best estimate?
   419,926 + 208,837
   F. 400,000 G. 500,000 **H. 600,000** J. 700,000

9. $35,326 + 3,908
   A. $38,224 B. $38,234 **C. $39,234** D. $39,324

10. 316,077 + 44,841
    F. 350,818 G. 356,918 H. 360,818 **J. 360,918**

GO ON

Grade 4 65

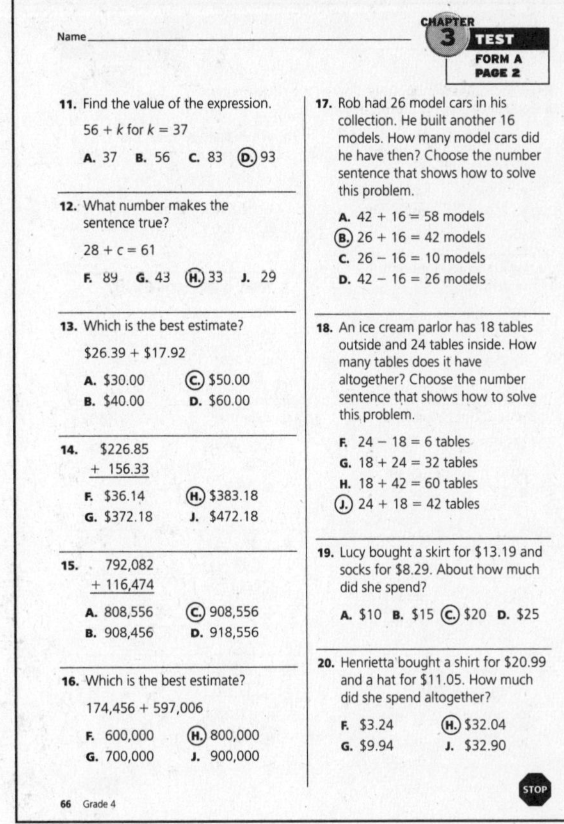

Name____________________

CHAPTER 3 TEST FORM A PAGE 2

11. Find the value of the expression.
    $56 + k$ for $k = 37$
    A. 37 B. 56 C. 83 **D. 93**

12. What number makes the sentence true?
    $28 + c = 61$
    F. 89 G. 43 **H. 33** J. 29

13. Which is the best estimate?
    $26.39 + $17.92
    A. $30.00 B. $40.00 **C. $50.00** D. $60.00

14. $226.85 + 156.33
    F. $36.14 G. $372.18 **H. $383.18** J. $472.18

15. 792,082 + 116,474
    A. 808,556 B. 908,456 **C. 908,556** D. 918,556

16. Which is the best estimate?
    174,456 + 597,006
    F. 600,000 G. 700,000 **H. 800,000** J. 900,000

17. Rob had 26 model cars in his collection. He built another 16 models. How many model cars did he have then? Choose the number sentence that shows how to solve this problem.
    A. 42 + 16 = 58 models
    B. 26 + 16 = 42 models
    C. 26 − 16 = 10 models
    D. 42 − 16 = 26 models

18. An ice cream parlor has 18 tables outside and 24 tables inside. How many tables does it have altogether? Choose the number sentence that shows how to solve this problem.
    F. 24 − 18 = 6 tables
    G. 18 + 24 = 32 tables
    H. 18 + 42 = 60 tables
    J. 24 + 18 = 42 tables

19. Lucy bought a skirt for $13.19 and socks for $8.29. About how much did she spend?
    A. $10 B. $15 **C. $20** D. $25

20. Henrietta bought a shirt for $20.99 and a hat for $11.05. How much did she spend altogether?
    F. $3.24 G. $9.94 **H. $32.04** J. $32.90

STOP

66 Grade 4

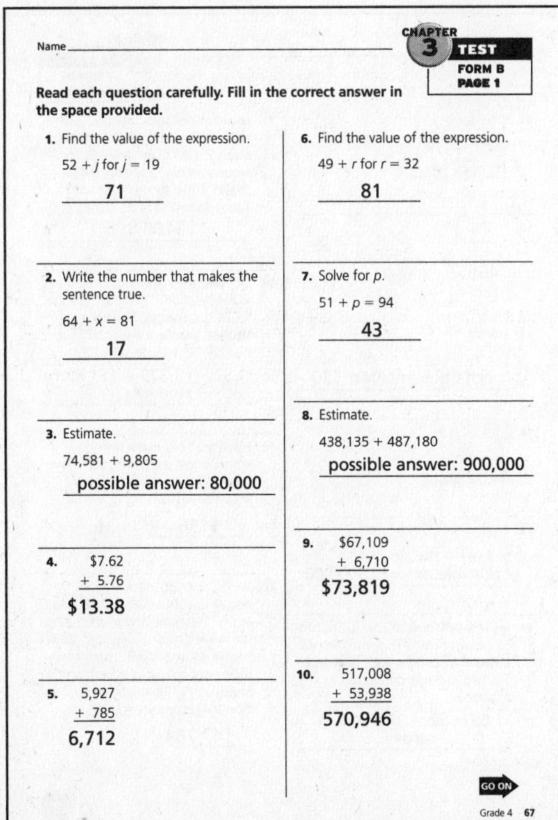

Name____________________

CHAPTER 3 TEST FORM B PAGE 1

Read each question carefully. Fill in the correct answer in the space provided.

1. Find the value of the expression.
   $52 + j$ for $j = 19$
   71

2. Write the number that makes the sentence true.
   $64 + x = 81$
   17

3. Estimate.
   74,581 + 9,805
   possible answer: 80,000

4. $7.62 + 5.76
   $13.38

5. 5,927 + 785
   6,712

6. Find the value of the expression.
   $49 + r$ for $r = 32$
   81

7. Solve for p.
   $51 + p = 94$
   43

8. Estimate.
   438,135 + 487,180
   possible answer: 900,000

9. $67,109 + 6,710
   $73,819

10. 517,008 + 53,938
    570,946

GO ON

Grade 4 67

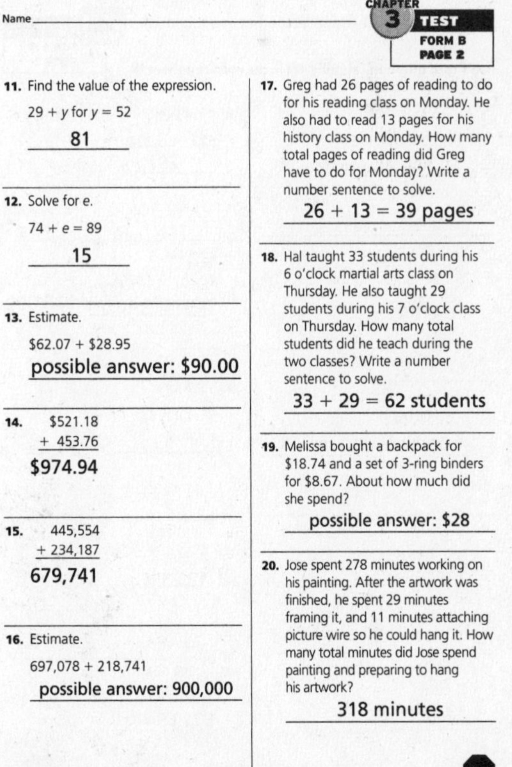

Name____________________

CHAPTER 3 TEST FORM B PAGE 2

11. Find the value of the expression.
    $29 + y$ for $y = 52$
    81

12. Solve for e.
    $74 + e = 89$
    15

13. Estimate.
    $62.07 + $28.95
    possible answer: $90.00

14. $521.18 + 453.76
    $974.94

15. 445,554 + 234,187
    679,741

16. Estimate.
    697,078 + 218,741
    possible answer: 900,000

17. Greg had 26 pages of reading to do for his reading class on Monday. He also had to read 13 pages for his history class on Monday. How many total pages of reading did Greg have to do for Monday? Write a number sentence to solve.
    26 + 13 = 39 pages

18. Hal taught 33 students during his 6 o'clock martial arts class on Thursday. He also taught 29 students during his 7 o'clock class on Thursday. How many total students did he teach during the two classes? Write a number sentence to solve.
    33 + 29 = 62 students

19. Melissa bought a backpack for $18.74 and a set of 3-ring binders for $8.67. About how much did she spend?
    possible answer: $28

20. Jose spent 278 minutes working on his painting. After the artwork was finished, he spent 29 minutes framing it, and 11 minutes attaching picture wire so he could hang it. How many total minutes did Jose spend painting and preparing to hang his artwork?
    318 minutes

STOP

68 Grade 4

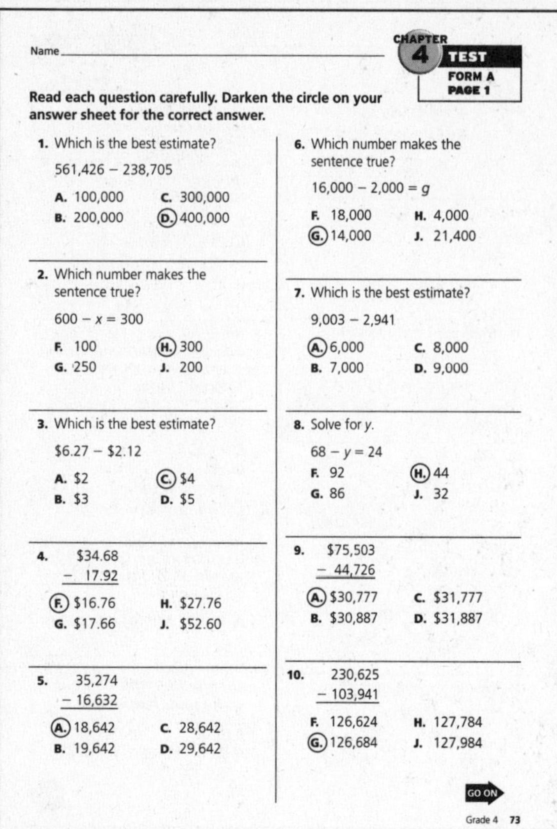

Name________________________

CHAPTER 4 TEST FORM A PAGE 1

Read each question carefully. Darken the circle on your answer sheet for the correct answer.

1. Which is the best estimate?
   561,426 − 238,705
   A. 100,000 B. 200,000 C. 300,000 **(D.) 400,000**

2. Which number makes the sentence true?
   600 − x = 300
   F. 100 G. 250 **(H.) 300** J. 200

3. Which is the best estimate?
   $6.27 − $2.12
   A. $2 B. $3 **(C.) $4** D. $5

4. $34.68 − 17.92
   (F.) $16.76 G. $17.66 H. $27.76 J. $52.60

5. 35,274 − 16,632
   (A.) 18,642 B. 19,642 C. 28,642 D. 29,642

6. Which number makes the sentence true?
   16,000 − 2,000 = g
   F. 18,000 **(G.) 14,000** H. 4,000 J. 21,400

7. Which is the best estimate?
   9,003 − 2,941
   (A.) 6,000 B. 7,000 C. 8,000 D. 9,000

8. Solve for y.
   68 − y = 24
   F. 92 G. 86 **(H.) 44** J. 32

9. $75,503 − 44,726
   (A.) $30,777 B. $30,887 C. $31,777 D. $31,887

10. 230,625 − 103,941
    F. 126,624 **(G.) 126,684** H. 127,784 J. 127,984

GO ON

Grade 4 73

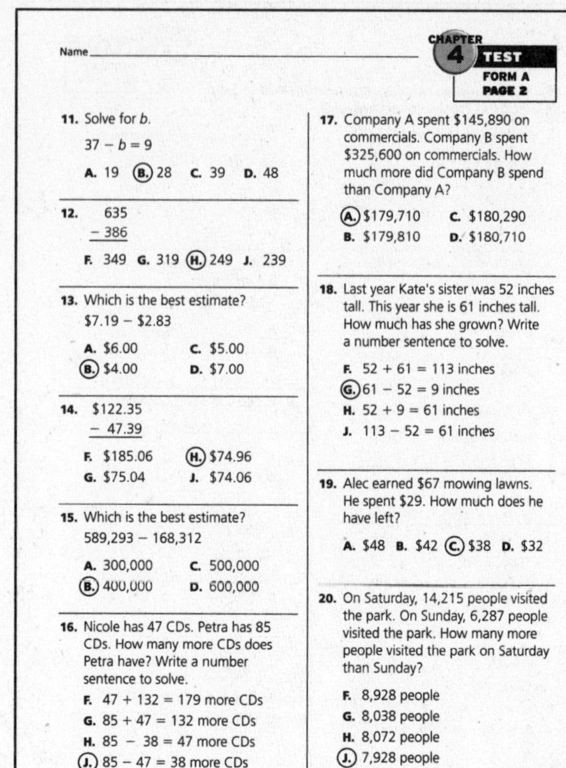

Name________________________

CHAPTER 4 TEST FORM A PAGE 2

11. Solve for b.
    37 − b = 9
    A. 19 **(B.) 28** C. 39 D. 48

12. 635 − 386
    F. 349 G. 319 **(H.) 249** J. 239

13. Which is the best estimate?
    $7.19 − $2.83
    A. $6.00 **(B.) $4.00** C. $5.00 D. $7.00

14. $122.35 − 47.39
    F. $185.06 G. $75.04 **(H.) $74.96** J. $74.06

15. Which is the best estimate?
    589,293 − 168,312
    A. 300,000 **(B.) 400,000** C. 500,000 D. 600,000

16. Nicole has 47 CDs. Petra has 85 CDs. How many more CDs does Petra have? Write a number sentence to solve.
    F. 47 + 132 = 179 more CDs
    G. 85 + 47 = 132 more CDs
    H. 85 − 38 = 47 more CDs
    (J.) 85 − 47 = 38 more CDs

17. Company A spent $145,890 on commercials. Company B spent $325,600 on commercials. How much more did Company B spend than Company A?
    (A.) $179,710 B. $179,810 C. $180,290 D. $180,710

18. Last year Kate's sister was 52 inches tall. This year she is 61 inches tall. How much has she grown? Write a number sentence to solve.
    F. 52 + 61 = 113 inches
    (G.) 61 − 52 = 9 inches
    H. 52 + 9 = 61 inches
    J. 113 − 52 = 61 inches

19. Alec earned $67 mowing lawns. He spent $29. How much does he have left?
    A. $48 B. $42 **(C.) $38** D. $32

20. On Saturday, 14,215 people visited the park. On Sunday, 6,287 people visited the park. How many more people visited the park on Saturday than Sunday?
    F. 8,928 people
    G. 8,038 people
    H. 8,072 people
    (J.) 7,928 people

STOP

74 Grade 4

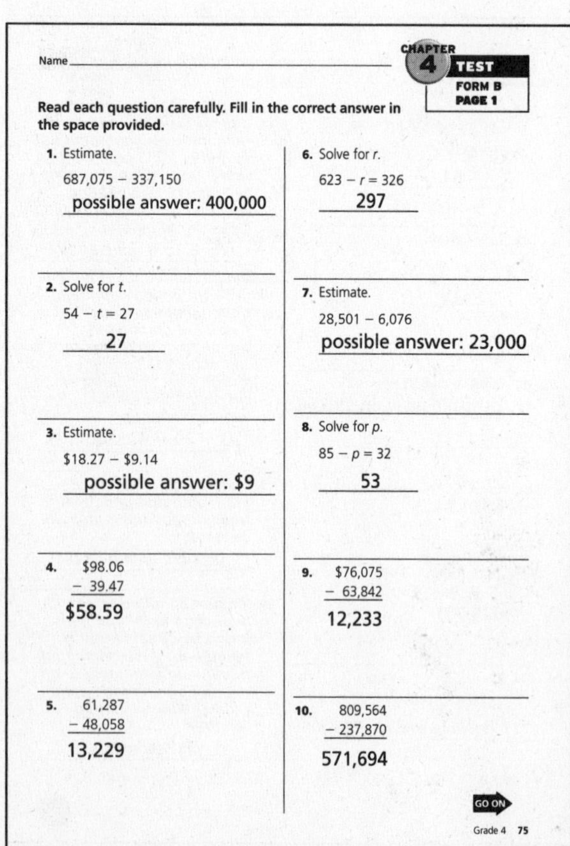

Name________________________

CHAPTER 4 TEST FORM B PAGE 1

Read each question carefully. Fill in the correct answer in the space provided.

1. Estimate.
   687,075 − 337,150
   possible answer: 400,000

2. Solve for t.
   54 − t = 27
   27

3. Estimate.
   $18.27 − $9.14
   possible answer: $9

4. $98.06 − 39.47
   $58.59

5. 61,287 − 48,058
   13,229

6. Solve for r.
   623 − r = 326
   297

7. Estimate.
   28,501 − 6,076
   possible answer: 23,000

8. Solve for p.
   85 − p = 32
   53

9. $76,075 − 63,842
   12,233

10. 809,564 − 237,870
    571,694

GO ON

Grade 4 75

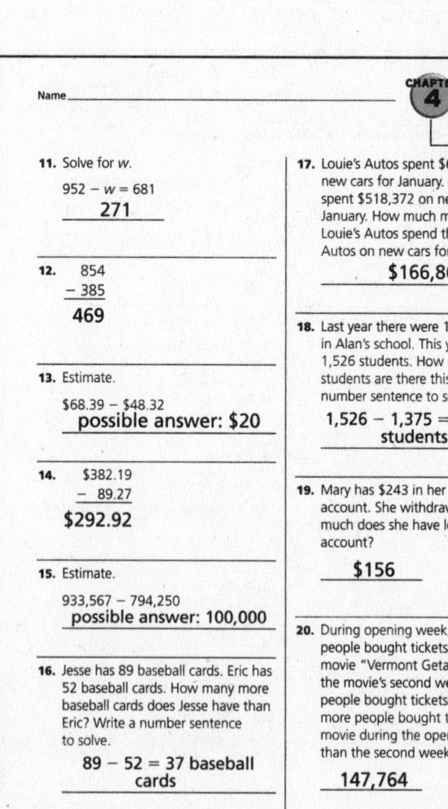

Name________________________

CHAPTER 4 TEST FORM B PAGE 2

11. Solve for w.
    952 − w = 681
    271

12. 854 − 385
    469

13. Estimate.
    $68.39 − $48.32
    possible answer: $20

14. $382.19 − 89.27
    $292.92

15. Estimate.
    933,567 − 794,250
    possible answer: 100,000

16. Jesse has 89 baseball cards. Eric has 52 baseball cards. How many more baseball cards does Jesse have than Eric? Write a number sentence to solve.
    89 − 52 = 37 baseball cards

17. Louie's Autos spent $685,237 on new cars for January. Phil's Autos spent $518,372 on new cars for January. How much more did Louie's Autos spend than Phil's Autos on new cars for January?
    $166,865

18. Last year there were 1,375 students in Alan's school. This year there are 1,526 students. How many more students are there this year? Write a number sentence to solve.
    1,526 − 1,375 = 151 more students

19. Mary has $243 in her savings account. She withdraws $87. How much does she have left in her account?
    $156

20. During opening week, 389,047 people bought tickets for the new movie "Vermont Getaway." During the movie's second week 241,283 people bought tickets. How many more people bought tickets for the movie during the opening week than the second week?
    147,764

STOP

76 Grade 4

Unit 2

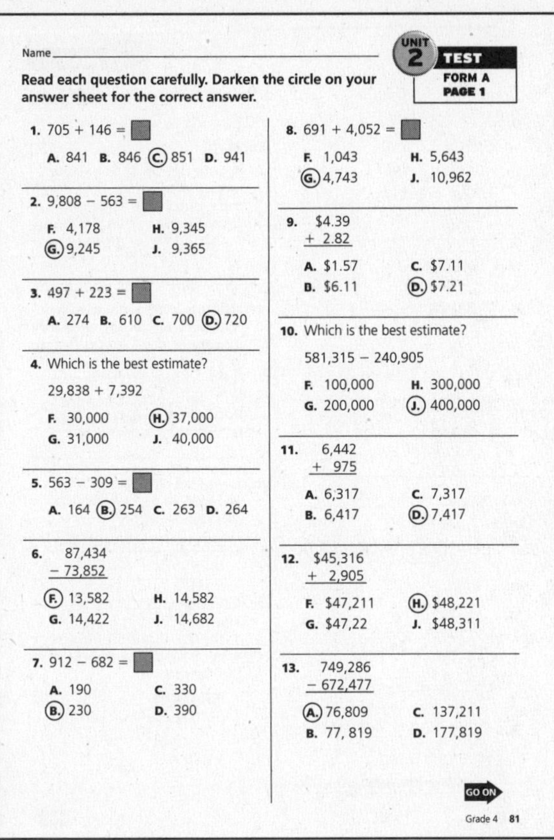

Name ____________________

UNIT 2 TEST FORM A PAGE 1

Read each question carefully. Darken the circle on your answer sheet for the correct answer.

1. 705 + 146 = ■
   A. 841 **B.** 846 (C) 851 **D.** 941

2. 9,808 − 563 = ■
   F. 4,178 **H.** 9,345
   (G) 9,245 **J.** 9,365

3. 497 + 223 = ■
   A. 274 **B.** 610 **C.** 700 (D) 720

4. Which is the best estimate?
   29,838 + 7,392
   F. 30,000 (H) 37,000
   G. 31,000 **J.** 40,000

5. 563 − 309 = ■
   A. 164 (B) 254 **C.** 263 **D.** 264

6. 87,434 − 73,852
   (F) 13,582 **H.** 14,582
   G. 14,422 **J.** 14,682

7. 912 − 682 = ■
   A. 190 **C.** 330
   (B) 230 **D.** 390

8. 691 + 4,052 = ■
   F. 1,043 **H.** 5,643
   (G) 4,743 **J.** 10,962

9. $4.39 + 2.82
   A. $1.57 **C.** $7.11
   B. $6.11 (D) $7.21

10. Which is the best estimate?
    581,315 − 240,905
    F. 100,000 **H.** 300,000
    G. 200,000 (J) 400,000

11. 6,442 + 975
    A. 6,317 **C.** 7,317
    B. 6,417 (D) 7,417

12. $45,316 + 2,905
    F. $47,211 (H) $48,221
    G. $47,22 **J.** $48,311

13. 749,286 − 672,477
    (A) 76,809 **C.** 137,211
    B. 77, 819 **D.** 177,819

GO ON

Grade 4 81

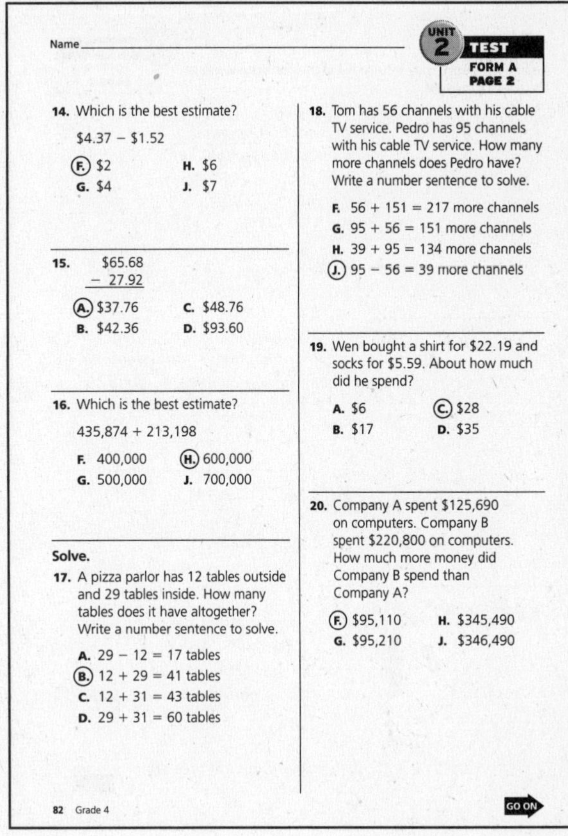

Name ____________________

UNIT 2 TEST FORM A PAGE 2

14. Which is the best estimate?
    $4.37 − $1.52
    (F) $2 **H.** $6
    G. $4 **J.** $7

15. $65.68 − 27.92
    (A) $37.76 **C.** $48.76
    B. $42.36 **D.** $93.60

16. Which is the best estimate?
    435,874 + 213,198
    F. 400,000 (H) 600,000
    G. 500,000 **J.** 700,000

Solve.

17. A pizza parlor has 12 tables outside and 29 tables inside. How many tables does it have altogether? Write a number sentence to solve.
    A. 29 − 12 = 17 tables
    (B) 12 + 29 = 41 tables
    C. 12 + 31 = 43 tables
    D. 29 + 31 = 60 tables

18. Tom has 56 channels with his cable TV service. Pedro has 95 channels with his cable TV service. How many more channels does Pedro have? Write a number sentence to solve.
    F. 56 + 151 = 217 more channels
    G. 95 + 56 = 151 more channels
    H. 39 + 95 = 134 more channels
    (J) 95 − 56 = 39 more channels

19. Wen bought a shirt for $22.19 and socks for $5.59. About how much did he spend?
    A. $6 (C) $28
    B. $17 **D.** $35

20. Company A spent $125,690 on computers. Company B spent $220,800 on computers. How much more money did Company B spend than Company A?
    (F) $95,110 **H.** $345,490
    G. $95,210 **J.** $346,490

82 Grade 4

GO ON

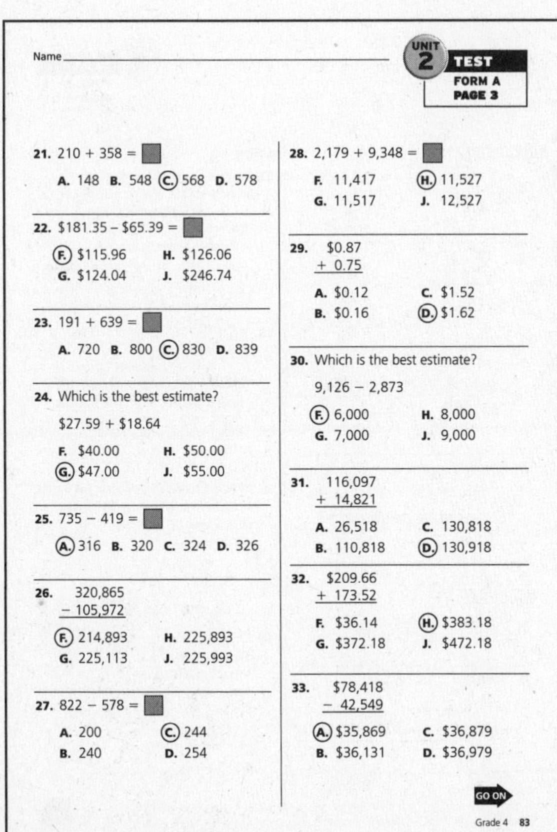

Name ____________________

UNIT 2 TEST FORM A PAGE 3

21. 210 + 358 = ■
    A. 148 **B.** 548 (C) 568 **D.** 578

22. $181.35 − $65.39 = ■
    (F) $115.96 **H.** $126.06
    G. $124.04 **J.** $246.74

23. 191 + 639 = ■
    A. 720 **B.** 800 (C) 830 **D.** 839

24. Which is the best estimate?
    $27.59 + $18.64
    F. $40.00 **H.** $50.00
    (G) $47.00 **J.** $55.00

25. 735 − 419 = ■
    (A) 316 **B.** 320 **C.** 324 **D.** 326

26. 320,865 − 105,972
    (F) 214,893 **H.** 225,893
    G. 225,113 **J.** 225,993

27. 822 − 578 = ■
    A. 200 (C) 244
    B. 240 **D.** 254

28. 2,179 + 9,348 = ■
    F. 11,417 (H) 11,527
    G. 11,517 **J.** 12,527

29. $0.87 + 0.75
    A. $0.12 **C.** $1.52
    B. $0.16 (D) $1.62

30. Which is the best estimate?
    9,126 − 2,873
    (F) 6,000 **H.** 8,000
    G. 7,000 **J.** 9,000

31. 116,097 + 14,821
    A. 26,518 **C.** 130,818
    B. 110,818 (D) 130,918

32. $209.66 + 173.52
    F. $36.14 (H) $383.18
    G. $372.18 **J.** $472.18

33. $78,418 − 42,549
    (A) $35,869 **C.** $36,879
    B. $36,131 **D.** $36,979

GO ON

Grade 4 83

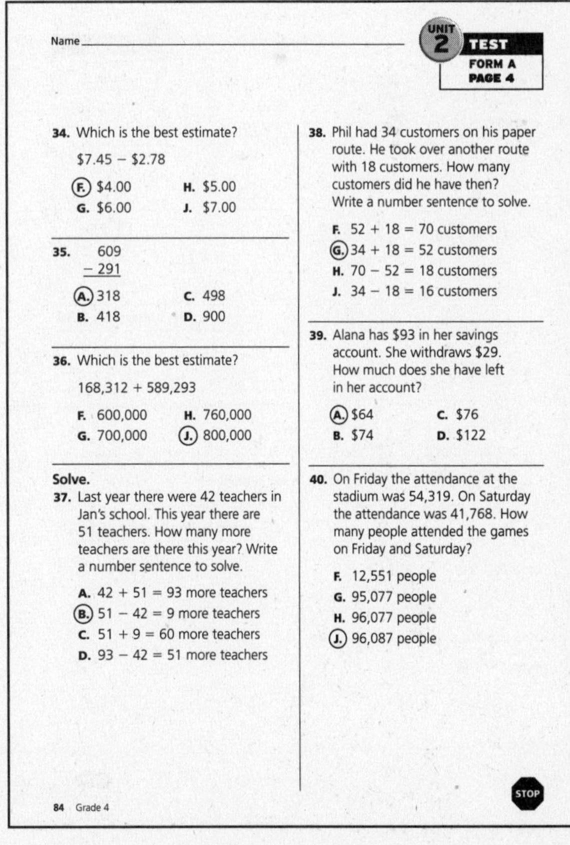

Name ____________________

UNIT 2 TEST FORM A PAGE 4

34. Which is the best estimate?
    $7.45 − $2.78
    (F) $4.00 **H.** $5.00
    G. $6.00 **J.** $7.00

35. 609 − 291
    (A) 318 **C.** 498
    B. 418 **D.** 900

36. Which is the best estimate?
    168,312 + 589,293
    F. 600,000 **H.** 760,000
    G. 700,000 (J) 800,000

Solve.

37. Last year there were 42 teachers in Jan's school. This year there are 51 teachers. How many more teachers are there this year? Write a number sentence to solve.
    A. 42 + 51 = 93 more teachers
    (B) 51 − 42 = 9 more teachers
    C. 51 + 9 = 60 more teachers
    D. 93 − 42 = 51 more teachers

38. Phil had 34 customers on his paper route. He took over another route with 18 customers. How many customers did he have then? Write a number sentence to solve.
    F. 52 + 18 = 70 customers
    (G) 34 + 18 = 52 customers
    H. 70 − 52 = 18 customers
    J. 34 − 18 = 16 customers

39. Alana has $93 in her savings account. She withdraws $29. How much does she have left in her account?
    (A) $64 **C.** $76
    B. $74 **D.** $122

40. On Friday the attendance at the stadium was 54,319. On Saturday the attendance was 41,768. How many people attended the games on Friday and Saturday?
    F. 12,551 people
    G. 95,077 people
    H. 96,077 people
    (J) 96,087 people

84 Grade 4

STOP

Unit 2

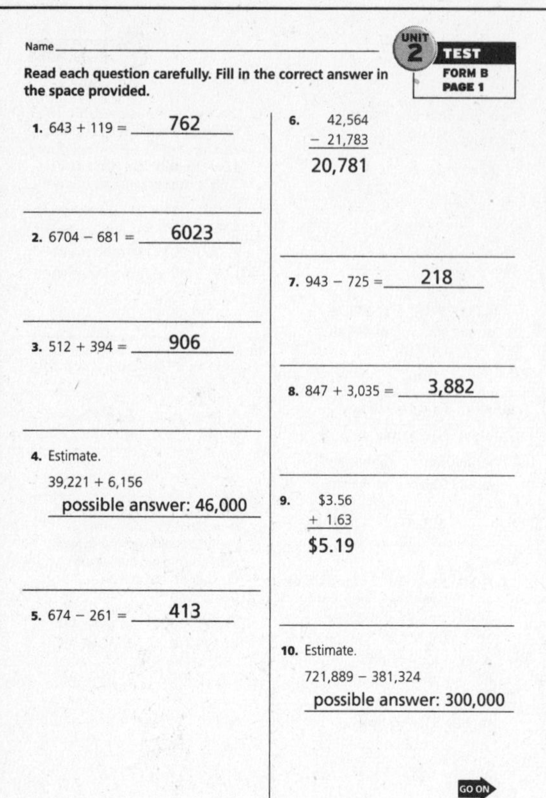

Name ______

UNIT 2 TEST FORM B PAGE 1

Read each question carefully. Fill in the correct answer in the space provided.

1. 643 + 119 = **762**
2. 6704 − 681 = **6023**
3. 512 + 394 = **906**
4. Estimate. 39,221 + 6,156 **possible answer: 46,000**
5. 674 − 261 = **413**
6. 42,564 − 21,783 = **20,781**
7. 943 − 725 = **218**
8. 847 + 3,035 = **3,882**
9. $3.56 + 1.63 = **$5.19**
10. Estimate. 721,889 − 381,324 **possible answer: 300,000**

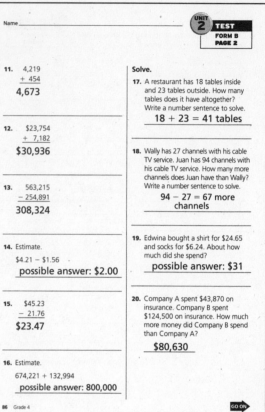

GO ON

Grade 4 85

Name ______

UNIT 2 TEST FORM B PAGE 2

11. 4,219 + 454 = **4,673**
12. $23,754 + 7,182 = **$30,936**
13. 563,215 − 254,891 = **308,324**
14. Estimate. $4.21 − $1.56 **possible answer: $2.00**
15. $45.23 − 21.76 = **$23.47**
16. Estimate. 674,221 + 132,994 **possible answer: 800,000**

Solve.

17. A restaurant has 18 tables inside and 23 tables outside. How many tables does it have altogether? Write a number sentence to solve. **18 + 23 = 41 tables**
18. Wally has 27 channels with his cable TV service. Juan has 94 channels with his cable TV service. How many more channels does Juan have than Wally? Write a number sentence to solve. **94 − 27 = 67 more channels**
19. Edwina bought a shirt for $24.65 and socks for $6.24. About how much did she spend? **possible answer: $31**
20. Company A spent $43,870 on insurance. Company B spent $124,500 on insurance. How much more money did Company B spend than Company A? **$80,630**

86 Grade 4

GO ON

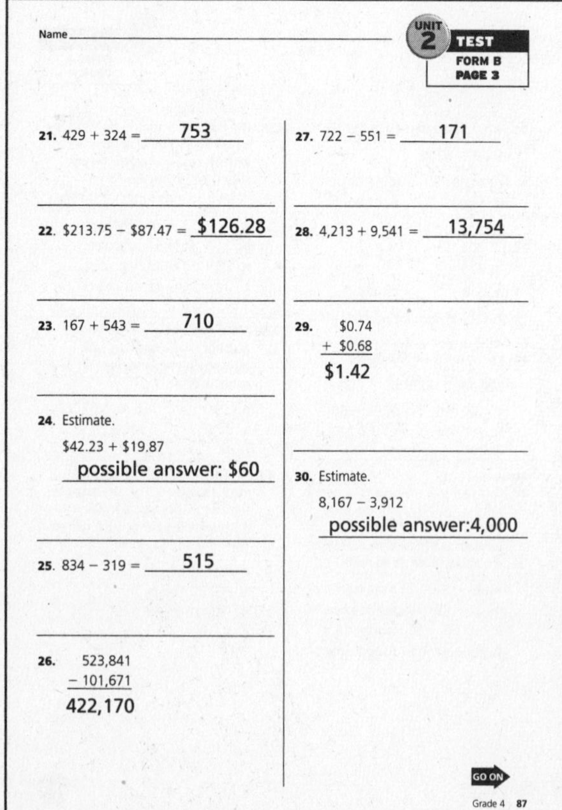

Name ______

UNIT 2 TEST FORM B PAGE 3

21. 429 + 324 = **753**
22. $213.75 − $87.47 = **$126.28**
23. 167 + 543 = **710**
24. Estimate. $42.23 + $19.87 **possible answer: $60**
25. 834 − 319 = **515**
26. 523,841 − 101,671 = **422,170**
27. 722 − 551 = **171**
28. 4,213 + 9,541 = **13,754**
29. $0.74 + $0.68 = **$1.42**
30. Estimate. 8,167 − 3,912 **possible answer:4,000**

GO ON

Grade 4 87

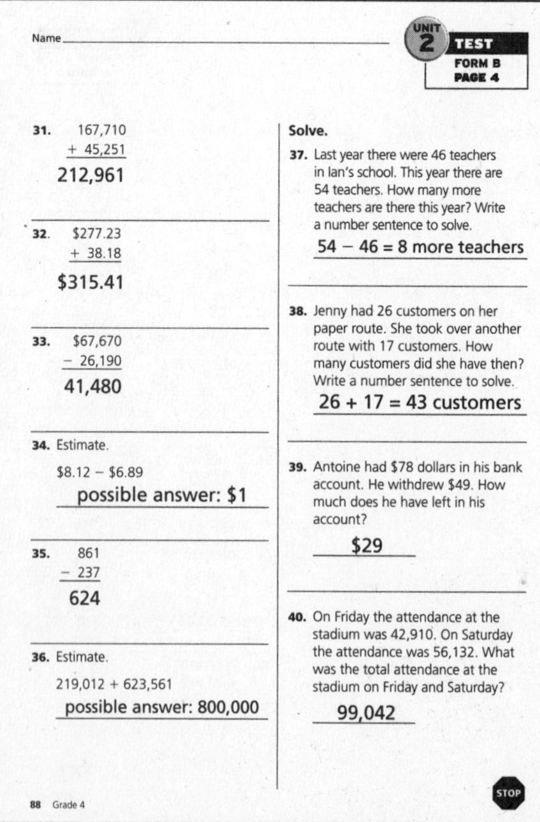

Name ______

UNIT 2 TEST FORM B PAGE 4

31. 167,710 + 45,251 = **212,961**
32. $277.23 + 38.18 = **$315.41**
33. $67,670 − 26,190 = **41,480**
34. Estimate. $8.12 − $6.89 **possible answer: $1**
35. 861 − 237 = **624**
36. Estimate. 219,012 + 623,561 **possible answer: 800,000**

Solve.

37. Last year there were 46 teachers in Ian's school. This year there are 54 teachers. How many more teachers are there this year? Write a number sentence to solve. **54 − 46 = 8 more teachers**
38. Jenny had 26 customers on her paper route. She took over another route with 17 customers. How many customers did she have then? Write a number sentence to solve. **26 + 17 = 43 customers**
39. Antoine had $78 dollars in his bank account. He withdrew $49. How much does he have left in his account? **$29**
40. On Friday the attendance at the stadium was 42,910. On Saturday the attendance was 56,132. What was the total attendance at the stadium on Friday and Saturday? **99,042**

STOP

88 Grade 4

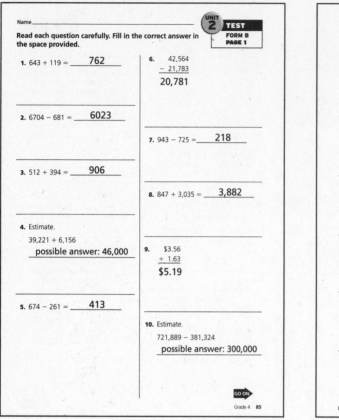

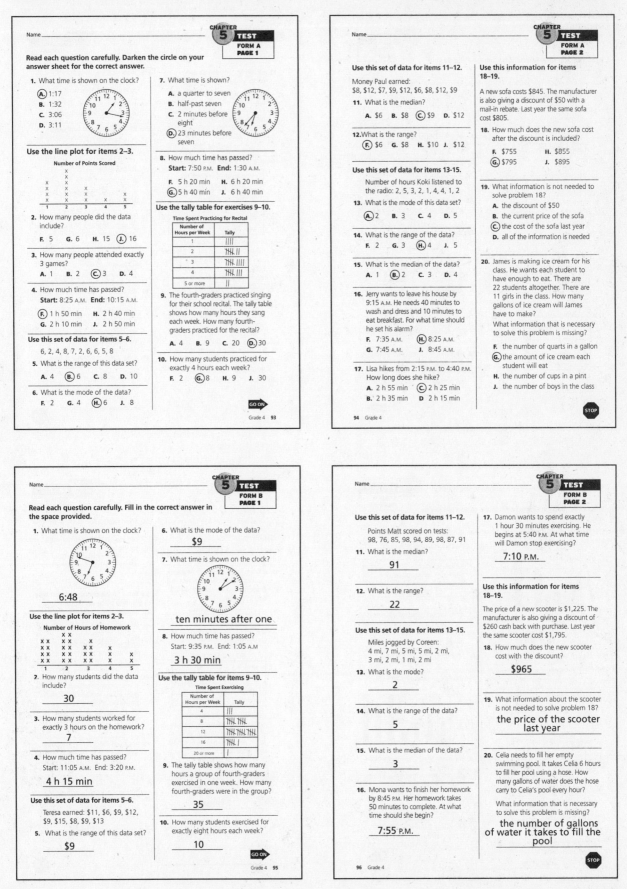

Name ____________________

CHAPTER 5 TEST FORM A PAGE 1

Read each question carefully. Darken the circle on your answer sheet for the correct answer.

1. What time is shown on the clock?
   (A.) 1:17
   B. 1:32
   C. 3:06
   D. 3:11

Use the line plot for items 2–3.

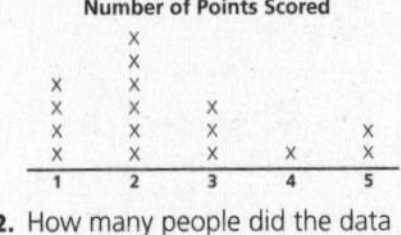

Number of Points Scored

1	2	3	4	5
XXXX	XXXXXX	XXX	X	XX

2. How many people did the data include?
   F. 5 G. 6 H. 15 (J.) 16

3. How many people attended exactly 3 games?
   A. 1 B. 2 (C.) 3 D. 4

4. How much time has passed?
   Start: 8:25 A.M. **End:** 10:15 A.M.
   (F.) 1 h 50 min H. 2 h 40 min
   G. 2 h 10 min J. 2 h 50 min

Use this set of data for items 5–6.

6, 2, 4, 8, 7, 2, 6, 6, 5, 8

5. What is the range of this data set?
   A. 4 (B.) 6 C. 8 D. 10

6. What is the mode of the data?
   F. 2 G. 4 (H.) 6 J. 8

7. What time is shown?
   A. a quarter to seven
   B. half-past seven
   C. 2 minutes before eight
   (D.) 23 minutes before seven

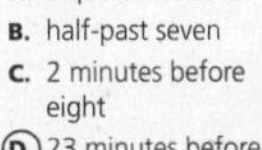

8. How much time has passed?
   Start: 7:50 P.M. **End:** 1:30 A.M.
   F. 5 h 20 min H. 6 h 20 min
   (G.) 5 h 40 min J. 6 h 40 min

Use the tally table for exercises 9–10.

Time Spent Practicing for Recital

Number of Hours per Week	Tally
1	||||
2	卌 ||
3	卌 ||||
4	卌 |||
5 or more	||

9. The fourth-graders practiced singing for their school recital. The tally table shows how many hours they sang each week. How many fourth-graders practiced for the recital?
   A. 4 B. 9 C. 20 (D.) 30

10. How many students practiced for exactly 4 hours each week?
    F. 2 (G.) 8 H. 9 J. 30

Name ____________________

CHAPTER 5 TEST FORM A PAGE 2

Use this set of data for items 11–12.

Money Paul earned:
$8, $12, $7, $9, $12, $6, $8, $12, $9

11. What is the median?
    A. $6 B. $8 (C.) $9 D. $12

12. What is the range?
    (F.) $6 G. $8 H. $10 J. $12

Use this set of data for items 13–15.

Number of hours Koki listened to the radio: 2, 5, 3, 2, 1, 4, 4, 1, 2

13. What is the mode of this data set?
    (A.) 2 B. 3 C. 4 D. 5

14. What is the range of the data?
    F. 2 G. 3 (H.) 4 J. 5

15. What is the median of the data?
    A. 1 (B.) 2 C. 3 D. 4

16. Jerry wants to leave his house by 9:15 A.M. He needs 40 minutes to wash and dress and 10 minutes to eat breakfast. For what time should he set his alarm?
    F. 7:35 A.M. (H.) 8:25 A.M.
    G. 7:45 A.M. J. 8:45 A.M.

17. Lisa hikes from 2:15 P.M. to 4:40 P.M. How long does she hike?
    A. 2 h 55 min (C.) 2 h 25 min
    B. 2 h 35 min D. 2 h 15 min

Use this information for items 18–19.

A new sofa costs $845. The manufacturer is also giving a discount of $50 with a mail-in rebate. Last year the same sofa cost $805.

18. How much does the new sofa cost after the discount is included?
    F. $755 H. $855
    (G.) $795 J. $895

19. What information is not needed to solve problem 18?
    A. the discount of $50
    B. the current price of the sofa
    (C.) the cost of the sofa last year
    D. all of the information is needed

20. James is making ice cream for his class. He wants each student to have enough to eat. There are 22 students altogether. There are 11 girls in the class. How many gallons of ice cream will James have to make?
    What information that is necessary to solve this problem is missing?
    F. the number of quarts in a gallon
    (G.) the amount of ice cream each student will eat
    H. the number of cups in a pint
    J. the number of boys in the class

Name ____________________

CHAPTER 5 TEST FORM B PAGE 1

Read each question carefully. Fill in the correct answer in the space provided.

1. What time is shown on the clock?

6:48

Use the line plot for items 2–3.

Number of Hours of Homework

1	2	3	4	5
XXXXXXXX	XXXXXXXXXX	XXXXXXX	XXX	XX

2. How many students did the data include?
   30

3. How many students worked for exactly 3 hours on the homework?
   7

4. How much time has passed?
   Start: 11:05 A.M. End: 3:20 P.M.
   4 h 15 min

Use this set of data for items 5–6.

Teresa earned: $11, $6, $9, $12, $9, $15, $8, $9, $13

5. What is the range of this data set?
   $9

6. What is the mode of the data?
   $9

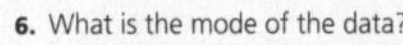

7. What time is shown on the clock?

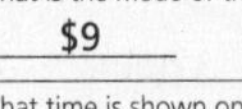

ten minutes after one

8. How much time has passed?
   Start: 9:35 P.M. End: 1:05 A.M
   3 h 30 min

Use the tally table for items 9–10.

Time Spent Exercising

Number of Hours per Week	Tally
4	|||
8	卌 卌
12	卌 卌 卌
16	卌 |
20 or more	|

9. The tally table shows how many hours a group of fourth-graders exercised in one week. How many fourth-graders were in the group?
   35

10. How many students exercised for exactly eight hours each week?
    10

Name ____________________

CHAPTER 5 TEST FORM B PAGE 2

Use this set of data for items 11–12.

Points Matt scored on tests:
98, 76, 85, 98, 94, 89, 98, 87, 91

11. What is the median?
    91

12. What is the range?
    22

Use this set of data for items 13–15.

Miles jogged by Coreen:
4 mi, 7 mi, 5 mi, 5 mi, 2 mi,
3 mi, 2 mi, 1 mi, 2 mi

13. What is the mode?
    2

14. What is the range of the data?
    5

15. What is the median of the data?
    3

16. Mona wants to finish her homework by 8:45 P.M. Her homework takes 50 minutes to complete. At what time should she begin?
    7:55 P.M.

17. Damon wants to spend exactly 1 hour 30 minutes exercising. He begins at 5:40 P.M. At what time will Damon stop exercising?
    7:10 P.M.

Use this information for items 18–19.

The price of a new scooter is $1,225. The manufacturer is also giving a discount of $260 cash back with purchase. Last year the same scooter cost $1,795.

18. How much does the new scooter cost with the discount?
    $965

19. What information about the scooter is not needed to solve problem 18?
    the price of the scooter last year

20. Celia needs to fill her empty swimming pool. It takes Celia 6 hours to fill her pool using a hose. How many gallons of water does the hose carry to Celia's pool every hour?
    What information that is necessary to solve this problem is missing?
    the number of gallons of water it takes to fill the pool

Chapter 6

Name____

Read each question carefully. Darken the circle on your answer sheet for the correct answer.

Use the bar graph for items 1–4.

1. How many votes did vanilla get?
A. 1 B. 2 C. 4 (D.) 5

2. Which flavor did girls like most?
F. vanilla H. mint
G. chocolate (J.) strawberry

3. How many boys like strawberry?
A. 1 (B.) 4 C. 8 D. 12

4. If 3 times as many girls voted for mint as is on the graph, what would be a good scale to use?
F. 0-3 G. 0-12 (H.) 0-20 J. 0-30

Use the pictograph for items 5–8.

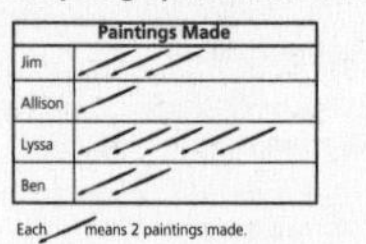

5. How many more paintings did Jim make than Allison?
A. 2 B. 3 (C.) 4 D. 6

6. Who made the most paintings?
F. Jim (H.) Lyssa
G. Allison J. Ben

7. Erika made 18 paintings. How many brushes would be next to her name?
A. 6 (B.) 9 C. 12 D. 18

8. If the number of brushes next to Lyssa represented 15 paintings instead of 10, how many paintings made would each picture represent in the key?
F. 1 G. 2 (H.) 3 J. 4

Use the line graph for items 9–12.

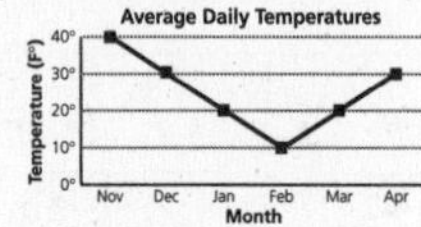

9. What was the average daily temperature for February?
(A.) 10° B. 20° C. 30° D. 40°

10. How much higher was the average daily temperature in December than in February?
F. 10° (G.) 20° H. 30° J. 40°

Name____

11. What was the average daily temperature for all six months?
A. 15° B. 16° (C.) 25° D. 30°

12. October had an average daily temperature of 50°. By how much would the range change if you added October to the graph?
(F.) 10° G. 15° H. 20° J. 25°

Use this set of data for items 13–16.

Number of Players on Each Soccer Team	
Green	24
Blue	12
Black	16
Red	20

13. If you made a pictograph of the data using a soccer ball as a symbol, how many soccer balls would be next to the Red team if each ball represented 4 players?
A. 20 B. 10 (C.) 5 D. 4

14. How many soccer balls would be next to the Green team if each ball represented 8 players?
F. 4 (G.) 3 H. 16 J. 2

15. If you made a bar graph of the data, which would be the best scale?
A. 0-4 B. 0-12 (C.) 0-24 D. 0-48

16. If you made a line graph of the data, which team would correspond to the lowest point on the line?
F. Green H. Black
(G.) Blue J. Red

For 17–20, choose the best graph.

17. Four students compare the number of boxes of cookies they sold. Each cookie symbol represents 3 boxes.
A. line graph
B. double bar graph
C. Venn diagram
(D.) pictograph

18. 32 students play baseball, soccer or track. 18 play 2 of the sports, and 5 play all 3 sports.
F. line graph
G. double bar graph
(H.) Venn diagram
J. pictograph

19. Ben and Amy compare their math and reading scores.
A. line graph
(B.) double bar graph
C. Venn diagram
D. pictograph

20. Ticket sales at a movie theater increase over a 6-month period.
(F.) line graph
G. double bar graph
H. Venn diagram
J. pictograph

Name____

CHAPTER 6 TEST FORM B PAGE 1

Read each question carefully. Fill in the correct answer in the space provided.

Use the bar graph for items 1–4.

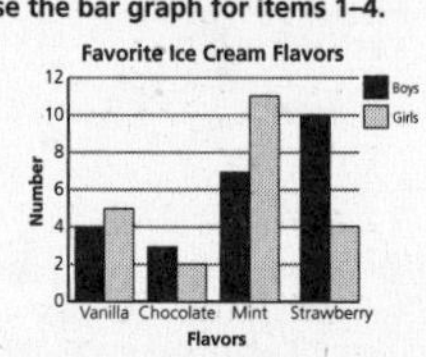

1. How many votes did mint get?
18 votes

2. Which flavor had the most votes by boys?
strawberry

3. How many girls like vanilla best?
5 girls

4. If 4 times as many boys voted for strawberry as shown on the graph, what would be a good scale?
possible answer: 0–40

Use the pictograph for items 5–8.

5. How many more points did Alice score than Jason?
6 points

6. Who scored the least points?
Louis

7. William scored 14 points. How many basketballs would you put next to his name?
7 basketballs

8. If the number of basketballs next to Francis represented 12 points instead of 8, how many points would each picture represent in the key?
3 points

Use the line graph for items 9–12.

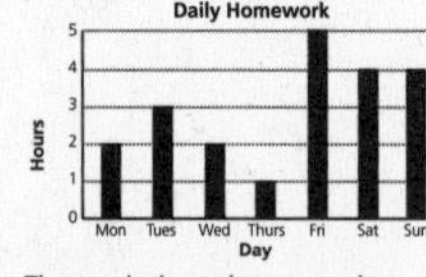

9. The graph shows how many hours of homework Kevin had for each day of the week. How many hours did he have on Tuesday?
3 hours

10. How many more hours of homework did Kevin have on Friday than on Thursday?
4 hours

GO ON

Name____

11. What was the average number of hours of homework for all seven days?
3 hours

12. If Kevin had 6 hours of homework on Sunday, by how much would the range change if you changed this data in the graph?
1 hour

Use this set of data for items 13–16.

Students Favorite School Subjects	
Math	42
Science	35
English	63
History	56

13. Imagine that you made a pictograph of the data using a book as a symbol. How many books would you show next to English if each book represented 7 students?
9 books

14. How many books would be next to History if each book represented 8 students?
7 books

15. If you made a bar graph of the data, which would be the best scale to use?
0–7, 0–35, or 0–70
0–70

16. If you made a line graph of the data in the table, which subject would correspond to the highest point on the line?
English

For items 17–20, choose the best type of graph to show each data set.

17. The class compared the number of pizza slices they ate. Each pizza pie symbol represents 2 slices.
pictograph

18. 24 students enjoy action movies, comedies, or cartoons. Some enjoy only action, some only comedies, others like all three.
venn diagram

19. Matt and Jasira earn money each week working at their summer jobs.
double bar graph

20. Daily sales at Morgan's Hardware Store increase over a 3-month period.
line graph

Unit 3

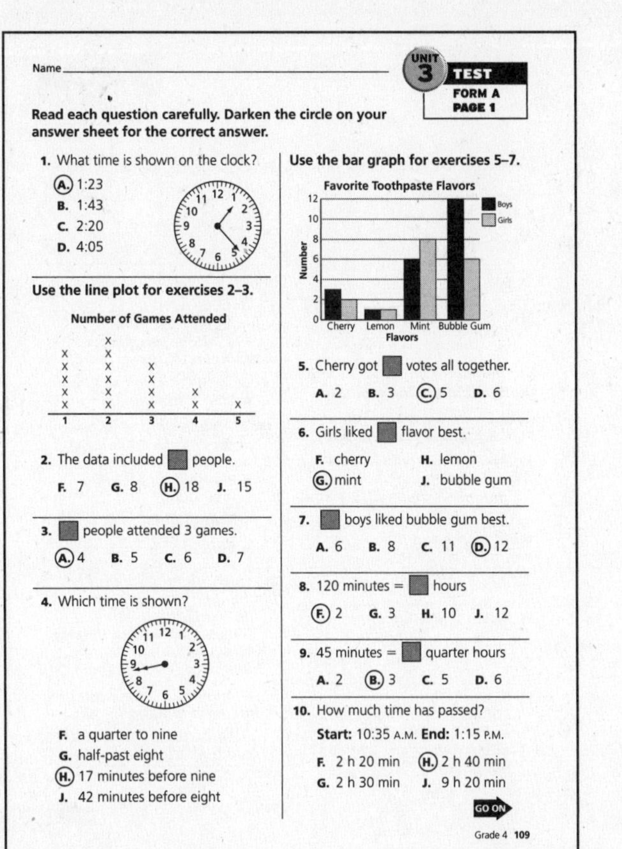

Name ____________________

UNIT 3 TEST FORM A PAGE 1

Read each question carefully. Darken the circle on your answer sheet for the correct answer.

1. What time is shown on the clock?
   (A.) 1:23
   B. 1:43
   C. 2:20
   D. 4:05

Use the line plot for exercises 2–3.

Number of Games Attended

1 2 3 4 5

2. The data included ☐ people.
   F. 7 G. 8 (H.) 18 J. 15

3. ☐ people attended 3 games.
   (A.) 4 B. 5 C. 6 D. 7

4. Which time is shown?
   F. a quarter to nine
   G. half-past eight
   (H.) 17 minutes before nine
   J. 42 minutes before eight

Use the bar graph for exercises 5–7.

Favorite Toothpaste Flavors

Number; Flavors: Cherry, Lemon, Mint, Bubble Gum; Boys, Girls

5. Cherry got ☐ votes all together.
   A. 2 B. 3 (C.) 5 D. 6

6. Girls liked ☐ flavor best.
   F. cherry H. lemon
   (G.) mint J. bubble gum

7. ☐ boys liked bubble gum best.
   A. 6 B. 8 C. 11 (D.) 12

8. 120 minutes = ☐ hours
   (F.) 2 G. 3 H. 10 J. 12

9. 45 minutes = ☐ quarter hours
   A. 2 (B.) 3 C. 5 D. 6

10. How much time has passed?
    Start: 10:35 A.M. **End:** 1:15 P.M.
    F. 2 h 20 min (H.) 2 h 40 min
    G. 2 h 30 min J. 9 h 20 min

GO ON

Grade 4 109

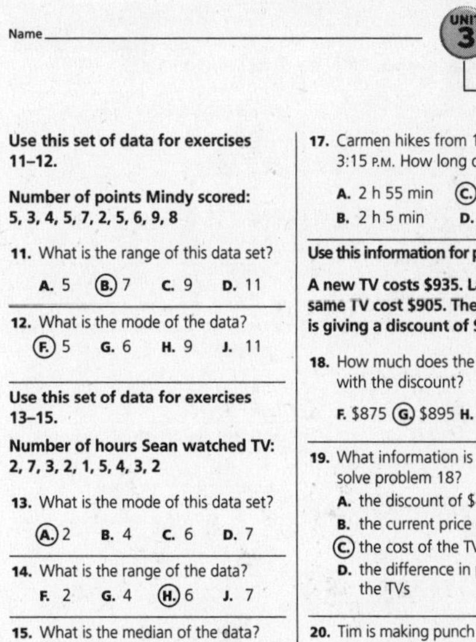

Name ____________________

UNIT 3 TEST FORM A PAGE 2

Use this set of data for exercises 11–12.

Number of points Mindy scored: 5, 3, 4, 5, 7, 2, 5, 6, 9, 8

11. What is the range of this data set?
    A. 5 (B.) 7 C. 9 D. 11

12. What is the mode of the data?
    (F.) 5 G. 6 H. 9 J. 11

Use this set of data for exercises 13–15.

Number of hours Sean watched TV: 2, 7, 3, 2, 1, 5, 4, 3, 2

13. What is the mode of this data set?
    (A.) 2 B. 4 C. 6 D. 7

14. What is the range of the data?
    F. 2 G. 4 (H.) 6 J. 7

15. What is the median of the data?
    A. 2 (B.) 3 C. 4 D. 7

Solve.

16. Tom wants to leave his house by 8:45 A.M. He needs 30 minutes to wash and dress and 20 minutes to eat breakfast. For what time should he set his alarm?
    (F.) 7:55 A.M. H. 8:15 A.M.
    G. 8:05 A.M. J. 8:25 A.M.

17. Carmen hikes from 1:20 P.M. to 3:15 P.M. How long does she hike?
    A. 2 h 55 min (C.) 1 h 55 min
    B. 2 h 5 min D. 1 h 35 min

Use this information for problems 18–19.

A new TV costs $935. Last year the same TV cost $905. The manufacturer is giving a discount of $40.

18. How much does the new TV cost with the discount?
    F. $875 (G.) $895 H. $965 J. $975

19. What information is not needed to solve problem 18?
    A. the discount of $40
    B. the current price of the TV
    (C.) the cost of the TV last year
    D. the difference in price between the TVs

20. Tim is making punch for his class. He wants each student to have enough to drink. There are 30 students all together. There are 15 girls in the class. How many gallons of punch will Tim have to make?
    What information that is necessary to solve this problem is missing?
    F. the number of quarts in a gallon
    (G.) the amount of punch each student will drink
    H. the number of cups in a pint
    J. the number of boys in the class

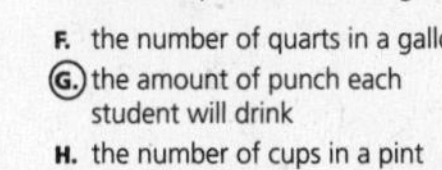

110 Grade 4

GO ON

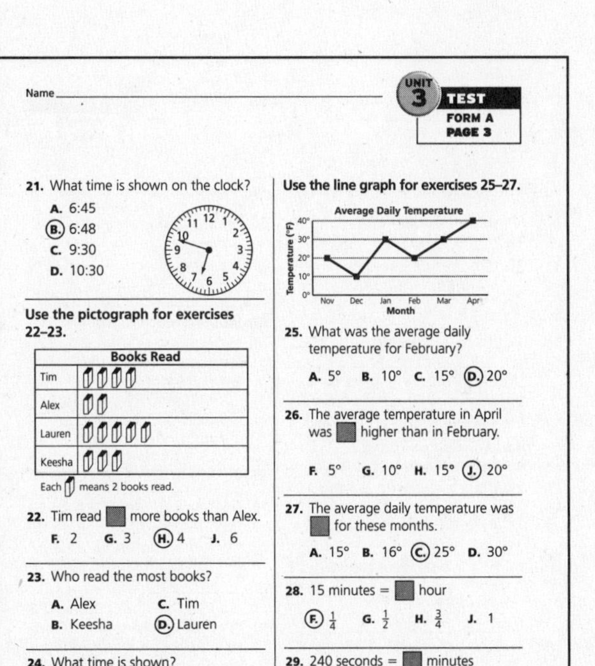

Name ____________________

UNIT 3 TEST FORM A PAGE 3

21. What time is shown on the clock?
    A. 6:45
    (B.) 6:48
    C. 9:30
    D. 10:30

Use the pictograph for exercises 22–23.

Books Read	
Tim	▯▯▯▯
Alex	▯▯
Lauren	▯▯▯▯▯
Keesha	▯▯▯

Each ▯ means 2 books read.

22. Tim read ☐ more books than Alex.
    F. 2 G. 3 (H.) 4 J. 6

23. Who read the most books?
    A. Alex C. Tim
    B. Keesha (D.) Lauren

24. What time is shown?
    (F.) ten minutes after one
    G. quarter past one
    H. ten minutes to one
    J. five minutes after two

Use the line graph for exercises 25–27.

Average Daily Temperature

Temperature (°F): 0°, 10°, 20°, 30°, 40°; Month: Nov, Dec, Jan, Feb, Mar, Apr

25. What was the average daily temperature for February?
    A. 5° B. 10° C. 15° (D.) 20°

26. The average temperature in April was ☐ higher than in February.
    F. 5° G. 10° H. 15° (J.) 20°

27. The average daily temperature was ☐ for these months.
    A. 15° B. 16° (C.) 25° D. 30°

28. 15 minutes = ☐ hour
    (F.) $\frac{1}{4}$ G. $\frac{1}{2}$ H. $\frac{3}{4}$ J. 1

29. 240 seconds = ☐ minutes
    A. 2 B. 3 (C.) 4 D. 5

30. How much time has passed?
    Start: 11:50 P.M. End: 2:30 A.M.
    F. 2 h 20 min H. 3 h 20 min
    (G.) 2 h 40 min J. 9 h 20 min

GO ON

Grade 4 111

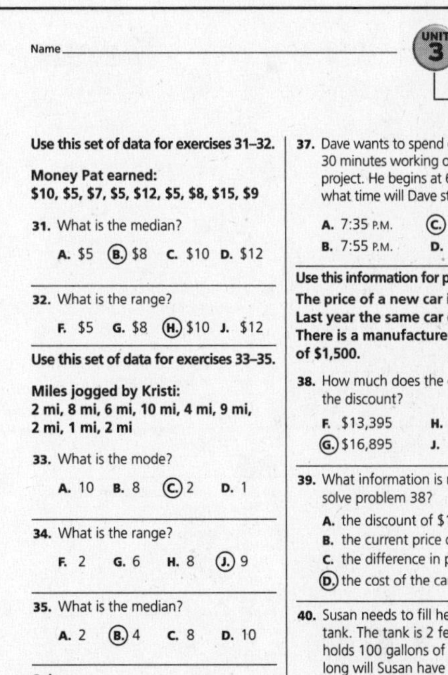

Name ____________________

UNIT 3 TEST FORM A PAGE 4

Use this set of data for exercises 31–32.

Money Pat earned: $10, $5, $7, $5, $12, $5, $8, $15, $9

31. What is the median?
    A. $5 (B.) $8 C. $10 D. $12

32. What is the range?
    F. $5 G. $8 (H.) $10 J. $12

Use this set of data for exercises 33–35.

Miles jogged by Kristi: 2 mi, 8 mi, 6 mi, 10 mi, 4 mi, 9 mi, 2 mi, 1 mi, 2 mi

33. What is the mode?
    A. 10 B. 8 (C.) 2 D. 1

34. What is the range?
    F. 2 G. 6 H. 8 (J.) 9

35. What is the median?
    A. 2 (B.) 4 C. 8 D. 10

Solve.

36. Linda wants to finish her paper route by 8:15 A.M. Her paper route takes 50 minutes to complete. At what time should she leave?
    (F.) 7:25 A.M. H. 7:55 A.M.
    G. 7:45 A.M. J. 9:05 A.M.

37. Dave wants to spend exactly 1 hour 30 minutes working on his science project. He begins at 6:55 P.M. At what time will Dave stop working?
    A. 7:35 P.M. (C.) 8:25 P.M.
    B. 7:55 P.M. D. 8:35 P.M.

Use this information for problems 38–39.

The price of a new car is $18,395. Last year the same car cost $17,295. There is a manufacturer's discount of $1,500.

38. How much does the car cost with the discount?
    F. $13,395 H. $17,295
    (G.) $16,895 J. $18,395

39. What information is not needed to solve problem 38?
    A. the discount of $1,500
    B. the current price of the car
    C. the difference in price
    (D.) the cost of the car last year

40. Susan needs to fill her empty fish tank. The tank is 2 feet high and holds 100 gallons of water. How long will Susan have to wait until the tank is full? What information necessary to solve this problem is missing?
    F. the number of quarts in a gallon
    G. the width of the tank
    (H.) the amount of time needed to add one gallon of water to the tank
    J. the number of fish

STOP

112 Grade 4

Unit 3

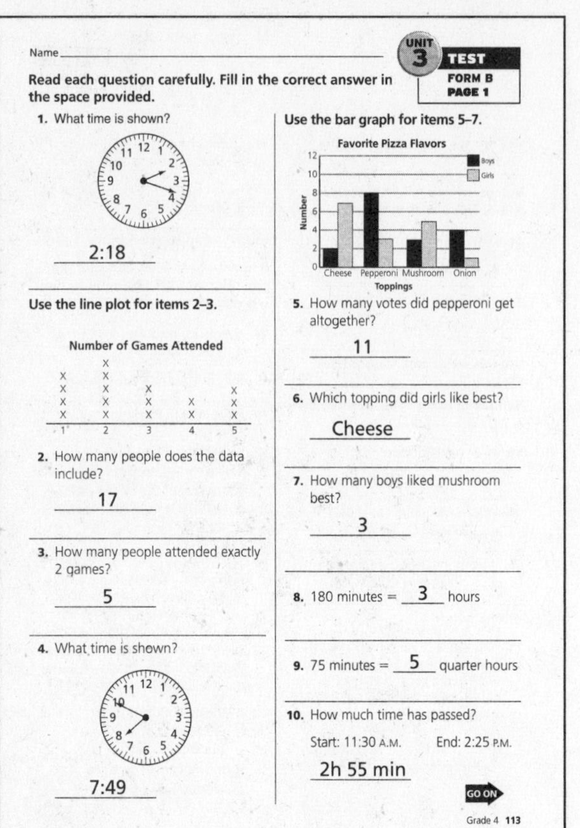

Name ______________________

UNIT 3 TEST FORM B PAGE 1

Read each question carefully. Fill in the correct answer in the space provided.

1. What time is shown?

2:18

Use the line plot for items 2–3.

Number of Games Attended

2. How many people does the data include?

17

3. How many people attended exactly 2 games?

5

4. What time is shown?

7:49

Use the bar graph for items 5–7.

Favorite Pizza Flavors (Boys, Girls; Number; Toppings: Cheese, Pepperoni, Mushroom, Onion)

5. How many votes did pepperoni get altogether?

11

6. Which topping did girls like best?

Cheese

7. How many boys liked mushroom best?

3

8. 180 minutes = 3 hours

9. 75 minutes = 5 quarter hours

10. How much time has passed?

Start: 11:30 A.M. End: 2:25 P.M.

2h 55 min

GO ON

Grade 4 113

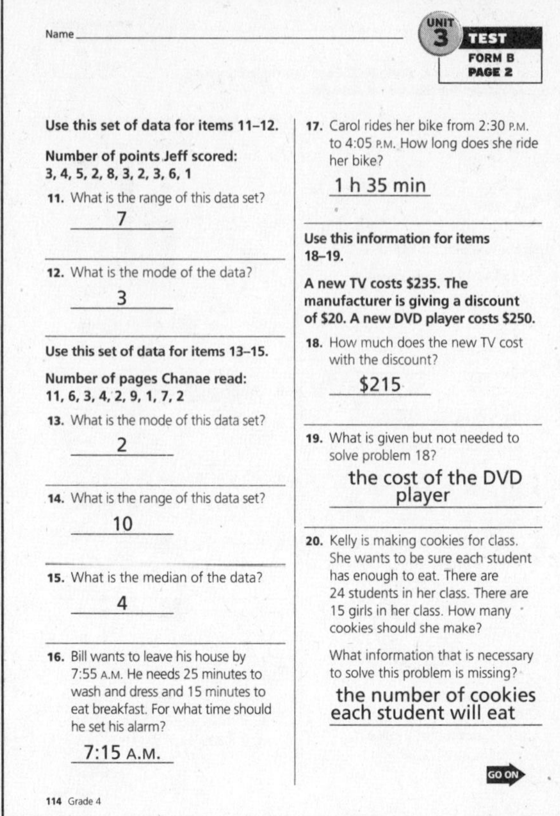

Name ______________________

UNIT 3 TEST FORM B PAGE 2

Use this set of data for items 11–12.

Number of points Jeff scored: 3, 4, 5, 2, 8, 3, 2, 3, 6, 1

11. What is the range of this data set?

7

12. What is the mode of the data?

3

Use this set of data for items 13–15.

Number of pages Chanae read: 11, 6, 3, 4, 2, 9, 1, 7, 2

13. What is the mode of this data set?

2

14. What is the range of this data set?

10

15. What is the median of the data?

4

16. Bill wants to leave his house by 7:55 A.M. He needs 25 minutes to wash and dress and 15 minutes to eat breakfast. For what time should he set his alarm?

7:15 A.M.

17. Carol rides her bike from 2:30 P.M. to 4:05 P.M. How long does she ride her bike?

1 h 35 min

Use this information for items 18–19.

A new TV costs $235. The manufacturer is giving a discount of $20. A new DVD player costs $250.

18. How much does the new TV cost with the discount?

$215

19. What is given but not needed to solve problem 18?

the cost of the DVD player

20. Kelly is making cookies for class. She wants to be sure each student has enough to eat. There are 24 students in her class. There are 15 girls in her class. How many cookies should she make?

What information that is necessary to solve this problem is missing?

the number of cookies each student will eat

GO ON

114 Grade 4

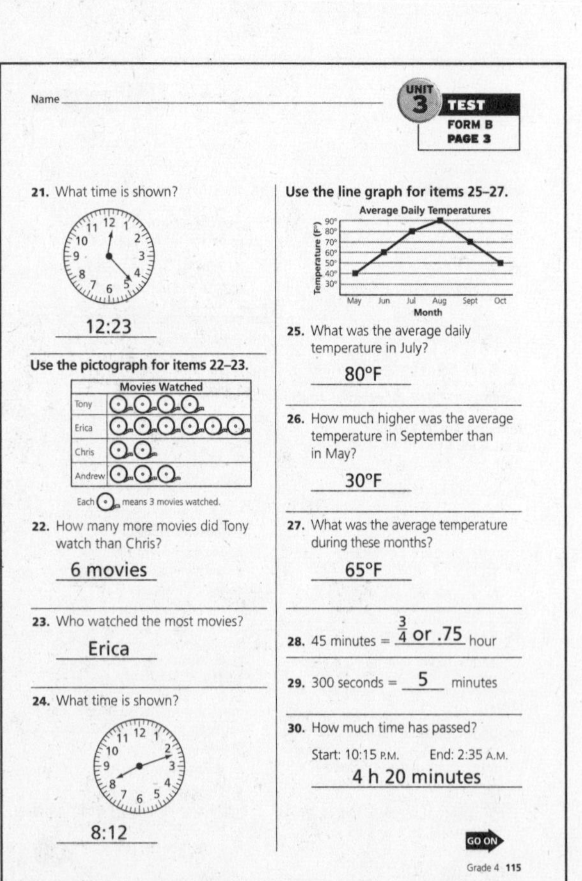

Name ______________________

UNIT 3 TEST FORM B PAGE 3

21. What time is shown?

12:23

Use the pictograph for items 22–23.

Movies Watched (Tony, Erica, Chris, Andrew)

Each ☉ means 3 movies watched.

22. How many more movies did Tony watch than Chris?

6 movies

23. Who watched the most movies?

Erica

24. What time is shown?

8:12

Use the line graph for items 25–27.

Average Daily Temperatures (Temperature (F°); Month: May, Jun, Jul, Aug, Sept, Oct)

25. What was the average daily temperature in July?

80°F

26. How much higher was the average temperature in September than in May?

30°F

27. What was the average temperature during these months?

65°F

28. 45 minutes = $\frac{3}{4}$ or .75 hour

29. 300 seconds = 5 minutes

30. How much time has passed?

Start: 10:15 P.M. End: 2:35 A.M.

4 h 20 minutes

GO ON

Grade 4 115

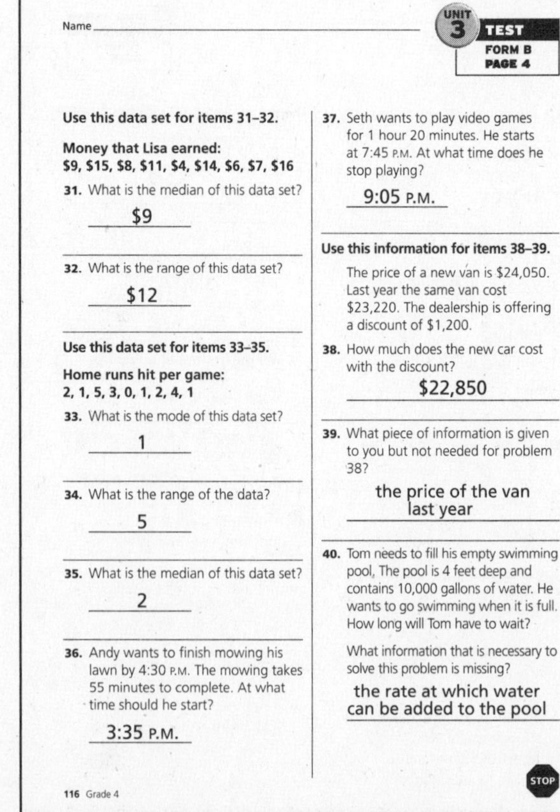

Name ______________________

UNIT 3 TEST FORM B PAGE 4

Use this data set for items 31–32.

Money that Lisa earned: $9, $15, $8, $11, $4, $14, $6, $7, $16

31. What is the median of this data set?

$9

32. What is the range of this data set?

$12

Use this data set for items 33–35.

Home runs hit per game: 2, 1, 5, 3, 0, 1, 2, 4, 1

33. What is the mode of this data set?

1

34. What is the range of the data?

5

35. What is the median of this data set?

2

36. Andy wants to finish mowing his lawn by 4:30 P.M. The mowing takes 55 minutes to complete. At what time should he start?

3:35 P.M.

37. Seth wants to play video games for 1 hour 20 minutes. He starts at 7:45 P.M. At what time does he stop playing?

9:05 P.M.

Use this information for items 38–39.

The price of a new van is $24,050. Last year the same van cost $23,220. The dealership is offering a discount of $1,200.

38. How much does the new car cost with the discount?

$22,850

39. What piece of information is given to you but not needed for problem 38?

the price of the van last year

40. Tom needs to fill his empty swimming pool, The pool is 4 feet deep and contains 10,000 gallons of water. He wants to go swimming when it is full. How long will Tom have to wait?

What information that is necessary to solve this problem is missing?

the rate at which water can be added to the pool

STOP

116 Grade 4

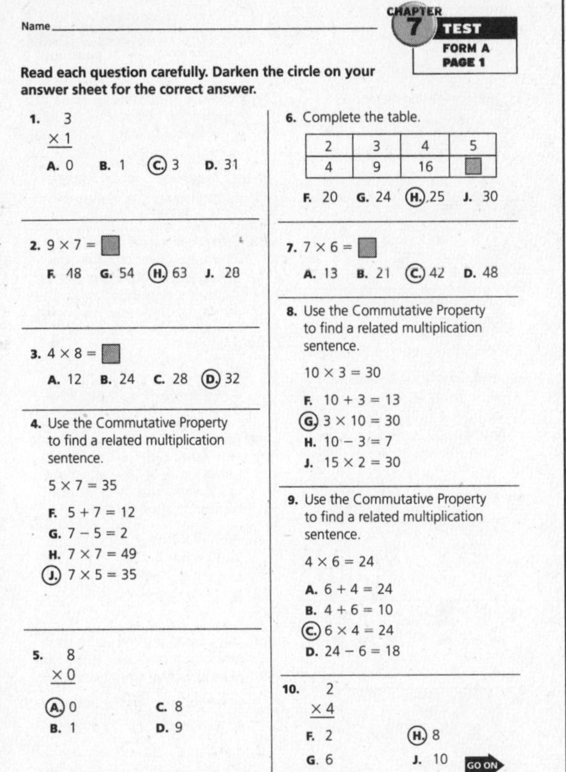

Name______________________

CHAPTER 7 TEST FORM A PAGE 1

Read each question carefully. Darken the circle on your answer sheet for the correct answer.

1. 3 × 1

A. 0 B. 1 (C.) 3 D. 31

2. 9 × 7 = ▢

F. 48 G. 54 (H.) 63 J. 28

3. 4 × 8 = ▢

A. 12 B. 24 C. 28 (D.) 32

4. Use the Commutative Property to find a related multiplication sentence.

5 × 7 = 35

F. 5 + 7 = 12
G. 7 − 5 = 2
H. 7 × 7 = 49
(J.) 7 × 5 = 35

5. 8 × 0

(A.) 0 C. 8
B. 1 D. 9

6. Complete the table.

2	3	4	5
4	9	16	▢

F. 20 G. 24 (H.) 25 J. 30

7. 7 × 6 = ▢

A. 13 B. 21 (C.) 42 D. 48

8. Use the Commutative Property to find a related multiplication sentence.

10 × 3 = 30

F. 10 + 3 = 13
(G.) 3 × 10 = 30
H. 10 − 3 = 7
J. 15 × 2 = 30

9. Use the Commutative Property to find a related multiplication sentence.

4 × 6 = 24

A. 6 + 4 = 24
B. 4 + 6 = 10
(C.) 6 × 4 = 24
D. 24 − 6 = 18

10. 2 × 4

F. 2 (H.) 8
G. 6 J. 10

GO ON

Grade 4 121

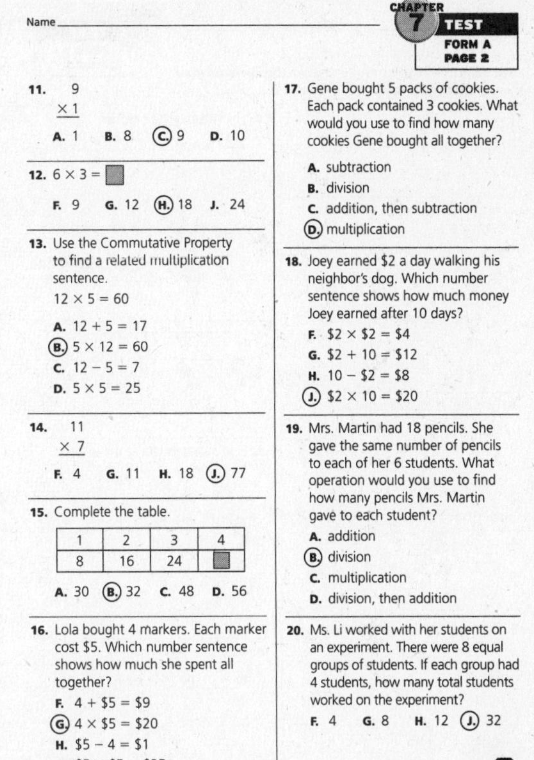

Name______________________

CHAPTER 7 TEST FORM A PAGE 2

11. 9 × 1

A. 1 B. 8 (C.) 9 D. 10

12. 6 × 3 = ▢

F. 9 G. 12 (H.) 18 J. 24

13. Use the Commutative Property to find a related multiplication sentence.

12 × 5 = 60

A. 12 + 5 = 17
(B.) 5 × 12 = 60
C. 12 − 5 = 7
D. 5 × 5 = 25

14. 11 × 7

F. 4 G. 11 H. 18 (J.) 77

15. Complete the table.

1	2	3	4
8	16	24	▢

A. 30 (B.) 32 C. 48 D. 56

16. Lola bought 4 markers. Each marker cost $5. Which number sentence shows how much she spent all together?

F. 4 + $5 = $9
(G.) 4 × $5 = $20
H. $5 − 4 = $1
J. $5 × $5 = $25

17. Gene bought 5 packs of cookies. Each pack contained 3 cookies. What would you use to find how many cookies Gene bought all together?

A. subtraction
B. division
C. addition, then subtraction
(D.) multiplication

18. Joey earned $2 a day walking his neighbor's dog. Which number sentence shows how much money Joey earned after 10 days?

F. $2 × $2 = $4
G. $2 + 10 = $12
H. 10 − $2 = $8
(J.) $2 × 10 = $20

19. Mrs. Martin had 18 pencils. She gave the same number of pencils to each of her 6 students. What operation would you use to find how many pencils Mrs. Martin gave to each student?

A. addition
(B.) division
C. multiplication
D. division, then addition

20. Ms. Li worked with her students on an experiment. There were 8 equal groups of students. If each group had 4 students, how many total students worked on the experiment?

F. 4 G. 8 H. 12 (J.) 32

STOP

122 Grade 4

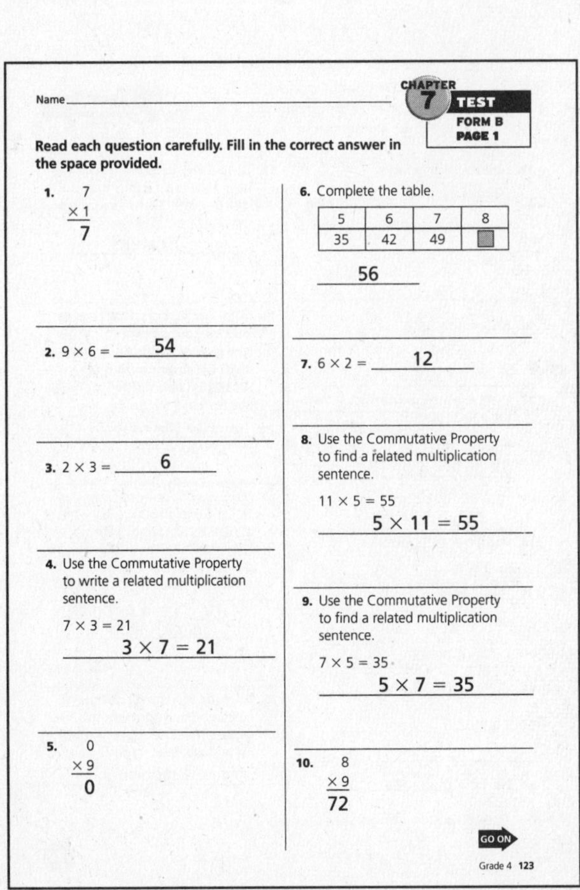

Name______________________

CHAPTER 7 TEST FORM B PAGE 1

Read each question carefully. Fill in the correct answer in the space provided.

1. 7 × 1 = 7

2. 9 × 6 = 54

3. 2 × 3 = 6

4. Use the Commutative Property to write a related multiplication sentence.

7 × 3 = 21

3 × 7 = 21

5. 0 × 9 = 0

6. Complete the table.

5	6	7	8
35	42	49	▢

56

7. 6 × 2 = 12

8. Use the Commutative Property to find a related multiplication sentence.

11 × 5 = 55

5 × 11 = 55

9. Use the Commutative Property to find a related multiplication sentence.

7 × 5 = 35

5 × 7 = 35

10. 8 × 9 = 72

GO ON

Grade 4 123

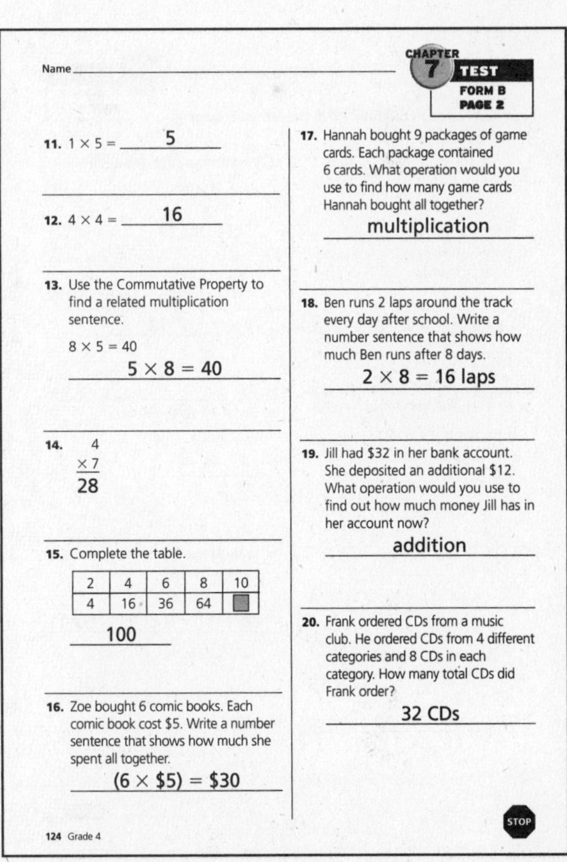

Name______________________

CHAPTER 7 TEST FORM B PAGE 2

11. 1 × 5 = 5

12. 4 × 4 = 16

13. Use the Commutative Property to find a related multiplication sentence.

8 × 5 = 40

5 × 8 = 40

14. 4 × 7 = 28

15. Complete the table.

2	4	6	8	10
4	16	36	64	▢

100

16. Zoe bought 6 comic books. Each comic book cost $5. Write a number sentence that shows how much she spent all together.

(6 × $5) = $30

17. Hannah bought 9 packages of game cards. Each package contained 6 cards. What operation would you use to find how many game cards Hannah bought all together?

multiplication

18. Ben runs 2 laps around the track every day after school. Write a number sentence that shows how much Ben runs after 8 days.

2 × 8 = 16 laps

19. Jill had $32 in her bank account. She deposited an additional $12. What operation would you use to find out how much money Jill has in her account now?

addition

20. Frank ordered CDs from a music club. He ordered CDs from 4 different categories and 8 CDs in each category. How many total CDs did Frank order?

32 CDs

STOP

124 Grade 4

Chapter 8

Name

CHAPTER 8 TEST — FORM A — PAGE 1

Read each question carefully. Darken the circle on your answer sheet for the correct answer.

1. $24 \div 8 = \square$

(A) 3 **B.** 4 **C.** 5 **D.** 6

2. Find a related fact in the same fact family.

$5 \times 6 = 30$

(F) $30 \div 5 = 6$
G. $30 \div 2 = 15$
H. $30 \div 3 = 10$
J. $30 \div 1 = 30$

3. Find the missing number.

$35 \div 5 = t$

A. 4 **B.** 5 **C.** 6 (D) 7

4. $6\overline{)72} = \square$

F. 9 **G.** 10 **H.** 11 (J) 12

5. Find a related fact in the same fact family.

$9 \times 5 = 45$

A. $9 + 5 = 14$
B. $9 - 5 = 4$
C. $45 \times 1 = 45$
(D) $45 \div 9 = 5$

6. Find the missing number.

$36 \div 3 = x$

(F) 12 **G.** 11 **H.** 10 **J.** 9

7. $7\overline{)21} = \square$

A. 2 (B) 3 **C.** 4 **D.** 5

8. Find the missing number.

$54 \div 6 = a$

F. 8 (G) 9 **H.** 10 **J.** 11

9. Find a related fact in the same fact family.

$2 \times 8 = 16$

A. $16 \div 4 = 4$
B. $16 \div 1 = 16$
C. $16 \div 4 = 5$
(D) $16 \div 2 = 8$

10. $49 \div 7 = \square$

F. 6 (G) 7 **H.** 8 **J.** 9

Grade 4 129

Name

CHAPTER 8 TEST — FORM A — PAGE 2

11. Find the missing factor.

$d \times 12 = 96$

A. 7 (B) 8 **C.** 9 **D.** 10

12. $4\overline{)24} = \square$

(F) 6 **G.** 7 **H.** 8 **J.** 9

13. Find a related fact in the same fact family.

$6 \times 4 = 24$

A. $4 + 6 = 10$
B. $6 - 4 = 3$
C. $12 \times 2 = 22$
(D) $24 \div 6 = 4$

14. Find the missing factor.

$f \times 10 = 60$

F. 0 **G.** 1 (H) 6 **J.** 10

15. $3\overline{)33} = \square$

A. 8 **B.** 9 **C.** 10 (D) 11

16. $72 \div 9 = \square$

F. 6 **G.** 7 (H) 8 **J.** 9

17. There are 21 climbers signed up for rope lessons. Each teacher will take 3 climbers. How many teachers are needed?

(A) 7 teachers **C.** 24 teachers
B. 81 teachers **D.** 63 teachers

18. Glen had 8 magnets. Then his mother gave him some packages of magnets. Each package had 4 magnets. Now Glen has 36 magnets. How many packages of magnets did Glen's mother give him?

(F) 7 packages **H.** 5 packages
G. 6 packages **J.** 4 packages

19. Trina has 12 CDs. She put them into 6 CD cases. Each case held the same number of CDs. How many CDs did each case hold? Write a number sentence to solve.

(A) $12 \div 6 = 2$
B. $12 - 6 = 6$
C. $12 + 6 = 18$
D. $12 \times 6 = 72$

20. There are 48 children signed up to play softball. There are 4 teams. How many players are on each team?

F. 10 players (H) 12 players
G. 11 players **J.** 13 players

130 Grade 4

Name

CHAPTER 8 TEST — FORM B — PAGE 1

Read each question carefully. Fill in the correct answer in the space provided.

1. $64 \div 8 =$ 8

2. Write a related division fact in the same fact family.

$5 \times 9 = 45$

$45 \div 9 = 5$ or $45 \div 5 = 9$

3. Find the missing number.

$72 \div 6 = s$

12

4. $8\overline{)56} =$ 7

5. Write a related division fact in the same fact family.

$8 \times 3 = 24$

$24 \div 8 = 3$ or $24 \div 3 = 8$

6. Find the missing number.

$44 \div 11 = a$

4

7. $5\overline{)60} =$ 12

8. Find the missing number.

$81 \div 9 = z$

9

9. Write a related division fact in the same fact family.

$9 \times 11 = 99$

$99 \div 11 = 9$ or $99 \div 9 = 11$

10. $108 \div 12 =$ 9

GO ON

Grade 4 131

Name

CHAPTER 8 TEST — FORM B — PAGE 2

11. Find the missing factor.

$d \times 7 = 63$

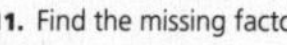

9

12. $8\overline{)88} =$ 11

13. Write a related division fact in the same fact family.

$6 \div 3 = 18$

$18 \div 6 = 3$ or $18 \div 3 = 6$

14. Find the missing factor.

$j \times 7 = 84$

12

15. $5\overline{)55} =$ 11

16. $24 \div 4 =$ 6

17. There are 42 people in line for the train. Each cabin on the train will hold 6 people. How many cabins will all 42 people fill?

7 cabins

18. Marcy had 3 pencils. Then her sister gave her some packages of pencils. Each package had 6 pencils. Now Marcy has 33 pencils. How many packages of pencils did Marcy's sister give her?

5 packages

19. Marty has 15 soccer trophies. He would like to place an equal number of trophies on each of 5 shelves. How many trophies should he put on each shelf? Write a number sentence to solve.

$15 \div 5 = 3$ trophies on each shelf

20. There are 36 students going on a field trip. The children are split into groups. There are 9 groups. How many students are in each group?

4 students

132 Grade 4

Unit 4

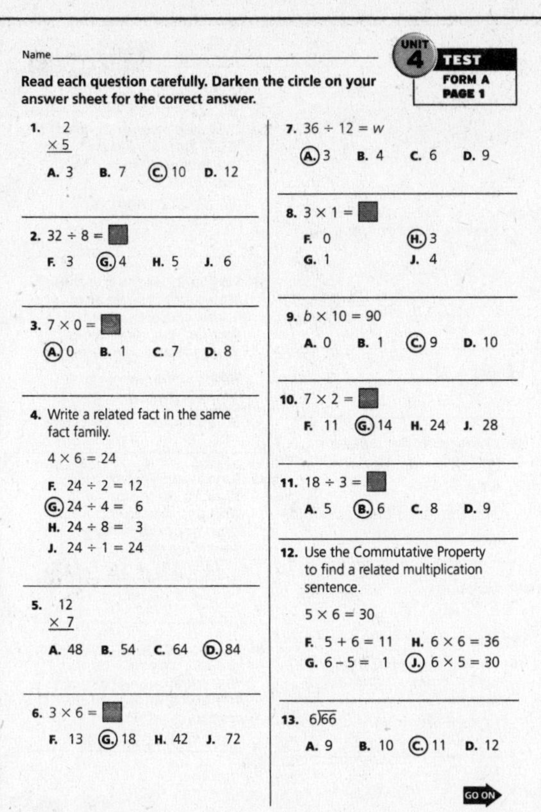

Name______________________________

UNIT 4 TEST FORM A PAGE 1

Read each question carefully. Darken the circle on your answer sheet for the correct answer.

1. $\begin{array}{r} 2 \\ \times 5 \\ \hline \end{array}$

A. 3 B. 7 **(C.) 10** D. 12

2. 32 ÷ 8 = ■

F. 3 **(G.) 4** H. 5 J. 6

3. 7 × 0 = ■

(A.) 0 B. 1 C. 7 D. 8

4. Write a related fact in the same fact family.

4 × 6 = 24

F. 24 ÷ 2 = 12
(G.) 24 ÷ 4 = 6
H. 24 ÷ 8 = 3
J. 24 ÷ 1 = 24

5. $\begin{array}{r} 12 \\ \times 7 \\ \hline \end{array}$

A. 48 B. 54 C. 64 **(D.) 84**

6. 3 × 6 = ■

F. 13 **(G.) 18** H. 42 J. 72

7. 36 ÷ 12 = w

(A.) 3 B. 4 C. 6 D. 9

8. 3 × 1 = ■

F. 0 **(H.) 3**
G. 1 J. 4

9. b × 10 = 90

A. 0 B. 1 **(C.) 9** D. 10

10. 7 × 2 = ■

F. 11 **(G.) 14** H. 24 J. 28

11. 18 ÷ 3 = ■

A. 5 **(B.) 6** C. 8 D. 9

12. Use the Commutative Property to find a related multiplication sentence.

5 × 6 = 30

F. 5 + 6 = 11 H. 6 × 6 = 36
G. 6 − 5 = 1 **(J.) 6 × 5 = 30**

13. $6\overline{)66}$

A. 9 B. 10 **(C.) 11** D. 12

GO ON

Grade 4 137

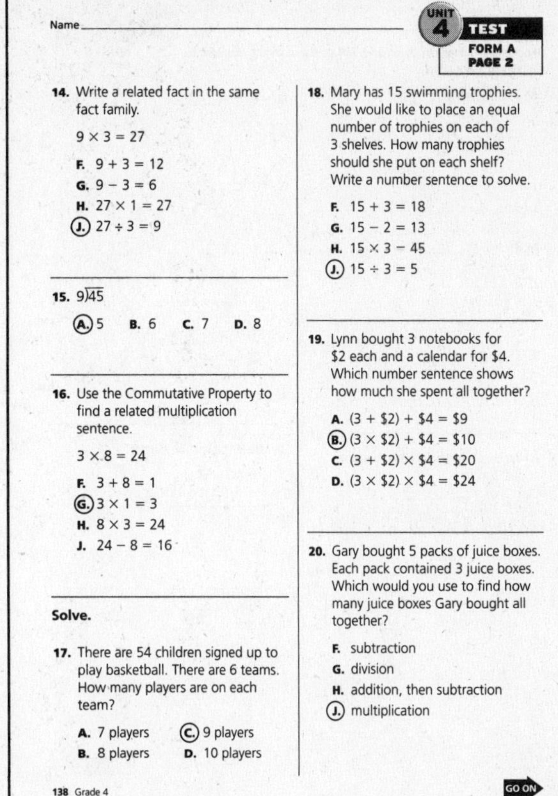

Name______________________________

UNIT 4 TEST FORM A PAGE 2

14. Write a related fact in the same fact family.

9 × 3 = 27

F. 9 + 3 = 12
G. 9 − 3 = 6
H. 27 × 1 = 27
(J.) 27 ÷ 3 = 9

15. $9\overline{)45}$

(A.) 5 B. 6 C. 7 D. 8

16. Use the Commutative Property to find a related multiplication sentence.

3 × 8 = 24

F. 3 + 8 = 1
(G.) 3 × 1 = 3
H. 8 × 3 = 24
J. 24 − 8 = 16

Solve.

17. There are 54 children signed up to play basketball. There are 6 teams. How many players are on each team?

A. 7 players **(C.) 9 players**
B. 8 players D. 10 players

18. Mary has 15 swimming trophies. She would like to place an equal number of trophies on each of 3 shelves. How many trophies should she put on each shelf? Write a number sentence to solve.

F. 15 + 3 = 18
G. 15 − 2 = 13
H. 15 × 3 = 45
(J.) 15 ÷ 3 = 5

19. Lynn bought 3 notebooks for $2 each and a calendar for $4. Which number sentence shows how much she spent all together?

A. (3 + $2) + $4 = $9
(B.) (3 × $2) + $4 = $10
C. (3 + $2) × $4 = $20
D. (3 × $2) × $4 = $24

20. Gary bought 5 packs of juice boxes. Each pack contained 3 juice boxes. Which would you use to find how many juice boxes Gary bought all together?

F. subtraction
G. division
H. addition, then subtraction
(J.) multiplication

138 Grade 4

GO ON

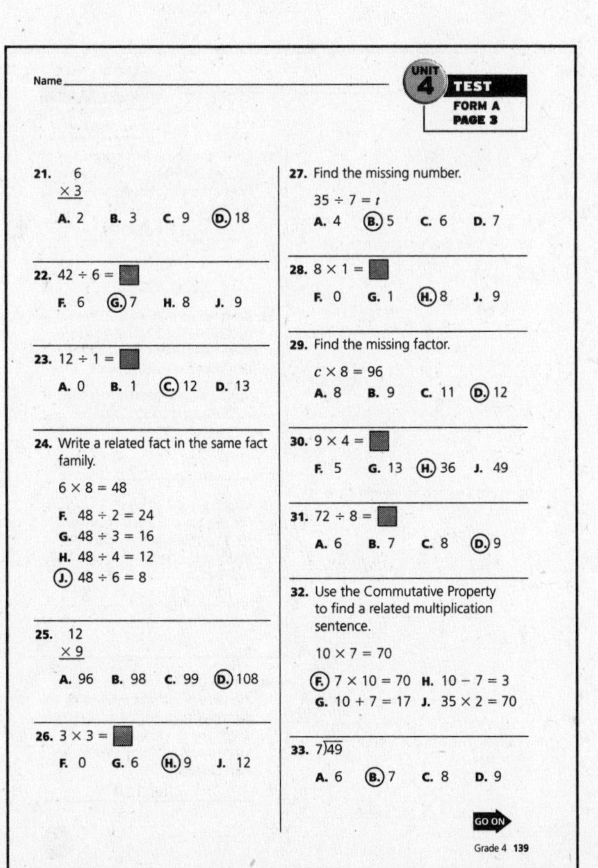

Name______________________________

UNIT 4 TEST FORM A PAGE 3

21. $\begin{array}{r} 6 \\ \times 3 \\ \hline \end{array}$

A. 2 B. 3 C. 9 **(D.) 18**

22. 42 ÷ 6 = ■

F. 6 **(G.) 7** H. 8 J. 9

23. 12 ÷ 1 = ■

A. 0 B. 1 **(C.) 12** D. 13

24. Write a related fact in the same fact family.

6 × 8 = 48

F. 48 ÷ 2 = 24
G. 48 ÷ 3 = 16
H. 48 ÷ 4 = 12
(J.) 48 ÷ 6 = 8

25. $\begin{array}{r} 12 \\ \times 9 \\ \hline \end{array}$

A. 96 B. 98 C. 99 **(D.) 108**

26. 3 × 3 = ■

F. 0 G. 6 **(H.) 9** J. 12

27. Find the missing number.

35 ÷ 7 = t

A. 4 **(B.) 5** C. 6 D. 7

28. 8 × 1 = ■

F. 0 G. 1 **(H.) 8** J. 9

29. Find the missing factor.

c × 8 = 96

A. 8 B. 9 C. 11 **(D.) 12**

30. 9 × 4 = ■

F. 5 G. 13 **(H.) 36** J. 49

31. 72 ÷ 8 = ■

A. 6 B. 7 C. 8 **(D.) 9**

32. Use the Commutative Property to find a related multiplication sentence.

10 × 7 = 70

(F.) 7 × 10 = 70 H. 10 − 7 = 3
G. 10 + 7 = 17 J. 35 × 2 = 70

33. $7\overline{)49}$

A. 6 **(B.) 7** C. 8 D. 9

GO ON

Grade 4 139

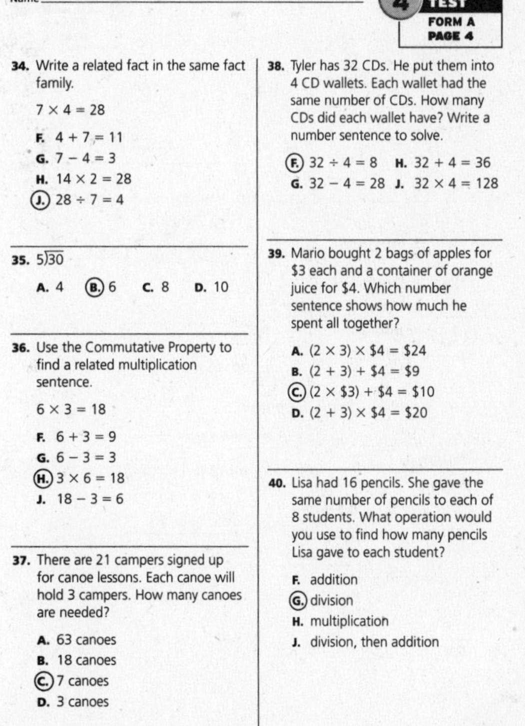

Name______________________________

UNIT 4 TEST FORM A PAGE 4

34. Write a related fact in the same fact family.

7 × 4 = 28

F. 4 + 7 = 11
G. 7 − 4 = 3
H. 14 × 2 = 28
(J.) 28 ÷ 7 = 4

35. $5\overline{)30}$

A. 4 **(B.) 6** C. 8 D. 10

36. Use the Commutative Property to find a related multiplication sentence.

6 × 3 = 18

F. 6 + 3 = 9
G. 6 − 3 = 3
(H.) 3 × 6 = 18
J. 18 − 3 = 6

37. There are 21 campers signed up for canoe lessons. Each canoe will hold 3 campers. How many canoes are needed?

A. 63 canoes
B. 18 canoes
(C.) 7 canoes
D. 3 canoes

38. Tyler has 32 CDs. He put them into 4 CD wallets. Each wallet had the same number of CDs. How many CDs did each wallet have? Write a number sentence to solve.

(F.) 32 ÷ 4 = 8 H. 32 + 4 = 36
G. 32 − 4 = 28 J. 32 × 4 = 128

39. Mario bought 2 bags of apples for $3 each and a container of orange juice for $4. Which number sentence shows how much he spent all together?

A. (2 × 3) × $4 = $24
B. (2 + 3) + $4 = $9
(C.) (2 × $3) + $4 = $10
D. (2 + 3) × $4 = $20

40. Lisa had 16 pencils. She gave the same number of pencils to each of 8 students. What operation would you use to find how many pencils Lisa gave to each student?

F. addition
(G.) division
H. multiplication
J. division, then addition

140 Grade 4

STOP

Unit 4

Name

Read each question carefully. Fill in the correct answer in the space provided.

1. $3 \times 6 = 18$

2. $36 \div 9 =$ 4

3. $11 \times 0 =$ 0

4. Write a related fact in the same fact family.
$5 \times 3 = 15$
$15 \div 3 = 5$ or $15 \div 5 = 3$

5. $14 \times 5 = 70$

6. $4 \times 7 =$ 28

7. $48 \div 4 =$ 12

8. $5 \times 1 =$ 5

9. Write the missing factor.
$b \times 10 = 60$
6

10. $7 \times 7 =$ 49

Name

11. $14 \div 2 =$ 7

12. Use the Commutative Property to write a related multiplication sentence.
$4 \times 7 = 28$
$7 \times 4 = 28$

13. $6\overline{)48} =$ 8

14. Write a related fact in the same fact family.
$6 \times 4 = 24$
$24 \div 4 = 6$ or $24 \div 6 = 4$

15. $7\overline{)35} =$ 5

16. Use the Commutative Property to write a related multiplication sentence.
$12 \times 8 = 96$
$8 \times 12 = 96$

17. There are 60 children signed up to play baseball. There are 5 teams. How many players are on each team?
12 players

18. Mary has 20 swimming trophies. She would like to place an equal number of trophies on each of 4 shelves. How many trophies should she place on each shelf?
Write a number sentence to solve.
$20 \div 4 = 5$

19. David bought 4 notebooks for \$3 each and a calendar for \$5. Write a number sentence that shows how much money he spent all together.
$(4 \times \$3) + \$5 = \$17$

20. Eddie bought 4 packs of batteries. Each pack contained 6 batteries. What operation would you use to find out how many batteries Eddie bought all together?
multiplication

Name

21. $7 \times 3 = 21$

22. $66 \div 6 =$ 11

23. $15 \div 1 =$ 15

24. Write a related fact in the same fact family.
$7 \times 9 = 63$
$63 \div 7 = 9$ or $63 \div 9 = 7$

25. $12 \times 7 = 84$

26. $5 \times 2 =$ 10

27. Write the missing number.
$64 \div 8 = t$
$t = 8$

28. $19 \times 1 =$ 19

29. Write the missing factor.
$c \times 4 = 44$
$c = 11$

30. $9 \times 11 =$ 99

GO ON

Name

31. $56 \div 7 =$ 8

32. Use the Commutative Property to write a related multiplication sentence.
$9 \times 8 = 72$
$8 \times 9 = 72$

33. $5\overline{)25} =$ 5

34. Write a related fact in the same fact family.
$2 \times 9 = 18$
$18 \div 2 = 9$ or $18 \div 9 = 2$

35. $4\overline{)12} =$ 3

36. Use the Commutative Property to write a related multiplication sentence.
$5 \times 6 = 30$
$6 \times 5 = 30$

37. There are 22 campers signed up to go canoeing. Each canoe will hold 2 campers. How many canoes are needed?
11 canoes

38. Scott has 45 CDs. He put them into 5 CD wallets. Each wallet has the same number of CDs. How many CDs does each wallet hold?
Write a number sentence to solve.
$45 \div 5 = 9$

39. Luigi bought 2 boxes of doughnuts for \$5 each and a cup of coffee for \$1. Write a number sentence that shows how much he spent all together.
$(2 \times \$5) + \$1 = \$11$

40. Patricia had 18 markers. She gave the same number of markers to each of 6 students. What operation would you use to find out how many markers Patricia gave to each student?
division

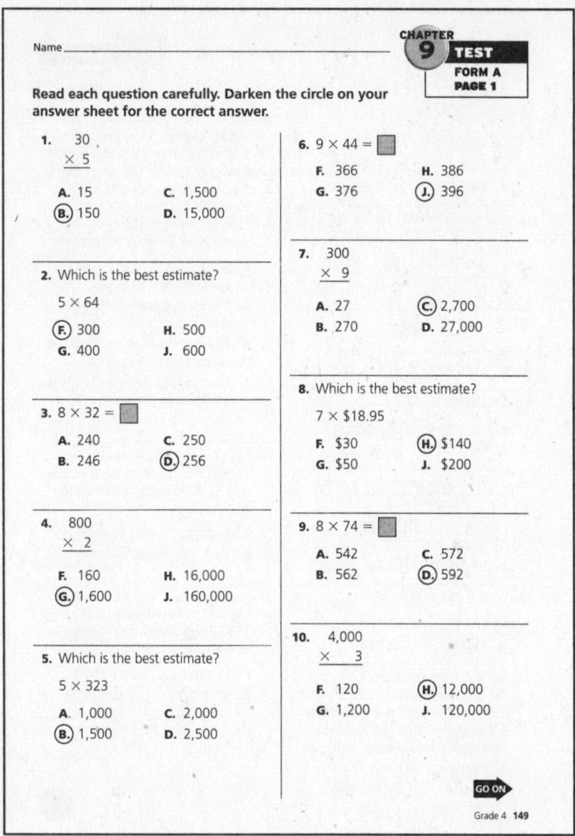

Name_______________

CHAPTER 9 TEST FORM A PAGE 1

Read each question carefully. Darken the circle on your answer sheet for the correct answer.

1. 30 × 5
   A. 15 (B.) 150 C. 1,500 D. 15,000

2. Which is the best estimate? 5 × 64
   (F.) 300 G. 400 H. 500 J. 600

3. 8 × 32 = ☐
   A. 240 B. 246 C. 250 (D.) 256

4. 800 × 2
   F. 160 (G.) 1,600 H. 16,000 J. 160,000

5. Which is the best estimate? 5 × 323
   A. 1,000 (B.) 1,500 C. 2,000 D. 2,500

6. 9 × 44 = ☐
   F. 366 G. 376 H. 386 (J.) 396

7. 300 × 9
   A. 27 B. 270 (C.) 2,700 D. 27,000

8. Which is the best estimate? 7 × $18.95
   F. $30 G. $50 (H.) $140 J. $200

9. 8 × 74 = ☐
   A. 542 B. 562 C. 572 (D.) 592

10. 4,000 × 3
    F. 120 G. 1,200 (H.) 12,000 J. 120,000

GO ON

Grade 4 149

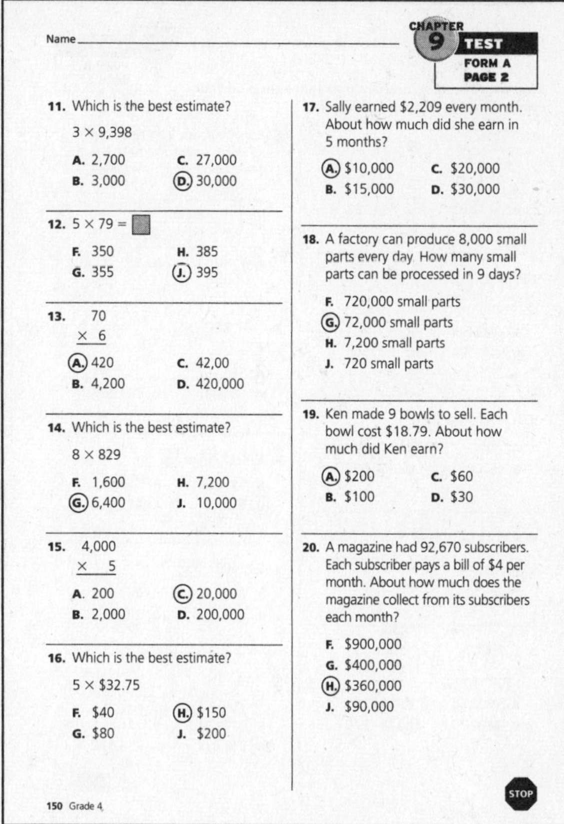

Name_______________

CHAPTER 9 TEST FORM A PAGE 2

11. Which is the best estimate? 3 × 9,398
    A. 2,700 B. 3,000 C. 27,000 (D.) 30,000

12. 5 × 79 = ☐
    F. 350 G. 355 H. 385 (J.) 395

13. 70 × 6
    (A.) 420 B. 4,200 C. 42,00 D. 420,000

14. Which is the best estimate? 8 × 829
    F. 1,600 (G.) 6,400 H. 7,200 J. 10,000

15. 4,000 × 5
    A. 200 B. 2,000 (C.) 20,000 D. 200,000

16. Which is the best estimate? 5 × $32.75
    F. $40 G. $80 (H.) $150 J. $200

17. Sally earned $2,209 every month. About how much did she earn in 5 months?
    (A.) $10,000 B. $15,000 C. $20,000 D. $30,000

18. A factory can produce 8,000 small parts every day. How many small parts can be processed in 9 days?
    F. 720,000 small parts
    (G.) 72,000 small parts
    H. 7,200 small parts
    J. 720 small parts

19. Ken made 9 bowls to sell. Each bowl cost $18.79. About how much did Ken earn?
    (A.) $200 B. $100 C. $60 D. $30

20. A magazine had 92,670 subscribers. Each subscriber pays a bill of $4 per month. About how much does the magazine collect from its subscribers each month?
    F. $900,000
    G. $400,000
    (H.) $360,000
    J. $90,000

STOP

150 Grade 4

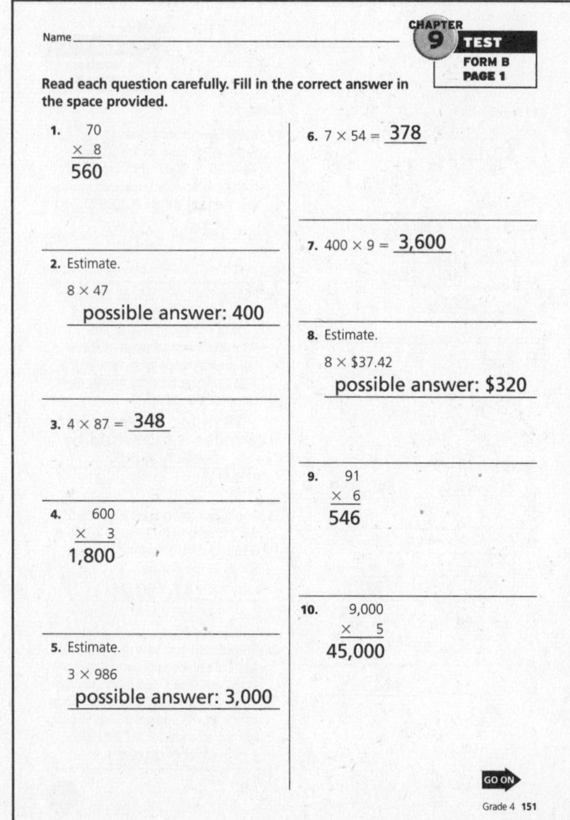

Name_______________

CHAPTER 9 TEST FORM B PAGE 1

Read each question carefully. Fill in the correct answer in the space provided.

1. 70 × 8 = 560

2. Estimate. 8 × 47 possible answer: 400

3. 4 × 87 = 348

4. 600 × 3 = 1,800

5. Estimate. 3 × 986 possible answer: 3,000

6. 7 × 54 = 378

7. 400 × 9 = 3,600

8. Estimate. 8 × $37.42 possible answer: $320

9. 91 × 6 = 546

10. 9,000 × 5 = 45,000

GO ON

Grade 4 151

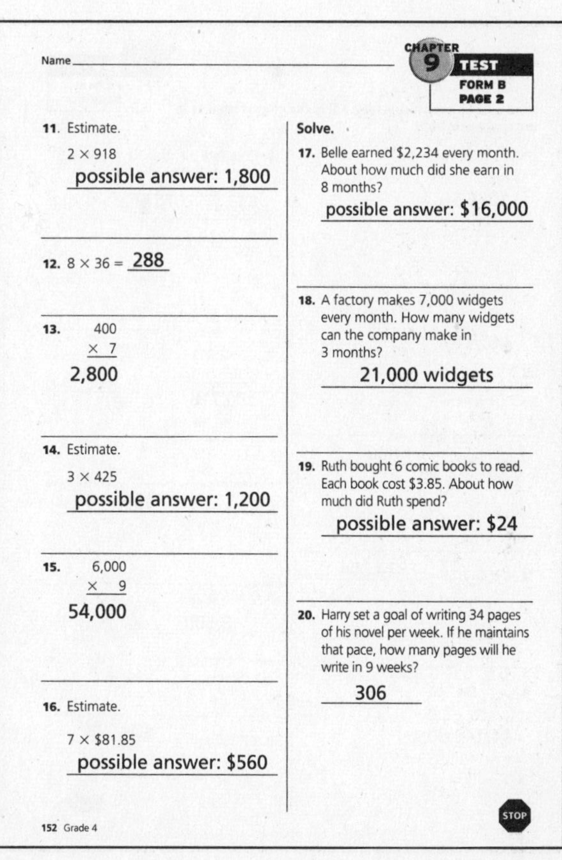

Name_______________

CHAPTER 9 TEST FORM B PAGE 2

11. Estimate. 2 × 918 possible answer: 1,800

12. 8 × 36 = 288

13. 400 × 7 = 2,800

14. Estimate. 3 × 425 possible answer: 1,200

15. 6,000 × 9 = 54,000

16. Estimate. 7 × $81.85 possible answer: $560

Solve.

17. Belle earned $2,234 every month. About how much did she earn in 8 months? possible answer: $16,000

18. A factory makes 7,000 widgets every month. How many widgets can the company make in 3 months? 21,000 widgets

19. Ruth bought 6 comic books to read. Each book cost $3.85. About how much did Ruth spend? possible answer: $24

20. Harry set a goal of writing 34 pages of his novel per week. If he maintains that pace, how many pages will he write in 9 weeks? 306

STOP

152 Grade 4

Chapter 10

Name ______________________________

CHAPTER 10 TEST FORM A PAGE 1

Read each question carefully. Darken the circle on your answer sheet for the correct answer.

1. $53.28 × 4

A. $212.32 C. $213.12
B. $212.82 D. $213.32

2. 400,297 × 2

F. 800,494 H. 800,604
G. 800,594 J. 900,594

3. 6 × 5,000 = ■

A. 300 C. 30,000
B. 3,000 D. 300,000

4. 4 × 23,623 = ■

F. 94,492 H. 92,482
G. 92,492 J. 82,482

5. $162.74 × 5

A. $800.50 C. $813.50
B. $800.70 D. $813.70

6. Annette drinks 1 bottle of water for every 2 miles she runs. How far does she run when she drinks 4 bottles?

x	1	2	3	4
y	2	4	6	■

F. 7 G. 8 H. 9 J. 10

7. 82,981 × 7

A. 580,867 C. 581,767
B. 580,887 D. 581,867

8. $92.15 × 6 = ■

F. $550.90 H. $555.60
G. $552.90 J. $558.30

9. 5 × 400 = ■

A. 2 C. 200
B. 20 D. 2,000

10. 53,206 × 4

F. 212,804 H. 214,804
G. 212,824 J. 214,824

GO ON

Grade 4 157

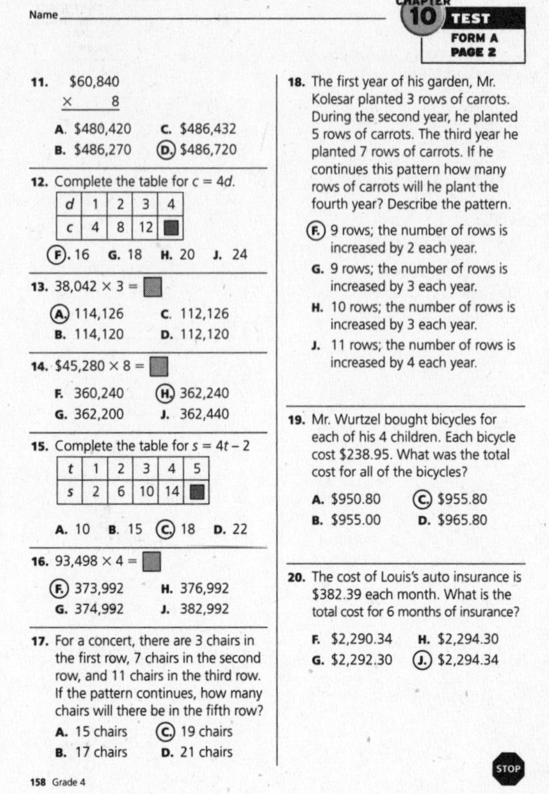

Name ______________________________

CHAPTER 10 TEST FORM A PAGE 2

11. $60,840 × 8

A. $480,420 C. $486,432
B. $486,270 D. $486,720

12. Complete the table for $c = 4d$.

d	1	2	3	4
c	4	8	12	■

F. 16 G. 18 H. 20 J. 24

13. 38,042 × 3 = ■

A. 114,126 C. 112,126
B. 114,120 D. 112,120

14. $45,280 × 8 = ■

F. 360,240 H. 362,240
G. 362,200 J. 362,440

15. Complete the table for $s = 4t - 2$

t	1	2	3	4	5
s	2	6	10	14	■

A. 10 B. 15 C. 18 D. 22

16. 93,498 × 4 = ■

F. 373,992 H. 376,992
G. 374,992 J. 382,992

17. For a concert, there are 3 chairs in the first row, 7 chairs in the second row, and 11 chairs in the third row. If the pattern continues, how many chairs will there be in the fifth row?

A. 15 chairs C. 19 chairs
B. 17 chairs D. 21 chairs

18. The first year of his garden, Mr. Kolesar planted 3 rows of carrots. During the second year, he planted 5 rows of carrots. The third year he planted 7 rows of carrots. If he continues this pattern how many rows of carrots will he plant the fourth year? Describe the pattern.

F. 9 rows; the number of rows is increased by 2 each year.
G. 9 rows; the number of rows is increased by 3 each year.
H. 10 rows; the number of rows is increased by 3 each year.
J. 11 rows; the number of rows is increased by 4 each year.

19. Mr. Wurtzel bought bicycles for each of his 4 children. Each bicycle cost $238.95. What was the total cost for all of the bicycles?

A. $950.80 C. $955.80
B. $955.00 D. $965.80

20. The cost of Louis's auto insurance is $382.39 each month. What is the total cost for 6 months of insurance?

F. $2,290.34 H. $2,294.30
G. $2,292.30 J. $2,294.34

STOP

158 Grade 4

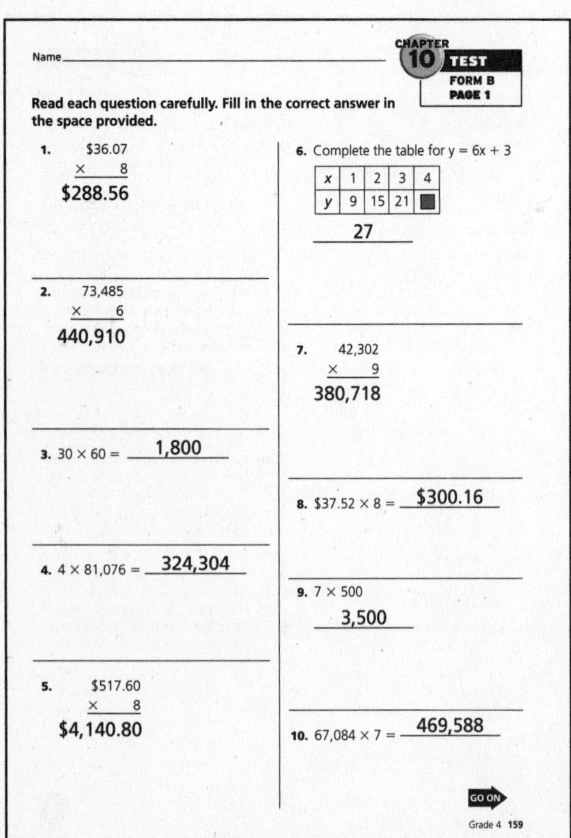

Name ______________________________

CHAPTER 10 TEST FORM B PAGE 1

Read each question carefully. Fill in the correct answer in the space provided.

1. $36.07 × 8 — **$288.56**

2. 73,485 × 6 — **440,910**

3. 30 × 60 = **1,800**

4. 4 × 81,076 = **324,304**

5. $517.60 × 8 — **$4,140.80**

6. Complete the table for y = 6x + 3

x	1	2	3	4
y	9	15	21	■

27

7. 42,302 × 9 — **380,718**

8. $37.52 × 8 = **$300.16**

9. 7 × 500 — **3,500**

10. 67,084 × 7 = **469,588**

GO ON

Grade 4 159

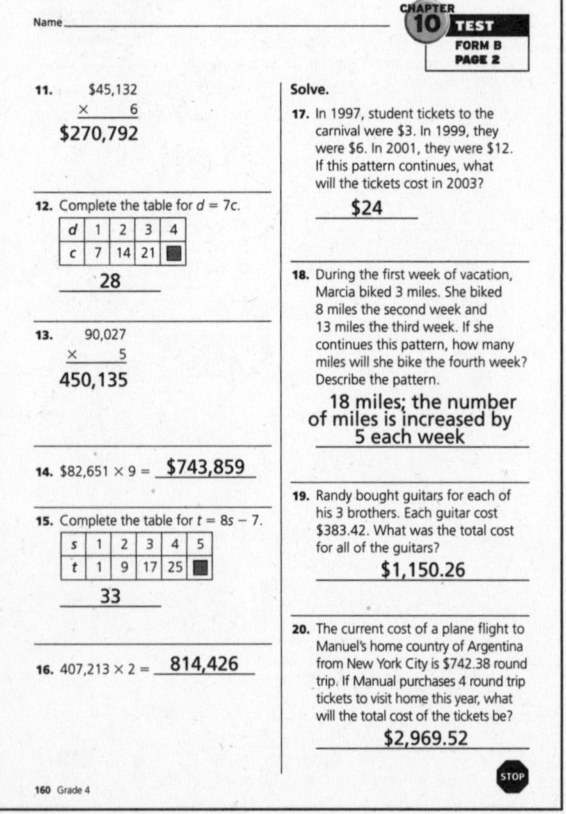

Name ______________________________

CHAPTER 10 TEST FORM B PAGE 2

11. $45,132 × 6 — **$270,792**

12. Complete the table for $d = 7c$.

d	1	2	3	4
c	7	14	21	■

28

13. 90,027 × 5 — **450,135**

14. $82,651 × 9 = **$743,859**

15. Complete the table for $t = 8s - 7$.

s	1	2	3	4	5
t	1	9	17	25	■

33

16. 407,213 × 2 = **814,426**

Solve.

17. In 1997, student tickets to the carnival were $3. In 1999, they were $6. In 2001, they were $12. If this pattern continues, what will the tickets cost in 2003?

$24

18. During the first week of vacation, Marcia biked 3 miles. She biked 8 miles the second week and 13 miles the third week. If she continues this pattern, how many miles will she bike the fourth week? Describe the pattern.

18 miles; the number of miles is increased by 5 each week

19. Randy bought guitars for each of his 3 brothers. Each guitar cost $383.42. What was the total cost for all of the guitars?

$1,150.26

20. The current cost of a plane flight to Manuel's home country of Argentina from New York City is $742.38 round trip. If Manual purchases 4 round trip tickets to visit home this year, what will the total cost of the tickets be?

$2,969.52

STOP

160 Grade 4

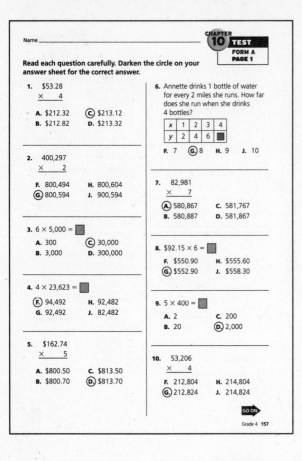

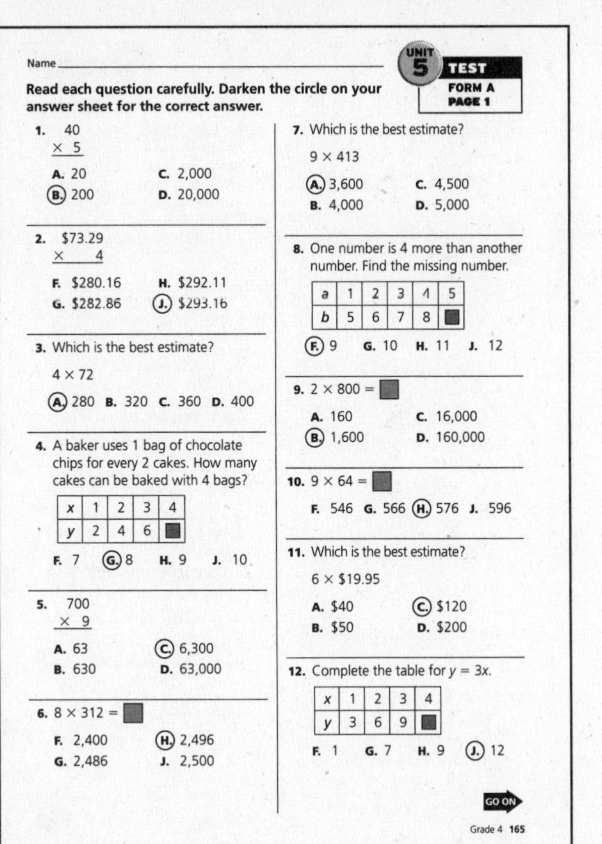

Name

UNIT 5 TEST FORM A PAGE 1

Read each question carefully. Darken the circle on your answer sheet for the correct answer.

1. 40 × 5

A. 20 B. 200 C. 2,000 D. 20,000

2. $73.29 × 4

F. $280.16 G. $282.86 H. $292.11 J. $293.16

3. Which is the best estimate?

4 × 72

A. 280 B. 320 C. 360 D. 400

4. A baker uses 1 bag of chocolate chips for every 2 cakes. How many cakes can be baked with 4 bags?

x	1	2	3	4
y	2	4	6	■

F. 7 G. 8 H. 9 J. 10

5. 700 × 9

A. 63 B. 630 C. 6,300 D. 63,000

6. 8 × 312 = ■

F. 2,400 G. 2,486 H. 2,496 J. 2,500

7. Which is the best estimate?

9 × 413

A. 3,600 B. 4,000 C. 4,500 D. 5,000

8. One number is 4 more than another number. Find the missing number.

a	1	2	3	4	5
b	5	6	7	8	■

F. 9 G. 10 H. 11 J. 12

9. 2 × 800 = ■

A. 160 B. 1,600 C. 16,000 D. 160,000

10. 9 × 64 = ■

F. 546 G. 566 H. 576 J. 596

11. Which is the best estimate?

6 × $19.95

A. $40 B. $50 C. $120 D. $200

12. Complete the table for $y = 3x$.

x	1	2	3	4
y	3	6	9	■

F. 1 G. 7 H. 9 J. 12

GO ON

Grade 4 165

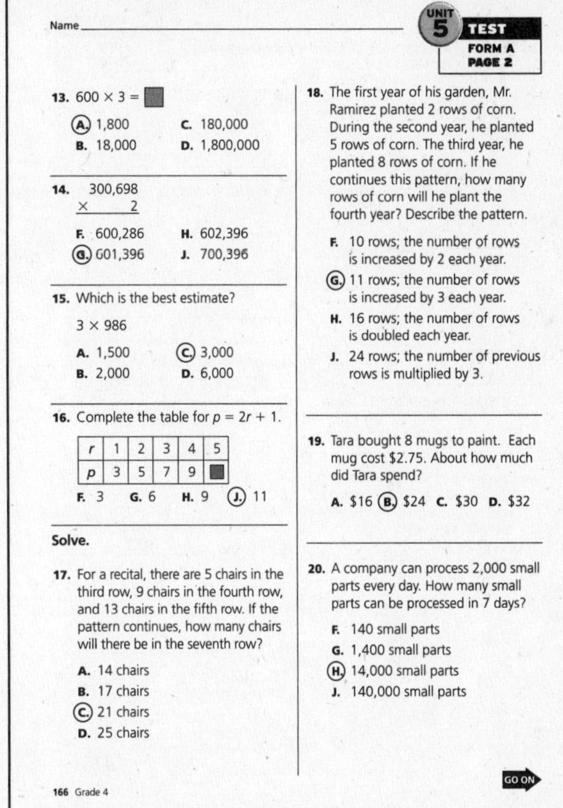

Name

UNIT 5 TEST FORM A PAGE 2

13. 600 × 3 = ■

A. 1,800 B. 18,000 C. 180,000 D. 1,800,000

14. 300,698 × 2

F. 600,286 G. 601,396 H. 602,396 J. 700,396

15. Which is the best estimate?

3 × 986

A. 1,500 B. 2,000 C. 3,000 D. 6,000

16. Complete the table for $p = 2r + 1$.

r	1	2	3	4	5
p	3	5	7	9	■

F. 3 G. 6 H. 9 J. 11

Solve.

17. For a recital, there are 5 chairs in the third row, 9 chairs in the fourth row, and 13 chairs in the fifth row. If the pattern continues, how many chairs will there be in the seventh row?

A. 14 chairs
B. 17 chairs
C. 21 chairs
D. 25 chairs

18. The first year of his garden, Mr. Ramirez planted 2 rows of corn. During the second year, he planted 5 rows of corn. The third year, he planted 8 rows of corn. If he continues this pattern, how many rows of corn will he plant the fourth year? Describe the pattern.

F. 10 rows; the number of rows is increased by 2 each year.
G. 11 rows; the number of rows is increased by 3 each year.
H. 16 rows; the number of rows is doubled each year.
J. 24 rows; the number of previous rows is multiplied by 3.

19. Tara bought 8 mugs to paint. Each mug cost $2.75. About how much did Tara spend?

A. $16 B. $24 C. $30 D. $32

20. A company can process 2,000 small parts every day. How many small parts can be processed in 7 days?

F. 140 small parts
G. 1,400 small parts
H. 14,000 small parts
J. 140,000 small parts

GO ON

166 Grade 4

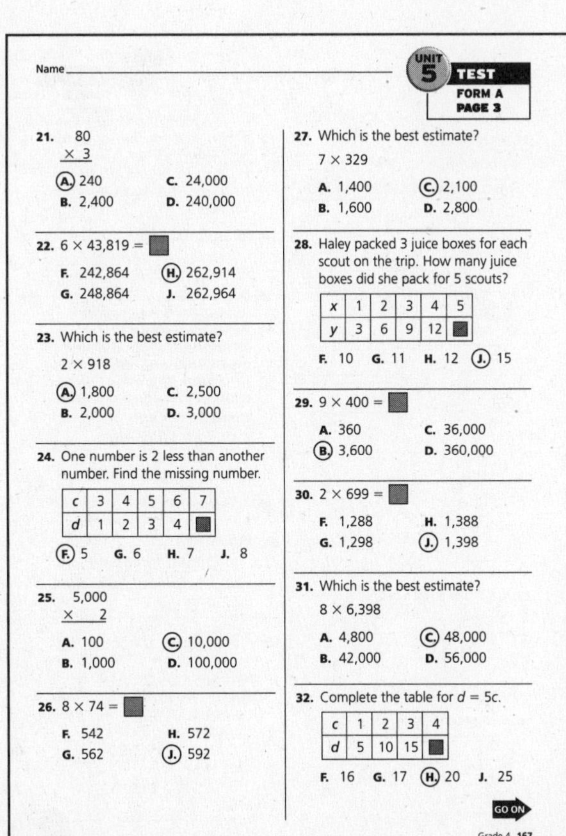

Name

UNIT 5 TEST FORM A PAGE 3

21. 80 × 3

A. 240 B. 2,400 C. 24,000 D. 240,000

22. 6 × 43,819 = ■

F. 242,864 G. 248,864 H. 262,914 J. 262,964

23. Which is the best estimate?

2 × 918

A. 1,800 B. 2,000 C. 2,500 D. 3,000

24. One number is 2 less than another number. Find the missing number.

c	3	4	5	6	7
d	1	2	3	4	■

F. 5 G. 6 H. 7 J. 8

25. 5,000 × 2

A. 100 B. 1,000 C. 10,000 D. 100,000

26. 8 × 74 = ■

F. 542 G. 562 H. 572 J. 592

27. Which is the best estimate?

7 × 329

A. 1,400 B. 1,600 C. 2,100 D. 2,800

28. Haley packed 3 juice boxes for each scout on the trip. How many juice boxes did she pack for 5 scouts?

x	1	2	3	4	5
y	3	6	9	12	■

F. 10 G. 11 H. 12 J. 15

29. 9 × 400 = ■

A. 360 B. 3,600 C. 36,000 D. 360,000

30. 2 × 699 = ■

F. 1,288 G. 1,298 H. 1,388 J. 1,398

31. Which is the best estimate?

8 × 6,398

A. 4,800 B. 42,000 C. 48,000 D. 56,000

32. Complete the table for $d = 5c$.

c	1	2	3	4
d	5	10	15	■

F. 16 G. 17 H. 20 J. 25

GO ON

Grade 4 167

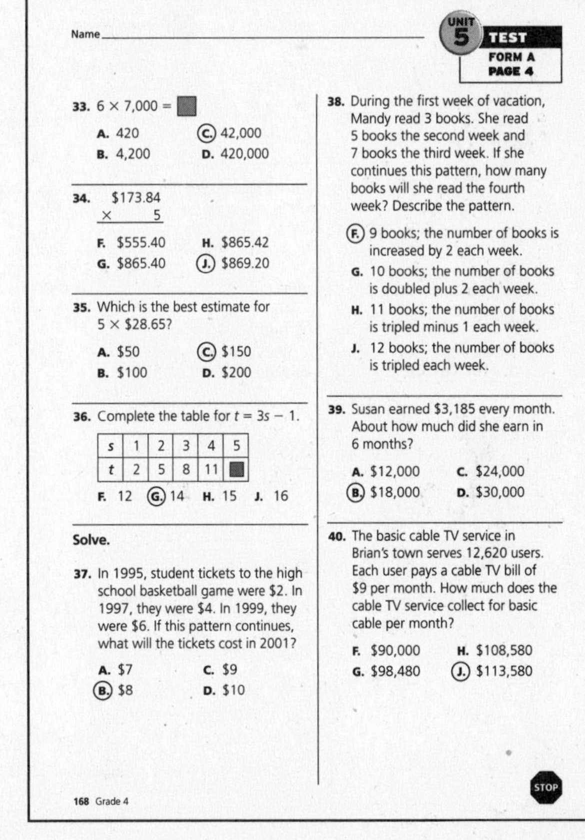

Name

UNIT 5 TEST FORM A PAGE 4

33. 6 × 7,000 = ■

A. 420 B. 4,200 C. 42,000 D. 420,000

34. $173.84 × 5

F. $555.40 G. $865.40 H. $865.42 J. $869.20

35. Which is the best estimate for 5 × $28.65?

A. $50 B. $100 C. $150 D. $200

36. Complete the table for $t = 3s - 1$.

s	1	2	3	4	5
t	2	5	8	11	■

F. 12 G. 14 H. 15 J. 16

Solve.

37. In 1995, student tickets to the high school basketball game were $2. In 1997, they were $4. In 1999, they were $6. If this pattern continues, what will the tickets cost in 2001?

A. $7 B. $8 C. $9 D. $10

38. During the first week of vacation, Mandy read 3 books. She read 5 books the second week and 7 books the third week. If she continues this pattern, how many books will she read the fourth week? Describe the pattern.

F. 9 books; the number of books is increased by 2 each week.
G. 10 books; the number of books is doubled plus 2 each week.
H. 11 books; the number of books is tripled minus 1 each week.
J. 12 books; the number of books is tripled each week.

39. Susan earned $3,185 every month. About how much did she earn in 6 months?

A. $12,000 B. $18,000 C. $24,000 D. $30,000

40. The basic cable TV service in Brian's town serves 12,620 users. Each user pays a cable TV bill of $9 per month. How much does the cable TV service collect for basic cable per month?

F. $90,000 G. $98,480 H. $108,580 J. $113,580

STOP

168 Grade 4

Unit 5

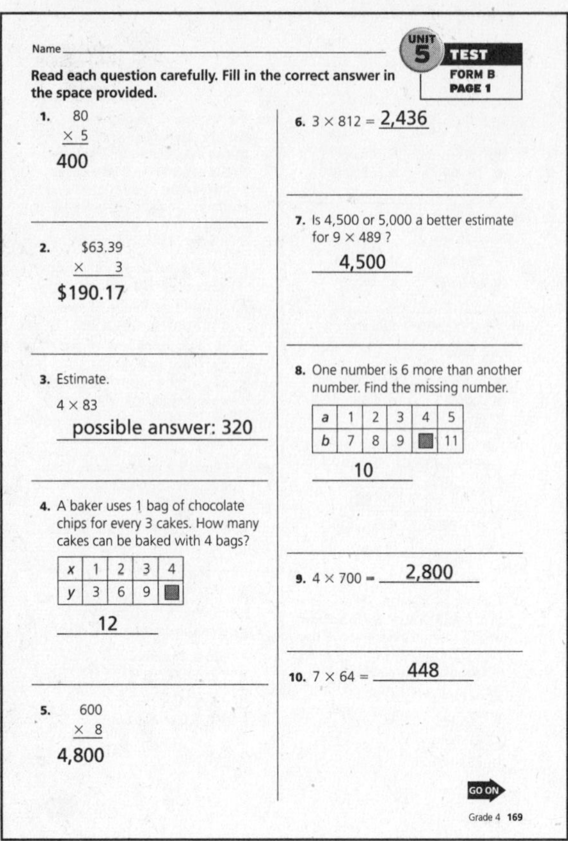

Name

Read each question carefully. Fill in the correct answer in the space provided.

UNIT 5 TEST FORM B PAGE 1

1. 80 × 5
400

2. \$63.39 × 3
\$190.17

3. Estimate.
4 × 83
possible answer: 320

4. A baker uses 1 bag of chocolate chips for every 3 cakes. How many cakes can be baked with 4 bags?

x	1	2	3	4
y	3	6	9	■

12

5. 600 × 8
4,800

6. 3 × 812 = 2,436

7. Is 4,500 or 5,000 a better estimate for 9 × 489 ?
4,500

8. One number is 6 more than another number. Find the missing number.

a	1	2	3	4	5
b	7	8	9	■	11

10

9. 4 × 700 = 2,800

10. 7 × 64 = 448

GO ON

Grade 4 169

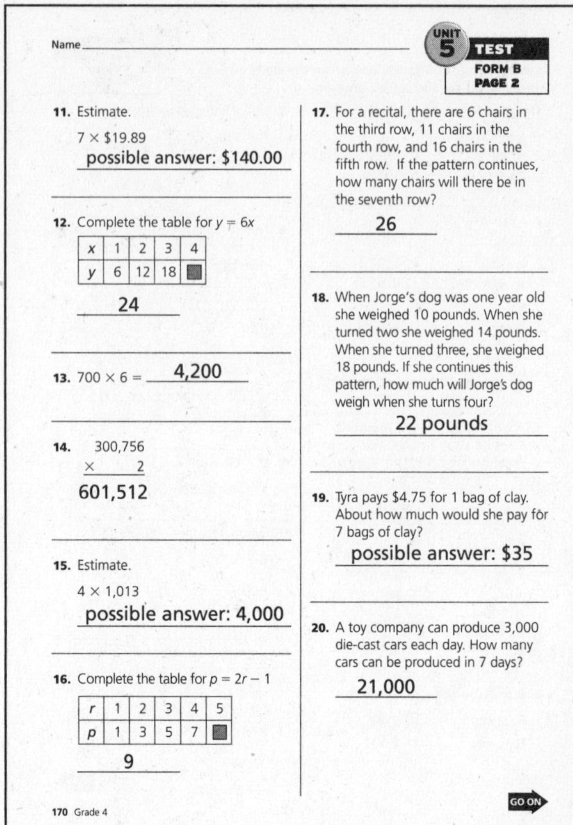

Name

UNIT 5 TEST FORM B PAGE 2

11. Estimate.
7 × \$19.89
possible answer: \$140.00

12. Complete the table for $y = 6x$

x	1	2	3	4
y	6	12	18	■

24

13. 700 × 6 = 4,200

14. 300,756 × 2
601,512

15. Estimate.
4 × 1,013
possible answer: 4,000

16. Complete the table for $p = 2r - 1$

r	1	2	3	4	5
p	1	3	5	7	■

9

17. For a recital, there are 6 chairs in the third row, 11 chairs in the fourth row, and 16 chairs in the fifth row. If the pattern continues, how many chairs will there be in the seventh row?
26

18. When Jorge's dog was one year old she weighed 10 pounds. When she turned two she weighed 14 pounds. When she turned three, she weighed 18 pounds. If she continues this pattern, how much will Jorge's dog weigh when she turns four?
22 pounds

19. Tyra pays \$4.75 for 1 bag of clay. About how much would she pay for 7 bags of clay?
possible answer: \$35

20. A toy company can produce 3,000 die-cast cars each day. How many cars can be produced in 7 days?
21,000

170 Grade 4

GO ON

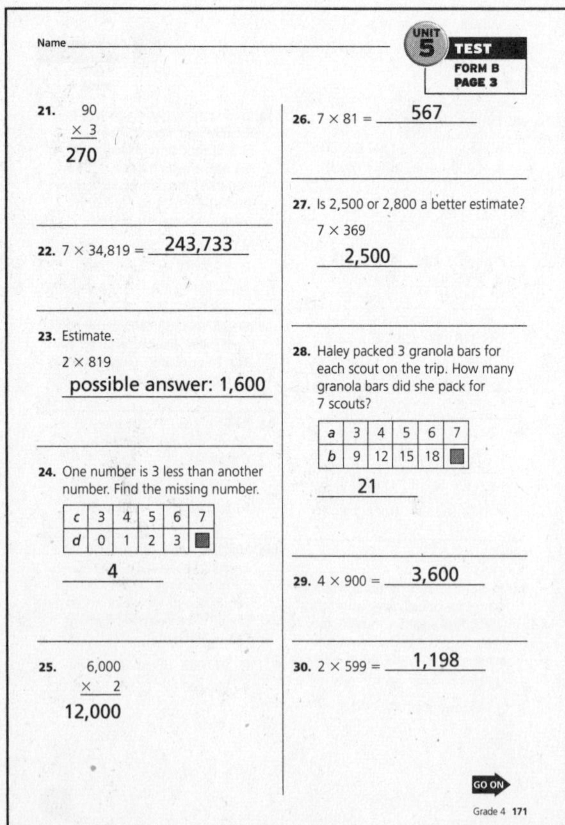

Name

UNIT 5 TEST FORM B PAGE 3

21. 90 × 3
270

22. 7 × 34,819 = 243,733

23. Estimate.
2 × 819
possible answer: 1,600

24. One number is 3 less than another number. Find the missing number.

c	3	4	5	6	7
d	0	1	2	3	■

4

25. 6,000 × 2
12,000

26. 7 × 81 = 567

27. Is 2,500 or 2,800 a better estimate?
7 × 369
2,500

28. Haley packed 3 granola bars for each scout on the trip. How many granola bars did she pack for 7 scouts?

a	3	4	5	6	7
b	9	12	15	18	■

21

29. 4 × 900 = 3,600

30. 2 × 599 = 1,198

GO ON

Grade 4 171

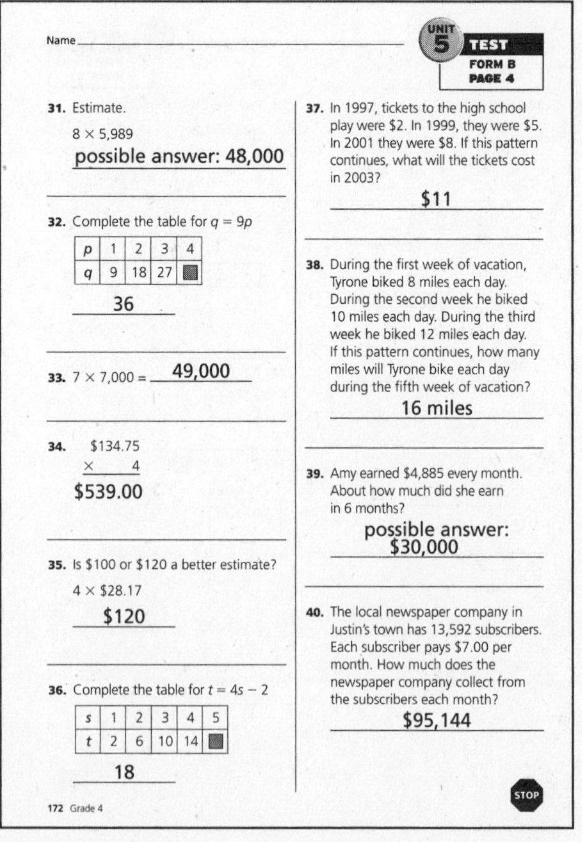

Name

UNIT 5 TEST FORM B PAGE 4

31. Estimate.
8 × 5,989
possible answer: 48,000

32. Complete the table for $q = 9p$

p	1	2	3	4
q	9	18	27	■

36

33. 7 × 7,000 = 49,000

34. \$134.75 × 4
\$539.00

35. Is \$100 or \$120 a better estimate?
4 × \$28.17
\$120

36. Complete the table for $t = 4s - 2$

s	1	2	3	4	5
t	2	6	10	14	■

18

37. In 1997, tickets to the high school play were \$2. In 1999, they were \$5. In 2001 they were \$8. If this pattern continues, what will the tickets cost in 2003?
\$11

38. During the first week of vacation, Tyrone biked 8 miles each day. During the second week he biked 10 miles each day. During the third week he biked 12 miles each day. If this pattern continues, how many miles will Tyrone bike each day during the fifth week of vacation?
16 miles

39. Amy earned \$4,885 every month. About how much did she earn in 6 months?
possible answer: \$30,000

40. The local newspaper company in Justin's town has 13,592 subscribers. Each subscriber pays \$7.00 per month. How much does the newspaper company collect from the subscribers each month?
\$95,144

172 Grade 4

STOP

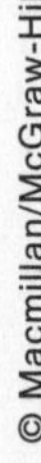

Chapter 11

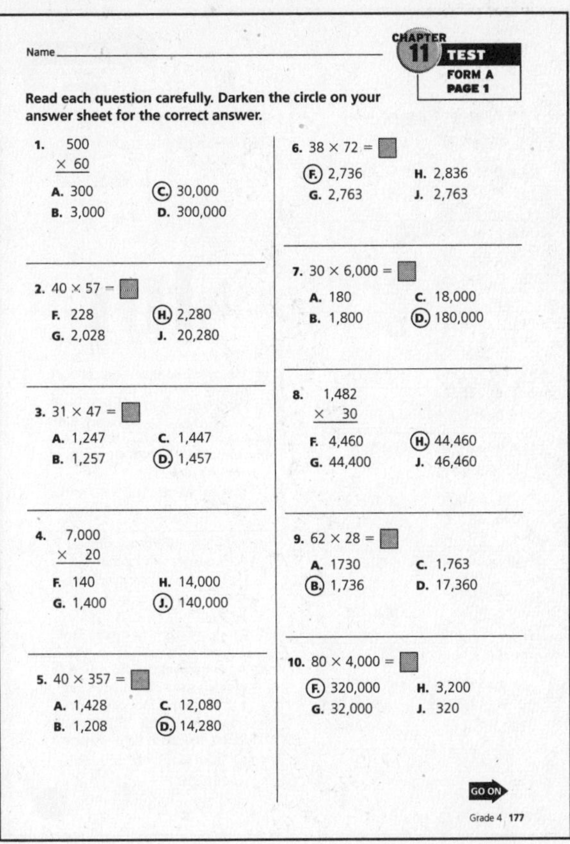

Name ______________________

CHAPTER 11 TEST FORM A PAGE 1

Read each question carefully. Darken the circle on your answer sheet for the correct answer.

1. 500 × 60
   A. 300 (C) 30,000
   B. 3,000 D. 300,000

2. 40 × 57 = ▢
   F. 228 (H) 2,280
   G. 2,028 J. 20,280

3. 31 × 47 = ▢
   A. 1,247 C. 1,447
   B. 1,257 (D) 1,457

4. 7,000 × 20
   F. 140 H. 14,000
   G. 1,400 (J) 140,000

5. 40 × 357 = ▢
   A. 1,428 C. 12,080
   B. 1,208 (D) 14,280

6. 38 × 72 = ▢
   (F) 2,736 H. 2,836
   G. 2,763 J. 2,763

7. 30 × 6,000 = ▢
   A. 180 C. 18,000
   B. 1,800 (D) 180,000

8. 1,482 × 30
   F. 4,460 (H) 44,460
   G. 44,400 J. 46,460

9. 62 × 28 = ▢
   A. 1730 C. 1,763
   (B) 1,736 D. 17,360

10. 80 × 4,000 = ▢
    (F) 320,000 H. 3,200
    G. 32,000 J. 320

GO ON

Grade 4 177

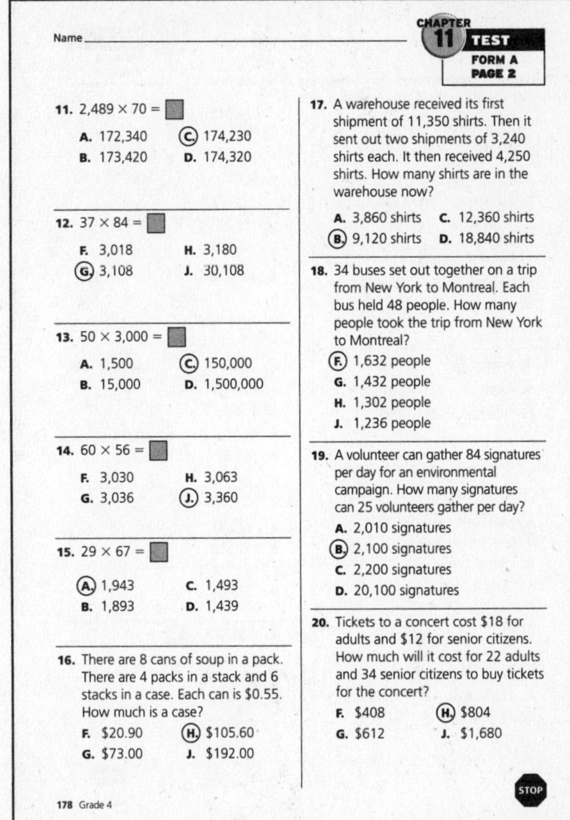

Name ______________________

CHAPTER 11 TEST FORM A PAGE 2

11. 2,489 × 70 = ▢
    A. 172,340 (C) 174,230
    B. 173,420 D. 174,320

12. 37 × 84 = ▢
    F. 3,018 H. 3,180
    (G) 3,108 J. 30,108

13. 50 × 3,000 = ▢
    A. 1,500 (C) 150,000
    B. 15,000 D. 1,500,000

14. 60 × 56 = ▢
    F. 3,030 H. 3,063
    G. 3,036 (J) 3,360

15. 29 × 67 = ▢
    (A) 1,943 C. 1,493
    B. 1,893 D. 1,439

16. There are 8 cans of soup in a pack. There are 4 packs in a stack and 6 stacks in a case. Each can is $0.55. How much is a case?
    F. $20.90 (H) $105.60
    G. $73.00 J. $192.00

17. A warehouse received its first shipment of 11,350 shirts. Then it sent out two shipments of 3,240 shirts each. It then received 4,250 shirts. How many shirts are in the warehouse now?
    A. 3,860 shirts C. 12,360 shirts
    (B) 9,120 shirts D. 18,840 shirts

18. 34 buses set out together on a trip from New York to Montreal. Each bus held 48 people. How many people took the trip from New York to Montreal?
    (F) 1,632 people
    G. 1,432 people
    H. 1,302 people
    J. 1,236 people

19. A volunteer can gather 84 signatures per day for an environmental campaign. How many signatures can 25 volunteers gather per day?
    A. 2,010 signatures
    (B) 2,100 signatures
    C. 2,200 signatures
    D. 20,100 signatures

20. Tickets to a concert cost $18 for adults and $12 for senior citizens. How much will it cost for 22 adults and 34 senior citizens to buy tickets for the concert?
    F. $408 (H) $804
    G. $612 J. $1,680

STOP

178 Grade 4

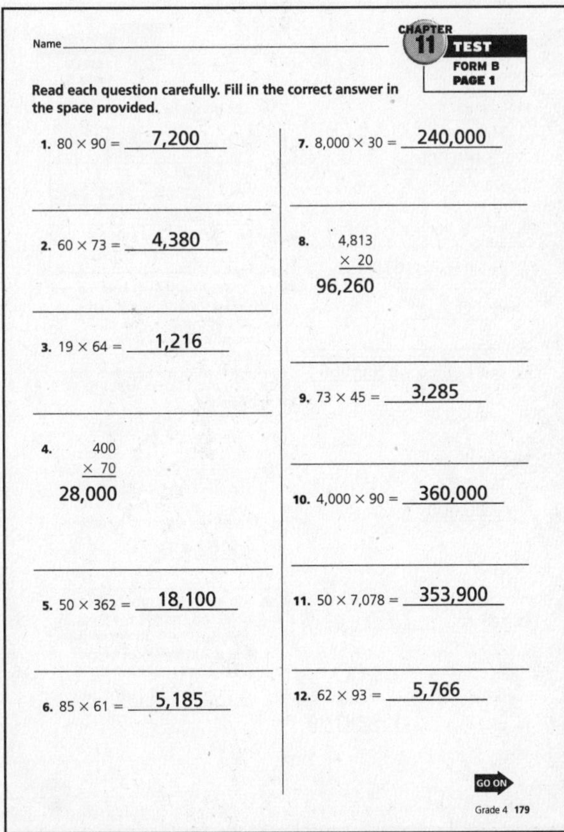

Name ______________________

CHAPTER 11 TEST FORM B PAGE 1

Read each question carefully. Fill in the correct answer in the space provided.

1. 80 × 90 = 7,200

2. 60 × 73 = 4,380

3. 19 × 64 = 1,216

4. 400 × 70 = 28,000

5. 50 × 362 = 18,100

6. 85 × 61 = 5,185

7. 8,000 × 30 = 240,000

8. 4,813 × 20 = 96,260

9. 73 × 45 = 3,285

10. 4,000 × 90 = 360,000

11. 50 × 7,078 = 353,900

12. 62 × 93 = 5,766

GO ON

Grade 4 179

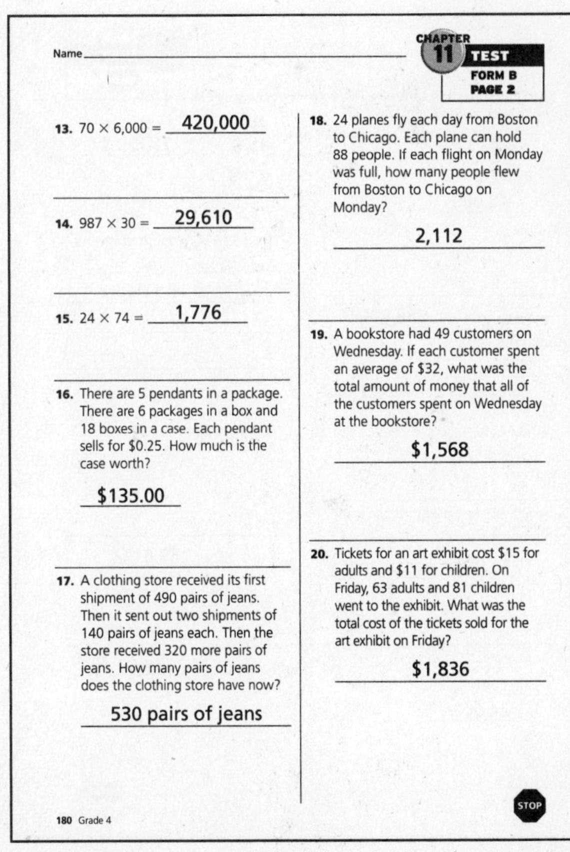

Name ______________________

CHAPTER 11 TEST FORM B PAGE 2

13. 70 × 6,000 = 420,000

14. 987 × 30 = 29,610

15. 24 × 74 = 1,776

16. There are 5 pendants in a package. There are 6 packages in a box and 18 boxes in a case. Each pendant sells for $0.25. How much is the case worth?
    $135.00

17. A clothing store received its first shipment of 490 pairs of jeans. Then it sent out two shipments of 140 pairs of jeans each. Then the store received 320 more pairs of jeans. How many pairs of jeans does the clothing store have now?
    530 pairs of jeans

18. 24 planes fly each day from Boston to Chicago. Each plane can hold 88 people. If each flight on Monday was full, how many people flew from Boston to Chicago on Monday?
    2,112

19. A bookstore had 49 customers on Wednesday. If each customer spent an average of $32, what was the total amount of money that all of the customers spent on Wednesday at the bookstore?
    $1,568

20. Tickets for an art exhibit cost $15 for adults and $11 for children. On Friday, 63 adults and 81 children went to the exhibit. What was the total cost of the tickets sold for the art exhibit on Friday?
    $1,836

STOP

180 Grade 4

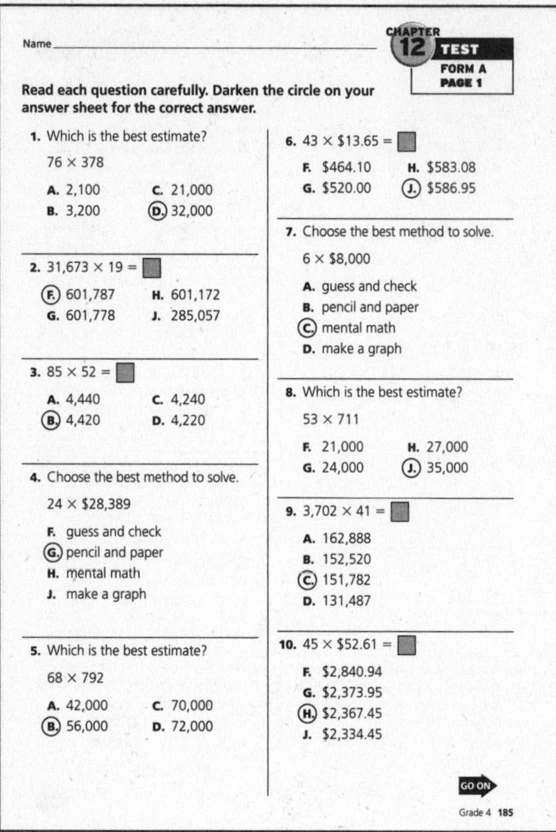

Name ____________

CHAPTER 12 TEST FORM A PAGE 1

Read each question carefully. Darken the circle on your answer sheet for the correct answer.

1. Which is the best estimate?

76 × 378

A. 2,100 **C.** 21,000
B. 3,200 (**D.**) 32,000

2. 31,673 × 19 = ▢

(**F.**) 601,787 **H.** 601,172
G. 601,778 **J.** 285,057

3. 85 × 52 = ▢

A. 4,440 **C.** 4,240
(**B.**) 4,420 **D.** 4,220

4. Choose the best method to solve.

24 × $28,389

F. guess and check
(**G.**) pencil and paper
H. mental math
J. make a graph

5. Which is the best estimate?

68 × 792

A. 42,000 **C.** 70,000
(**B.**) 56,000 **D.** 72,000

6. 43 × $13.65 = ▢

F. $464.10 **H.** $583.08
G. $520.00 (**J.**) $586.95

7. Choose the best method to solve.

6 × $8,000

A. guess and check
B. pencil and paper
(**C.**) mental math
D. make a graph

8. Which is the best estimate?

53 × 711

F. 21,000 **H.** 27,000
G. 24,000 (**J.**) 35,000

9. 3,702 × 41 = ▢

A. 162,888
B. 152,520
(**C.**) 151,782
D. 131,487

10. 45 × $52.61 = ▢

F. $2,840.94
G. $2,373.95
(**H.**) $2,367.45
J. $2,334.45

GO ON

Grade 4 185

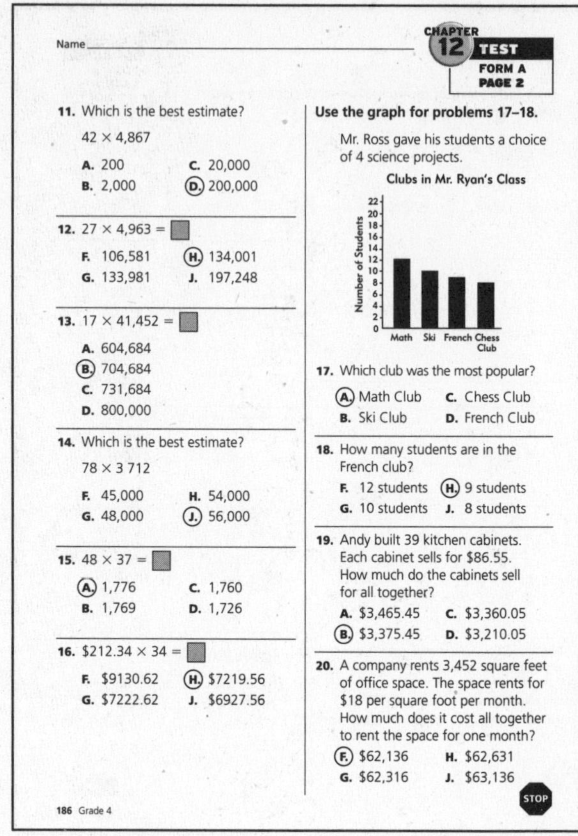

Name ____________

CHAPTER 12 TEST FORM A PAGE 2

11. Which is the best estimate?

42 × 4,867

A. 200 **C.** 20,000
B. 2,000 (**D.**) 200,000

12. 27 × 4,963 = ▢

F. 106,581 (**H.**) 134,001
G. 133,981 **J.** 197,248

13. 17 × 41,452 = ▢

A. 604,684
(**B.**) 704,684
C. 731,684
D. 800,000

14. Which is the best estimate?

78 × 3 712

F. 45,000 **H.** 54,000
G. 48,000 (**J.**) 56,000

15. 48 × 37 = ▢

(**A.**) 1,776 **C.** 1,760
B. 1,769 **D.** 1,726

16. $212.34 × 34 = ▢

F. $9130.62 (**H.**) $7219.56
G. $7222.62 **J.** $6927.56

Use the graph for problems 17–18.

Mr. Ross gave his students a choice of 4 science projects.

17. Which club was the most popular?

(**A.**) Math Club **C.** Chess Club
B. Ski Club **D.** French Club

18. How many students are in the French club?

F. 12 students (**H.**) 9 students
G. 10 students **J.** 8 students

19. Andy built 39 kitchen cabinets. Each cabinet sells for $86.55. How much do the cabinets sell for all together?

A. $3,465.45 **C.** $3,360.05
(**B.**) $3,375.45 **D.** $3,210.05

20. A company rents 3,452 square feet of office space. The space rents for $18 per square foot per month. How much does it cost all together to rent the space for one month?

(**F.**) $62,136 **H.** $62,631
G. $62,316 **J.** $63,136

STOP

186 Grade 4

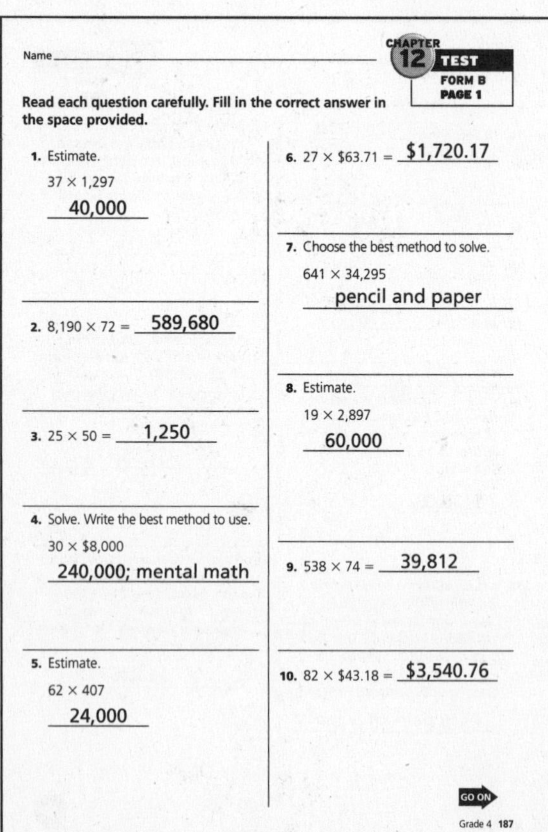

Name ____________

CHAPTER 12 TEST FORM B PAGE 1

Read each question carefully. Fill in the correct answer in the space provided.

1. Estimate.

37 × 1,297

40,000

2. 8,190 × 72 = 589,680

3. 25 × 50 = 1,250

4. Solve. Write the best method to use.

30 × $8,000

240,000; mental math

5. Estimate.

62 × 407

24,000

6. 27 × $63.71 = $1,720.17

7. Choose the best method to solve.

641 × 34,295

pencil and paper

8. Estimate.

19 × 2,897

60,000

9. 538 × 74 = 39,812

10. 82 × $43.18 = $3,540.76

GO ON

Grade 4 187

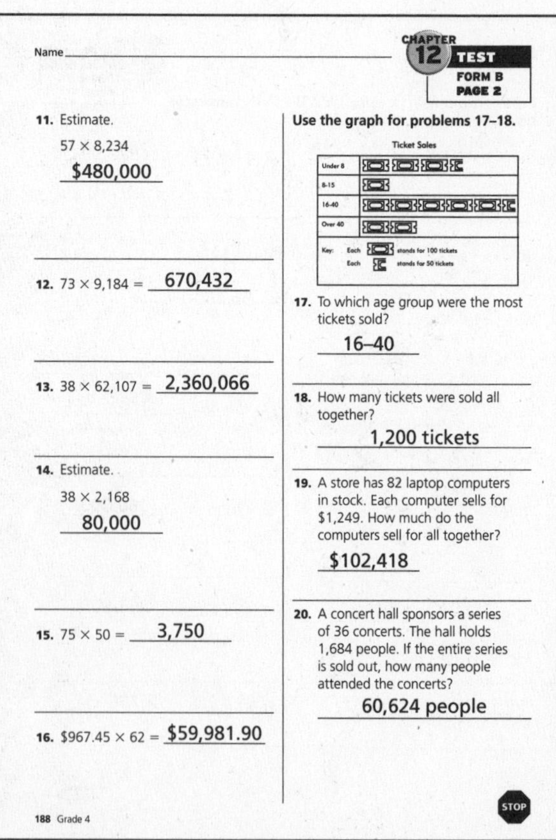

Name ____________

CHAPTER 12 TEST FORM B PAGE 2

11. Estimate.

57 × 8,234

$480,000

12. 73 × 9,184 = 670,432

13. 38 × 62,107 = 2,360,066

14. Estimate.

38 × 2,168

80,000

15. 75 × 50 = 3,750

16. $967.45 × 62 = $59,981.90

Use the graph for problems 17–18.

17. To which age group were the most tickets sold?

16–40

18. How many tickets were sold all together?

1,200 tickets

19. A store has 82 laptop computers in stock. Each computer sells for $1,249. How much do the computers sell for all together?

$102,418

20. A concert hall sponsors a series of 36 concerts. The hall holds 1,684 people. If the entire series is sold out, how many people attended the concerts?

60,624 people

STOP

188 Grade 4

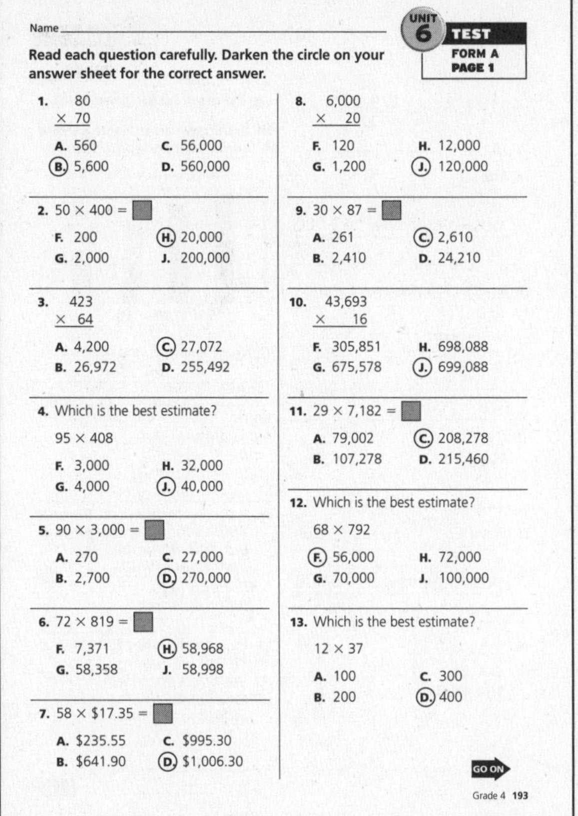

Name________________________________

UNIT 6 TEST FORM A PAGE 1

Read each question carefully. Darken the circle on your answer sheet for the correct answer.

1. 80 × 70
   A. 560 Ⓑ 5,600 C. 56,000 D. 560,000

2. 50 × 400 = ▢
   F. 200 G. 2,000 Ⓗ 20,000 J. 200,000

3. 423 × 64
   A. 4,200 B. 26,972 Ⓒ 27,072 D. 255,492

4. Which is the best estimate?
   95 × 408
   F. 3,000 G. 4,000 H. 32,000 Ⓙ 40,000

5. 90 × 3,000 = ▢
   A. 270 B. 2,700 C. 27,000 Ⓓ 270,000

6. 72 × 819 = ▢
   F. 7,371 G. 58,358 Ⓗ 58,968 J. 58,998

7. 58 × $17.35 = ▢
   A. $235.55 B. $641.90 C. $995.30 Ⓓ $1,006.30

8. 6,000 × 20
   F. 120 G. 1,200 H. 12,000 Ⓙ 120,000

9. 30 × 87 = ▢
   A. 261 B. 2,410 Ⓒ 2,610 D. 24,210

10. 43,693 × 16
    F. 305,851 G. 675,578 H. 698,088 Ⓙ 699,088

11. 29 × 7,182 = ▢
    A. 79,002 B. 107,278 Ⓒ 208,278 D. 215,460

12. Which is the best estimate?
    68 × 792
    Ⓕ 56,000 G. 70,000 H. 72,000 J. 100,000

13. Which is the best estimate?
    12 × 37
    A. 100 B. 200 C. 300 Ⓓ 400

GO ON

Grade 4 193

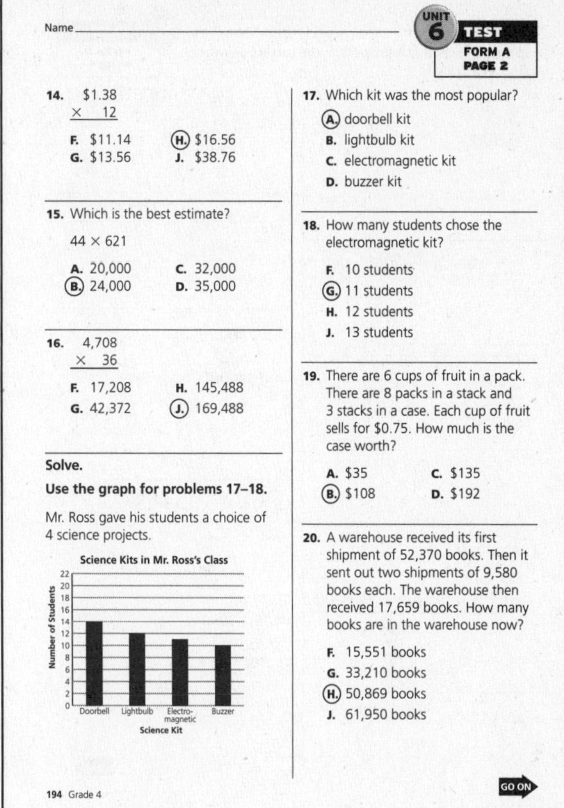

Name________________________________

UNIT 6 TEST FORM A PAGE 2

14. $1.38 × 12
    F. $11.14 G. $13.56 Ⓗ $16.56 J. $38.76

15. Which is the best estimate?
    44 × 621
    A. 20,000 Ⓑ 24,000 C. 32,000 D. 35,000

16. 4,708 × 36
    F. 17,208 G. 42,372 H. 145,488 Ⓙ 169,488

Solve.

Use the graph for problems 17–18.

Mr. Ross gave his students a choice of 4 science projects.

17. Which kit was the most popular?
    Ⓐ doorbell kit
    B. lightbulb kit
    C. electromagnetic kit
    D. buzzer kit

18. How many students chose the electromagnetic kit?
    F. 10 students
    Ⓖ 11 students
    H. 12 students
    J. 13 students

19. There are 6 cups of fruit in a pack. There are 8 packs in a stack and 3 stacks in a case. Each cup of fruit sells for $0.75. How much is the case worth?
    A. $35 Ⓑ $108 C. $135 D. $192

20. A warehouse received its first shipment of 52,370 books. Then it sent out two shipments of 9,580 books each. The warehouse then received 17,659 books. How many books are in the warehouse now?
    F. 15,551 books
    G. 33,210 books
    Ⓗ 50,869 books
    J. 61,950 books

194 Grade 4

GO ON

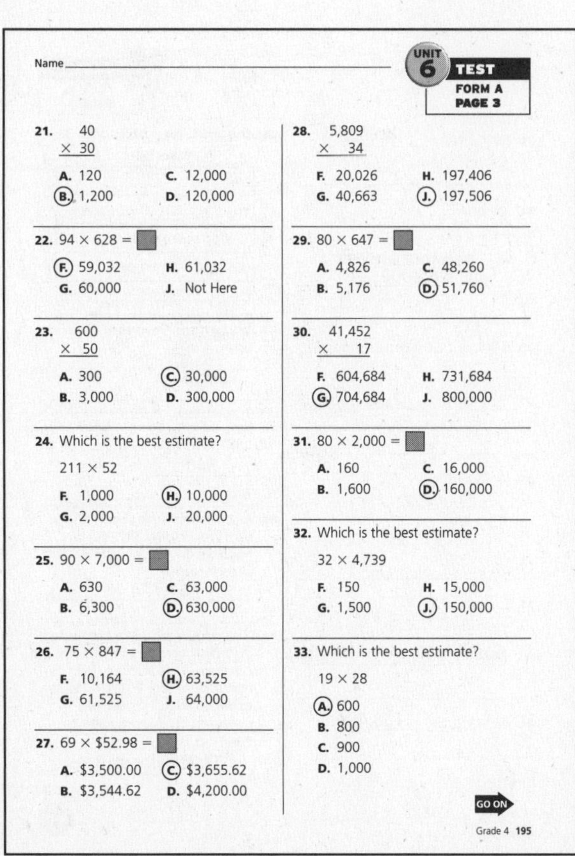

Name________________________________

UNIT 6 TEST FORM A PAGE 3

21. 40 × 30
    A. 120 Ⓑ 1,200 C. 12,000 D. 120,000

22. 94 × 628 = ▢
    Ⓕ 59,032 G. 60,000 H. 61,032 J. Not Here

23. 600 × 50
    A. 300 B. 3,000 Ⓒ 30,000 D. 300,000

24. Which is the best estimate?
    211 × 52
    F. 1,000 G. 2,000 Ⓗ 10,000 J. 20,000

25. 90 × 7,000 = ▢
    A. 630 B. 6,300 C. 63,000 Ⓓ 630,000

26. 75 × 847 = ▢
    F. 10,164 G. 61,525 Ⓗ 63,525 J. 64,000

27. 69 × $52.98 = ▢
    A. $3,500.00 B. $3,544.62 Ⓒ $3,655.62 D. $4,200.00

28. 5,809 × 34
    F. 20,026 G. 40,663 H. 197,406 Ⓙ 197,506

29. 80 × 647 = ▢
    A. 4,826 B. 5,176 C. 48,260 Ⓓ 51,760

30. 41,452 × 17
    F. 604,684 Ⓖ 704,684 H. 731,684 J. 800,000

31. 80 × 2,000 = ▢
    A. 160 B. 1,600 C. 16,000 Ⓓ 160,000

32. Which is the best estimate?
    32 × 4,739
    F. 150 G. 1,500 H. 15,000 Ⓙ 150,000

33. Which is the best estimate?
    19 × 28
    Ⓐ 600
    B. 800
    C. 900
    D. 1,000

GO ON

Grade 4 195

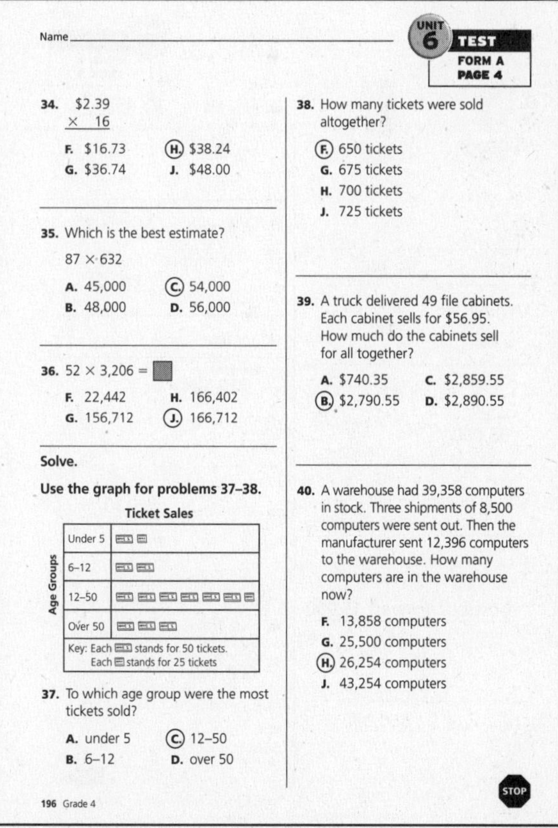

Name________________________________

UNIT 6 TEST FORM A PAGE 4

34. $2.39 × 16
    F. $16.73 G. $36.74 Ⓗ $38.24 J. $48.00

35. Which is the best estimate?
    87 × 632
    A. 45,000 B. 48,000 Ⓒ 54,000 D. 56,000

36. 52 × 3,206 = ▢
    F. 22,442 G. 156,712 H. 166,402 Ⓙ 166,712

Solve.

Use the graph for problems 37–38.

37. To which age group were the most tickets sold?
    A. under 5 B. 6–12 Ⓒ 12–50 D. over 50

38. How many tickets were sold altogether?
    Ⓕ 650 tickets
    G. 675 tickets
    H. 700 tickets
    J. 725 tickets

39. A truck delivered 49 file cabinets. Each cabinet sells for $56.95. How much do the cabinets sell for all together?
    A. $740.35 Ⓑ $2,790.55 C. $2,859.55 D. $2,890.55

40. A warehouse had 39,358 computers in stock. Three shipments of 8,500 computers were sent out. Then the manufacturer sent 12,396 computers to the warehouse. How many computers are in the warehouse now?
    F. 13,858 computers
    G. 25,500 computers
    Ⓗ 26,254 computers
    J. 43,254 computers

196 Grade 4

STOP

Unit 6

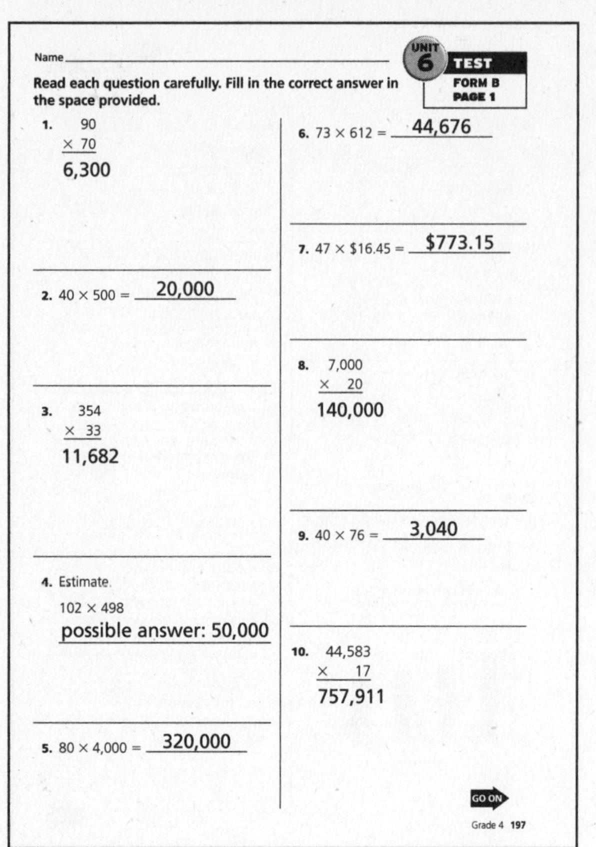

Name________________ UNIT 6 TEST FORM B PAGE 1

Read each question carefully. Fill in the correct answer in the space provided.

1. 90 × 70 = 6,300
2. 40 × 500 = 20,000
3. 354 × 33 = 11,682
4. Estimate. 102 × 498 possible answer: 50,000
5. 80 × 4,000 = 320,000
6. 73 × 612 = 44,676
7. 47 × $16.45 = $773.15
8. 7,000 × 20 = 140,000
9. 40 × 76 = 3,040
10. 44,583 × 17 = 757,911

GO ON

Grade 4 197

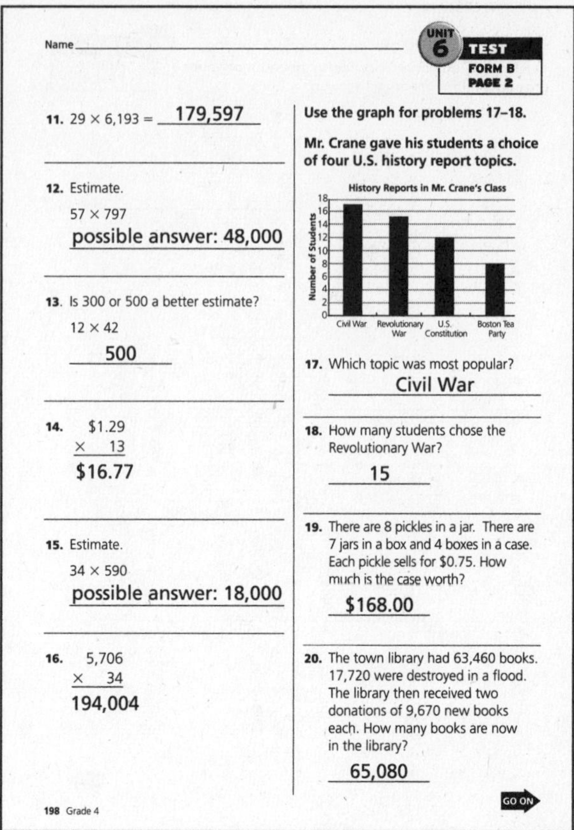

Name________________ UNIT 6 TEST FORM B PAGE 2

11. 29 × 6,193 = 179,597
12. Estimate. 57 × 797 possible answer: 48,000
13. Is 300 or 500 a better estimate? 12 × 42 500
14. $1.29 × 13 = $16.77
15. Estimate. 34 × 590 possible answer: 18,000
16. 5,706 × 34 = 194,004

Use the graph for problems 17–18.

Mr. Crane gave his students a choice of four U.S. history report topics.

17. Which topic was most popular? Civil War
18. How many students chose the Revolutionary War? 15
19. There are 8 pickles in a jar. There are 7 jars in a box and 4 boxes in a case. Each pickle sells for $0.75. How much is the case worth? $168.00
20. The town library had 63,460 books. 17,720 were destroyed in a flood. The library then received two donations of 9,670 new books each. How many books are now in the library? 65,080

198 Grade 4

GO ON

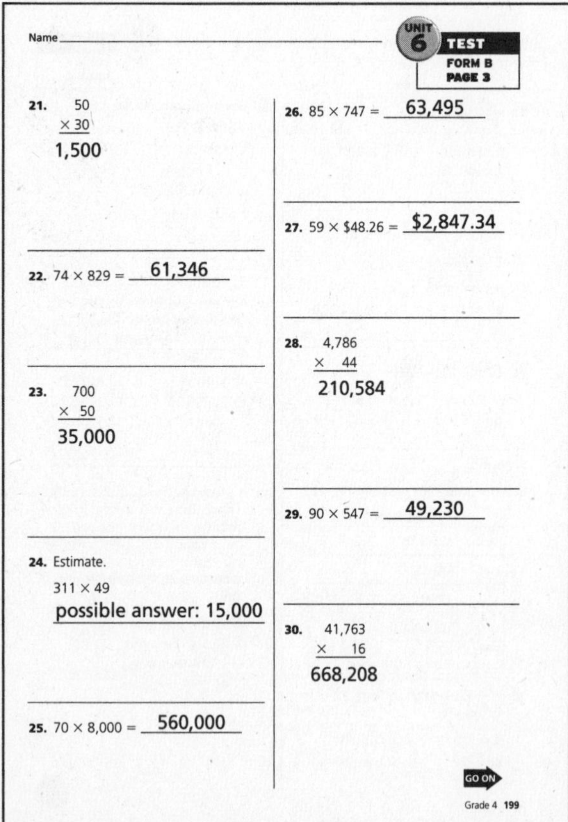

Name________________ UNIT 6 TEST FORM B PAGE 3

21. 50 × 30 = 1,500
22. 74 × 829 = 61,346
23. 700 × 50 = 35,000
24. Estimate. 311 × 49 possible answer: 15,000
25. 70 × 8,000 = 560,000
26. 85 × 747 = 63,495
27. 59 × $48.26 = $2,847.34
28. 4,786 × 44 = 210,584
29. 90 × 547 = 49,230
30. 41,763 × 16 = 668,208

GO ON

Grade 4 199

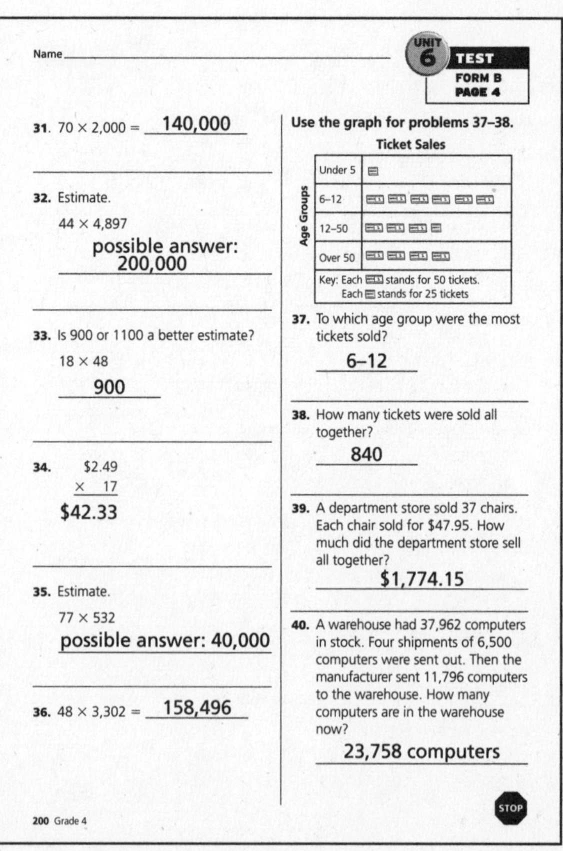

Name________________ UNIT 6 TEST FORM B PAGE 4

31. 70 × 2,000 = 140,000
32. Estimate. 44 × 4,897 possible answer: 200,000
33. Is 900 or 1100 a better estimate? 18 × 48 900
34. $2.49 × 17 = $42.33
35. Estimate. 77 × 532 possible answer: 40,000
36. 48 × 3,302 = 158,496

Use the graph for problems 37–38.

Ticket Sales

37. To which age group were the most tickets sold? 6–12
38. How many tickets were sold all together? 840
39. A department store sold 37 chairs. Each chair sold for $47.95. How much did the department store sell all together? $1,774.15
40. A warehouse had 37,962 computers in stock. Four shipments of 6,500 computers were sent out. Then the manufacturer sent 11,796 computers to the warehouse. How many computers are in the warehouse now? 23,758 computers

200 Grade 4

STOP

Chapter 13

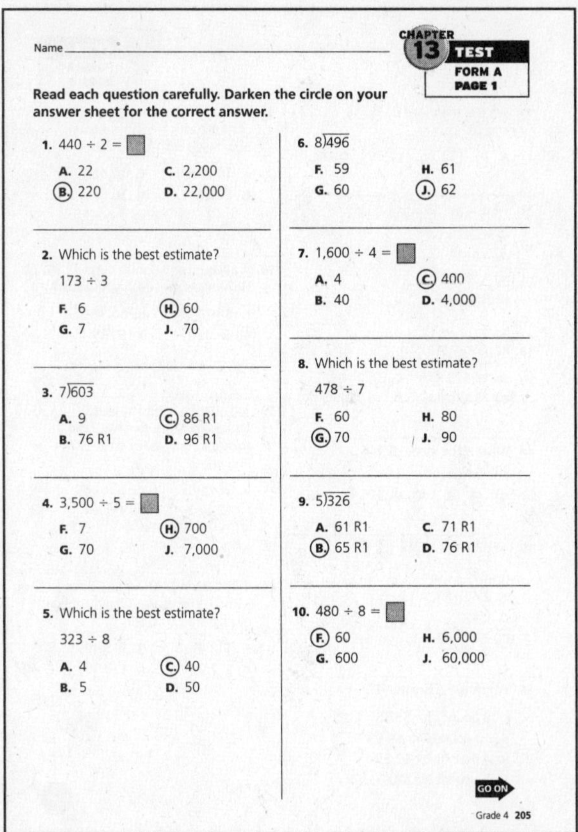

Name ______________________

CHAPTER 13 TEST
FORM A
PAGE 1

Read each question carefully. Darken the circle on your answer sheet for the correct answer.

1. 440 ÷ 2 = ■
   A. 22 Ⓑ 220 C. 2,200 D. 22,000

2. Which is the best estimate?
   173 ÷ 3
   F. 6 G. 7 Ⓗ 60 J. 70

3. 7)603
   A. 9 B. 76 R1 Ⓒ 86 R1 D. 96 R1

4. 3,500 ÷ 5 = ■
   F. 7 G. 70 Ⓗ 700 J. 7,000

5. Which is the best estimate?
   323 ÷ 8
   A. 4 B. 5 Ⓒ 40 D. 50

6. 8)496
   F. 59 G. 60 H. 61 Ⓙ 62

7. 1,600 ÷ 4 = ■
   A. 4 B. 40 Ⓒ 400 D. 4,000

8. Which is the best estimate?
   478 ÷ 7
   F. 60 Ⓖ 70 H. 80 J. 90

9. 5)326
   A. 61 R1 Ⓑ 65 R1 C. 71 R1 D. 76 R1

10. 480 ÷ 8 = ■
    Ⓕ 60 G. 600 H. 6,000 J. 60,000

GO ON

Grade 4 205

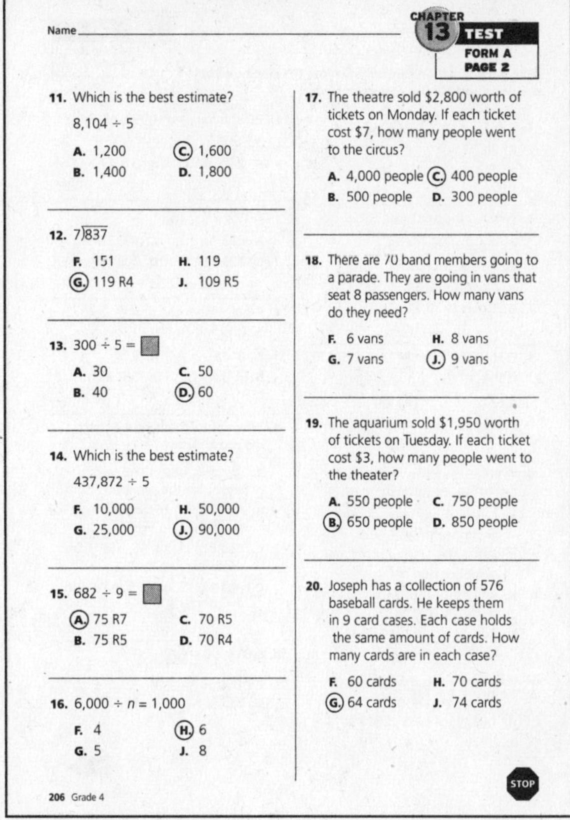

Name ______________________

CHAPTER 13 TEST
FORM A
PAGE 2

11. Which is the best estimate?
    8,104 ÷ 5
    A. 1,200 B. 1,400 Ⓒ 1,600 D. 1,800

12. 7)837
    F. 151 Ⓖ 119 R4 H. 119 J. 109 R5

13. 300 ÷ 5 = ■
    A. 30 B. 40 C. 50 Ⓓ 60

14. Which is the best estimate?
    437,872 ÷ 5
    F. 10,000 G. 25,000 H. 50,000 Ⓙ 90,000

15. 682 ÷ 9 = ■
    Ⓐ 75 R7 B. 75 R5 C. 70 R5 D. 70 R4

16. 6,000 ÷ n = 1,000
    F. 4 G. 5 Ⓗ 6 J. 8

17. The theatre sold $2,800 worth of tickets on Monday. If each ticket cost $7, how many people went to the circus?
    A. 4,000 people B. 500 people Ⓒ 400 people D. 300 people

18. There are 70 band members going to a parade. They are going in vans that seat 8 passengers. How many vans do they need?
    F. 6 vans G. 7 vans H. 8 vans Ⓙ 9 vans

19. The aquarium sold $1,950 worth of tickets on Tuesday. If each ticket cost $3, how many people went to the theater?
    A. 550 people Ⓑ 650 people C. 750 people D. 850 people

20. Joseph has a collection of 576 baseball cards. He keeps them in 9 card cases. Each case holds the same amount of cards. How many cards are in each case?
    F. 60 cards Ⓖ 64 cards H. 70 cards J. 74 cards

STOP

206 Grade 4

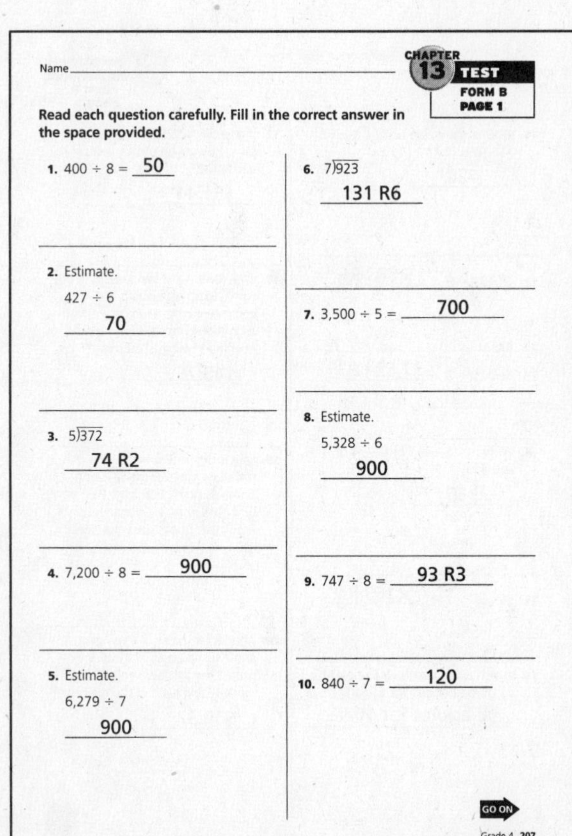

Name ______________________

CHAPTER 13 TEST
FORM B
PAGE 1

Read each question carefully. Fill in the correct answer in the space provided.

1. 400 ÷ 8 = **50**

2. Estimate.
   427 ÷ 6
   70

3. 5)372
   74 R2

4. 7,200 ÷ 8 = **900**

5. Estimate.
   6,279 ÷ 7
   900

6. 7)923
   131 R6

7. 3,500 ÷ 5 = **700**

8. Estimate.
   5,328 ÷ 6
   900

9. 747 ÷ 8 = **93 R3**

10. 840 ÷ 7 = **120**

GO ON

Grade 4 207

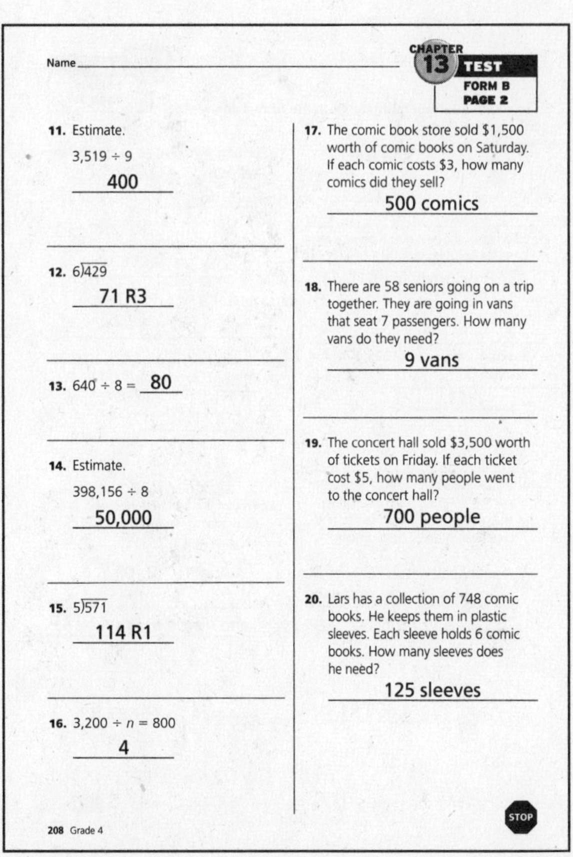

Name ______________________

CHAPTER 13 TEST
FORM B
PAGE 2

11. Estimate.
    3,519 ÷ 9
    400

12. 6)429
    71 R3

13. 640 ÷ 8 = **80**

14. Estimate.
    398,156 ÷ 8
    50,000

15. 5)571
    114 R1

16. 3,200 ÷ n = 800
    4

17. The comic book store sold $1,500 worth of comic books on Saturday. If each comic costs $3, how many comics did they sell?
    500 comics

18. There are 58 seniors going on a trip together. They are going in vans that seat 7 passengers. How many vans do they need?
    9 vans

19. The concert hall sold $3,500 worth of tickets on Friday. If each ticket cost $5, how many people went to the concert hall?
    700 people

20. Lars has a collection of 748 comic books. He keeps them in plastic sleeves. Each sleeve holds 6 comic books. How many sleeves does he need?
    125 sleeves

STOP

208 Grade 4

Chapter 14

Name________________________________

CHAPTER 14 TEST FORM A PAGE 1

Read each question carefully. Darken the circle on your answer sheet for the correct answer.

1. 4,928 ÷ 7 = ▢
   A. 70 (B) 704 C. 704 R3 D. 740

2. Which is the best buy?
   F. 9 ounces for $3.33
   G. 7 ounces for $2.52
   (H) 5 ounces for $1.75
   J. 3 ounces for $1.11

3. What is the mean of 211, 313, 256, and 308?
   A. 242 B. 252 (C) 272 D. 1,088

4. Which of the following is a correct method to determine the mean?
   F. Add 614, 752, 431 and 907, and divide the sum by 3.
   (G) Add 1,005, 456, and 201 and divide the sum by 3.
   H. Add 32, 55, 19, 94, and 31 and divide the sum by 6.
   J. Add 20, 25, 35, and 25 and divide the sum by 3.

5. 13,489 ÷ 7 = ▢
   (A) 1,927 B. 1,729 C. 1,729 R4 D. 1,279

6. What is the mean of 32, 45, 38, 37, and 53?
   F. 27 G. 31 H. 37 (J) 41

7. 7,498 ÷ 9 = ▢
   A. 689 (B) 833 R1 C. 833 R6 D. 388 R6

8. What is the mean of 305, 0, 297, 416, 376, 601, and 210?
   (F) 315 G. 320 R1 H. 335 J. 367 R3

9. Which of the following is a correct method to determine the mean?
   A. Add 360, 980, 1,016, and 10 and divide the sum by 3.
   B. Add 17, 17, 26, and 30 and divide the sum by 3.
   C. Add 37, 99, 28, 66, and 19 and divide the sum by 6.
   (D) Add 18, 15, and 11 and divide the sum by 3.

10. 6,683 ÷ 8 = ▢
    F. 835 (G) 835 R3 H. 853 J. 853 R3

GO ON

Name________________________________

CHAPTER 14 TEST FORM A PAGE 2

11. What is the mean of 30, 16, 51, 23, and 20?
    A. 20 (B) 28 C. 30 D. 38

12. 34,872 ÷ 7 = ▢
    F. 4,891 R5
    G. 4,981
    (H) 4,981 R5
    J. 5,981 R4

13. 82,379 ÷ 5 = ▢
    A. 16,475 R3 (B) 16,475 R4 C. 16,754 R4 D. 16,754 R5

14. What is the mean of 116, 128, 115, and 221?
    (F) 145 G. 140 H. 125 J. 120

15. 14,829 ÷ 6 = ▢
    A. 2,417
    B. 2,417 R3
    C. 2,471
    (D) 2,471 R3

16. Which is the best buy?
    F. 8 pounds for $5.25
    (G) 10 pounds for $6.05
    H. 4 pounds for $2.85
    J. 3 pounds for $2.03

17. If Lee spent $6.03 on 9 pens and each pen cost the same amount, how much did 1 pen cost?
    A. $0.58 B. $0.60 C. $0.62 (D) $0.67

18. A package of 6 donuts costs $1.50. How much does each donut cost?
    F. $0.20 (G) $0.25 H. $0.30 J. $0.35

19. Together Ron and Tori have 35 trading cards. Ron has 9 more than Tori. How many does Ron have?
    A. 26 cards (B) 22 cards C. 13 cards D. 9 cards

20. If Tami spent $38.97 on 3 CDs and each CD cost the same amount, how much did 1 CD cost?
    F. $12.49 (G) $12.99 H. $13.49 J. $13.99

Name________________________________

Read each question carefully. Fill in the correct answer in the space provided.

1. 7,124 ÷ 8 = 890 R4

2. Which is the best buy: 8 pounds for $15.43 or 4 pounds for $7.79?
   8 pounds for $15.43

3. What is the mean of 323, 374, 184, and 575?
   364

4. If you add a 0 to a set of 5 different numbers, how does that change the method you would use to find the mean of all of the numbers?
   You would divide the sum of all the numbers by 6, not 5, to find the mean.

5. 23,451 ÷ 5 = 4,690 R1

6. What is the mean of 36, 42, 39, 48, and 50?
   43

7. 7,045 ÷ 8 = 880 R5

8. What is the mean of 752, 148, 0, 18, 478, 657, and 894?
   421

9. What is a correct method of determining the mean of 16, 12, 14, 7, 6, and 17?
   Add 16, 12, 14, 7, 6, and 17 and divide the sum by 6.

10. 82,125 ÷ 6 = 13,687 R3

Name________________________________

CHAPTER 14 TEST FORM B PAGE 2

11. What is the mean of 534, 1, 962, 456, and 187?
    428

12. 48,453 ÷ 9 = 5,383 R6

13. 61,075 ÷ 8 = 7,634 R3

14. What is the mean of 327, 418, 166, and 489?
    350

15. 36,187 ÷ 7 = 5,169 R4

16. Which is the best buy: 6 apples for $3.45 or 2 apples for $0.98?
    2 apples for $0.98

17. If you divide $205.76 into 4 even piles, how much money will be in each pile?
    $51.44

18. Ezra, Kristin, and Mindy want to buy some stereo equipment. The equipment costs $146.28. If they each contribute the same amount, how much will they each pay?
    $48.76

19. Lara is organizing her books. She has three times as many fiction books as nonfiction. Lara has 60 books in all. How many nonfiction books does she have?
    15

20. Altogether, Jonas, Kareem, Ben, and Allie earned $77.48. If they shared the money evenly, how much would each of them receive?
    $19.37

STOP

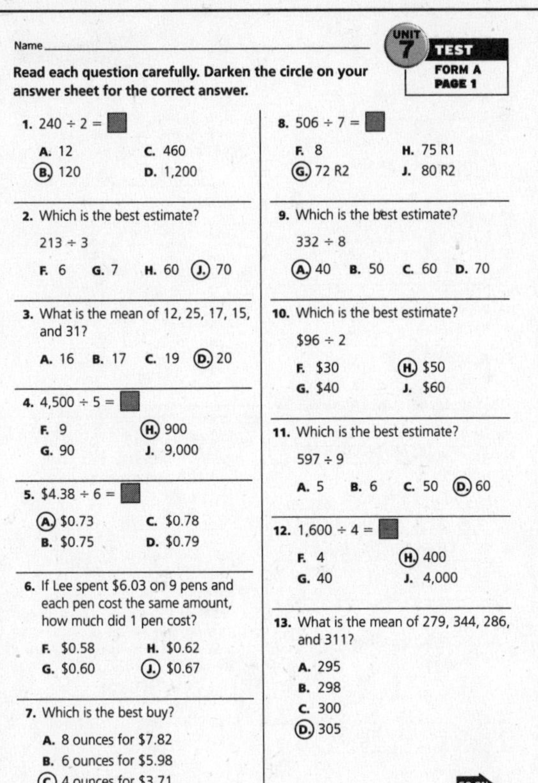

Name ________________

UNIT 7 TEST FORM A PAGE 1

Read each question carefully. Darken the circle on your answer sheet for the correct answer.

1. 240 ÷ 2 = ■
   A. 12 C. 460
   Ⓑ 120 D. 1,200

2. Which is the best estimate?
   213 ÷ 3
   F. 6 G. 7 H. 60 Ⓙ 70

3. What is the mean of 12, 25, 17, 15, and 31?
   A. 16 B. 17 C. 19 Ⓓ 20

4. 4,500 ÷ 5 = ■
   F. 9 Ⓗ 900
   G. 90 J. 9,000

5. $4.38 ÷ 6 = ■
   Ⓐ $0.73 C. $0.78
   B. $0.75 D. $0.79

6. If Lee spent $6.03 on 9 pens and each pen cost the same amount, how much did 1 pen cost?
   F. $0.58 H. $0.62
   G. $0.60 Ⓙ $0.67

7. Which is the best buy?
   A. 8 ounces for $7.82
   B. 6 ounces for $5.98
   Ⓒ 4 ounces for $3.71
   D. 2 ounces for $1.92

8. 506 ÷ 7 = ■
   F. 8 H. 75 R1
   Ⓖ 72 R2 J. 80 R2

9. Which is the best estimate?
   332 ÷ 8
   Ⓐ 40 B. 50 C. 60 D. 70

10. Which is the best estimate?
    $96 ÷ 2
    F. $30 Ⓗ $50
    G. $40 J. $60

11. Which is the best estimate?
    597 ÷ 9
    A. 5 B. 6 C. 50 Ⓓ 60

12. 1,600 ÷ 4 = ■
    F. 4 Ⓗ 400
    G. 40 J. 4,000

13. What is the mean of 279, 344, 286, and 311?
    A. 295
    B. 298
    C. 300
    Ⓓ 305

GO ON

Grade 4 221

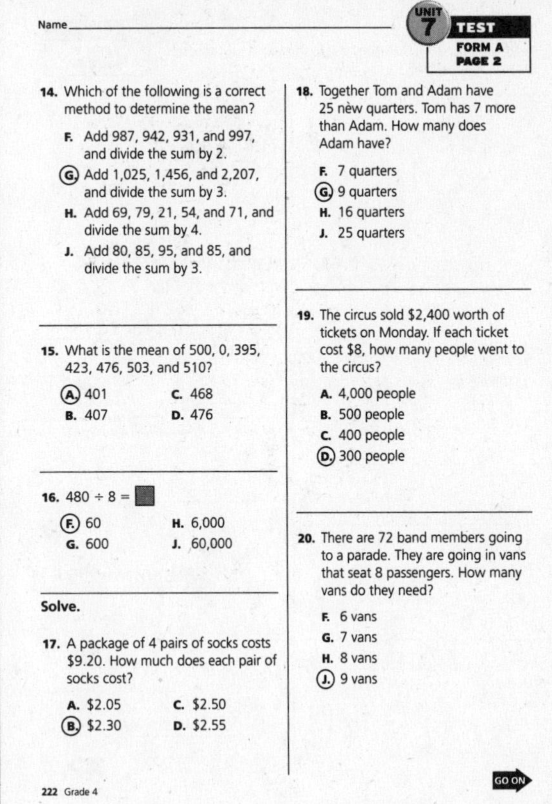

Name ________________

UNIT 7 TEST FORM A PAGE 2

14. Which of the following is a correct method to determine the mean?
    F. Add 987, 942, 931, and 997, and divide the sum by 2.
    Ⓖ Add 1,025, 1,456, and 2,207, and divide the sum by 3.
    H. Add 69, 79, 21, 54, and 71, and divide the sum by 4.
    J. Add 80, 85, 95, and 85, and divide the sum by 3.

15. What is the mean of 500, 0, 395, 423, 476, 503, and 510?
    Ⓐ 401 C. 468
    B. 407 D. 476

16. 480 ÷ 8 = ■
    Ⓕ 60 H. 6,000
    G. 600 J. 60,000

Solve.

17. A package of 4 pairs of socks costs $9.20. How much does each pair of socks cost?
    A. $2.05 C. $2.50
    Ⓑ $2.30 D. $2.55

18. Together Tom and Adam have 25 new quarters. Tom has 7 more than Adam. How many does Adam have?
    F. 7 quarters
    Ⓖ 9 quarters
    H. 16 quarters
    J. 25 quarters

19. The circus sold $2,400 worth of tickets on Monday. If each ticket cost $8, how many people went to the circus?
    A. 4,000 people
    B. 500 people
    C. 400 people
    Ⓓ 300 people

20. There are 72 band members going to a parade. They are going in vans that seat 8 passengers. How many vans do they need?
    F. 6 vans
    G. 7 vans
    H. 8 vans
    Ⓙ 9 vans

222 Grade 4

GO ON

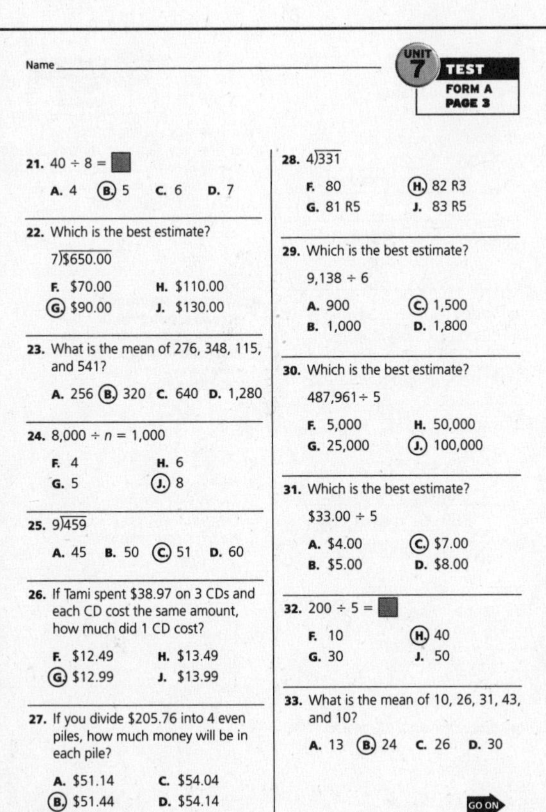

Name ________________

UNIT 7 TEST FORM A PAGE 3

21. 40 ÷ 8 = ■
    A. 4 Ⓑ 5 C. 6 D. 7

22. Which is the best estimate?
    7)$650.00
    F. $70.00 H. $110.00
    Ⓖ $90.00 J. $130.00

23. What is the mean of 276, 348, 115, and 541?
    A. 256 Ⓑ 320 C. 640 D. 1,280

24. 8,000 ÷ n = 1,000
    F. 4 H. 6
    G. 5 Ⓙ 8

25. 9)459
    A. 45 B. 50 Ⓒ 51 D. 60

26. If Tami spent $38.97 on 3 CDs and each CD cost the same amount, how much did 1 CD cost?
    F. $12.49 H. $13.49
    Ⓖ $12.99 J. $13.99

27. If you divide $205.76 into 4 even piles, how much money will be in each pile?
    A. $51.14 C. $54.04
    Ⓑ $51.44 D. $54.14

28. 4)331
    F. 80 Ⓗ 82 R3
    G. 81 R5 J. 83 R5

29. Which is the best estimate?
    9,138 ÷ 6
    A. 900 Ⓒ 1,500
    B. 1,000 D. 1,800

30. Which is the best estimate?
    487,961 ÷ 5
    F. 5,000 H. 50,000
    G. 25,000 Ⓙ 100,000

31. Which is the best estimate?
    $33.00 ÷ 5
    A. $4.00 Ⓒ $7.00
    B. $5.00 D. $8.00

32. 200 ÷ 5 = ■
    F. 10 Ⓗ 40
    G. 30 J. 50

33. What is the mean of 10, 26, 31, 43, and 10?
    A. 13 Ⓑ 24 C. 26 D. 30

GO ON

Grade 4 223

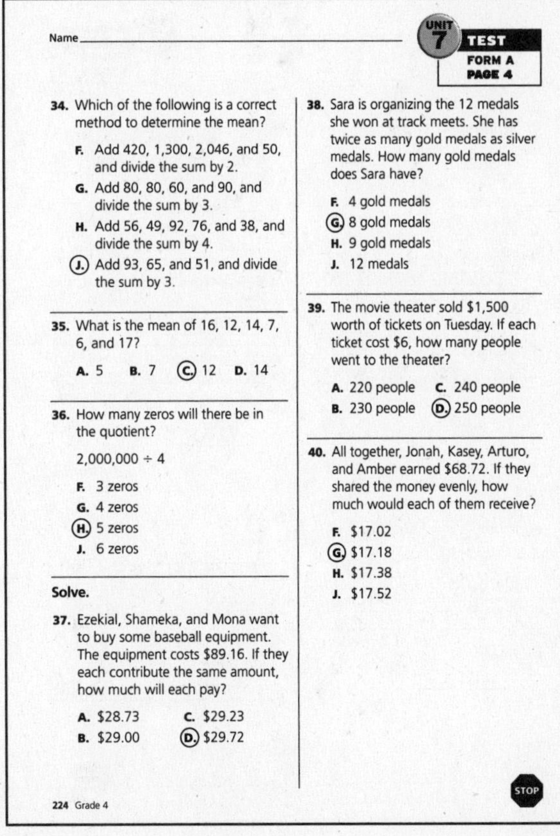

Name ________________

UNIT 7 TEST FORM A PAGE 4

34. Which of the following is a correct method to determine the mean?
    F. Add 420, 1,300, 2,046, and 50, and divide the sum by 2.
    G. Add 80, 80, 60, and 90, and divide the sum by 3.
    H. Add 56, 49, 92, 76, and 38, and divide the sum by 4.
    Ⓙ Add 93, 65, and 51, and divide the sum by 3.

35. What is the mean of 16, 12, 14, 7, 6, and 17?
    A. 5 B. 7 Ⓒ 12 D. 14

36. How many zeros will there be in the quotient?
    2,000,000 ÷ 4
    F. 3 zeros
    G. 4 zeros
    Ⓗ 5 zeros
    J. 6 zeros

Solve.

37. Ezekial, Shameka, and Mona want to buy some baseball equipment. The equipment costs $89.16. If they each contribute the same amount, how much will each pay?
    A. $28.73 C. $29.23
    B. $29.00 Ⓓ $29.72

38. Sara is organizing the 12 medals she won at track meets. She has twice as many gold medals as silver medals. How many gold medals does Sara have?
    F. 4 gold medals
    Ⓖ 8 gold medals
    H. 9 gold medals
    J. 12 medals

39. The movie theater sold $1,500 worth of tickets on Tuesday. If each ticket cost $6, how many people went to the theater?
    A. 220 people C. 240 people
    B. 230 people Ⓓ 250 people

40. All together, Jonah, Kasey, Arturo, and Amber earned $68.72. If they shared the money evenly, how much would each of them receive?
    F. $17.02
    Ⓖ $17.18
    H. $17.38
    J. $17.52

224 Grade 4

STOP

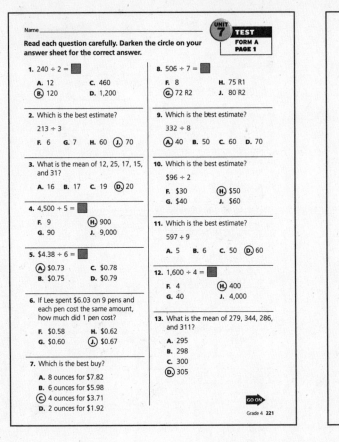

Unit 7

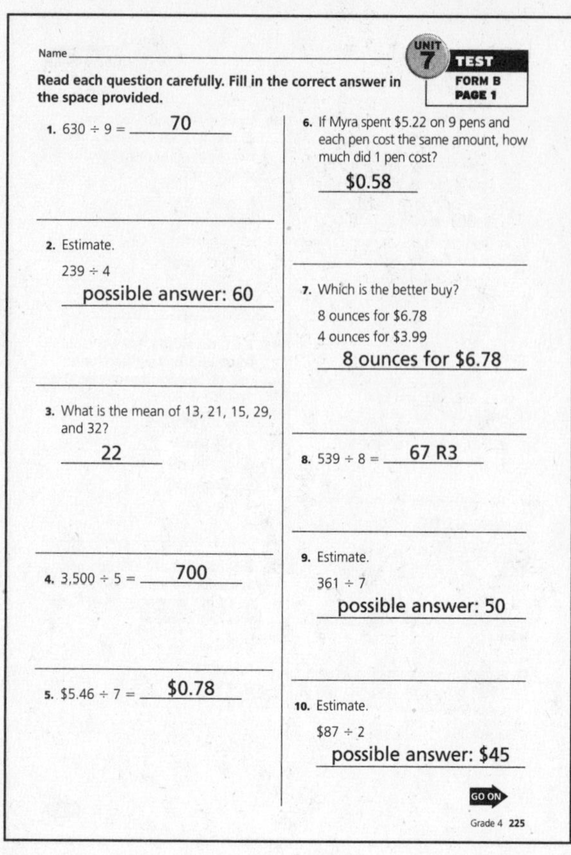

Name

Read each question carefully. Fill in the correct answer in the space provided.

UNIT 7 TEST FORM B PAGE 1

1. 630 ÷ 9 = 70

2. Estimate.

   239 ÷ 4

   possible answer: 60

3. What is the mean of 13, 21, 15, 29, and 32?

   22

4. 3,500 ÷ 5 = 700

5. $5.46 ÷ 7 = $0.78

6. If Myra spent $5.22 on 9 pens and each pen cost the same amount, how much did 1 pen cost?

   $0.58

7. Which is the better buy?

   8 ounces for $6.78

   4 ounces for $3.99

   8 ounces for $6.78

8. 539 ÷ 8 = 67 R3

9. Estimate.

   361 ÷ 7

   possible answer: 50

10. Estimate.

    $87 ÷ 2

    possible answer: $45

GO ON

Grade 4 225

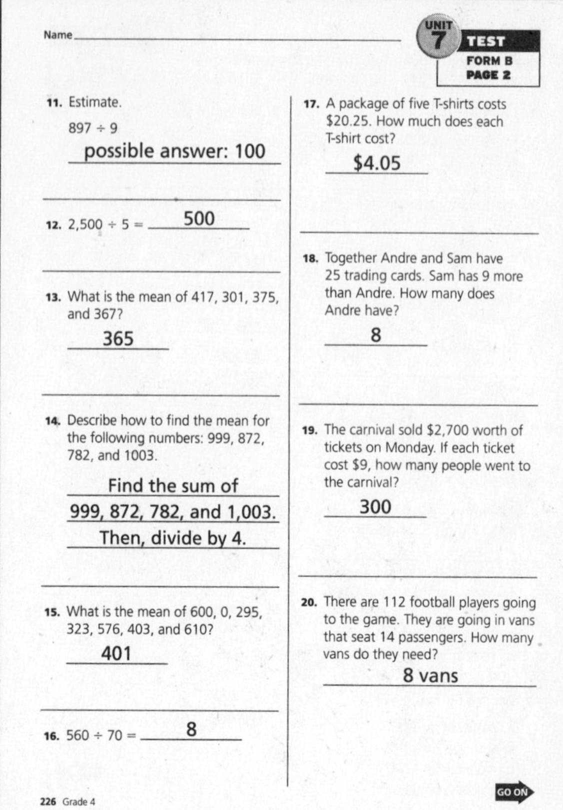

Name

UNIT 7 TEST FORM B PAGE 2

11. Estimate.

    897 ÷ 9

    possible answer: 100

12. 2,500 ÷ 5 = 500

13. What is the mean of 417, 301, 375, and 367?

    365

14. Describe how to find the mean for the following numbers: 999, 872, 782, and 1003.

    Find the sum of 999, 872, 782, and 1,003. Then, divide by 4.

15. What is the mean of 600, 0, 295, 323, 576, 403, and 610?

    401

16. 560 ÷ 70 = 8

17. A package of five T-shirts costs $20.25. How much does each T-shirt cost?

    $4.05

18. Together Andre and Sam have 25 trading cards. Sam has 9 more than Andre. How many does Andre have?

    8

19. The carnival sold $2,700 worth of tickets on Monday. If each ticket cost $9, how many people went to the carnival?

    300

20. There are 112 football players going to the game. They are going in vans that seat 14 passengers. How many vans do they need?

    8 vans

226 Grade 4

GO ON

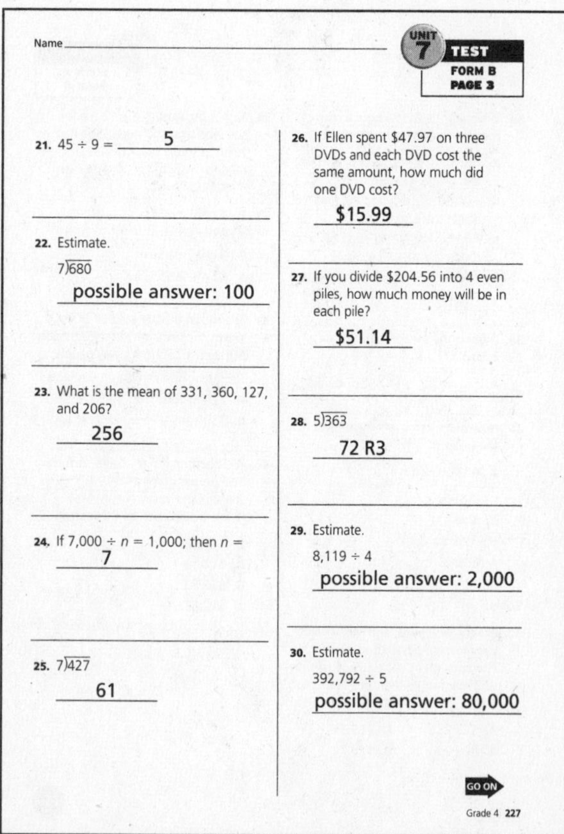

Name

UNIT 7 TEST FORM B PAGE 3

21. 45 ÷ 9 = 5

22. Estimate.

    7)680

    possible answer: 100

23. What is the mean of 331, 360, 127, and 206?

    256

24. If 7,000 ÷ n = 1,000; then n =

    7

25. 7)427

    61

26. If Ellen spent $47.97 on three DVDs and each DVD cost the same amount, how much did one DVD cost?

    $15.99

27. If you divide $204.56 into 4 even piles, how much money will be in each pile?

    $51.14

28. 5)363

    72 R3

29. Estimate.

    8,119 ÷ 4

    possible answer: 2,000

30. Estimate.

    392,792 ÷ 5

    possible answer: 80,000

GO ON

Grade 4 227

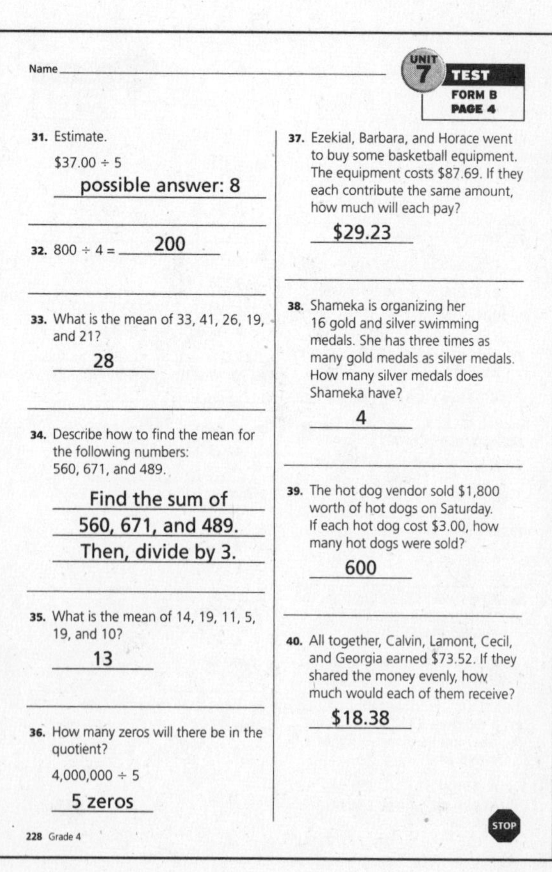

Name

UNIT 7 TEST FORM B PAGE 4

31. Estimate.

    $37.00 ÷ 5

    possible answer: 8

32. 800 ÷ 4 = 200

33. What is the mean of 33, 41, 26, 19, and 21?

    28

34. Describe how to find the mean for the following numbers: 560, 671, and 489.

    Find the sum of 560, 671, and 489. Then, divide by 3.

35. What is the mean of 14, 19, 11, 5, 19, and 10?

    13

36. How many zeros will there be in the quotient?

    4,000,000 ÷ 5

    5 zeros

37. Ezekial, Barbara, and Horace went to buy some basketball equipment. The equipment costs $87.69. If they each contribute the same amount, how much will each pay?

    $29.23

38. Shameka is organizing her 16 gold and silver swimming medals. She has three times as many gold medals as silver medals. How many silver medals does Shameka have?

    4

39. The hot dog vendor sold $1,800 worth of hot dogs on Saturday. If each hot dog cost $3.00, how many hot dogs were sold?

    600

40. All together, Calvin, Lamont, Cecil, and Georgia earned $73.52. If they shared the money evenly, how much would each of them receive?

    $18.38

228 Grade 4

STOP

Chapter 15

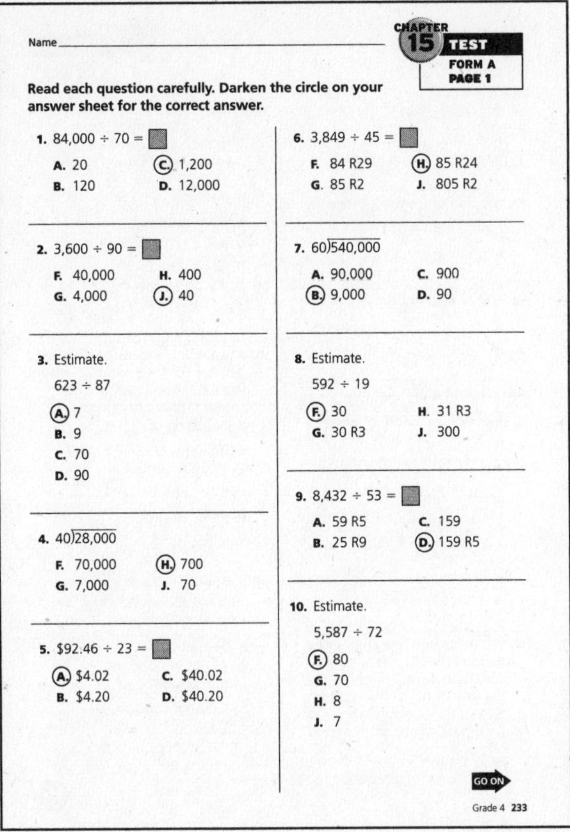

Name________________

CHAPTER 15 TEST FORM A PAGE 1

Read each question carefully. Darken the circle on your answer sheet for the correct answer.

1. 84,000 ÷ 70 = ☐
   A. 20 (C.) 1,200
   B. 120 D. 12,000

2. 3,600 ÷ 90 = ☐
   F. 40,000 H. 400
   G. 4,000 (J.) 40

3. Estimate.
   623 ÷ 87
   (A.) 7
   B. 9
   C. 70
   D. 90

4. $40\overline{)28,000}$
   F. 70,000 (H.) 700
   G. 7,000 J. 70

5. $92.46 ÷ 23 = ☐
   (A.) $4.02 C. $40.02
   B. $4.20 D. $40.20

6. 3,849 ÷ 45 = ☐
   F. 84 R29 (H.) 85 R24
   G. 85 R2 J. 805 R2

7. $60\overline{)540,000}$
   A. 90,000 C. 900
   (B.) 9,000 D. 90

8. Estimate.
   592 ÷ 19
   (F.) 30 H. 31 R3
   G. 30 R3 J. 300

9. 8,432 ÷ 53 = ☐
   A. 59 R5 C. 159
   B. 25 R9 (D.) 159 R5

10. Estimate.
    5,587 ÷ 72
    (F.) 80
    G. 70
    H. 8
    J. 7

GO ON

Grade 4 233

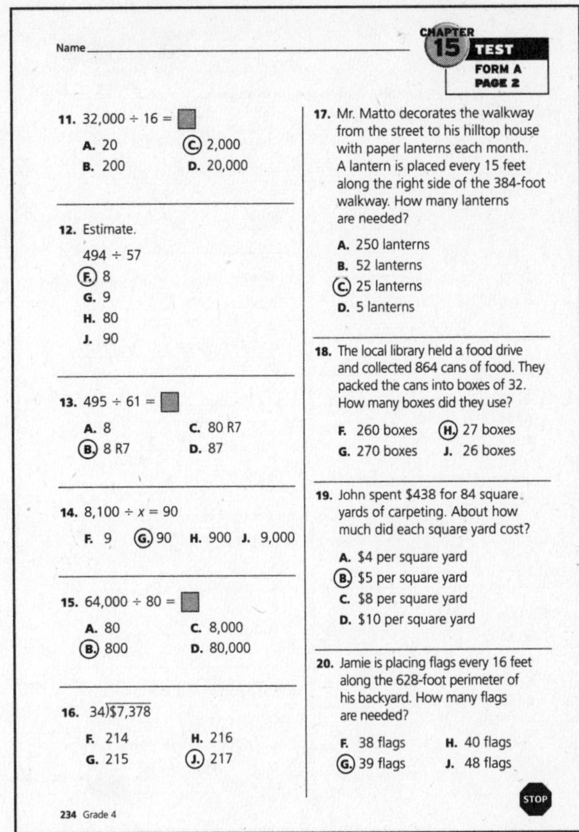

Name________________

CHAPTER 15 TEST FORM A PAGE 2

11. 32,000 ÷ 16 = ☐
    A. 20 (C.) 2,000
    B. 200 D. 20,000

12. Estimate.
    494 ÷ 57
    (F.) 8
    G. 9
    H. 80
    J. 90

13. 495 ÷ 61 = ☐
    A. 8 C. 80 R7
    (B.) 8 R7 D. 87

14. 8,100 ÷ x = 90
    F. 9 (G.) 90 H. 900 J. 9,000

15. 64,000 ÷ 80 = ☐
    A. 80 C. 8,000
    (B.) 800 D. 80,000

16. $34\overline{)\$7,378}$
    F. 214 H. 216
    G. 215 (J.) 217

17. Mr. Matto decorates the walkway from the street to his hilltop house with paper lanterns each month. A lantern is placed every 15 feet along the right side of the 384-foot walkway. How many lanterns are needed?
    A. 250 lanterns
    B. 52 lanterns
    (C.) 25 lanterns
    D. 5 lanterns

18. The local library held a food drive and collected 864 cans of food. They packed the cans into boxes of 32. How many boxes did they use?
    F. 260 boxes (H.) 27 boxes
    G. 270 boxes J. 26 boxes

19. John spent $438 for 84 square yards of carpeting. About how much did each square yard cost?
    A. $4 per square yard
    (B.) $5 per square yard
    C. $8 per square yard
    D. $10 per square yard

20. Jamie is placing flags every 16 feet along the 628-foot perimeter of his backyard. How many flags are needed?
    F. 38 flags H. 40 flags
    (G.) 39 flags J. 48 flags

STOP

234 Grade 4

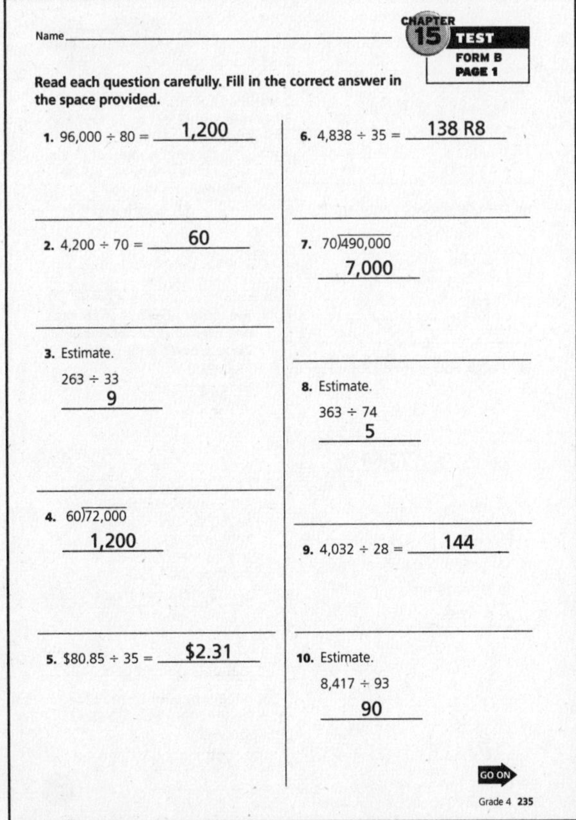

Name________________

CHAPTER 15 TEST FORM B PAGE 1

Read each question carefully. Fill in the correct answer in the space provided.

1. 96,000 ÷ 80 = 1,200

2. 4,200 ÷ 70 = 60

3. Estimate.
   263 ÷ 33
   9

4. $60\overline{)72,000}$
   1,200

5. $80.85 ÷ 35 = $2.31

6. 4,838 ÷ 35 = 138 R8

7. $70\overline{)490,000}$
   7,000

8. Estimate.
   363 ÷ 74
   5

9. 4,032 ÷ 28 = 144

10. Estimate.
    8,417 ÷ 93
    90

GO ON

Grade 4 235

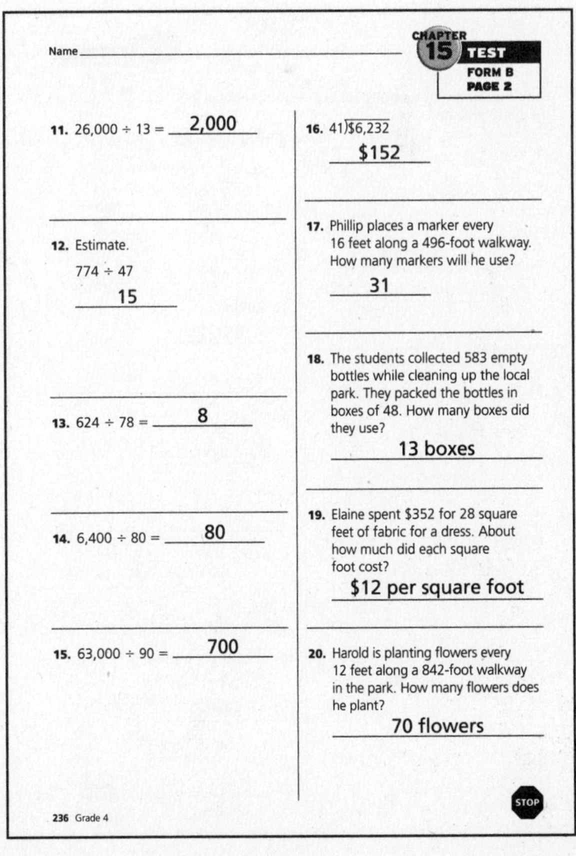

Name________________

CHAPTER 15 TEST FORM B PAGE 2

11. 26,000 ÷ 13 = 2,000

12. Estimate.
    774 ÷ 47
    15

13. 624 ÷ 78 = 8

14. 6,400 ÷ 80 = 80

15. 63,000 ÷ 90 = 700

16. $41\overline{)\$6,232}$
    $152

17. Phillip places a marker every 16 feet along a 496-foot walkway. How many markers will he use?
    31

18. The students collected 583 empty bottles while cleaning up the local park. They packed the bottles in boxes of 48. How many boxes did they use?
    13 boxes

19. Elaine spent $352 for 28 square feet of fabric for a dress. About how much did each square foot cost?
    $12 per square foot

20. Harold is planting flowers every 12 feet along a 842-foot walkway in the park. How many flowers does he plant?
    70 flowers

STOP

236 Grade 4

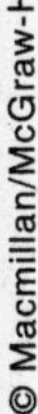

Chapter 16

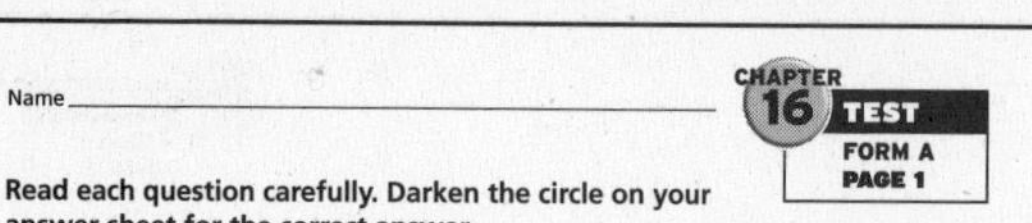

Name ________________

CHAPTER 16 TEST FORM A PAGE 1

Read each question carefully. Darken the circle on your answer sheet for the correct answer.

1. 139 ÷ 9 = ▢

A. 14 C. 15
B. 14 R4 **D.** 15 R4

2. 308 ÷ 7 = ▢

F. 44 H. 43 R7
G. 43 R7 J. 42

3. Use order of operations to simplify.
4 × (5 + 9)

A. 56 C. 18
B. 29 D. 11

4. $6\overline{)149}$

F. 23 R5 **H.** 24 R5
G. 24 J. 25

5. 173 ÷ 9 = ▢

A. 19 R2
B. 19
C. 18 R2
D. 18

6. Use order of operations to simplify.
42 ÷ (2 + 5) × 6

F. 156 H. 7
G. 36 J. 1

7. $54\overline{)429}$

A. 80
B. 70 R1
C. 8 R51
D. 7 R51

8. 473 ÷ 39 = ▢

F. 12 H. 13
G. 12 R5 J. 13 R5

9. 29,394 ÷ 18 = ▢

A. 1,633
B. 1,633 R4
C. 1,733
D. 1,733 R3

10. Use order of operations to simplify.
(5 × 3) × (1 + 5)

F. 20 H. 80
G. 21 **J.** 90

GO ON

Name ________________

CHAPTER 16 TEST FORM A PAGE 2

11. 297 ÷ 31 = ▢

A. 9 C. 10
B. 9 R18 D. 10 R18

12. Use order of operations to simplify.
(8 + 3) × 4 + 7

F. 22 G. 27 **H.** 51 J. 121

13. 58,273 ÷ 41 = ▢

A. 142 **C.** 1,421 R12
B. 1,421 D. 10,421 R12

14. 387 ÷ 52 = ▢

F. 7 R23 H. 6 R32
G. 7 J. 5

15. Use order of operations to simplify.
(4 × 9) ÷ (8 − 2)

A. 3 **B.** 6 C. 36 D. 216

16. $63\overline{)72{,}398}$

F. 1,148 H. 1,149
G. 1,148 R11 **J.** 1,149 R11

17. The Weintraubs have a flowerbed that measures 52 feet by 18 feet. They are building a fence around the flowerbed. The fence comes in 6-foot sections. How many sections are needed around the flowerbed?

A. 20 sections **C.** 24 sections
B. 23 sections D. 30 sections

18. Joseph is leasing a new computer. The computer costs a total of $1,449.72. He will make equal payments over 36 months. How much will each monthly payment be?

F. $40 per month
G. $40.27 per month
H. $41.27 per month
J. $52.38 per month

19. A parking lot measures 420 feet by 180 feet. The fence comes in 12-foot sections. How many sections are needed to build a fence around the entire parking lot?

A. 10 sections
B. 100 sections
C. 120 sections
D. 1,000 sections

20. A company spent $4,829.08 on 58 filing cabinets. How much did each filing cabinet cost?

F. $80 per cabinet
G. $82.00 per cabinet
H. $82.36 per cabinet
J. $83.26 per cabinet

Name ________________

CHAPTER 16 TEST FORM B PAGE 1

Read each question carefully. Fill in the correct answer in the space provided.

1. 794 ÷ 9 = 88 R2

2. 4,853 ÷ 6 = 808 R5

3. Use order of operations to simplify.
7 × (6 + 8)
98

4. $7\overline{)831}$
118 R5

5. 381 ÷ 8 = 47 R5

6. Use order of operations to simplify.
56 ÷ (1 + 7) × 3
21

7. $62\overline{)518}$
8 R22

8. 813 ÷ 28 = 29 R1

9. 83,067 ÷ 47 = 1,767 R18

10. Use order of operations to simplify.
(2 × 8) × (7 − 2)
80

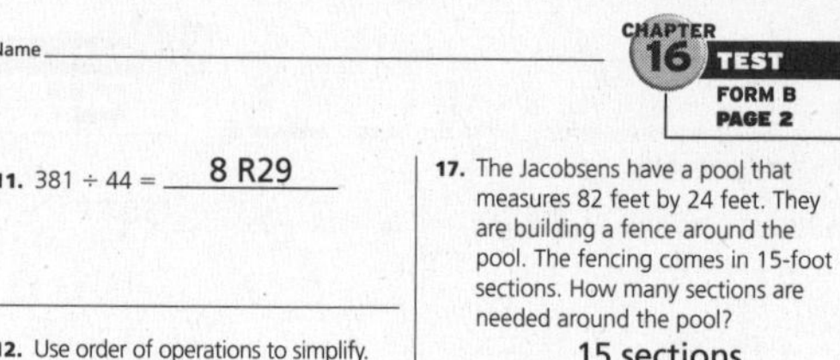

Name ________________

CHAPTER 16 TEST FORM B PAGE 2

11. 381 ÷ 44 = 8 R29

12. Use order of operations to simplify.
(6 + 9) × 7 − 12
93

13. 71,018 ÷ 25 = 2,840 R18

14. 586 ÷ 74 = 7 R68

15. Use order of operations to simplify.
(8 × 7) ÷ (9 − 5)
14

16. $55\overline{)94{,}751}$
1,722 R41

17. The Jacobsens have a pool that measures 82 feet by 24 feet. They are building a fence around the pool. The fencing comes in 15-foot sections. How many sections are needed around the pool?
15 sections

18. Zoe spends $2,398.30 on 58 art prints. If each print costs the same amount, how much did she pay for each print?
$41.35

19. A schoolyard measures 640 feet by 280 feet. The fencing comes in 18-foot sections. How many sections are needed around the schoolyard?
103 sections

20. A company spent $6,180.72 on 24 desks. How much did each desk cost?
$257.53

Unit 8

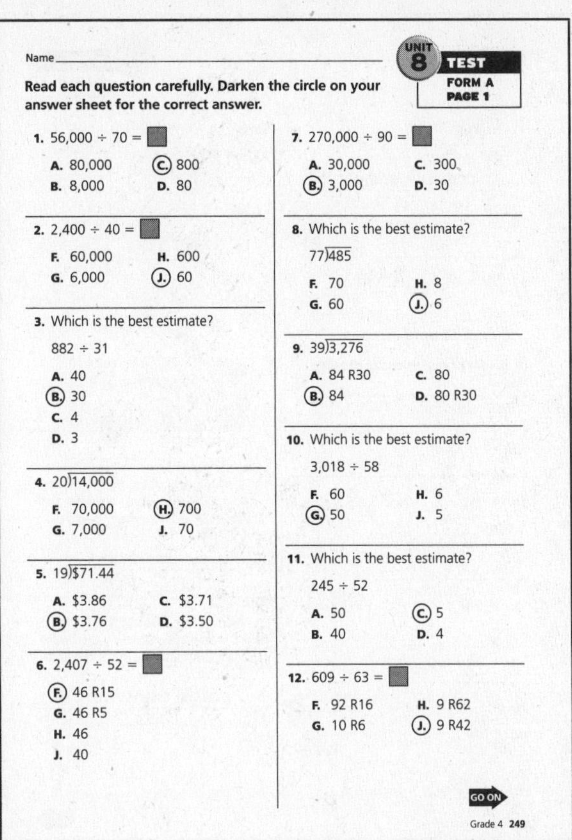

Name

UNIT 8 TEST FORM A PAGE 1

Read each question carefully. Darken the circle on your answer sheet for the correct answer.

1. 56,000 ÷ 70 =
   A. 80,000 C. 800
   B. 8,000 D. 80

2. 2,400 ÷ 40 =
   F. 60,000 H. 600
   G. 6,000 J. 60

3. Which is the best estimate?
   882 ÷ 31
   A. 40
   B. 30
   C. 4
   D. 3

4. 20)14,000
   F. 70,000 H. 700
   G. 7,000 J. 70

5. 19)$71.44
   A. $3.86 C. $3.71
   B. $3.76 D. $3.50

6. 2,407 ÷ 52 =
   F. 46 R15
   G. 46 R5
   H. 46
   J. 40

7. 270,000 ÷ 90 =
   A. 30,000 C. 300
   B. 3,000 D. 30

8. Which is the best estimate?
   77)485
   F. 70 H. 8
   G. 60 J. 6

9. 39)3,276
   A. 84 R30 C. 80
   B. 84 D. 80 R30

10. Which is the best estimate?
    3,018 ÷ 58
    F. 60 H. 6
    G. 50 J. 5

11. Which is the best estimate?
    245 ÷ 52
    A. 50 C. 5
    B. 40 D. 4

12. 609 ÷ 63 =
    F. 92 R16 H. 9 R62
    G. 10 R6 J. 9 R42

GO ON

Grade 4 249

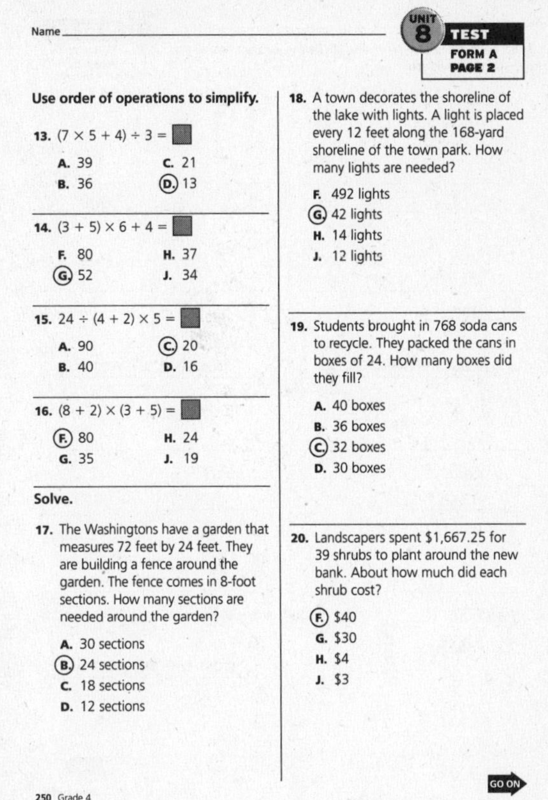

Name

UNIT 8 TEST FORM A PAGE 2

Use order of operations to simplify.

13. (7 × 5 + 4) ÷ 3 =
    A. 39 C. 21
    B. 36 D. 13

14. (3 + 5) × 6 + 4 =
    F. 80 H. 37
    G. 52 J. 34

15. 24 ÷ (4 + 2) × 5 =
    A. 90 C. 20
    B. 40 D. 16

16. (8 + 2) × (3 + 5) =
    F. 80 H. 24
    G. 35 J. 19

Solve.

17. The Washingtons have a garden that measures 72 feet by 24 feet. They are building a fence around the garden. The fence comes in 8-foot sections. How many sections are needed around the garden?
    A. 30 sections
    B. 24 sections
    C. 18 sections
    D. 12 sections

18. A town decorates the shoreline of the lake with lights. A light is placed every 12 feet along the 168-yard shoreline of the town park. How many lights are needed?
    F. 492 lights
    G. 42 lights
    H. 14 lights
    J. 12 lights

19. Students brought in 768 soda cans to recycle. They packed the cans in boxes of 24. How many boxes did they fill?
    A. 40 boxes
    B. 36 boxes
    C. 32 boxes
    D. 30 boxes

20. Landscapers spent $1,667.25 for 39 shrubs to plant around the new bank. About how much did each shrub cost?
    F. $40
    G. $30
    H. $4
    J. $3

GO ON

250 Grade 4

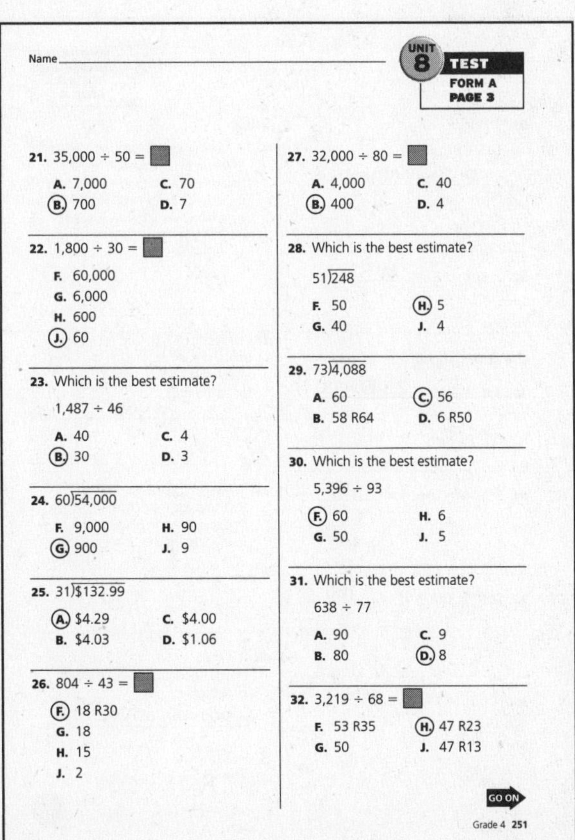

Name

UNIT 8 TEST FORM A PAGE 3

21. 35,000 ÷ 50 =
    A. 7,000 C. 70
    B. 700 D. 7

22. 1,800 ÷ 30 =
    F. 60,000
    G. 6,000
    H. 600
    J. 60

23. Which is the best estimate?
    1,487 ÷ 46
    A. 40 C. 4
    B. 30 D. 3

24. 60)54,000
    F. 9,000 H. 90
    G. 900 J. 9

25. 31)$132.99
    A. $4.29 C. $4.00
    B. $4.03 D. $1.06

26. 804 ÷ 43 =
    F. 18 R30
    G. 18
    H. 15
    J. 2

27. 32,000 ÷ 80 =
    A. 4,000 C. 40
    B. 400 D. 4

28. Which is the best estimate?
    51)248
    F. 50 H. 5
    G. 40 J. 4

29. 73)4,088
    A. 60 C. 56
    B. 58 R64 D. 6 R50

30. Which is the best estimate?
    5,396 ÷ 93
    F. 60 H. 6
    G. 50 J. 5

31. Which is the best estimate?
    638 ÷ 77
    A. 90 C. 9
    B. 80 D. 8

32. 3,219 ÷ 68 =
    F. 53 R35 H. 47 R23
    G. 50 J. 47 R13

GO ON

Grade 4 251

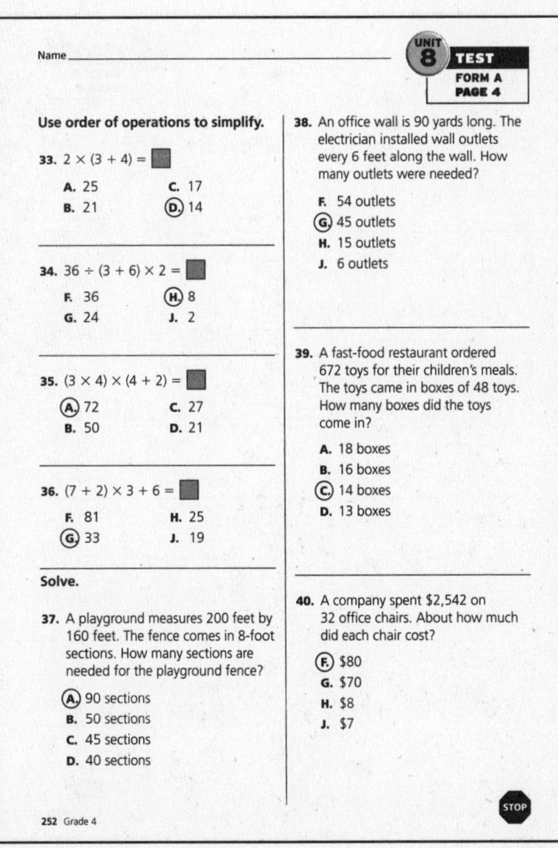

Name

UNIT 8 TEST FORM A PAGE 4

Use order of operations to simplify.

33. 2 × (3 + 4) =
    A. 25 C. 17
    B. 21 D. 14

34. 36 ÷ (3 + 6) × 2 =
    F. 36 H. 8
    G. 24 J. 2

35. (3 × 4) × (4 + 2) =
    A. 72 C. 27
    B. 50 D. 21

36. (7 + 2) × 3 + 6 =
    F. 81 H. 25
    G. 33 J. 19

Solve.

37. A playground measures 200 feet by 160 feet. The fence comes in 8-foot sections. How many sections are needed for the playground fence?
    A. 90 sections
    B. 50 sections
    C. 45 sections
    D. 40 sections

38. An office wall is 90 yards long. The electrician installed wall outlets every 6 feet along the wall. How many outlets were needed?
    F. 54 outlets
    G. 45 outlets
    H. 15 outlets
    J. 6 outlets

39. A fast-food restaurant ordered 672 toys for their children's meals. The toys came in boxes of 48 toys. How many boxes did the toys come in?
    A. 18 boxes
    B. 16 boxes
    C. 14 boxes
    D. 13 boxes

40. A company spent $2,542 on 32 office chairs. About how much did each chair cost?
    F. $80
    G. $70
    H. $8
    J. $7

STOP

252 Grade 4

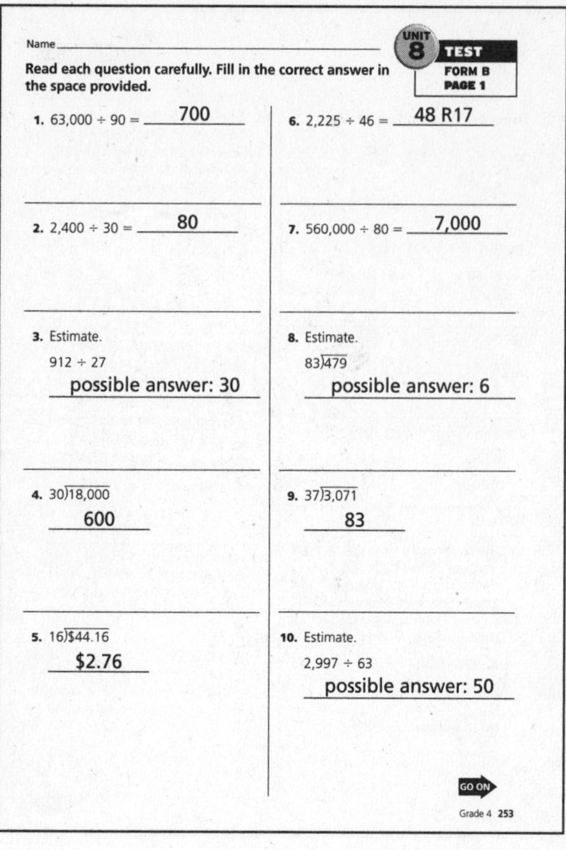

Name____________________

UNIT 8 TEST FORM B PAGE 1

Read each question carefully. Fill in the correct answer in the space provided.

1. 63,000 ÷ 90 = 700

2. 2,400 ÷ 30 = 80

3. Estimate.
912 ÷ 27
possible answer: 30

4. 30)18,000
600

5. 16)$44.16
$2.76

6. 2,225 ÷ 46 = 48 R17

7. 560,000 ÷ 80 = 7,000

8. Estimate.
83)479
possible answer: 6

9. 37)3,071
83

10. Estimate.
2,997 ÷ 63
possible answer: 50

GO ON

Grade 4 253

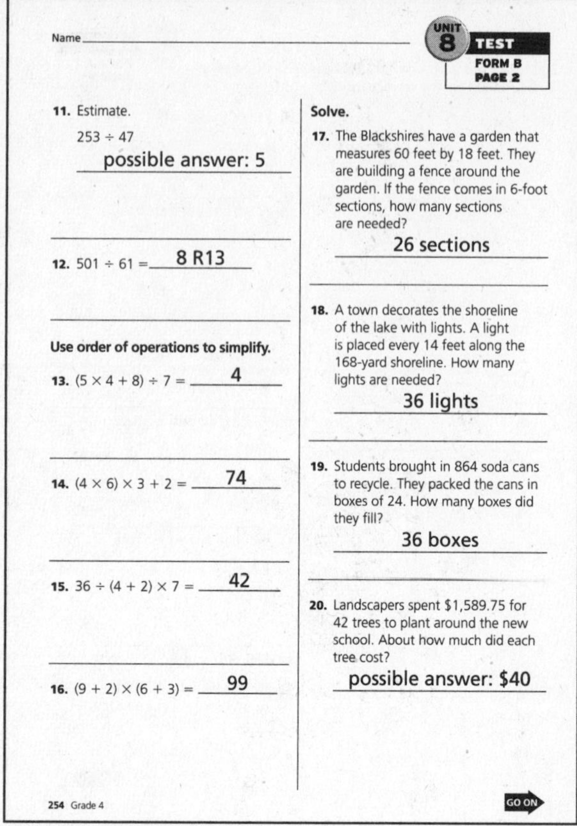

Name____________________

UNIT 8 TEST FORM B PAGE 2

11. Estimate.
253 ÷ 47
possible answer: 5

12. 501 ÷ 61 = 8 R13

Use order of operations to simplify.

13. (5 × 4 + 8) ÷ 7 = 4

14. (4 × 6) × 3 + 2 = 74

15. 36 ÷ (4 + 2) × 7 = 42

16. (9 + 2) × (6 + 3) = 99

Solve.

17. The Blackshires have a garden that measures 60 feet by 18 feet. They are building a fence around the garden. If the fence comes in 6-foot sections, how many sections are needed?
26 sections

18. A town decorates the shoreline of the lake with lights. A light is placed every 14 feet along the 168-yard shoreline. How many lights are needed?
36 lights

19. Students brought in 864 soda cans to recycle. They packed the cans in boxes of 24. How many boxes did they fill?
36 boxes

20. Landscapers spent $1,589.75 for 42 trees to plant around the new school. About how much did each tree cost?
possible answer: $40

254 Grade 4

GO ON

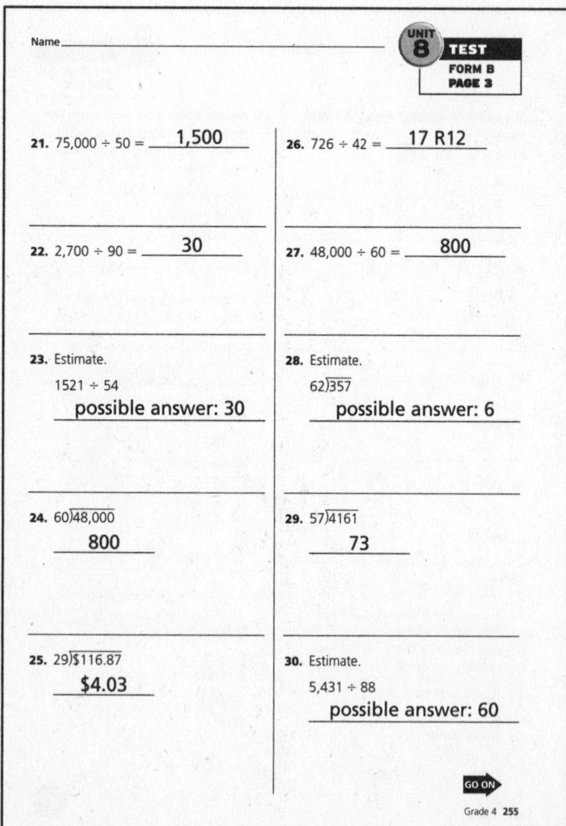

Name____________________

UNIT 8 TEST FORM B PAGE 3

21. 75,000 ÷ 50 = 1,500

22. 2,700 ÷ 90 = 30

23. Estimate.
1521 ÷ 54
possible answer: 30

24. 60)48,000
800

25. 29)$116.87
$4.03

26. 726 ÷ 42 = 17 R12

27. 48,000 ÷ 60 = 800

28. Estimate.
62)357
possible answer: 6

29. 57)4161
73

30. Estimate.
5,431 ÷ 88
possible answer: 60

GO ON

Grade 4 255

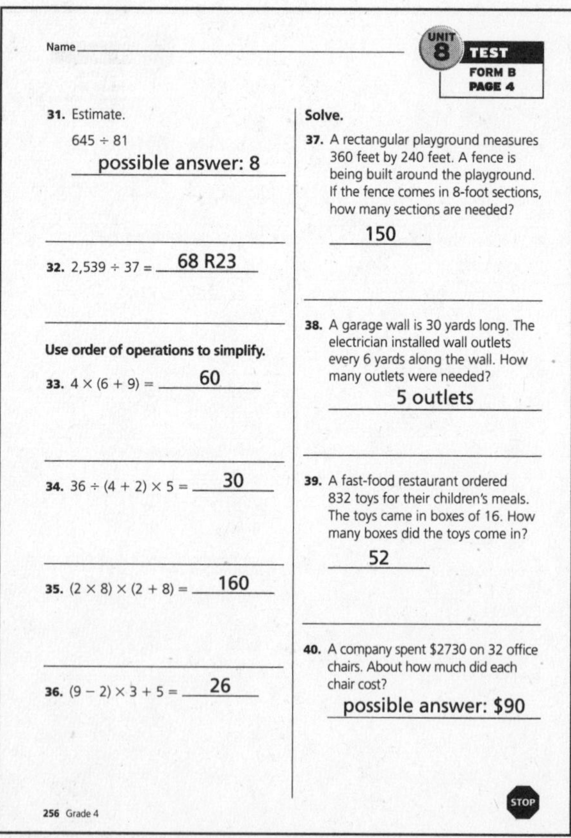

Name____________________

UNIT 8 TEST FORM B PAGE 4

31. Estimate.
645 ÷ 81
possible answer: 8

32. 2,539 ÷ 37 = 68 R23

Use order of operations to simplify.

33. 4 × (6 + 9) = 60

34. 36 ÷ (4 + 2) × 5 = 30

35. (2 × 8) × (2 + 8) = 160

36. (9 − 2) × 3 + 5 = 26

Solve.

37. A rectangular playground measures 360 feet by 240 feet. A fence is being built around the playground. If the fence comes in 8-foot sections, how many sections are needed?
150

38. A garage wall is 30 yards long. The electrician installed wall outlets every 6 yards along the wall. How many outlets were needed?
5 outlets

39. A fast-food restaurant ordered 832 toys for their children's meals. The toys came in boxes of 16. How many boxes did the toys come in?
52

40. A company spent $2730 on 32 office chairs. About how much did each chair cost?
possible answer: $90

256 Grade 4

STOP

Chapter 17

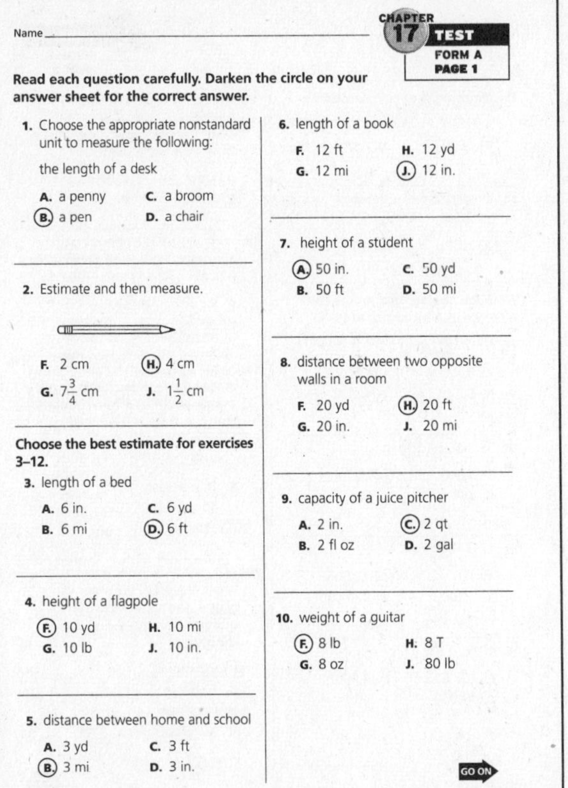

Name ____________ CHAPTER 17 TEST FORM A PAGE 1

Read each question carefully. Darken the circle on your answer sheet for the correct answer.

1. Choose the appropriate nonstandard unit to measure the following: the length of a desk
A. a penny C. a broom
(B.) a pen D. a chair

2. Estimate and then measure.
F. 2 cm (H.) 4 cm
G. $7\frac{3}{4}$ cm J. $1\frac{1}{2}$ cm

Choose the best estimate for exercises 3–12.

3. length of a bed
A. 6 in. C. 6 yd
B. 6 mi (D.) 6 ft

4. height of a flagpole
(F.) 10 yd H. 10 mi
G. 10 lb J. 10 in.

5. distance between home and school
A. 3 yd C. 3 ft
(B.) 3 mi D. 3 in.

6. length of a book
F. 12 ft H. 12 yd
G. 12 mi (J.) 12 in.

7. height of a student
(A.) 50 in. C. 50 yd
B. 50 ft D. 50 mi

8. distance between two opposite walls in a room
F. 20 yd (H.) 20 ft
G. 20 in. J. 20 mi

9. capacity of a juice pitcher
A. 2 in. (C.) 2 qt
B. 2 fl oz D. 2 gal

10. weight of a guitar
(F.) 8 lb H. 8 T
G. 8 oz J. 80 lb

GO ON

Grade 4 261

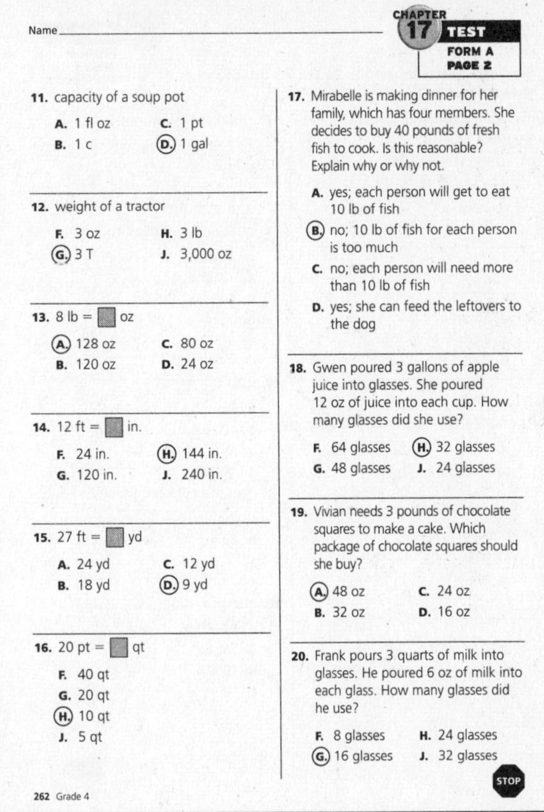

Name ____________ CHAPTER 17 TEST FORM A PAGE 2

11. capacity of a soup pot
A. 1 fl oz C. 1 pt
B. 1 c (D.) 1 gal

12. weight of a tractor
F. 3 oz H. 3 lb
(G.) 3 T J. 3,000 oz

13. 8 lb = ▢ oz
(A.) 128 oz C. 80 oz
B. 120 oz D. 24 oz

14. 12 ft = ▢ in.
F. 24 in. (H.) 144 in.
G. 120 in. J. 240 in.

15. 27 ft = ▢ yd
A. 24 yd C. 12 yd
B. 18 yd (D.) 9 yd

16. 20 pt = ▢ qt
F. 40 qt
G. 20 qt
(H.) 10 qt
J. 5 qt

17. Mirabelle is making dinner for her family, which has four members. She decides to buy 40 pounds of fresh fish to cook. Is this reasonable? Explain why or why not.
A. yes; each person will get to eat 10 lb of fish
(B.) no; 10 lb of fish for each person is too much
C. no; each person will need more than 10 lb of fish
D. yes; she can feed the leftovers to the dog

18. Gwen poured 3 gallons of apple juice into glasses. She poured 12 oz of juice into each cup. How many glasses did she use?
F. 64 glasses (H.) 32 glasses
G. 48 glasses J. 24 glasses

19. Vivian needs 3 pounds of chocolate squares to make a cake. Which package of chocolate squares should she buy?
(A.) 48 oz C. 24 oz
B. 32 oz D. 16 oz

20. Frank pours 3 quarts of milk into glasses. He poured 6 oz of milk into each glass. How many glasses did he use?
F. 8 glasses H. 24 glasses
(G.) 16 glasses J. 32 glasses

STOP

262 Grade 4

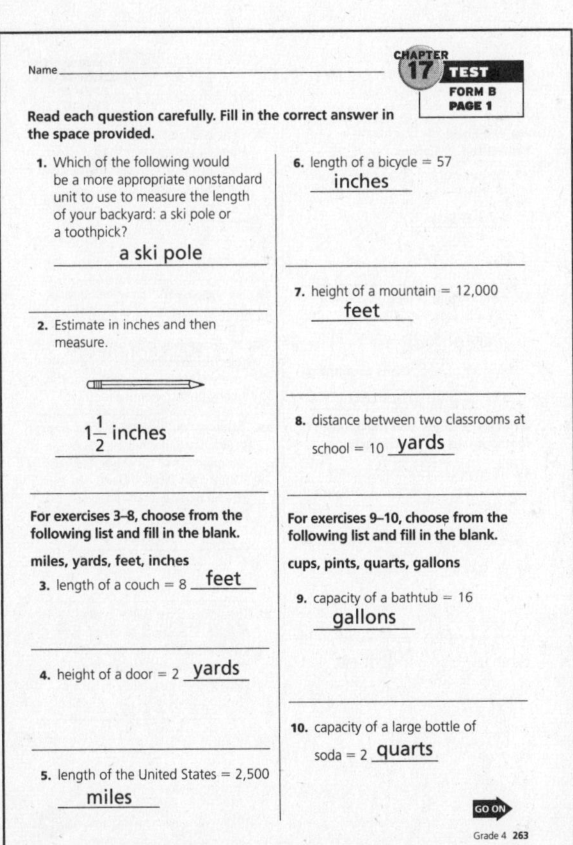

Name ____________ CHAPTER 17 TEST FORM B PAGE 1

Read each question carefully. Fill in the correct answer in the space provided.

1. Which of the following would be a more appropriate nonstandard unit to use to measure the length of your backyard: a ski pole or a toothpick?
a ski pole

2. Estimate in inches and then measure.
$1\frac{1}{2}$ inches

For exercises 3–8, choose from the following list and fill in the blank.

miles, yards, feet, inches

3. length of a couch = 8 feet

4. height of a door = 2 yards

5. length of the United States = 2,500 miles

6. length of a bicycle = 57 inches

7. height of a mountain = 12,000 feet

8. distance between two classrooms at school = 10 yards

For exercises 9–10, choose from the following list and fill in the blank.

cups, pints, quarts, gallons

9. capacity of a bathtub = 16 gallons

10. capacity of a large bottle of soda = 2 quarts

GO ON

Grade 4 263

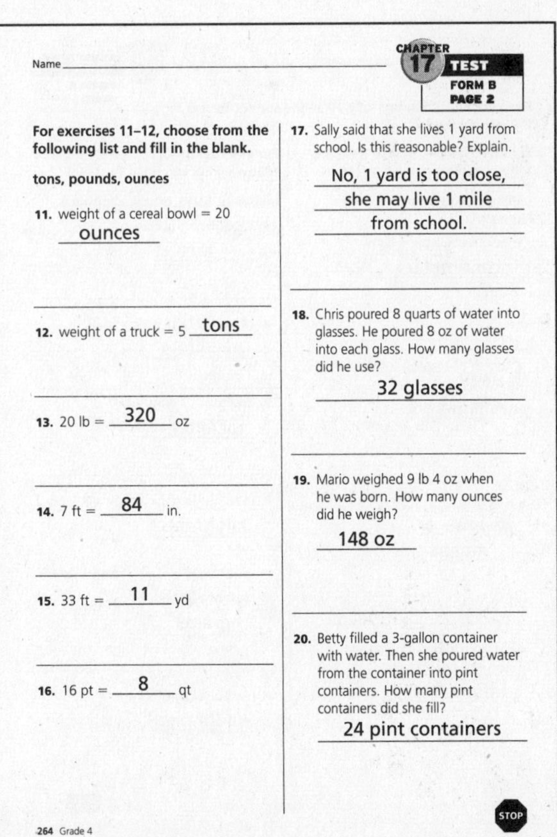

Name ____________ CHAPTER 17 TEST FORM B PAGE 2

For exercises 11–12, choose from the following list and fill in the blank.

tons, pounds, ounces

11. weight of a cereal bowl = 20 ounces

12. weight of a truck = 5 tons

13. 20 lb = 320 oz

14. 7 ft = 84 in.

15. 33 ft = 11 yd

16. 16 pt = 8 qt

17. Sally said that she lives 1 yard from school. Is this reasonable? Explain.
No, 1 yard is too close, she may live 1 mile from school.

18. Chris poured 8 quarts of water into glasses. He poured 8 oz of water into each glass. How many glasses did he use?
32 glasses

19. Mario weighed 9 lb 4 oz when he was born. How many ounces did he weigh?
148 oz

20. Betty filled a 3-gallon container with water. Then she poured water from the container into pint containers. How many pint containers did she fill?
24 pint containers

STOP

264 Grade 4

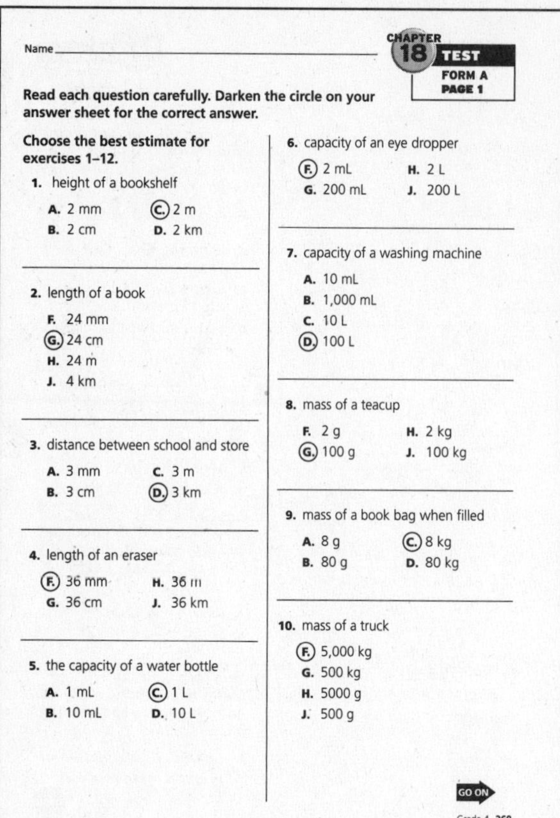

Name ______

CHAPTER 18 TEST FORM A PAGE 1

Read each question carefully. Darken the circle on your answer sheet for the correct answer.

Choose the best estimate for exercises 1–12.

1. height of a bookshelf
   A. 2 mm (C) 2 m
   B. 2 cm D. 2 km

2. length of a book
   F. 24 mm
   (G) 24 cm
   H. 24 m
   J. 4 km

3. distance between school and store
   A. 3 mm C. 3 m
   B. 3 cm (D) 3 km

4. length of an eraser
   (F) 36 mm H. 36 m
   G. 36 cm J. 36 km

5. the capacity of a water bottle
   A. 1 mL (C) 1 L
   B. 10 mL D. 10 L

6. capacity of an eye dropper
   (F) 2 mL H. 2 L
   G. 200 mL J. 200 L

7. capacity of a washing machine
   A. 10 mL
   B. 1,000 mL
   C. 10 L
   (D) 100 L

8. mass of a teacup
   F. 2 g H. 2 kg
   (G) 100 g J. 100 kg

9. mass of a book bag when filled
   A. 8 g (C) 8 kg
   B. 80 g D. 80 kg

10. mass of a truck
    (F) 5,000 kg
    G. 500 kg
    H. 5000 g
    J. 500 g

GO ON

Grade 4 269

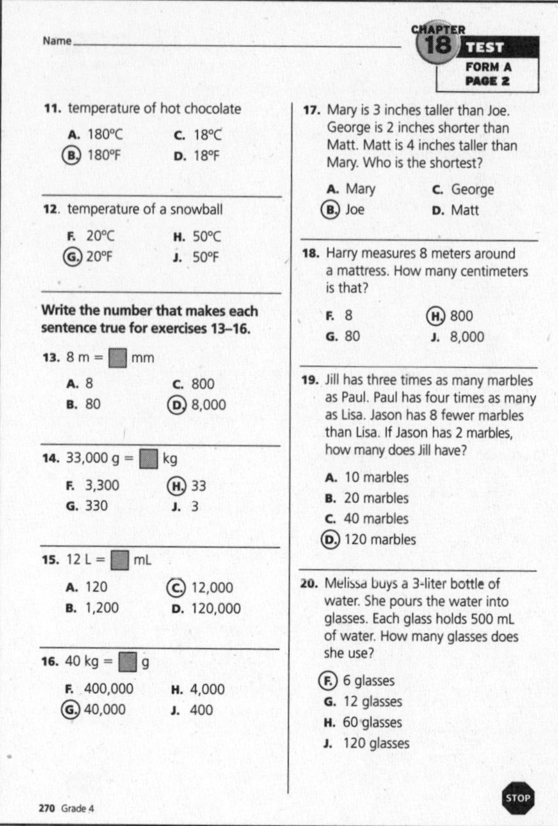

Name ______

CHAPTER 18 TEST FORM A PAGE 2

11. temperature of hot chocolate
    A. 180°C C. 18°C
    (B) 180°F D. 18°F

12. temperature of a snowball
    F. 20°C H. 50°C
    (G) 20°F J. 50°F

Write the number that makes each sentence true for exercises 13–16.

13. 8 m = ■ mm
    A. 8 C. 800
    B. 80 (D) 8,000

14. 33,000 g = ■ kg
    F. 3,300 (H) 33
    G. 330 J. 3

15. 12 L = ■ mL
    A. 120 (C) 12,000
    B. 1,200 D. 120,000

16. 40 kg = ■ g
    F. 400,000 H. 4,000
    (G) 40,000 J. 400

17. Mary is 3 inches taller than Joe. George is 2 inches shorter than Matt. Matt is 4 inches taller than Mary. Who is the shortest?
    A. Mary C. George
    (B) Joe D. Matt

18. Harry measures 8 meters around a mattress. How many centimeters is that?
    F. 8 (H) 800
    G. 80 J. 8,000

19. Jill has three times as many marbles as Paul. Paul has four times as many as Lisa. Jason has 8 fewer marbles than Lisa. If Jason has 2 marbles, how many does Jill have?
    A. 10 marbles
    B. 20 marbles
    C. 40 marbles
    (D) 120 marbles

20. Melissa buys a 3-liter bottle of water. She pours the water into glasses. Each glass holds 500 mL of water. How many glasses does she use?
    (F) 6 glasses
    G. 12 glasses
    H. 60 glasses
    J. 120 glasses

270 Grade 4

STOP

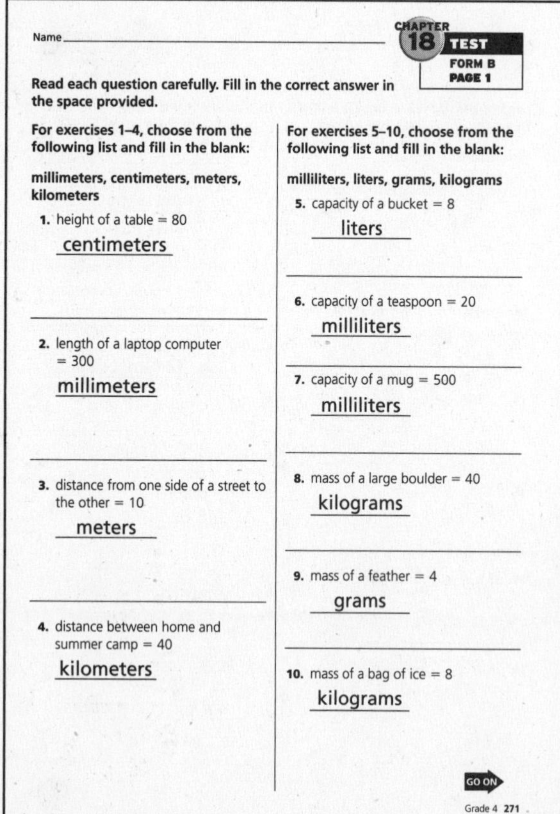

Name ______

CHAPTER 18 TEST FORM B PAGE 1

Read each question carefully. Fill in the correct answer in the space provided.

For exercises 1–4, choose from the following list and fill in the blank:

millimeters, centimeters, meters, kilometers

1. height of a table = 80
   centimeters

2. length of a laptop computer = 300
   millimeters

3. distance from one side of a street to the other = 10
   meters

4. distance between home and summer camp = 40
   kilometers

For exercises 5–10, choose from the following list and fill in the blank:

milliliters, liters, grams, kilograms

5. capacity of a bucket = 8
   liters

6. capacity of a teaspoon = 20
   milliliters

7. capacity of a mug = 500
   milliliters

8. mass of a large boulder = 40
   kilograms

9. mass of a feather = 4
   grams

10. mass of a bag of ice = 8
    kilograms

GO ON

Grade 4 271

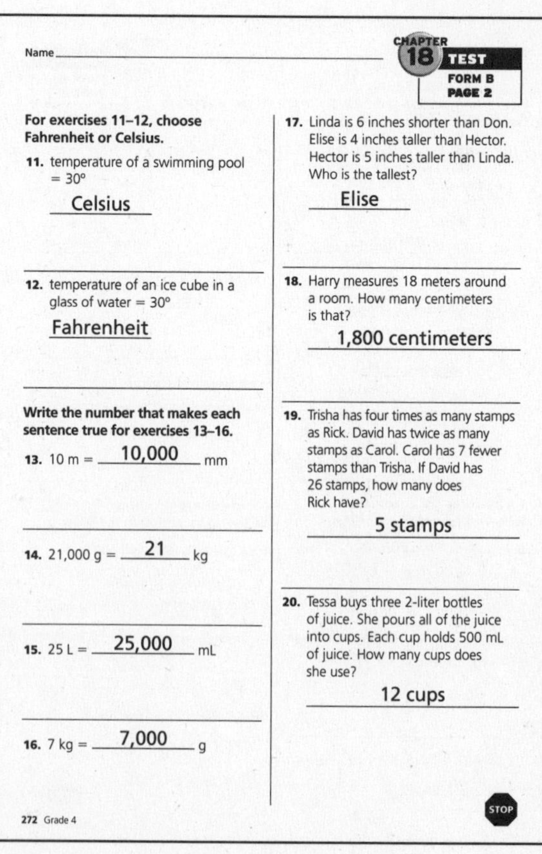

Name ______

CHAPTER 18 TEST FORM B PAGE 2

For exercises 11–12, choose Fahrenheit or Celsius.

11. temperature of a swimming pool = 30°
    Celsius

12. temperature of an ice cube in a glass of water = 30°
    Fahrenheit

Write the number that makes each sentence true for exercises 13–16.

13. 10 m = 10,000 mm

14. 21,000 g = 21 kg

15. 25 L = 25,000 mL

16. 7 kg = 7,000 g

17. Linda is 6 inches shorter than Don. Elise is 4 inches taller than Hector. Hector is 5 inches taller than Linda. Who is the tallest?
    Elise

18. Harry measures 18 meters around a room. How many centimeters is that?
    1,800 centimeters

19. Trisha has four times as many stamps as Rick. David has twice as many stamps as Carol. Carol has 7 fewer stamps than Trisha. If David has 26 stamps, how many does Rick have?
    5 stamps

20. Tessa buys three 2-liter bottles of juice. She pours all of the juice into cups. Each cup holds 500 mL of juice. How many cups does she use?
    12 cups

272 Grade 4

STOP

Unit 9

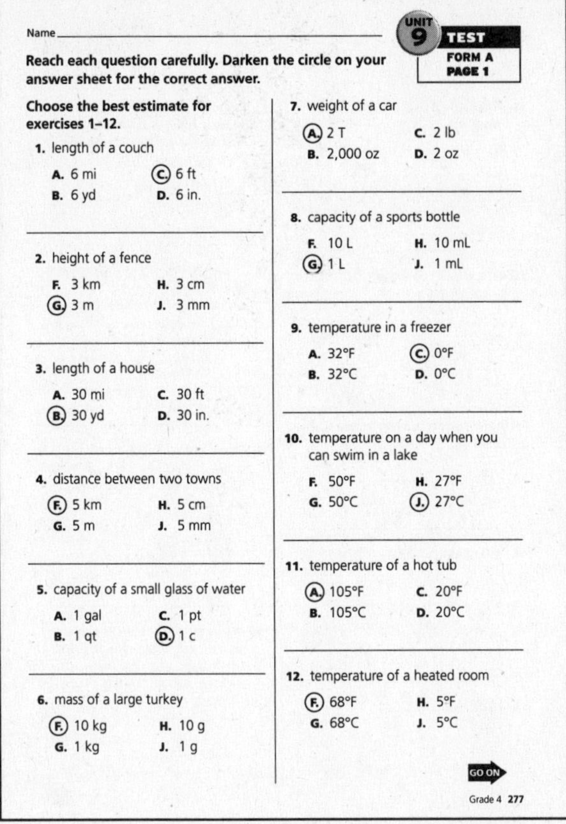

Name ______________________

UNIT 9 TEST FORM A PAGE 1

Reach each question carefully. Darken the circle on your answer sheet for the correct answer.

Choose the best estimate for exercises 1–12.

1. length of a couch
   A. 6 mi C. 6 ft
   B. 6 yd D. 6 in.

2. height of a fence
   F. 3 km H. 3 cm
   G. 3 m J. 3 mm

3. length of a house
   A. 30 mi C. 30 ft
   B. 30 yd D. 30 in.

4. distance between two towns
   F. 5 km H. 5 cm
   G. 5 m J. 5 mm

5. capacity of a small glass of water
   A. 1 gal C. 1 pt
   B. 1 qt D. 1 c

6. mass of a large turkey
   F. 10 kg H. 10 g
   G. 1 kg J. 1 g

7. weight of a car
   A. 2 T C. 2 lb
   B. 2,000 oz D. 2 oz

8. capacity of a sports bottle
   F. 10 L H. 10 mL
   G. 1 L J. 1 mL

9. temperature in a freezer
   A. 32°F C. 0°F
   B. 32°C D. 0°C

10. temperature on a day when you can swim in a lake
   F. 50°F H. 27°F
   G. 50°C J. 27°C

11. temperature of a hot tub
   A. 105°F C. 20°F
   B. 105°C D. 20°C

12. temperature of a heated room
   F. 68°F H. 5°F
   G. 68°C J. 5°C

GO ON

Grade 4 277

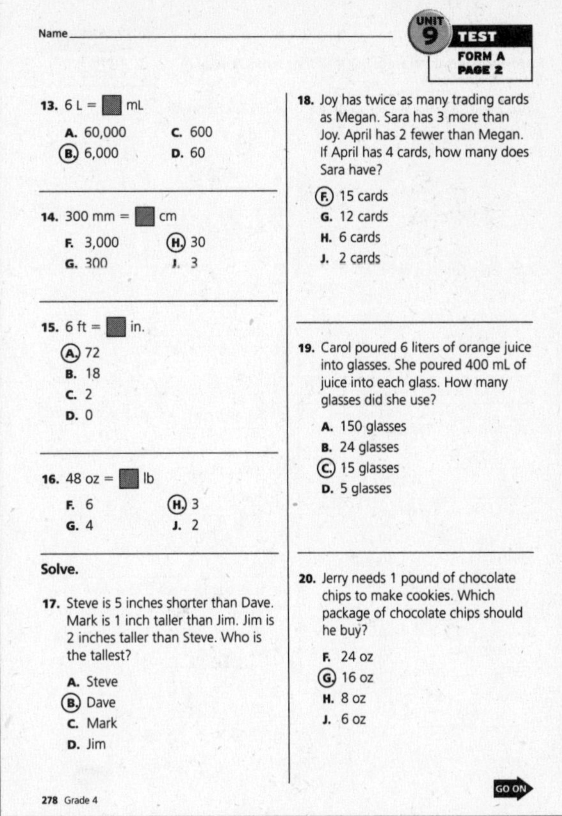

Name ______________________

UNIT 9 TEST FORM A PAGE 2

13. 6 L = ■ mL
   A. 60,000 C. 600
   B. 6,000 D. 60

14. 300 mm = ■ cm
   F. 3,000 H. 30
   G. 300 J. 3

15. 6 ft = ■ in.
   A. 72
   B. 18
   C. 2
   D. 0

16. 48 oz = ■ lb
   F. 6 H. 3
   G. 4 J. 2

Solve.

17. Steve is 5 inches shorter than Dave. Mark is 1 inch taller than Jim. Jim is 2 inches taller than Steve. Who is the tallest?
   A. Steve
   B. Dave
   C. Mark
   D. Jim

18. Joy has twice as many trading cards as Megan. Sara has 3 more than Joy. April has 2 fewer than Megan. If April has 4 cards, how many does Sara have?
   F. 15 cards
   G. 12 cards
   H. 6 cards
   J. 2 cards

19. Carol poured 6 liters of orange juice into glasses. She poured 400 mL of juice into each glass. How many glasses did she use?
   A. 150 glasses
   B. 24 glasses
   C. 15 glasses
   D. 5 glasses

20. Jerry needs 1 pound of chocolate chips to make cookies. Which package of chocolate chips should he buy?
   F. 24 oz
   G. 16 oz
   H. 8 oz
   J. 6 oz

278 Grade 4

GO ON

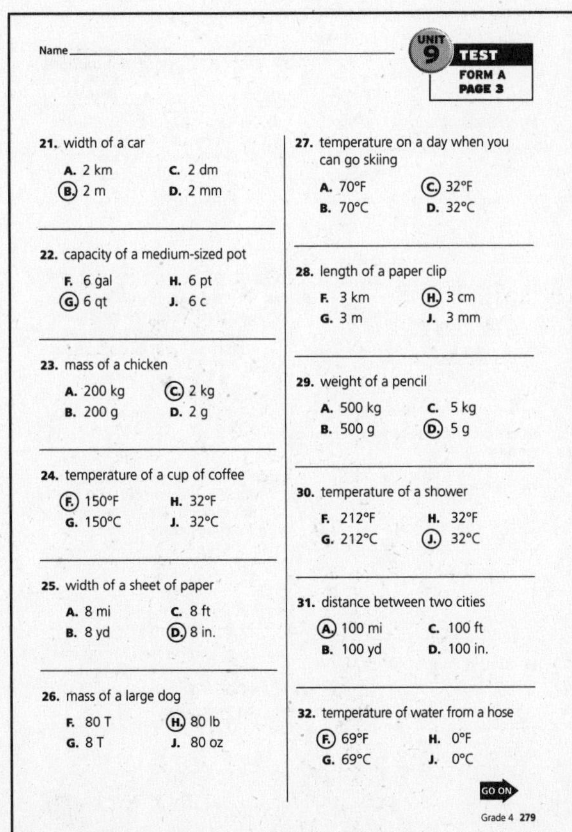

Name ______________________

UNIT 9 TEST FORM A PAGE 3

21. width of a car
   A. 2 km C. 2 dm
   B. 2 m D. 2 mm

22. capacity of a medium-sized pot
   F. 6 gal H. 6 pt
   G. 6 qt J. 6 c

23. mass of a chicken
   A. 200 kg C. 2 kg
   B. 200 g D. 2 g

24. temperature of a cup of coffee
   F. 150°F H. 32°F
   G. 150°C J. 32°C

25. width of a sheet of paper
   A. 8 mi C. 8 ft
   B. 8 yd D. 8 in.

26. mass of a large dog
   F. 80 T H. 80 lb
   G. 8 T J. 80 oz

27. temperature on a day when you can go skiing
   A. 70°F C. 32°F
   B. 70°C D. 32°C

28. length of a paper clip
   F. 3 km H. 3 cm
   G. 3 m J. 3 mm

29. weight of a pencil
   A. 500 kg C. 5 kg
   B. 500 g D. 5 g

30. temperature of a shower
   F. 212°F H. 32°F
   G. 212°C J. 32°C

31. distance between two cities
   A. 100 mi C. 100 ft
   B. 100 yd D. 100 in.

32. temperature of water from a hose
   F. 69°F H. 0°F
   G. 69°C J. 0°C

GO ON

Grade 4 279

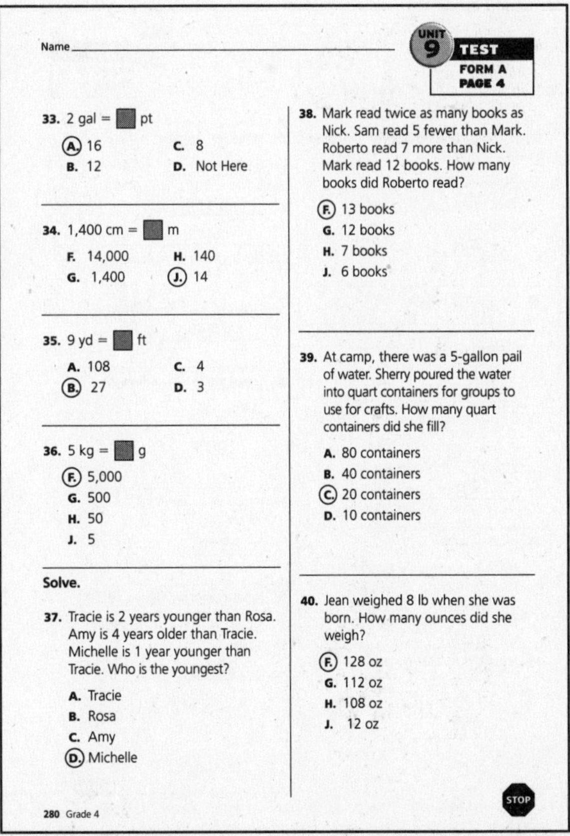

Name ______________________

UNIT 9 TEST FORM A PAGE 4

33. 2 gal = ■ pt
   A. 16 C. 8
   B. 12 D. Not Here

34. 1,400 cm = ■ m
   F. 14,000 H. 140
   G. 1,400 J. 14

35. 9 yd = ■ ft
   A. 108 C. 4
   B. 27 D. 3

36. 5 kg = ■ g
   F. 5,000
   G. 500
   H. 50
   J. 5

Solve.

37. Tracie is 2 years younger than Rosa. Amy is 4 years older than Tracie. Michelle is 1 year younger than Tracie. Who is the youngest?
   A. Tracie
   B. Rosa
   C. Amy
   D. Michelle

38. Mark read twice as many books as Nick. Sam read 5 fewer than Mark. Roberto read 7 more than Nick. Mark read 12 books. How many books did Roberto read?
   F. 13 books
   G. 12 books
   H. 7 books
   J. 6 books

39. At camp, there was a 5-gallon pail of water. Sherry poured the water into quart containers for groups to use for crafts. How many quart containers did she fill?
   A. 80 containers
   B. 40 containers
   C. 20 containers
   D. 10 containers

40. Jean weighed 8 lb when she was born. How many ounces did she weigh?
   F. 128 oz
   G. 112 oz
   H. 108 oz
   J. 12 oz

280 Grade 4

STOP

Name__________________

UNIT 9 TEST FORM B PAGE 1

Read each question carefully. Fill in the correct answer in the space provided.

Write the best estimate for exercises 1–12.

1. length of a table
   8 mi 8 ft
   8 yd 8 in.
   8 feet
2. distance between two towns
   4 km 4 cm
   4 m 4 mm
   4 km
3. length of a truck
   25 mi 25 ft
   25 yd 25 in.
   25 ft
4. height of an action figure
   10 km 10 cm
   10 m 10 mm
   10 cm
5. capacity of a small glass of orange juice
   1 gal 1 pt
   1 qt 1 c
   1 c
6. mass of a can of soda
   40 kg 400 g
   4 kg 40 g
   400 g
7. weight of a truck
   3 T 3 lb
   3,000 oz 3 oz
   3 T
8. capacity of a bath tub
   50 gal 50 pt
   50 qt 50 c
   50 gal
9. temperature of a bath
   100°C 50°C
   30°C 0°C
   30°C
10. temperature inside a classroom
    212°F 100°F
    65°F 32°F
    65°F

GO ON

Grade 4 281

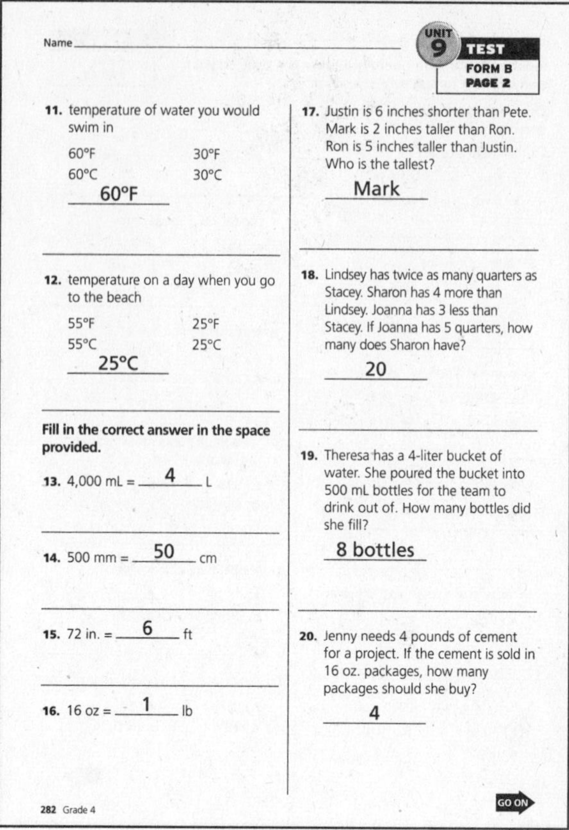

Name__________________

UNIT 9 TEST FORM B PAGE 2

11. temperature of water you would swim in
    60°F 30°F
    60°C 30°C
    60°F
12. temperature on a day when you go to the beach
    55°F 25°F
    55°C 25°C
    25°C

Fill in the correct answer in the space provided.

13. 4,000 mL = 4 L
14. 500 mm = 50 cm
15. 72 in. = 6 ft
16. 16 oz = 1 lb
17. Justin is 6 inches shorter than Pete. Mark is 2 inches taller than Ron. Ron is 5 inches taller than Justin. Who is the tallest?
    Mark
18. Lindsey has twice as many quarters as Stacey. Sharon has 4 more than Lindsey. Joanna has 3 less than Stacey. If Joanna has 5 quarters, how many does Sharon have?
    20
19. Theresa has a 4-liter bucket of water. She poured the bucket into 500 mL bottles for the team to drink out of. How many bottles did she fill?
    8 bottles
20. Jenny needs 4 pounds of cement for a project. If the cement is sold in 16 oz. packages, how many packages should she buy?
    4

282 Grade 4

GO ON

Name__________________

UNIT 9 TEST FORM B PAGE 3

Write the best estimate for exercises 21–32.

21. height of a car
    4 mi 4 ft
    4 yd 4 in.
    4 ft
22. weight of a potato
    1,000 lb 100 lb
    10 lb 1 lb
    1 lb
23. mass of a paper clip
    20 kg 2 kg
    20 g 2 g
    2 g
24. mass of a cat
    300 kg 30 kg
    3 kg 300 g
    3 kg
25. temperature of lemonade
    25°F 5°F
    25°C 5°C
    5°C
26. length of a bicycle
    5 mi 5 yd
    5 ft 5 in.
    5 ft
27. capacity of a large cooler
    5 gal 5 pt
    5 qt 5 c
    5 gal
28. temperature of warm soup
    200°F 100°F
    200°C 100°C
    100°F
29. Height of a basketball net—3 m or 180 in.
    3 m
30. capacity of a swimming pool
    5,000 gal 5,000 pt
    5,000 qt 5,000 c
    5,000 gal

GO ON

Grade 4 283

Name__________________

UNIT 9 TEST FORM B PAGE 4

31. temperature inside a freezer
    40°F 20°F
    40°C 20°C
    20°F
32. weight of a large dog
    50 T 50 lb
    5 T 5 lb
    50 lb

Fill in the correct answer in the space provided.

33. 1 gallon = 16 c
34. 15,000 mm = 15 m
35. 72 in. = 2 yd
36. 4 kg = 4,000 g
37. Janice is 3 years older than Patricia. April is 2 years younger than Janice. Michelle is 1 year older than Patricia. Who is the youngest?
    Patricia
38. Scott ran twice as many laps as Joe. Isaiah ran 7 more than Joe. Roberto ran 4 less than Scott. Roberto ran 6 laps. How many laps did Isaiah run?
    12
39. Jim poured one and a half gallons of milk into glasses. He poured 12 oz of milk into each glass. How many glasses did he use?
    16
40. Renee weighed 7 lb when she was born. How many ounces did she weigh?
    112 ounces

284 Grade 4

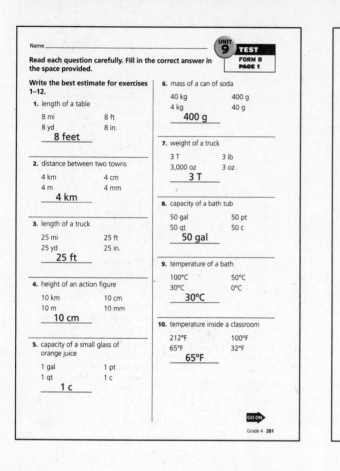

STOP

Chapter 19

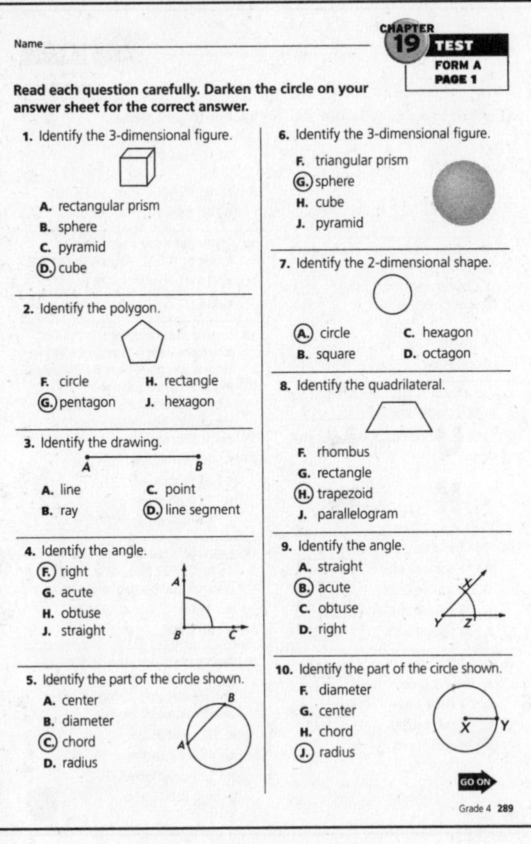

Name

CHAPTER 19 TEST FORM A PAGE 1

Read each question carefully. Darken the circle on your answer sheet for the correct answer.

1. Identify the 3-dimensional figure.
   A. rectangular prism
   B. sphere
   C. pyramid
   (D.) cube

2. Identify the polygon.
   F. circle
   H. rectangle
   (G.) pentagon
   J. hexagon

3. Identify the drawing.
   A. line
   C. point
   B. ray
   (D.) line segment

4. Identify the angle.
   (F.) right
   G. acute
   H. obtuse
   J. straight

5. Identify the part of the circle shown.
   A. center
   B. diameter
   (C.) chord
   D. radius

6. Identify the 3-dimensional figure.
   F. triangular prism
   (G.) sphere
   H. cube
   J. pyramid

7. Identify the 2-dimensional shape.
   (A.) circle
   C. hexagon
   B. square
   D. octagon

8. Identify the quadrilateral.
   F. rhombus
   G. rectangle
   (H.) trapezoid
   J. parallelogram

9. Identify the angle.
   A. straight
   (B.) acute
   C. obtuse
   D. right

10. Identify the part of the circle shown.
    F. diameter
    G. center
    H. chord
    (J.) radius

GO ON

Grade 4 289

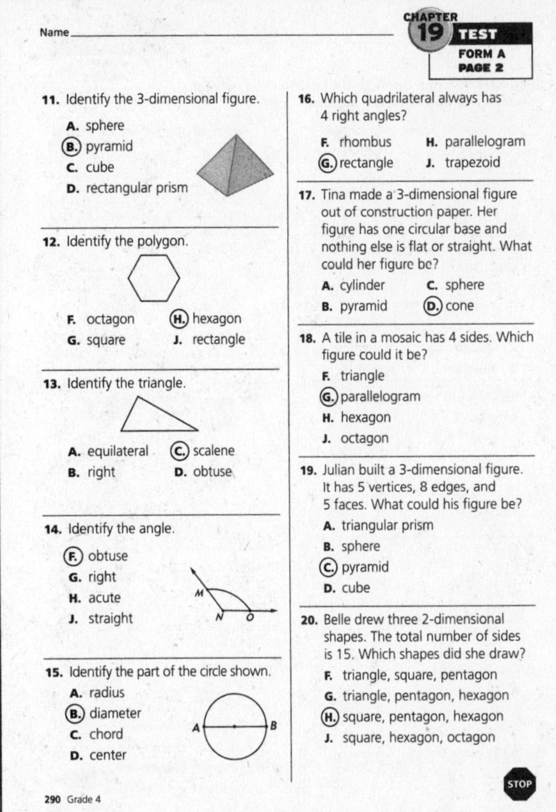

Name

CHAPTER 19 TEST FORM A PAGE 2

11. Identify the 3-dimensional figure.
    A. sphere
    (B.) pyramid
    C. cube
    D. rectangular prism

12. Identify the polygon.
    F. octagon
    (H.) hexagon
    G. square
    J. rectangle

13. Identify the triangle.
    A. equilateral
    (C.) scalene
    B. right
    D. obtuse

14. Identify the angle.
    (F.) obtuse
    G. right
    H. acute
    J. straight

15. Identify the part of the circle shown.
    A. radius
    (B.) diameter
    C. chord
    D. center

16. Which quadrilateral always has 4 right angles?
    F. rhombus
    H. parallelogram
    (G.) rectangle
    J. trapezoid

17. Tina made a 3-dimensional figure out of construction paper. Her figure has one circular base and nothing else is flat or straight. What could her figure be?
    A. cylinder
    C. sphere
    B. pyramid
    (D.) cone

18. A tile in a mosaic has 4 sides. Which figure could it be?
    F. triangle
    (G.) parallelogram
    H. hexagon
    J. octagon

19. Julian built a 3-dimensional figure. It has 5 vertices, 8 edges, and 5 faces. What could his figure be?
    A. triangular prism
    B. sphere
    (C.) pyramid
    D. cube

20. Belle drew three 2-dimensional shapes. The total number of sides is 15. Which shapes did she draw?
    F. triangle, square, pentagon
    G. triangle, pentagon, hexagon
    (H.) square, pentagon, hexagon
    J. square, hexagon, octagon

STOP

290 Grade 4

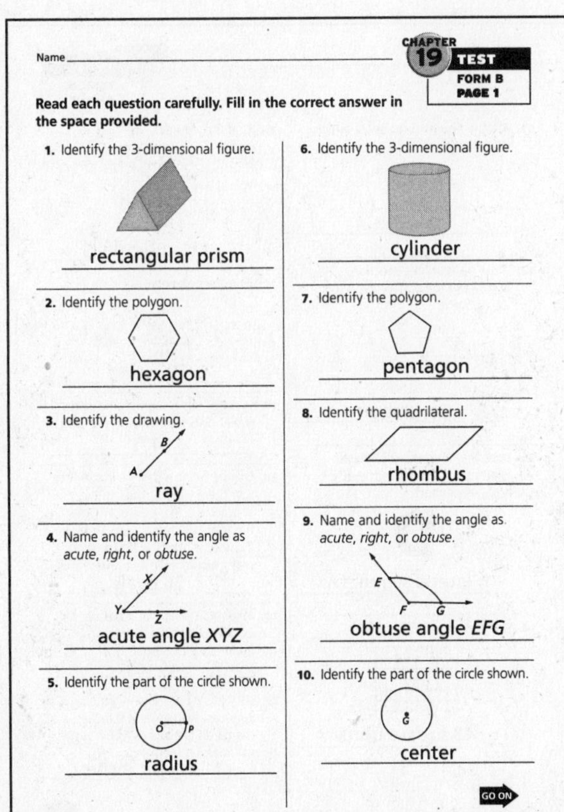

Name

CHAPTER 19 TEST FORM B PAGE 1

Read each question carefully. Fill in the correct answer in the space provided.

1. Identify the 3-dimensional figure.
   rectangular prism

2. Identify the polygon.
   hexagon

3. Identify the drawing.
   ray

4. Name and identify the angle as *acute*, *right*, or *obtuse*.
   acute angle *XYZ*

5. Identify the part of the circle shown.
   radius

6. Identify the 3-dimensional figure.
   cylinder

7. Identify the polygon.
   pentagon

8. Identify the quadrilateral.
   rhombus

9. Name and identify the angle as *acute*, *right*, or *obtuse*.
   obtuse angle *EFG*

10. Identify the part of the circle shown.
    center

GO ON

Grade 4 291

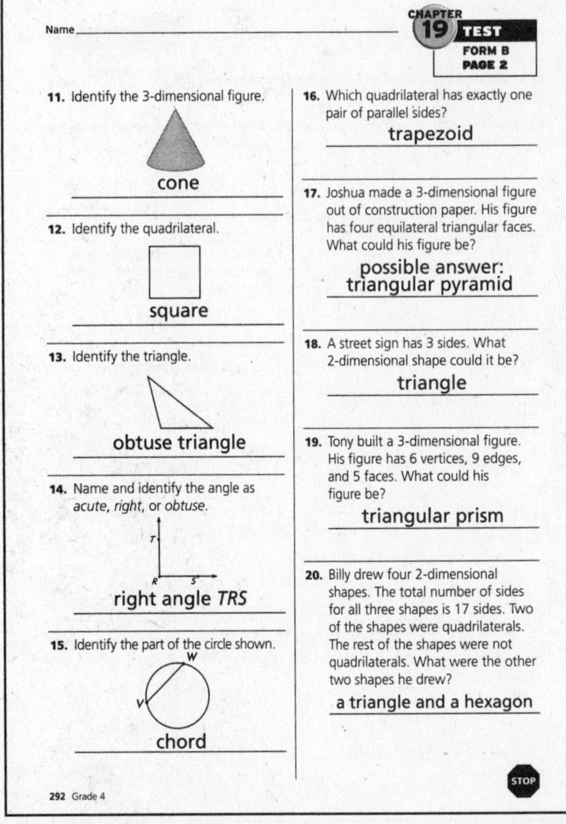

Name

CHAPTER 19 TEST FORM B PAGE 2

11. Identify the 3-dimensional figure.
    cone

12. Identify the quadrilateral.
    square

13. Identify the triangle.
    obtuse triangle

14. Name and identify the angle as *acute*, *right*, or *obtuse*.
    right angle *TRS*

15. Identify the part of the circle shown.
    chord

16. Which quadrilateral has exactly one pair of parallel sides?
    trapezoid

17. Joshua made a 3-dimensional figure out of construction paper. His figure has four equilateral triangular faces. What could his figure be?
    possible answer: triangular pyramid

18. A street sign has 3 sides. What 2-dimensional shape could it be?
    triangle

19. Tony built a 3-dimensional figure. His figure has 6 vertices, 9 edges, and 5 faces. What could his figure be?
    triangular prism

20. Billy drew four 2-dimensional shapes. The total number of sides for all three shapes is 17 sides. Two of the shapes were quadrilaterals. The rest of the shapes were not quadrilaterals. What were the other two shapes he drew?
    a triangle and a hexagon

STOP

292 Grade 4

Chapter 20

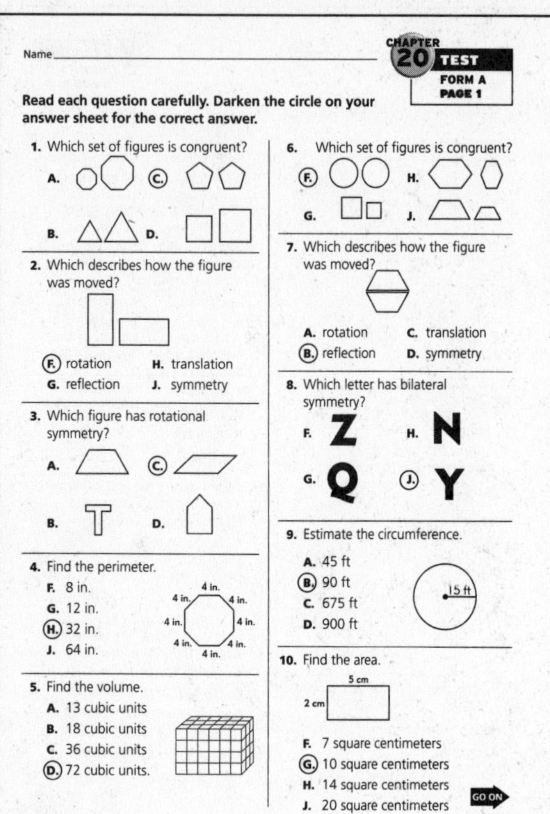

Name

CHAPTER 20 TEST FORM A PAGE 1

Read each question carefully. Darken the circle on your answer sheet for the correct answer.

1. Which set of figures is congruent?
A. B. (C.) D.

2. Which describes how the figure was moved?
(F.) rotation H. translation
G. reflection J. symmetry

3. Which figure has rotational symmetry?
A. (C.) B. D.

4. Find the perimeter.
F. 8 in.
G. 12 in.
(H.) 32 in.
J. 64 in.

5. Find the volume.
A. 13 cubic units
B. 18 cubic units
C. 36 cubic units
(D.) 72 cubic units.

6. Which set of figures is congruent?
(F.) H. G. J.

7. Which describes how the figure was moved?
A. rotation C. translation
(B.) reflection D. symmetry

8. Which letter has bilateral symmetry?
F. Z H. N
G. Q (J.) Y

9. Estimate the circumference.
A. 45 ft
(B.) 90 ft
C. 675 ft
D. 900 ft

10. Find the area.
F. 7 square centimeters
(G.) 10 square centimeters
H. 14 square centimeters
J. 20 square centimeters

GO ON

Grade 4 297

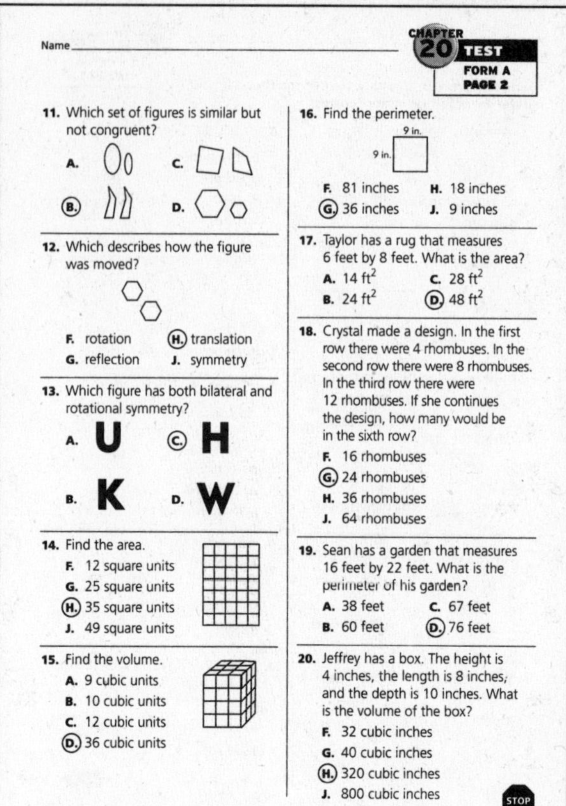

Name

CHAPTER 20 TEST FORM A PAGE 2

11. Which set of figures is similar but not congruent?
A. C. (B.) D.

12. Which describes how the figure was moved?
F. rotation (H.) translation
G. reflection J. symmetry

13. Which figure has both bilateral and rotational symmetry?
A. U (C.) H
B. K D. W

14. Find the area.
F. 12 square units
G. 25 square units
(H.) 35 square units
J. 49 square units

15. Find the volume.
A. 9 cubic units
B. 10 cubic units
C. 12 cubic units
(D.) 36 cubic units

16. Find the perimeter.
F. 81 inches H. 18 inches
(G.) 36 inches J. 9 inches

17. Taylor has a rug that measures 6 feet by 8 feet. What is the area?
A. 14 ft^2 C. 28 ft^2
B. 24 ft^2 (D.) 48 ft^2

18. Crystal made a design. In the first row there were 4 rhombuses. In the second row there were 8 rhombuses. In the third row there were 12 rhombuses. If she continues the design, how many would be in the sixth row?
F. 16 rhombuses
(G.) 24 rhombuses
H. 36 rhombuses
J. 64 rhombuses

19. Sean has a garden that measures 16 feet by 22 feet. What is the perimeter of his garden?
A. 38 feet C. 67 feet
B. 60 feet (D.) 76 feet

20. Jeffrey has a box. The height is 4 inches, the length is 8 inches, and the depth is 10 inches. What is the volume of the box?
F. 32 cubic inches
G. 40 cubic inches
(H.) 320 cubic inches
J. 800 cubic inches

STOP

298 Grade 4

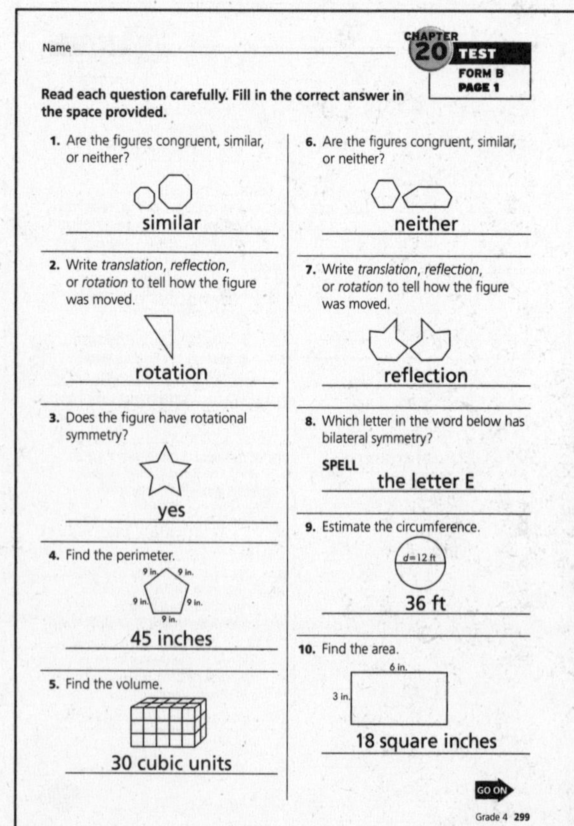

Name

CHAPTER 20 TEST FORM B PAGE 1

Read each question carefully. Fill in the correct answer in the space provided.

1. Are the figures congruent, similar, or neither?
similar

2. Write *translation*, *reflection*, or *rotation* to tell how the figure was moved.
rotation

3. Does the figure have rotational symmetry?
yes

4. Find the perimeter.
45 inches

5. Find the volume.
30 cubic units

6. Are the figures congruent, similar, or neither?
neither

7. Write *translation*, *reflection*, or *rotation* to tell how the figure was moved.
reflection

8. Which letter in the word below has bilateral symmetry?
SPELL
the letter E

9. Estimate the circumference.
36 ft

10. Find the area.
18 square inches

GO ON

Grade 4 299

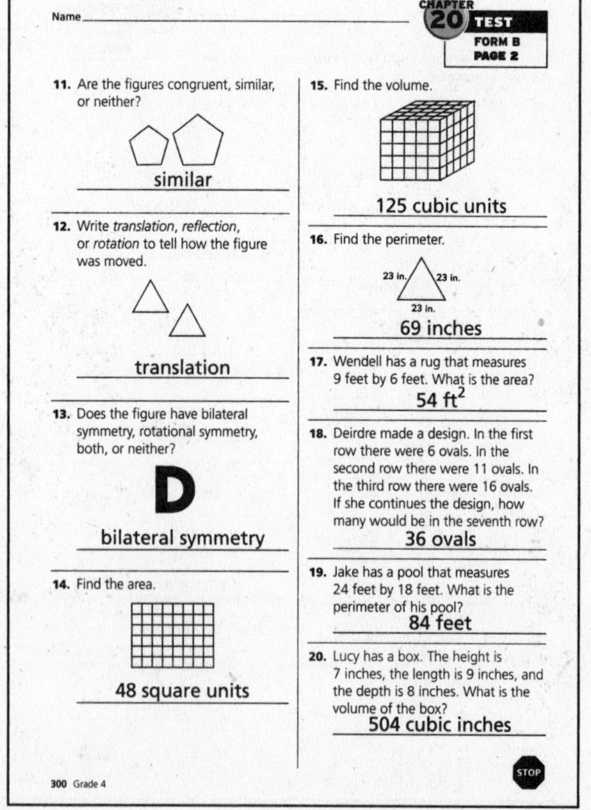

Name

CHAPTER 20 TEST FORM B PAGE 2

11. Are the figures congruent, similar, or neither?
similar

12. Write *translation*, *reflection*, or *rotation* to tell how the figure was moved.
translation

13. Does the figure have bilateral symmetry, rotational symmetry, both, or neither?
bilateral symmetry

14. Find the area.
48 square units

15. Find the volume.
125 cubic units

16. Find the perimeter.
69 inches

17. Wendell has a rug that measures 9 feet by 6 feet. What is the area?
54 ft^2

18. Deirdre made a design. In the first row there were 6 ovals. In the second row there were 11 ovals. In the third row there were 16 ovals. If she continues the design, how many would be in the seventh row?
36 ovals

19. Jake has a pool that measures 24 feet by 18 feet. What is the perimeter of his pool?
84 feet

20. Lucy has a box. The height is 7 inches, the length is 9 inches, and the depth is 8 inches. What is the volume of the box?
504 cubic inches

STOP

300 Grade 4

Unit 10

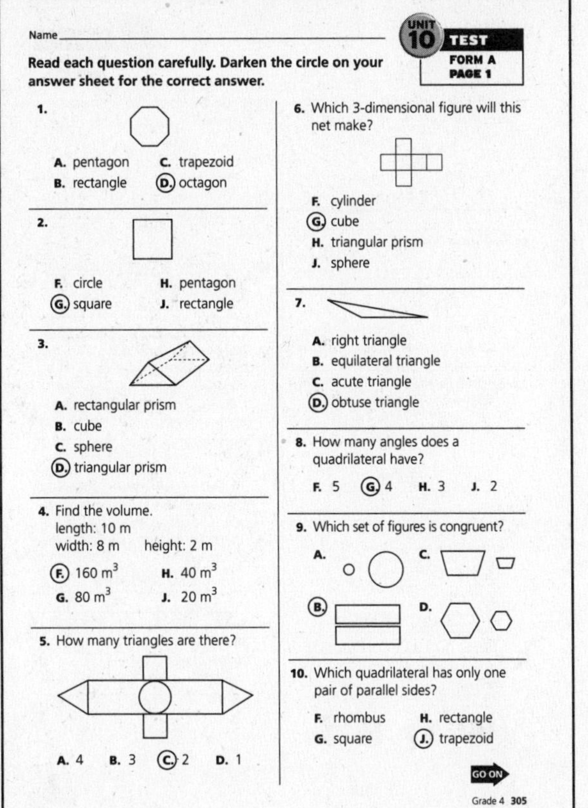

Name ____________________

UNIT 10 TEST
FORM A
PAGE 1

Read each question carefully. Darken the circle on your answer sheet for the correct answer.

1.

A. pentagon C. trapezoid
B. rectangle Ⓓ octagon

2.

F. circle H. pentagon
Ⓖ square J. rectangle

3.

A. rectangular prism
B. cube
C. sphere
Ⓓ triangular prism

4. Find the volume.
length: 10 m
width: 8 m height: 2 m

Ⓕ 160 m^3 H. 40 m^3
G. 80 m^3 J. 20 m^3

5. How many triangles are there?

A. 4 B. 3 Ⓒ 2 D. 1

6. Which 3-dimensional figure will this net make?

F. cylinder
Ⓖ cube
H. triangular prism
J. sphere

7.

A. right triangle
B. equilateral triangle
C. acute triangle
Ⓓ obtuse triangle

8. How many angles does a quadrilateral have?

F. 5 Ⓖ 4 H. 3 J. 2

9. Which set of figures is congruent?

A. C.

Ⓑ D.

10. Which quadrilateral has only one pair of parallel sides?

F. rhombus H. rectangle
G. square Ⓙ trapezoid

GO ON

Grade 4 305

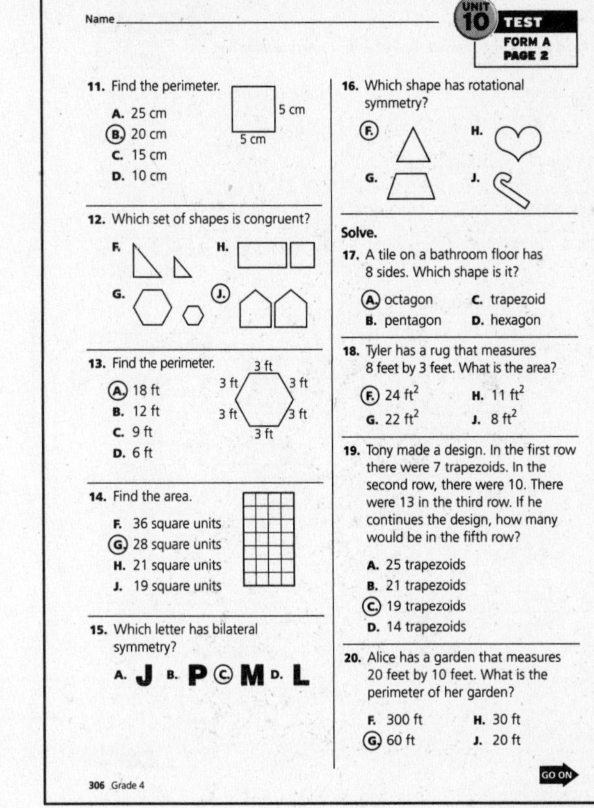

Name ____________________

UNIT 10 TEST
FORM A
PAGE 2

11. Find the perimeter.

5 cm
5 cm

A. 25 cm
Ⓑ 20 cm
C. 15 cm
D. 10 cm

12. Which set of shapes is congruent?

F. H.

G. Ⓙ

13. Find the perimeter.

3 ft 3 ft 3 ft 3 ft 3 ft 3 ft

Ⓐ 18 ft
B. 12 ft
C. 9 ft
D. 6 ft

14. Find the area.

F. 36 square units
Ⓖ 28 square units
H. 21 square units
J. 19 square units

15. Which letter has bilateral symmetry?

A. J B. P Ⓒ M D. L

16. Which shape has rotational symmetry?

Ⓕ H.

G. J.

Solve.

17. A tile on a bathroom floor has 8 sides. Which shape is it?

Ⓐ octagon C. trapezoid
B. pentagon D. hexagon

18. Tyler has a rug that measures 8 feet by 3 feet. What is the area?

Ⓕ 24 ft^2 H. 11 ft^2
G. 22 ft^2 J. 8 ft^2

19. Tony made a design. In the first row there were 7 trapezoids. In the second row, there were 10. There were 13 in the third row. If he continues the design, how many would be in the fifth row?

A. 25 trapezoids
B. 21 trapezoids
Ⓒ 19 trapezoids
D. 14 trapezoids

20. Alice has a garden that measures 20 feet by 10 feet. What is the perimeter of her garden?

F. 300 ft H. 30 ft
Ⓖ 60 ft J. 20 ft

306 Grade 4

GO ON

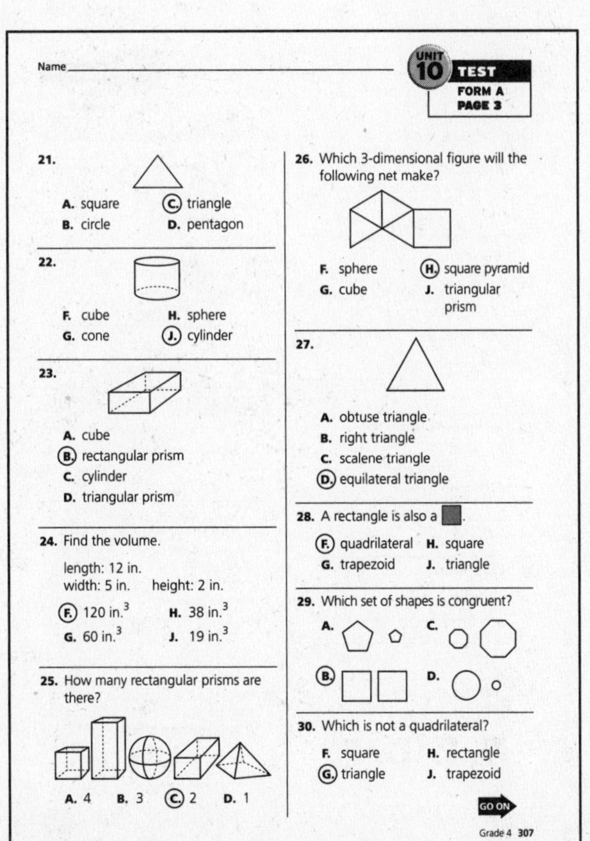

Name ____________________

UNIT 10 TEST
FORM A
PAGE 3

21.

A. square Ⓒ triangle
B. circle D. pentagon

22.

F. cube H. sphere
G. cone Ⓙ cylinder

23.

A. cube
Ⓑ rectangular prism
C. cylinder
D. triangular prism

24. Find the volume.

length: 12 in.
width: 5 in. height: 2 in.

Ⓕ 120 $in.^3$ H. 38 $in.^3$
G. 60 $in.^3$ J. 19 $in.^3$

25. How many rectangular prisms are there?

A. 4 B. 3 Ⓒ 2 D. 1

26. Which 3-dimensional figure will the following net make?

F. sphere Ⓗ square pyramid
G. cube J. triangular prism

27.

A. obtuse triangle
B. right triangle
C. scalene triangle
Ⓓ equilateral triangle

28. A rectangle is also a ■.

Ⓕ quadrilateral H. square
G. trapezoid J. triangle

29. Which set of shapes is congruent?

A. C.

Ⓑ D.

30. Which is not a quadrilateral?

F. square H. rectangle
Ⓖ triangle J. trapezoid

GO ON

Grade 4 307

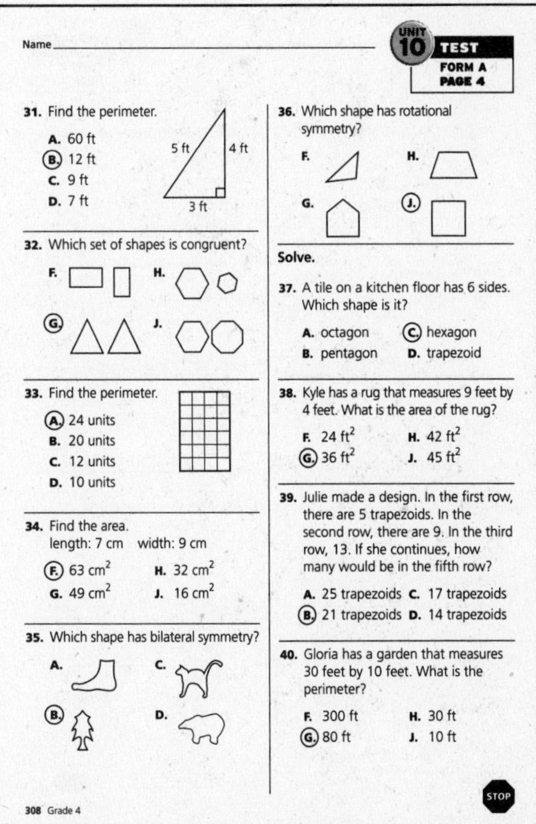

Name ____________________

UNIT 10 TEST
FORM A
PAGE 4

31. Find the perimeter.

5 ft 4 ft 3 ft

A. 60 ft
Ⓑ 12 ft
C. 9 ft
D. 7 ft

32. Which set of shapes is congruent?

F. H.

Ⓖ J.

33. Find the perimeter.

Ⓐ 24 units
B. 20 units
C. 12 units
D. 10 units

34. Find the area.
length: 7 cm width: 9 cm

Ⓕ 63 cm^2 H. 32 cm^2
G. 49 cm^2 J. 16 cm^2

35. Which shape has bilateral symmetry?

A. C.

Ⓑ D.

36. Which shape has rotational symmetry?

F. H.

G. Ⓙ

Solve.

37. A tile on a kitchen floor has 6 sides. Which shape is it?

A. octagon Ⓒ hexagon
B. pentagon D. trapezoid

38. Kyle has a rug that measures 9 feet by 4 feet. What is the area of the rug?

F. 24 ft^2 H. 42 ft^2
Ⓖ 36 ft^2 J. 45 ft^2

39. Julie made a design. In the first row, there are 5 trapezoids. In the second row, there are 9. In the third row, 13. If she continues, how many would be in the fifth row?

A. 25 trapezoids C. 17 trapezoids
Ⓑ 21 trapezoids D. 14 trapezoids

40. Gloria has a garden that measures 30 feet by 10 feet. What is the perimeter?

F. 300 ft H. 30 ft
Ⓖ 80 ft J. 10 ft

308 Grade 4

STOP

Unit 10

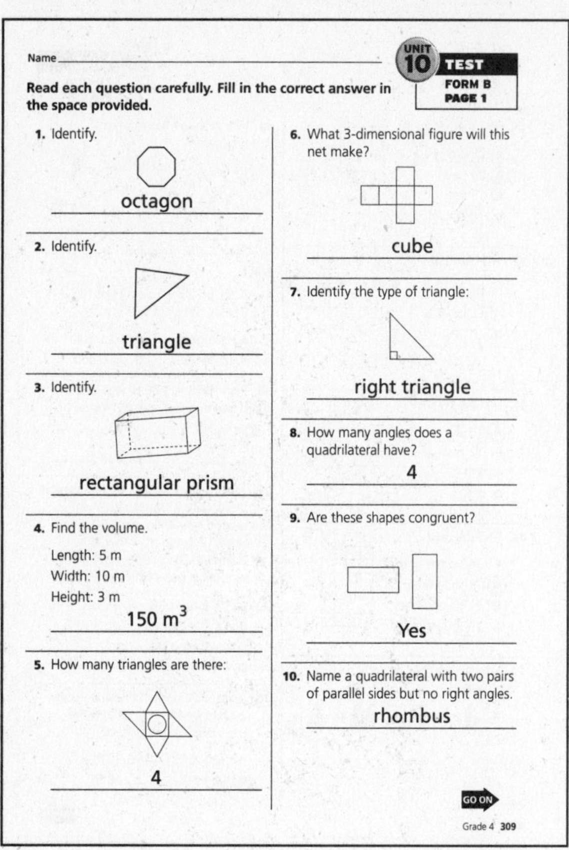

Name ________________

UNIT 10 TEST
FORM B
PAGE 1

Read each question carefully. Fill in the correct answer in the space provided.

1. Identify.

octagon

2. Identify.

triangle

3. Identify.

rectangular prism

4. Find the volume.

Length: 5 m
Width: 10 m
Height: 3 m

150 m^3

5. How many triangles are there:

4

6. What 3-dimensional figure will this net make?

cube

7. Identify the type of triangle:

right triangle

8. How many angles does a quadrilateral have?

4

9. Are these shapes congruent?

Yes

10. Name a quadrilateral with two pairs of parallel sides but no right angles.

rhombus

GO ON

Grade 4 309

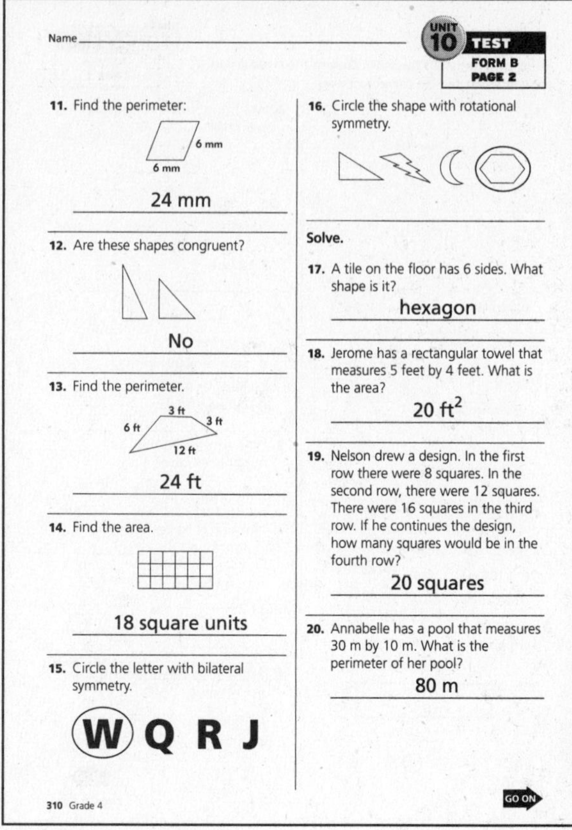

Name ________________

UNIT 10 TEST
FORM B
PAGE 2

11. Find the perimeter:

24 mm

12. Are these shapes congruent?

No

13. Find the perimeter.

24 ft

14. Find the area.

18 square units

15. Circle the letter with bilateral symmetry.

W Q R J

16. Circle the shape with rotational symmetry.

Solve.

17. A tile on the floor has 6 sides. What shape is it?

hexagon

18. Jerome has a rectangular towel that measures 5 feet by 4 feet. What is the area?

20 ft^2

19. Nelson drew a design. In the first row there were 8 squares. In the second row, there were 12 squares. There were 16 squares in the third row. If he continues the design, how many squares would be in the fourth row?

20 squares

20. Annabelle has a pool that measures 30 m by 10 m. What is the perimeter of her pool?

80 m

310 Grade 4

GO ON

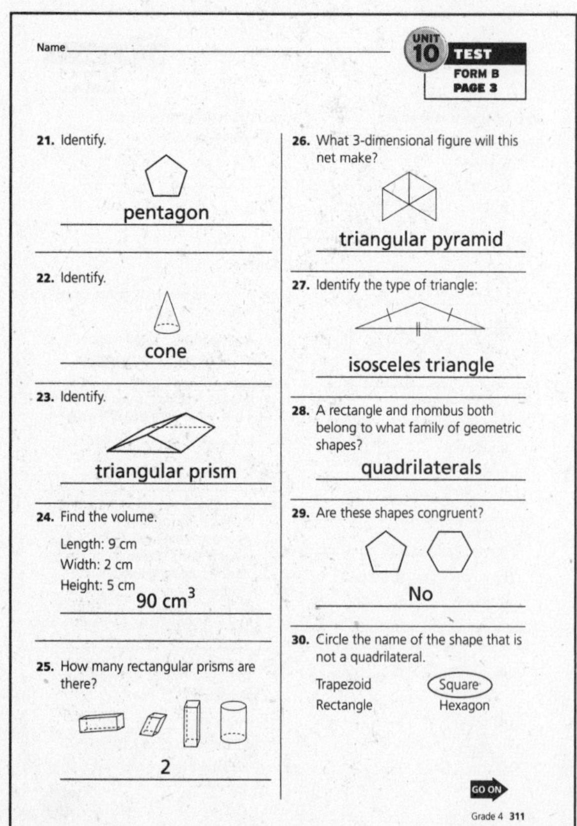

Name ________________

UNIT 10 TEST
FORM B
PAGE 3

21. Identify.

pentagon

22. Identify.

cone

23. Identify.

triangular prism

24. Find the volume.

Length: 9 cm
Width: 2 cm
Height: 5 cm

90 cm^3

25. How many rectangular prisms are there?

2

26. What 3-dimensional figure will this net make?

triangular pyramid

27. Identify the type of triangle:

isosceles triangle

28. A rectangle and rhombus both belong to what family of geometric shapes?

quadrilaterals

29. Are these shapes congruent?

No

30. Circle the name of the shape that is not a quadrilateral.

Trapezoid	Square
Rectangle	Hexagon

GO ON

Grade 4 311

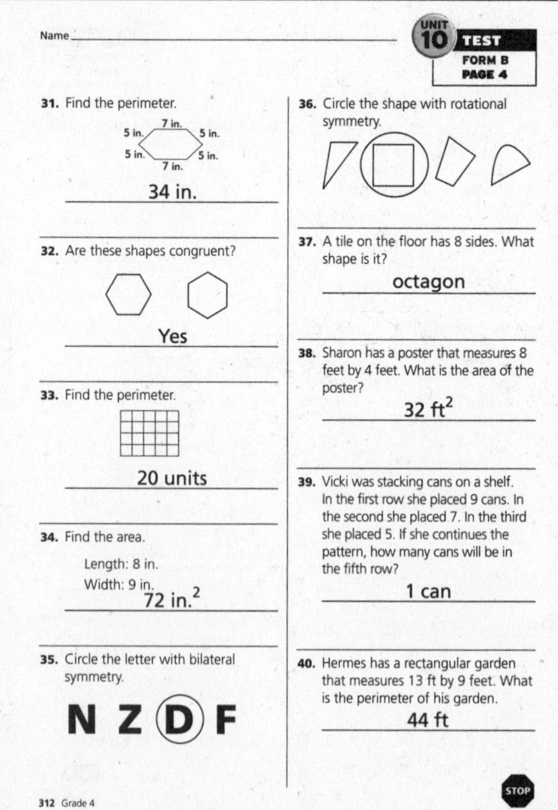

Name ________________

UNIT 10 TEST
FORM B
PAGE 4

31. Find the perimeter.

34 in.

32. Are these shapes congruent?

Yes

33. Find the perimeter.

20 units

34. Find the area.

Length: 8 in.
Width: 9 in.

72 in.^2

35. Circle the letter with bilateral symmetry.

N Z D F

36. Circle the shape with rotational symmetry.

37. A tile on the floor has 8 sides. What shape is it?

octagon

38. Sharon has a poster that measures 8 feet by 4 feet. What is the area of the poster?

32 ft^2

39. Vicki was stacking cans on a shelf. In the first row she placed 9 cans. In the second she placed 7. In the third she placed 5. If she continues the pattern, how many cans will be in the fifth row?

1 can

40. Hermes has a rectangular garden that measures 13 ft by 9 feet. What is the perimeter of his garden.

44 ft

312 Grade 4

STOP

Name ____________________

Read each question carefully. Darken the circle on your answer sheet for the correct answer.

For exercises 1–4, match the model with the fraction that correctly represents the shaded part of the model.

1. 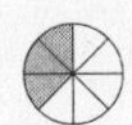

A. $\frac{8}{3}$ B. $\frac{1}{3}$ **C.** $\frac{3}{8}$ D. $\frac{5}{8}$

2. 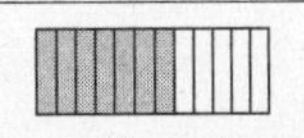

F. $\frac{1}{7}$ G. $\frac{12}{7}$ H. $\frac{5}{12}$ **J.** $\frac{7}{12}$

3. 

A. $\frac{2}{5}$ B. $\frac{5}{2}$ C. $\frac{3}{5}$ D. $\frac{1}{5}$

4. 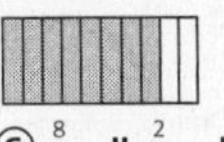

F. $\frac{10}{8}$ **G.** $\frac{8}{10}$ H. $\frac{2}{8}$ J. $\frac{2}{10}$

5. Which has the greatest value?
$\frac{3}{12}$ $\frac{1}{5}$ $\frac{2}{6}$ $\frac{3}{8}$
A. $\frac{3}{12}$ B. $\frac{1}{5}$ C. $\frac{2}{6}$ **D.** $\frac{3}{8}$

6. Order from least to greatest.
$\frac{2}{4}$ $\frac{3}{8}$ $\frac{7}{12}$
F. $\frac{3}{8}, \frac{7}{12}, \frac{2}{4}$ H. $\frac{7}{12}, \frac{3}{8}, \frac{2}{4}$
G. $\frac{2}{4}, \frac{3}{8}, \frac{7}{12}$ **J.** $\frac{3}{8}, \frac{2}{4}, \frac{7}{12}$

7. Write $\frac{27}{36}$ in simplest form.
A. $\frac{9}{4}$ B. $\frac{4}{9}$ **C.** $\frac{3}{4}$ D. $\frac{3}{9}$

8. Rename $\frac{19}{3}$ as a mixed number in simplest form.
F. $6\frac{3}{19}$ H. $\frac{6}{3}$
G. $6\frac{1}{3}$ J. $\frac{6}{19}$

9. Which has the least value?
$\frac{2}{10}$ $\frac{3}{5}$ $\frac{1}{4}$ $\frac{3}{20}$
A. $\frac{2}{10}$ B. $\frac{3}{5}$ C. $\frac{1}{4}$ **D.** $\frac{3}{20}$

10. Order from greatest to least.
$\frac{2}{8}$ $\frac{5}{16}$ $\frac{1}{2}$
F. $\frac{1}{2}, \frac{5}{16}, \frac{2}{8}$ H. $\frac{2}{8}, \frac{5}{16}, \frac{1}{2}$
G. $\frac{5}{16}, \frac{1}{2}, \frac{2}{8}$ J. $\frac{1}{2}, \frac{2}{8}, \frac{5}{16}$

Name ____________________

11. Write $\frac{7}{21}$ in simplest form.
A. $\frac{7}{14}$ B. $\frac{1}{7}$ **C.** $\frac{1}{3}$ D. $\frac{3}{21}$

12. Rename $\frac{35}{8}$ as a mixed number in simplest form.
F. $8\frac{3}{8}$ H. $4\frac{8}{35}$
G. $4\frac{3}{8}$ J. $3\frac{4}{35}$

13. Which has the greatest value?
$\frac{2}{3}$ $\frac{5}{6}$ $\frac{7}{9}$ $\frac{3}{4}$
A. $\frac{2}{3}$ **B.** $\frac{5}{6}$ C. $\frac{7}{9}$ D. $\frac{3}{4}$

14. Order from least to greatest.
$\frac{7}{8}$ $\frac{3}{4}$ $\frac{8}{12}$
F. $\frac{8}{12}, \frac{3}{4}, \frac{7}{8}$ H. $\frac{3}{4}, \frac{7}{8}, \frac{8}{12}$
G. $\frac{8}{12}, \frac{7}{8}, \frac{3}{4}$ J. $\frac{3}{4}, \frac{8}{12}, \frac{7}{8}$

15. Write $\frac{12}{20}$ in simplest form.
A. $\frac{4}{5}$ B. $\frac{3}{4}$ **C.** $\frac{3}{5}$ D. $\frac{6}{10}$

16. Rename $\frac{26}{5}$ as a mixed number in simplest form.
F. $5\frac{6}{5}$ H. $5\frac{1}{26}$
G. $\frac{5}{26}$ **J.** $5\frac{1}{5}$

17. A group of 40 students went to the museum. $\frac{3}{5}$ went to the Picasso exhibit and the rest went to the Matisse exhibit. How many went to the Picasso exhibit?
A. 15 students **C.** 24 students
B. 8 students D. 35 students

18. A group of 12 students performed a science experiment. Of the group, $\frac{2}{3}$ were girls. Which statement is most reasonable?
F. More than 9 were girls.
G. Less than 8 were girls.
H. More than $\frac{1}{4}$ were boys.
J. Less than $\frac{1}{3}$ were boys.

19. Missy has 38 marbles. She separates the marbles into piles of 4 marbles each. She is left with a pile that has less than 4 marbles. Write a fraction in simplest form that represents the piles of marbles.
A. $\frac{38}{4}$ **B.** $9\frac{1}{2}$ C. $9\frac{4}{38}$ D. $4\frac{9}{4}$

20. A group of 16 students met to play soccer. $\frac{1}{8}$ had never played soccer and had to have the rules explained. Which statement is most reasonable?
F. Fewer than 2 students had never played soccer.
G. More than 12 students had played soccer before.
H. Almost 10 students had played soccer before.
J. More than 2 students had never played soccer.

Name ____________________

CHAPTER 21 TEST FORM B PAGE 1

Read each question carefully. Fill in the correct answer in the space provided.

For exercises 1–4, write the fraction that correctly represents the shaded part of the model.

1. 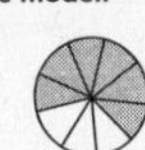

$\frac{6}{9}$

2. 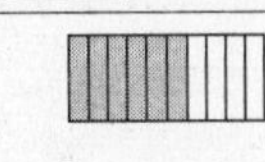

$\frac{6}{10}$

3. 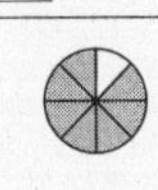

$\frac{7}{8}$

4. 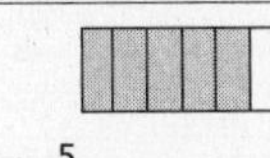

$\frac{5}{6}$

5. Which has the greatest value?
$\frac{4}{5}$ $\frac{3}{4}$ $\frac{4}{10}$ $\frac{12}{20}$
$\frac{4}{5}$

6. Order from least to greatest.
$\frac{3}{5}$ $\frac{4}{10}$ $\frac{5}{15}$
$\frac{5}{15}, \frac{4}{10}, \frac{3}{5}$

7. Write $\frac{18}{27}$ in simplest form.
$\frac{2}{3}$

8. Rename $\frac{17}{6}$ as a mixed number in simplest form.
$2\frac{5}{6}$

9. Which has the least value?
$\frac{1}{5}$ $\frac{3}{10}$ $\frac{5}{20}$ $\frac{10}{40}$
$\frac{1}{5}$

10. Order from greatest to least.
$\frac{5}{6}$ $\frac{7}{9}$ $\frac{13}{18}$
$\frac{5}{6}, \frac{7}{9}, \frac{13}{18}$

Name ____________________

11. Write $\frac{15}{25}$ in simplest form.
$\frac{3}{5}$

12. Rename $\frac{29}{7}$ as a mixed number in simplest form.
$4\frac{1}{7}$

13. Which has the greatest value?
$\frac{7}{10}$ $\frac{3}{5}$ $\frac{10}{15}$ $\frac{22}{30}$
$\frac{22}{30}$

14. Order from least to greatest.
$\frac{6}{9}$ $\frac{3}{6}$ $\frac{3}{4}$
$\frac{3}{6}, \frac{6}{9}, \frac{3}{4}$

15. Write $\frac{24}{36}$ in simplest form.
$\frac{2}{3}$

16. Rename $\frac{32}{6}$ as a mixed number in simplest form.
$5\frac{1}{3}$

17. A group of 30 students went to a ballet. $\frac{5}{6}$ had never seen a ballet performance before. How many had never seen a ballet?
25 students

18. 25 students attended the science fair. $\frac{3}{5}$ entered their projects into the competition. Is it reasonable to say that fewer than 12 students entered the competition? Write yes or no and explain your answer.
No, it is not reasonable because $\frac{3}{5}$ of 25 is 15 and 15 is more than 12, not less than 12.

19. Joseph has 47 coins. He separates them into piles of 8. He is left with a pile that has fewer than 8 coins. Write a fraction in simplest form that represents the piles of coins.
$8\frac{7}{8}$

20. 18 students met to rehearse for a school play. $\frac{1}{2}$ of the students had never been in a play before. Is it reasonable to say that fewer than 10 students had never been in a play? Write *yes* or *no* and explain your answer.
Yes, it is reasonable because $\frac{1}{2}$ of 18 is 9 and 9 is less than 10.

Chapter 22

Name

CHAPTER 22 TEST FORM A PAGE 1

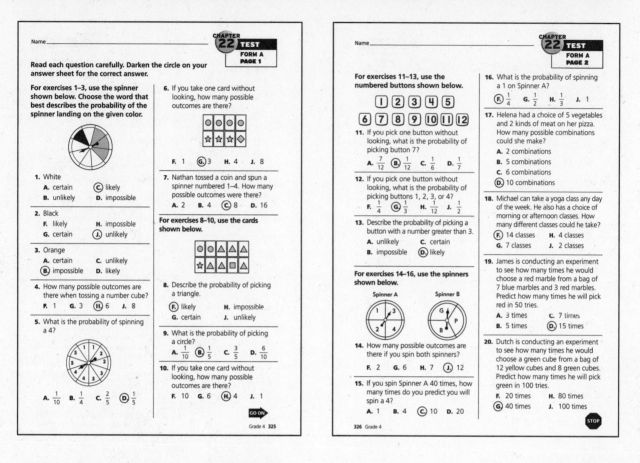

Read each question carefully. Darken the circle on your answer sheet for the correct answer.

For exercises 1–3, use the spinner shown below. Choose the word that best describes the probability of the spinner landing on the given color.

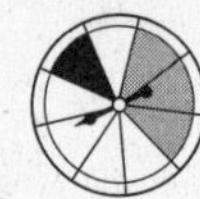

1. White
   A. certain (C.) likely
   B. unlikely D. impossible
2. Black
   F. likely H. impossible
   G. certain (J.) unlikely
3. Orange
   A. certain C. unlikely
   (B.) impossible D. likely
4. How many possible outcomes are there when tossing a number cube?
   F. 1 G. 3 (H.) 6 J. 8
5. What is the probability of spinning a 4?

A. $\frac{1}{10}$ B. $\frac{1}{4}$ C. $\frac{2}{5}$ (D.) $\frac{1}{5}$

6. If you take one card without looking, how many possible outcomes are there?

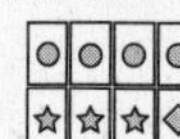

F. 1 (G.) 3 H. 4 J. 8

7. Nathan tossed a coin and spun a spinner numbered 1–4. How many possible outcomes were there?
   A. 2 B. 4 (C.) 8 D. 16

For exercises 8–10, use the cards shown below.

8. Describe the probability of picking a triangle.
   (F.) likely H. impossible
   G. certain J. unlikely
9. What is the probability of picking a circle?
   A. $\frac{1}{10}$ (B.) $\frac{1}{5}$ C. $\frac{3}{5}$ D. $\frac{6}{10}$
10. If you take one card without looking, how many possible outcomes are there?
    F. 10 G. 6 (H.) 4 J. 1

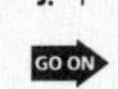

Name

CHAPTER 22 TEST FORM A PAGE 2

For exercises 11–13, use the numbered buttons shown below.

1 2 3 4 5
6 7 8 9 10 11 12

11. If you pick one button without looking, what is the probability of picking button 7?
    A. $\frac{7}{12}$ (B.) $\frac{1}{12}$ C. $\frac{1}{6}$ D. $\frac{1}{7}$
12. If you pick one button without looking, what is the probability of picking buttons 1, 2, 3, or 4?
    F. $\frac{1}{4}$ (G.) $\frac{1}{3}$ H. $\frac{1}{12}$ J. $\frac{1}{2}$
13. Describe the probability of picking a button with a number greater than 3.
    A. unlikely C. certain
    B. impossible (D.) likely

For exercises 14–16, use the spinners shown below.

Spinner A

Spinner B

14. How many possible outcomes are there if you spin both spinners?
    F. 2 G. 6 H. 7 (J.) 12
15. If you spin Spinner A 40 times, how many times do you predict you will spin a 4?
    A. 1 B. 4 (C.) 10 D. 20
16. What is the probability of spinning a 1 on Spinner A?
    (F.) $\frac{1}{4}$ G. $\frac{1}{2}$ H. $\frac{1}{3}$ J. 1
17. Helena had a choice of 5 vegetables and 2 kinds of meat on her pizza. How many possible combinations could she make?
    A. 2 combinations
    B. 5 combinations
    C. 6 combinations
    (D.) 10 combinations
18. Michael can take a yoga class any day of the week. He also has a choice of morning or afternoon classes. How many different classes could he take?
    (F.) 14 classes H. 4 classes
    G. 7 classes J. 2 classes
19. James is conducting an experiment to see how many times he would choose a red marble from a bag of 7 blue marbles and 3 red marbles. Predict how many times he will pick red in 50 tries.
    A. 3 times C. 7 times
    B. 5 times (D.) 15 times
20. Dutch is conducting an experiment to see how many times he would choose a green cube from a bag of 12 yellow cubes and 8 green cubes. Predict how many times he will pick green in 100 tries.
    F. 20 times H. 80 times
    (G.) 40 times J. 100 times

Name

CHAPTER 22 TEST FORM B PAGE 1

Read each question carefully. Fill in the correct answer in the space provided.

For exercises 1–3, use the spinner shown below. Write the words likely, certain, unlikely, or impossible to best describe the probability of the spinner landing on the given color.

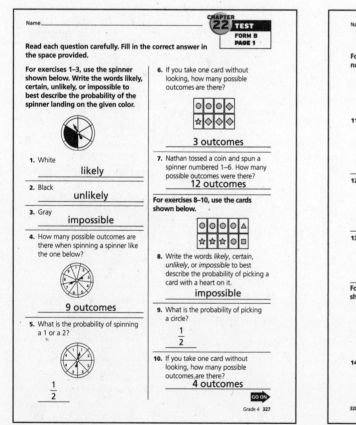

1. White
   likely
2. Black
   unlikely
3. Gray
   impossible
4. How many possible outcomes are there when spinning a spinner like the one below?

9 outcomes

5. What is the probability of spinning a 1 or a 2?

$\frac{1}{2}$

6. If you take one card without looking, how many possible outcomes are there?

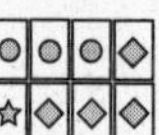

3 outcomes

7. Nathan tossed a coin and spun a spinner numbered 1–6. How many possible outcomes were there?
   12 outcomes

For exercises 8–10, use the cards shown below.

8. Write the words *likely*, *certain*, *unlikely*, or *impossible* to best describe the probability of picking a card with a heart on it.
   impossible
9. What is the probability of picking a circle?
   $\frac{1}{2}$
10. If you take one card without looking, how many possible outcomes are there?
    4 outcomes

GO ON

Name

CHAPTER 22 TEST FORM B PAGE 2

For exercises 11–13, use the numbered buttons shown below.

1 2 3 4 5
6 7 8 9 10

11. If you pick one button without looking, what is the probability of picking button 2?
    $\frac{1}{10}$
12. If you pick one button without looking, what is the probability of picking buttons 1, 4, 7, or 10?
    $\frac{2}{5}$
13. Write the words likely, certain, unlikely, or impossible to best describe the probability of picking a button with a number greater than 4.
    likely

For exercises 14–16, use the spinners shown below.

Spinner A

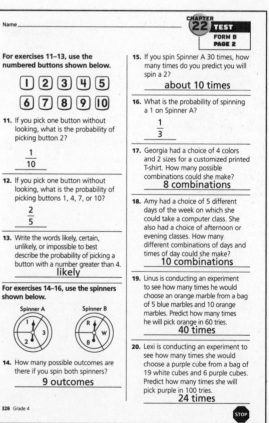

Spinner B

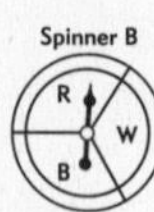

14. How many possible outcomes are there if you spin both spinners?
    9 outcomes
15. If you spin Spinner A 30 times, how many times do you predict you will spin a 2?
    about 10 times
16. What is the probability of spinning a 1 on Spinner A?
    $\frac{1}{3}$
17. Georgia had a choice of 4 colors and 2 sizes for a customized printed T-shirt. How many possible combinations could she make?
    8 combinations
18. Amy had a choice of 5 different days of the week on which she could take a computer class. She also had a choice of afternoon or evening classes. How many different combinations of days and times of day could she make?
    10 combinations
19. Linus is conducting an experiment to see how many times he would choose an orange marble from a bag of 5 blue marbles and 10 orange marbles. Predict how many times he will pick orange in 60 tries.
    40 times
20. Lexi is conducting an experiment to see how many times she would choose a purple cube from a bag of 19 white cubes and 6 purple cubes. Predict how many times she will pick purple in 100 tries.
    24 times

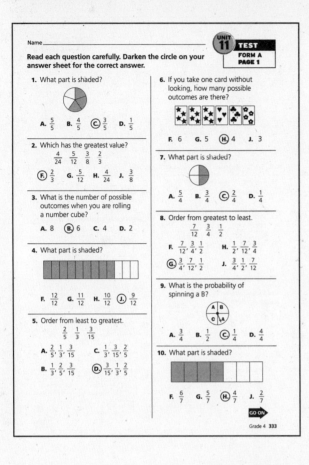

Name ____________________

UNIT 11 TEST FORM A PAGE 1

Read each question carefully. Darken the circle on your answer sheet for the correct answer.

1. What part is shaded?

A. $\frac{5}{5}$ B. $\frac{4}{5}$ (C.) $\frac{3}{5}$ D. $\frac{1}{5}$

2. Which has the greatest value?

$\frac{4}{24}$ $\frac{5}{12}$ $\frac{3}{8}$ $\frac{2}{3}$

(F.) $\frac{2}{3}$ G. $\frac{5}{12}$ H. $\frac{4}{24}$ J. $\frac{3}{8}$

3. What is the number of possible outcomes when you are rolling a number cube?

A. 8 (B.) 6 C. 4 D. 2

4. What part is shaded?

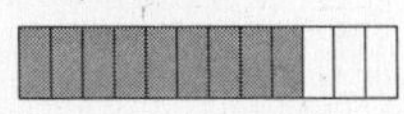

F. $\frac{12}{12}$ G. $\frac{11}{12}$ H. $\frac{10}{12}$ (J.) $\frac{9}{12}$

5. Order from least to greatest.

$\frac{2}{5}$ $\frac{1}{3}$ $\frac{3}{15}$

A. $\frac{2}{5}, \frac{1}{3}, \frac{3}{15}$ C. $\frac{1}{3}, \frac{3}{15}, \frac{2}{5}$

B. $\frac{1}{3}, \frac{2}{5}, \frac{3}{15}$ (D.) $\frac{3}{15}, \frac{1}{3}, \frac{2}{5}$

6. If you take one card without looking, how many possible outcomes are there?

F. 6 G. 5 (H.) 4 J. 3

7. What part is shaded?

A. $\frac{5}{4}$ B. $\frac{3}{4}$ (C.) $\frac{2}{4}$ D. $\frac{1}{4}$

8. Order from greatest to least.

$\frac{7}{12}$ $\frac{3}{4}$ $\frac{1}{2}$

F. $\frac{7}{12}, \frac{3}{4}, \frac{1}{2}$ H. $\frac{1}{2}, \frac{7}{12}, \frac{3}{4}$

(G.) $\frac{3}{4}, \frac{7}{12}, \frac{1}{2}$ J. $\frac{3}{4}, \frac{1}{2}, \frac{7}{12}$

9. What is the probability of spinning a B?

A. $\frac{3}{4}$ B. $\frac{1}{2}$ (C.) $\frac{1}{4}$ D. $\frac{4}{4}$

10. What part is shaded?

F. $\frac{6}{7}$ G. $\frac{5}{7}$ (H.) $\frac{4}{7}$ J. $\frac{2}{7}$

GO ON

Grade 4 333

Name ____________________

UNIT 11 TEST FORM A PAGE 2

11. Write $\frac{4}{32}$ in simplest form.

(A.) $\frac{1}{8}$ B. $\frac{2}{16}$ C. $\frac{1}{9}$ D. $\frac{1}{28}$

12. Cheyenne tossed 2 coins. How many possible outcomes were there?

F. 8 (G.) 4 H. 3 J. 2

13. Rename $\frac{27}{4}$ as a fraction in simplest form.

(A.) $6\frac{3}{4}$ B. $4\frac{3}{6}$ C. $4\frac{3}{7}$ D. $4\frac{1}{8}$

14. Write $\frac{24}{27}$ in simplest form.

(F.) $\frac{8}{9}$ G. $\frac{6}{7}$ H. $\frac{3}{4}$ J. $\frac{1}{3}$

Use the numbered buttons for exercises 15–16.

15. If you pick one button without looking, what is the probability of picking button 6?

A. $\frac{1}{2}$ B. $\frac{1}{4}$ C. $\frac{1}{6}$ (D.) $\frac{1}{8}$

16. If you pick one button without looking, what is the probability of picking buttons 2, 4, or 8?

F. $\frac{1}{2}$ (G.) $\frac{3}{8}$ H. $\frac{1}{4}$ J. $\frac{1}{8}$

Solve.

17. A group of 36 campers went for a hike. Afterward, $\frac{1}{3}$ of the campers went swimming. How many went swimming?

(A.) 12 campers C. 6 campers

B. 9 campers D. 3 campers

Use the cards for problems 18–19.

18. Describe the probability of picking a triangle.

F. certain H. likely

(G.) impossible J. unlikely

19. What is the probability of picking a star?

A. $\frac{1}{8}$ (B.) $\frac{1}{4}$ C. $\frac{3}{8}$ D. $\frac{7}{8}$

20. Mandy had a choice of 4 bats and 2 gloves in the sports store. How many possible combinations could she make?

(F.) 8 combinations

G. 6 combinations

H. 4 combinations

J. 2 combinations

GO ON

334 Grade 4

Name ____________________

UNIT 11 TEST FORM A PAGE 3

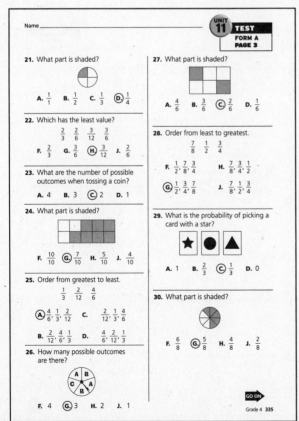

21. What part is shaded?

A. $\frac{1}{1}$ B. $\frac{1}{2}$ C. $\frac{1}{3}$ (D.) $\frac{1}{4}$

22. Which has the least value?

$\frac{2}{3}$ $\frac{2}{6}$ $\frac{3}{12}$ $\frac{3}{6}$

F. $\frac{2}{3}$ G. $\frac{3}{6}$ (H.) $\frac{3}{12}$ J. $\frac{2}{6}$

23. What are the number of possible outcomes when tossing a coin?

A. 4 B. 3 (C.) 2 D. 1

24. What part is shaded?

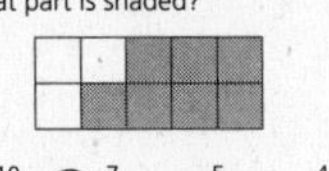

F. $\frac{10}{10}$ (G.) $\frac{7}{10}$ H. $\frac{5}{10}$ J. $\frac{4}{10}$

25. Order from greatest to least.

$\frac{1}{3}$ $\frac{2}{12}$ $\frac{4}{6}$

(A.) $\frac{4}{6}, \frac{1}{3}, \frac{2}{12}$ C. $\frac{2}{12}, \frac{1}{3}, \frac{4}{6}$

B. $\frac{2}{12}, \frac{4}{6}, \frac{1}{3}$ D. $\frac{4}{6}, \frac{2}{12}, \frac{1}{3}$

26. How many possible outcomes are there?

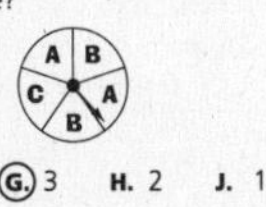

F. 4 (G.) 3 H. 2 J. 1

27. What part is shaded?

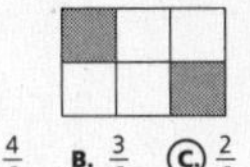

A. $\frac{4}{6}$ B. $\frac{3}{6}$ (C.) $\frac{2}{6}$ D. $\frac{1}{6}$

28. Order from least to greatest.

$\frac{7}{8}$ $\frac{1}{2}$ $\frac{3}{4}$

F. $\frac{1}{2}, \frac{7}{8}, \frac{3}{4}$ H. $\frac{7}{8}, \frac{3}{4}, \frac{1}{2}$

(G.) $\frac{1}{2}, \frac{3}{4}, \frac{7}{8}$ J. $\frac{7}{8}, \frac{1}{2}, \frac{3}{4}$

29. What is the probability of picking a card with a star?

A. 1 B. $\frac{2}{3}$ (C.) $\frac{1}{3}$ D. 0

30. What part is shaded?

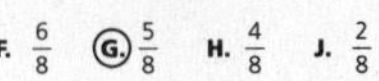

F. $\frac{6}{8}$ (G.) $\frac{5}{8}$ H. $\frac{4}{8}$ J. $\frac{2}{8}$

GO ON

Grade 4 335

Name ____________________

UNIT 11 TEST FORM A PAGE 4

31. Write $\frac{12}{18}$ in simplest form.

A. $\frac{3}{4}$ B. $\frac{4}{6}$ (C.) $\frac{2}{3}$ D. $\frac{6}{9}$

32. Ron tosses a coin and then rolls a number cube. How many possible outcomes are there?

(F.) 12 G. 8 H. 6 J. 2

33. Rename $\frac{10}{7}$ as a mixed number.

A. $1\frac{4}{7}$ (B.) $1\frac{3}{7}$ C. $1\frac{2}{7}$ D. $1\frac{1}{7}$

34. Write $\frac{45}{50}$ in simplest form.

(F.) $\frac{9}{10}$ G. $\frac{4}{5}$ H. $\frac{20}{25}$ J. $\frac{1}{10}$

Use the spinner for exercises 35–36.

35. What is the probability of spinning a 4?

A. $\frac{2}{3}$ B. $\frac{1}{2}$ C. $\frac{1}{3}$ (D.) $\frac{1}{6}$

36. What is the probability of spinning a 1 or a 2?

F. $\frac{2}{3}$ G. $\frac{1}{2}$ (H.) $\frac{1}{3}$ J. $\frac{1}{6}$

37. At lunch, Bob had a choice of 3 different sandwiches. He also had a choice of 2 different salads. How many possible combinations of salad and sandwich could he make?

(A.) 6 combinations

B. 5 combinations

C. 3 combinations

D. 2 combinations

Use the spinner for problems 38–39.

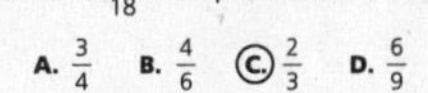

38. Describe the probability of spinning a 1.

F. certain (H.) likely

G. impossible J. unlikely

39. What is the probability of spinning a 4?

A. $\frac{1}{3}$ B. $\frac{1}{4}$ C. $\frac{1}{5}$ (D.) $\frac{1}{8}$

40. A class of 24 students voted on their favorite school lunch. One fourth of the students voted for tacos. How many students voted for tacos?

F. 8 students

(G.) 6 students

H. 4 students

J. 3 students

STOP

336 Grade 4

Name

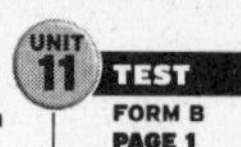

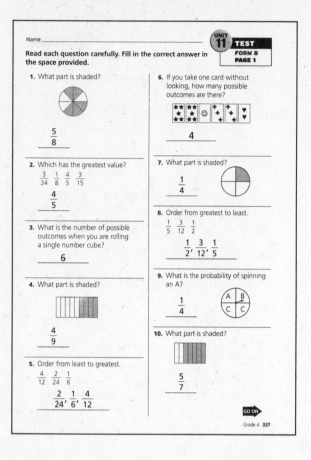

Read each question carefully. Fill in the correct answer in the space provided.

1. What part is shaded?

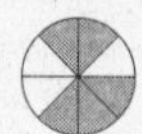

$\frac{5}{8}$

2. Which has the greatest value?

$\frac{3}{24}$ $\frac{1}{8}$ $\frac{4}{5}$ $\frac{3}{15}$

$\frac{4}{5}$

3. What is the number of possible outcomes when you are rolling a single number cube?

6

4. What part is shaded?

$\frac{4}{9}$

5. Order from least to greatest.

$\frac{4}{12}$ $\frac{2}{24}$ $\frac{1}{6}$

$\frac{2}{24}, \frac{1}{6}, \frac{4}{12}$

6. If you take one card without looking, how many possible outcomes are there?

4

7. What part is shaded?

$\frac{1}{4}$

8. Order from greatest to least.

$\frac{1}{5}$ $\frac{3}{12}$ $\frac{1}{2}$

$\frac{1}{2}, \frac{3}{12}, \frac{1}{5}$

9. What is the probability of spinning an A?

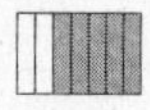

$\frac{1}{4}$

10. What part is shaded?

$\frac{5}{7}$

GO ON

Name

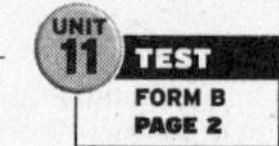

11. Write $\frac{8}{32}$ in simplest form.

$\frac{1}{4}$

12. Cheyenne tossed three coins. How many possible outcomes were there?

8

13. Rename $\frac{25}{3}$ as a fraction in simplest form.

$8\frac{1}{3}$

14. Write $\frac{35}{40}$ in simplest form.

$\frac{7}{8}$

Use the numbered buttons for exercises 15–16.

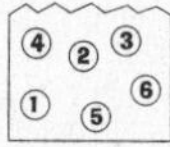

15. If you pick one button without looking, what is the probability of picking button 4?

$\frac{1}{6}$

16. If you pick one button without looking, what is the probability of picking buttons 2 or 5.

$\frac{2}{6}$ or $\frac{1}{3}$

17. A group of 42 students went to the playground for recess. During recess, $\frac{1}{3}$ of the students played tag. How many students played tag?

14 students

Use the cards for problems 18–19.

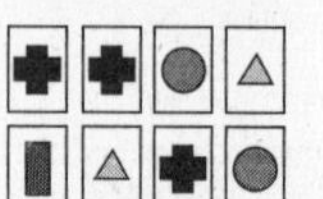

18. Is the probability of picking a heart certain, likely, or impossible?

impossible

19. What is the probability of picking a cross?

$\frac{3}{8}$

20. Mr. Tower has a choice of 3 shirts and 4 ties in his closet. How many possible combinations can he make?

12

GO ON

Name

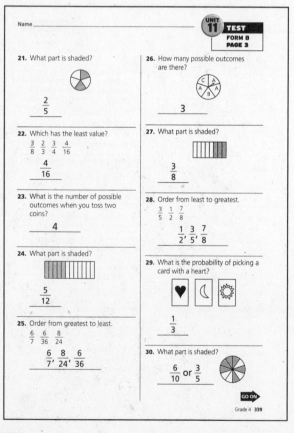

UNIT 11 TEST FORM B PAGE 3

21. What part is shaded?

$\frac{2}{5}$

22. Which has the least value?

$\frac{3}{8}$ $\frac{2}{3}$ $\frac{3}{4}$ $\frac{4}{16}$

$\frac{4}{16}$

23. What is the number of possible outcomes when you toss two coins?

4

24. What part is shaded?

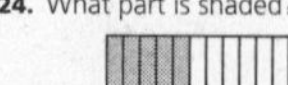

$\frac{5}{12}$

25. Order from greatest to least.

$\frac{6}{7}$ $\frac{6}{36}$ $\frac{8}{24}$

$\frac{6}{7}, \frac{8}{24}, \frac{6}{36}$

26. How many possible outcomes are there?

3

27. What part is shaded?

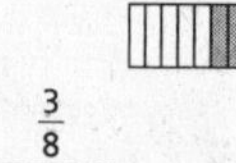

$\frac{3}{8}$

28. Order from least to greatest.

$\frac{3}{5}$ $\frac{1}{2}$ $\frac{7}{8}$

$\frac{1}{2}, \frac{3}{5}, \frac{7}{8}$

29. What is the probability of picking a card with a heart?

$\frac{1}{3}$

30. What part is shaded?

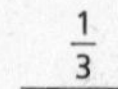
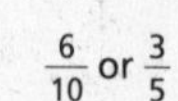

$\frac{6}{10}$ or $\frac{3}{5}$

GO ON

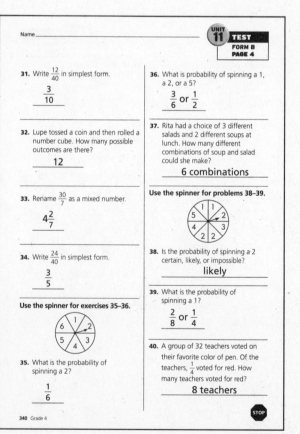

Name

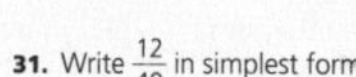

31. Write $\frac{12}{40}$ in simplest form.

$\frac{3}{10}$

32. Lupe tossed a coin and then rolled a number cube. How many possible outcomes are there?

12

33. Rename $\frac{30}{7}$ as a mixed number.

$4\frac{2}{7}$

34. Write $\frac{24}{40}$ in simplest form.

$\frac{3}{5}$

Use the spinner for exercises 35–36.

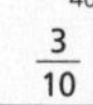
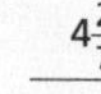
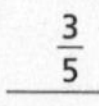
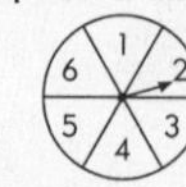

35. What is the probability of spinning a 2?

$\frac{1}{6}$

36. What is probability of spinning a 1, a 2, or a 5?

$\frac{3}{6}$ or $\frac{1}{2}$

37. Rita had a choice of 3 different salads and 2 different soups at lunch. How many different combinations of soup and salad could she make?

6 combinations

Use the spinner for problems 38–39.

38. Is the probability of spinning a 2 certain, likely, or impossible?

likely

39. What is the probability of spinning a 1?

$\frac{2}{8}$ or $\frac{1}{4}$

40. A group of 32 teachers voted on their favorite color of pen. Of the teachers, $\frac{1}{4}$ voted for red. How many teachers voted for red?

8 teachers

Chapter 23

Name________________

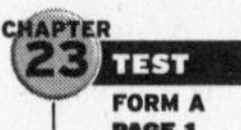

CHAPTER 23 TEST FORM A PAGE 1

Read each question carefully. Darken the circle on your answer sheet for the correct answer. Put all answers in simplest form.

1. $\frac{5}{9} + \frac{3}{9}$

A. $\frac{2}{9}$ B. $\frac{4}{9}$ C. $\frac{7}{9}$ (D.) $\frac{8}{9}$

2. $\frac{3}{8} + \frac{1}{4} = $ ■

F. $\frac{1}{8}$ G. $\frac{2}{8}$ H. $\frac{1}{3}$ (J.) $\frac{5}{8}$

3. $\frac{3}{4} + \frac{7}{8} = $ ■

A. $\frac{5}{6}$ B. $\frac{7}{8}$ C. $1\frac{3}{8}$ (D.) $1\frac{5}{8}$

4. $\frac{5}{7} + \frac{3}{7} + \frac{1}{5} = $ ■

(F.) $1\frac{12}{35}$ H. $1\frac{13}{35}$

G. $1\frac{1}{3}$ J. $\frac{9}{19}$

5. $\frac{6}{7} + \frac{5}{7} = $ ■

(A.) $1\frac{4}{7}$ C. $\frac{11}{14}$

B. $1\frac{4}{11}$ D. $\frac{7}{11}$

6. $\frac{5}{6} + \frac{3}{4}$

F. $\frac{3}{4}$ G. $\frac{13}{16}$ (H.) $1\frac{7}{12}$ J. $\frac{4}{5}$

7. $\frac{2}{5} + \frac{8}{15} = $ ■

A. $\frac{13}{15}$ (B.) $\frac{14}{15}$ C. 1 D. $1\frac{1}{15}$

8. $\frac{7}{8} + (\frac{3}{8} + \frac{3}{4}) = $ ■

F. $1\frac{3}{8}$ G. $1\frac{3}{4}$ H. $1\frac{7}{8}$ (J.) 2

9. $\frac{11}{24} + \frac{7}{24}$

A. $\frac{2}{3}$ B. $\frac{3}{8}$ (C.) $\frac{3}{4}$ D. $\frac{5}{6}$

10. $\frac{1}{3} + \frac{7}{9}$

(F.) $1\frac{1}{9}$ H. $\frac{10}{12}$

G. $\frac{11}{9}$ J. $\frac{4}{9}$

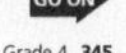

GO ON

Name________________

CHAPTER 23 TEST FORM A PAGE 2

11. $\frac{1}{12} + \frac{5}{6} = $ ■

A. $\frac{5}{6}$ (B.) $\frac{11}{12}$ C. 1 D. $1\frac{1}{12}$

12. $\frac{2}{5} + \frac{4}{5} + \frac{1}{8} = $ ■

(F.) $1\frac{13}{40}$ G. $1\frac{3}{10}$ H. $1\frac{1}{4}$ J. $1\frac{3}{20}$

13. $\frac{11}{15} + \frac{8}{15}$

A. $\frac{19}{30}$ (B.) $1\frac{4}{15}$ C. $1\frac{1}{5}$ D. $1\frac{1}{3}$

14. $\frac{4}{5} + \frac{4}{5} = $ ■

F. $\frac{4}{5}$ G. $1\frac{3}{10}$ H. $\frac{12}{15}$ (J.) $1\frac{3}{5}$

15. $\frac{11}{16} + \frac{7}{16} = $ ■

A. $\frac{1}{4}$ B. $\frac{9}{16}$ (C.) $1\frac{1}{8}$ D. $1\frac{1}{2}$

16. $\frac{5}{8} + \frac{2}{3} = $ ■

F. $1\frac{1}{4}$ (G.) $1\frac{7}{24}$ H. $1\frac{1}{3}$ J. $\frac{7}{8}$

17. Gina ate $\frac{1}{4}$ of a sandwich and Brianna ate $\frac{2}{3}$ of the sandwich. How much of the sandwich did the girls eat?

(A.) $\frac{11}{12}$ sandwich C. $\frac{3}{7}$ sandwich

B. $\frac{5}{6}$ sandwich D. 1 sandwich

18. One fillet of fish weighs $\frac{2}{3}$ of a pound. Another fillet weighs $\frac{3}{4}$ pound. How many pounds do the fillets weigh in all?

F. $\frac{5}{7}$ pound H. $1\frac{1}{4}$ pounds

G. $1\frac{1}{8}$ pounds (J.) $1\frac{5}{12}$ pounds

19. A recipe calls for $\frac{7}{8}$ cup of white sugar and $\frac{1}{4}$ cup of brown sugar. How many cups of sugar are in the recipe?

A. $1\frac{7}{8}$ cups C. $1\frac{1}{4}$ cups

(B.) $1\frac{1}{8}$ cups D. $\frac{2}{3}$ cup

20. Alberto ate $\frac{1}{8}$ of the chocolates in a box. Katlyn ate $\frac{1}{3}$ of the chocolates in a box. How much of the chocolate in the box did they eat?

F. $\frac{2}{11}$ box H. $\frac{1}{2}$ box

G. $\frac{5}{12}$ box (J.) $\frac{11}{24}$ box

STOP

Name________________

CHAPTER 23 TEST FORM B PAGE 1

Read each question carefully. Fill in the correct answer in the space provided. Put all answers in simplest form.

1. $\frac{2}{7} + \frac{4}{7}$ $\frac{6}{7}$

2. $\frac{5}{6} + \frac{1}{3} = $ $1\frac{1}{6}$

3. $\frac{2}{3} + \frac{5}{9} = $ $1\frac{2}{9}$

4. $\frac{1}{4} + \frac{4}{5} + \frac{3}{4} = $ $1\frac{4}{5}$

5. $\frac{8}{15} + \frac{4}{15} = $ $\frac{4}{5}$

6. $\frac{9}{10} + \frac{4}{5}$ $1\frac{7}{10}$

7. $\frac{3}{4} + \frac{1}{5} = $ $\frac{19}{20}$

8. $\frac{5}{12} + \frac{17}{20} + \frac{7}{12} = $ $1\frac{17}{20}$

9. $\frac{15}{18} + \frac{2}{18}$ $\frac{17}{18}$

10. $\frac{1}{5} + \frac{3}{20} = $ $\frac{7}{20}$

GO ON

Name________________

CHAPTER 23 TEST FORM B PAGE 2

11. $\frac{3}{5} + \frac{8}{9} = $ $1\frac{22}{45}$

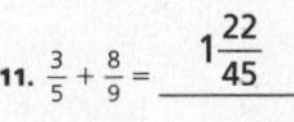

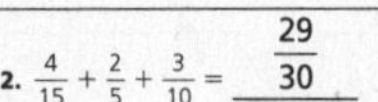

12. $\frac{4}{15} + \frac{2}{5} + \frac{3}{10} = $ $\frac{29}{30}$

13. $\frac{9}{20} + \frac{6}{20}$ $\frac{3}{4}$

14. $\frac{1}{4} + \frac{2}{4} = $ $\frac{3}{4}$

15. $\frac{7}{15} + \frac{4}{15} = $ $\frac{11}{15}$

16. $\frac{9}{10} + \frac{7}{20} = $ $1\frac{1}{4}$

17. Alex ate $\frac{3}{8}$ of a candy bar and Julie ate $\frac{1}{2}$ of the candy bar. How much of the candy bar did the girls eat?

$\frac{7}{8}$ candy bar

18. One apple weighs $\frac{1}{5}$ of a pound. Another apple weighs $\frac{3}{10}$ of a pound. How much do they weigh all together?

$\frac{1}{2}$

19. A recipe calls for $\frac{11}{16}$ cup of corn flour and $\frac{3}{4}$ cup of wheat flour. How many cups of flour are in the recipe?

$1\frac{7}{16}$ cups

20. Sarah ate $\frac{1}{3}$ of the cookies in a box. Penelope ate $\frac{1}{4}$ of the cookies in the box. How much of the box did they eat in all?

$\frac{7}{12}$ box

STOP

Name______________________________

CHAPTER 24 TEST FORM A PAGE 1

Read each question carefully. Darken the circle on your answer sheet for the correct answer. Put all answers in simplest form.

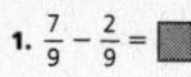

1. $\frac{7}{9} - \frac{2}{9} = ■$

   A. $\frac{2}{9}$ **(B.)** $\frac{5}{9}$ C. $\frac{7}{9}$ D. 1

2. $\frac{7}{10} - \frac{3}{5}$

   F. $\frac{1}{5}$ G. $\frac{4}{5}$ **(H.)** $\frac{1}{10}$ J. $\frac{4}{10}$

3. $\frac{5}{6} - \frac{1}{6} = ■$

   (A.) $\frac{2}{3}$ B. $\frac{1}{2}$ C. $\frac{1}{3}$ D. $\frac{1}{6}$

4. $\frac{4}{5} - \frac{7}{15}$

   F. $\frac{5}{7}$ G. $\frac{5}{12}$ **(H.)** $\frac{1}{3}$ J. $\frac{1}{5}$

5. $\frac{8}{9} - \frac{2}{3} = ■$

   A. $\frac{2}{3}$ B. $\frac{4}{9}$ C. $\frac{1}{3}$ **(D.)** $\frac{2}{9}$

6. $\frac{19}{20} - \frac{9}{10} = ■$

   (F.) $\frac{1}{20}$ G. $\frac{1}{10}$ H. $\frac{1}{2}$ J. 1

7. $\frac{8}{12} - \frac{5}{12}$

   A. $1\frac{1}{12}$ B. $\frac{3}{5}$ C. $\frac{1}{8}$ **(D.)** $\frac{1}{4}$

8. $\frac{3}{4} - \frac{5}{8} = ■$

   F. $\frac{1}{2}$ **(G.)** $\frac{1}{8}$ H. $\frac{1}{4}$ J. 1

9. $\frac{14}{15} - \frac{5}{15} = ■$

   (A.) $\frac{3}{5}$ B. $\frac{4}{5}$ C. $\frac{2}{3}$ D. $\frac{11}{15}$

10. $\frac{3}{4} - ■ = \frac{3}{4}$

    F. 1 G. $\frac{3}{4}$ H. $\frac{3}{8}$ **(J.)** 0

GO ON

Name______________________________

CHAPTER 24 TEST FORM A PAGE 2

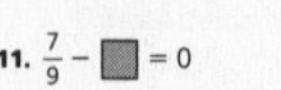

11. $\frac{7}{9} - ■ = 0$

    A. $\frac{1}{3}$ B. $\frac{1}{9}$ C. $\frac{4}{9}$ **(D.)** $\frac{7}{9}$

12. $\frac{14}{20} - \frac{3}{5} = ■$

    F. $\frac{1}{20}$ **(G.)** $\frac{1}{10}$ H. $\frac{1}{5}$ J. $\frac{11}{20}$

For Problems 13–16, use the circle graph below. The graph shows the results of a poll of 50 students who were asked what their favorite color was.

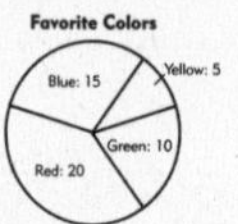

13. What fraction of the students polled choose red as their favorite color?

    A. $\frac{1}{5}$ **(B.)** $\frac{2}{5}$ C. $\frac{1}{2}$ D. $\frac{1}{3}$

14. What fraction of the students polled choose green as their favorite color?

    F. $\frac{1}{15}$ **(G.)** $\frac{1}{5}$ H. $\frac{1}{4}$ J. $\frac{1}{3}$

15. How many more students choose red than yellow? What is the fraction of the students polled?

    A. $\frac{7}{20}$ **(B.)** $\frac{3}{10}$ C. $\frac{2}{15}$ D. $\frac{1}{10}$

16. What fraction of the total students did not choose blue?

    F. $\frac{3}{10}$ G. $\frac{3}{5}$ **(H.)** $\frac{7}{10}$ J. $\frac{4}{5}$

17. Eric drank $\frac{3}{8}$ pint of juice. Mary drank $\frac{1}{4}$ pint of juice. How much more juice did Eric drink?

    A. $\frac{1}{4}$ pint C. $\frac{1}{6}$ pint **(B.)** $\frac{1}{8}$ pint D. $\frac{1}{12}$ pint

18. Penny had $\frac{3}{4}$ of a stick of butter. She used $\frac{1}{2}$ of the butter for a cookie recipe. How much of a stick of butter was left?

    (F.) $\frac{1}{4}$ stick H. $\frac{1}{12}$ stick G. $\frac{1}{2}$ stick J. $\frac{8}{12}$ stick

19. Lars drank $\frac{1}{8}$ of a quart of milk. David drank $\frac{1}{4}$ of the quart of milk. How much more did David drink than Lars?

    (A.) $\frac{1}{8}$ quart C. $\frac{1}{6}$ quart B. $\frac{1}{4}$ quart D. $\frac{3}{8}$ quart

20. Orin made $\frac{3}{4}$ cup of raspberry sauce. He used $\frac{1}{8}$ cup for a layer in a chocolate cake and the rest for the cake topping. How many cups of sauce did he use for the topping?

    F. $\frac{3}{8}$ cup **(H.)** $\frac{5}{8}$ cup G. $\frac{7}{8}$ cup J. $\frac{5}{4}$ cup

STOP

Name______________________________

CHAPTER 24 TEST FORM B PAGE 1

Read each question carefully. Fill in the correct answer in the space provided. Put all answers in simplest form.

1. $\frac{11}{20} - \frac{7}{20}$ = $\frac{1}{5}$

2. $\frac{3}{4} - \frac{5}{12}$ = $\frac{1}{3}$

3. $\frac{8}{11} - \frac{3}{11} =$ $\frac{5}{11}$

4. $\frac{1}{2} - \frac{3}{8}$ = $\frac{1}{8}$

5. $\frac{4}{5} - \frac{2}{15} =$ $\frac{2}{3}$

6. $\frac{3}{4} - \frac{1}{8} =$ $\frac{5}{8}$

7. $\frac{11}{12} - \frac{7}{12}$ = $\frac{4}{12}$ or $\frac{1}{3}$

8. $\frac{8}{15} - \frac{1}{5} =$ $\frac{1}{3}$

9. $\frac{13}{20} - \frac{9}{20} =$ $\frac{1}{5}$

10. $\frac{5}{6} -$ 0 $= \frac{5}{6}$

11. $\frac{1}{3} -$ $\frac{1}{3}$ $= 0$

12. $\frac{9}{10} - \frac{1}{5} =$ $\frac{7}{10}$

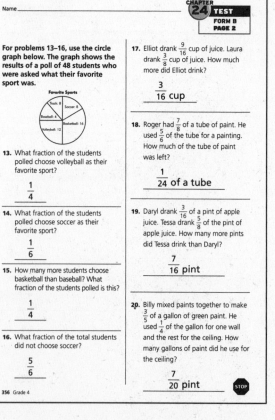

GO ON

Name______________________________

CHAPTER 24 TEST FORM B PAGE 2

For problems 13–16, use the circle graph below. The graph shows the results of a poll of 48 students who were asked what their favorite sport was.

13. What fraction of the students polled choose volleyball as their favorite sport?

    $\frac{1}{4}$

14. What fraction of the students polled choose soccer as their favorite sport?

    $\frac{1}{6}$

15. How many more students choose basketball than baseball? What fraction of the students polled is this?

    $\frac{1}{4}$

16. What fraction of the total students did not choose soccer?

    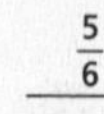

    $\frac{5}{6}$

17. Elliot drank $\frac{9}{16}$ cup of juice. Laura drank $\frac{3}{8}$ cup of juice. How much more did Elliot drink?

    $\frac{3}{16}$ cup

18. Roger had $\frac{7}{8}$ of a tube of paint. He used $\frac{5}{6}$ of the tube for a painting. How much of the tube of paint was left?

    $\frac{1}{24}$ of a tube

19. Daryl drank $\frac{3}{16}$ of a pint of apple juice. Tessa drank $\frac{5}{8}$ of the pint of apple juice. How many more pints did Tessa drink than Daryl?

    $\frac{7}{16}$ pint

20. Billy mixed paints together to make $\frac{3}{5}$ of a gallon of green paint. He used $\frac{1}{4}$ of the gallon for one wall and the rest for the ceiling. How many gallons of paint did he use for the ceiling?

    $\frac{7}{20}$ pint

STOP

Unit 12

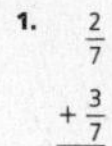

Name ______________________

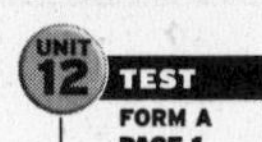

UNIT 12 TEST FORM A PAGE 1

Read each question carefully. Darken the circle on your answer sheet for the correct answer.

1. $\frac{2}{7} + \frac{3}{7}$

A. $\frac{6}{7}$ (B.) $\frac{5}{7}$ C. $\frac{4}{7}$ D. $\frac{5}{14}$

2. $\frac{10}{12} - \frac{6}{12} = ■$

F. $1\frac{1}{4}$ (G.) $\frac{1}{3}$ H. $\frac{1}{6}$ J. $\frac{1}{8}$

3. $\frac{4}{5} - \frac{2}{5} = ■$

A. $\frac{2}{10}$ (B.) $\frac{2}{5}$ C. $\frac{6}{10}$ D. $\frac{6}{5}$

4. $\frac{4}{9} + \frac{2}{3}$

F. $1\frac{5}{9}$ (G.) $1\frac{1}{9}$ H. $\frac{2}{3}$ J. $\frac{1}{2}$

5. $\frac{5}{7} - \frac{1}{2}$

A. $\frac{13}{14}$ B. $\frac{4}{5}$ C. $\frac{4}{14}$ (D.) $\frac{3}{14}$

6. $\frac{3}{8} + \frac{5}{6} = ■$

F. $\frac{1}{3}$ G. $\frac{8}{14}$ H. 1 (J.) $1\frac{5}{24}$

7. $\frac{3}{4} + \frac{2}{4}$

A. $1\frac{1}{2}$ (B.) $1\frac{1}{4}$ C. 1 D. $\frac{5}{8}$

8. $\frac{4}{5} - \frac{3}{10}$

F. $1\frac{4}{5}$ (G.) $\frac{1}{2}$ H. $\frac{1}{5}$ J. $\frac{1}{10}$

9. $\frac{5}{8} + \frac{3}{8} = ■$

A. $\frac{1}{8}$ (B.) $\frac{1}{4}$ C. $\frac{1}{2}$ D. 1

10. $\frac{7}{11} + \frac{8}{11} = ■$

(F.) $1\frac{4}{11}$ G. $1\frac{3}{11}$ H. $\frac{11}{15}$ J. $\frac{15}{22}$

GO ON

Grade 4 361

Name ______________________

UNIT 12 TEST FORM A PAGE 2

11. $\frac{7}{8} - \frac{1}{4} = ■$

A. $1\frac{1}{2}$ B. $1\frac{1}{8}$ C. $\frac{3}{4}$ (D.) $\frac{5}{8}$

12. $\frac{5}{8} - \frac{3}{8} = ■$

F. $\frac{1}{8}$ (G.) $\frac{1}{4}$ H. $\frac{1}{2}$ J. 1

13. $\frac{2}{3} + \frac{5}{6}$

(A.) $1\frac{1}{2}$ B. $1\frac{1}{3}$ C. $\frac{7}{9}$ D. $\frac{3}{4}$

14. $\frac{8}{9} - \frac{1}{9} = ■$

F. $1\frac{1}{9}$ G. 1 (H.) $\frac{7}{9}$ J. $\frac{2}{3}$

15. $\frac{3}{5} + \frac{1}{2} = ■$

(A.) $1\frac{1}{10}$ B. $\frac{4}{7}$ C. $\frac{11}{20}$ D. $\frac{2}{5}$

16. $\frac{5}{6} - \frac{1}{2}$

F. $\frac{2}{3}$ G. $\frac{1}{2}$ (H.) $\frac{1}{3}$ J. $\frac{1}{6}$

17. Roberto ate $\frac{1}{3}$ of a pizza and Aaron ate $\frac{1}{4}$ of the pizza. How much of the pizza did the boys eat?

A. $\frac{3}{4}$ pizza C. $\frac{1}{2}$ pizza (B.) $\frac{7}{12}$ pizza D. $\frac{2}{7}$ pizza

18. Marcie drank $\frac{3}{4}$ cup of juice. Yolanda drank $\frac{1}{2}$ cup of juice. How much more juice did Marcie drink?

F. $1\frac{1}{4}$ cups H. $\frac{1}{2}$ cup G. $\frac{3}{4}$ cup (J.) $\frac{1}{4}$ cup

19. A recipe calls for $\frac{3}{4}$ cup of granulated sugar and $\frac{2}{3}$ cup of powdered sugar. How much sugar is in the recipe?

(A.) $1\frac{5}{12}$ cups C. $\frac{5}{12}$ cup B. $\frac{5}{7}$ cup D. $\frac{1}{12}$ cup

20. Brandon had $\frac{1}{2}$ gallon of windshield washer fluid. He poured $\frac{1}{3}$ gallon into his car. How much was left?

F. $\frac{5}{6}$ gallon (H.) $\frac{1}{6}$ gallon G. $\frac{1}{3}$ gallon J. $\frac{1}{8}$ gallon

362 Grade 4

GO ON

Name ______________________

UNIT 12 TEST FORM A PAGE 3

21. $\frac{9}{11} + \frac{9}{11}$

A. $1\frac{8}{11}$ C. $\frac{9}{11}$ (B.) $1\frac{7}{11}$ D. $\frac{1}{11}$

22. $\frac{4}{7} - \frac{1}{7} = ■$

F. $\frac{5}{7}$ G. $\frac{4}{7}$ (H.) $\frac{3}{7}$ J. $\frac{2}{7}$

23. $\frac{7}{11} - \frac{5}{11} = ■$

(A.) $\frac{2}{11}$ B. $\frac{7}{11}$ C. $\frac{12}{22}$ D. $1\frac{1}{11}$

24. $\frac{5}{10} + \frac{3}{10}$

F. $1\frac{1}{2}$ G. 1 (H.) $\frac{4}{5}$ J. $\frac{2}{5}$

25. $\frac{7}{12} + \frac{2}{3}$

A. $3\frac{3}{4}$ B. $1\frac{3}{4}$ C. $1\frac{1}{2}$ (D.) $1\frac{1}{4}$

26. $\frac{1}{4} + \frac{2}{3} = ■$

F. $\frac{3}{7}$ (H.) $\frac{11}{12}$ G. $\frac{3}{4}$ J. $1\frac{1}{12}$

27. $\frac{5}{6} - \frac{1}{2}$

A. $1\frac{1}{3}$ B. 1 (C.) $\frac{1}{3}$ D. $\frac{1}{6}$

Use the circle graph for questions 28–30.

28. How many more people liked apple pie than cherry pie?

F. 0 (G.) 2 H. 4 J. 6

29. How many people liked ice cream or brownies?

A. 6 B. 12 C. 16 (D.) 18

30. How many people were surveyed?

F. 40 G. 44 (H.) 48 J. 32

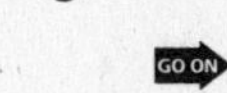

GO ON

Grade 4 363

Name ______________________

UNIT 12 TEST FORM A PAGE 4

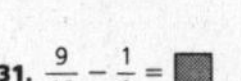

31. $\frac{9}{10} - \frac{1}{3} = ■$

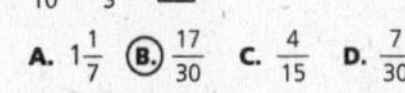

A. $1\frac{1}{7}$ (B.) $\frac{17}{30}$ C. $\frac{4}{15}$ D. $\frac{7}{30}$

32. $\frac{3}{7} + \frac{5}{14} = ■$

F. $\frac{3}{14}$ G. $\frac{4}{7}$ (H.) $\frac{11}{14}$ J. $1\frac{4}{7}$

33. $\frac{1}{2} + \frac{5}{8}$

A. $1\frac{3}{4}$ B. $1\frac{1}{4}$ (C.) $1\frac{1}{8}$ D. $\frac{3}{5}$

34. $\frac{7}{8} - \frac{1}{4}$

F. $1\frac{1}{12}$ G. $\frac{3}{4}$ (H.) $\frac{5}{8}$ J. $\frac{1}{2}$

35. $\frac{3}{4} + \frac{2}{9}$

(A.) $\frac{35}{36}$ B. $\frac{29}{36}$ C. $\frac{5}{13}$ D. $\frac{5}{36}$

36. $\frac{9}{11} - \frac{6}{11} = ■$

F. $1\frac{4}{11}$ (G.) $\frac{3}{11}$ H. $\frac{2}{11}$ J. $\frac{1}{11}$

37. Katie ate $\frac{1}{6}$ of a cheesecake and Lauren ate $\frac{1}{12}$ of the cake. How much did they eat in all?

A. $\frac{1}{3}$ (B.) $\frac{1}{4}$ C. $\frac{1}{6}$ D. $\frac{1}{9}$

38. Al made a mixture of $\frac{3}{4}$ cup of orange juice and $\frac{2}{3}$ cup of pineapple juice. How much more orange juice was there than pineapple juice?

F. $1\frac{5}{12}$ cups (H.) $\frac{1}{12}$ cup G. $\frac{1}{3}$ cup J. $\frac{1}{6}$ cup

39. Tony used $\frac{7}{8}$ cup of chocolate chips and $\frac{3}{4}$ cup of butterscotch chips. How many cups of chips did he use altogether?

(A.) $1\frac{5}{8}$ cups C. $\frac{1}{2}$ cup B. $1\frac{1}{8}$ cups D. $\frac{1}{8}$ cup

40. Meghan had $\frac{1}{2}$ cup of taco sauce. She used $\frac{1}{4}$ cup for the taco filling and the rest for the topping. How much sauce did she use for the topping?

F. $\frac{3}{4}$ cup (H.) $\frac{1}{4}$ cup G. $\frac{3}{8}$ cup J. $\frac{1}{8}$ cup

STOP

364 Grade 4

Unit 12

Name

UNIT 12 TEST FORM B PAGE 1

Read each question carefully. Fill in the correct answer in the space provided.

Write all fraction answers in *simplest form.*

1. $\frac{3}{5} + \frac{1}{5}$ = $\frac{4}{5}$

2. $\frac{4}{7} - \frac{1}{7} =$ $\frac{3}{7}$

3. $\frac{7}{8} - \frac{1}{8} =$ $\frac{3}{4}$

4. $\frac{5}{9} + \frac{2}{3}$ = $1\frac{2}{9}$

5. $\frac{4}{5} - \frac{1}{2}$ = $\frac{3}{10}$

6. $\frac{3}{5} + \frac{1}{15} =$ $\frac{2}{3}$

7. $\frac{2}{3} + \frac{2}{3}$ = $1\frac{1}{3}$

8. $\frac{5}{6} - \frac{7}{12}$ = $\frac{1}{4}$

9. $\frac{2}{3} + \frac{4}{5} =$ $1\frac{7}{15}$

10. $\frac{4}{11} + \frac{10}{11} =$ $1\frac{3}{11}$

GO ON

Grade 4 365

Name

UNIT 12 TEST FORM B PAGE 2

11. $\frac{5}{9} - \frac{1}{3} =$ $\frac{2}{9}$

12. $\frac{5}{6} - \frac{1}{6} =$ $\frac{2}{3}$

13. $\frac{7}{8} + \frac{1}{4}$ = $1\frac{1}{8}$

14. $\frac{5}{7} - \frac{1}{7} =$ $\frac{4}{7}$

15. $\frac{5}{7} + \frac{1}{2} =$ $1\frac{3}{14}$

16. $\frac{3}{4} - \frac{1}{2}$ = $\frac{1}{4}$

17. Jake ate $\frac{1}{4}$ of the pizza and Aaron ate $\frac{1}{2}$ of the pizza. How much of the pizza did the boys eat?

$\frac{3}{4}$

18. Peggy swam $\frac{5}{6}$ of a lap under water and Pete swam $\frac{1}{2}$ of a lap underwater. How much more did Peggy swim?

$\frac{1}{3}$ lap

19. Lenora added $\frac{3}{4}$ cup of juice to a glass and $\frac{3}{4}$ cup water. How much liquid is in the glass?

$1\frac{1}{2}$ cups

20. Laurie had $\frac{1}{2}$ gallon of milk. She drank $\frac{1}{7}$ gallon today. How much does she have left?

$\frac{5}{14}$

366 Grade 4

GO ON

Name

UNIT 12 TEST FORM B PAGE 3

21. $\frac{7}{12} + \frac{7}{12}$ = $1\frac{1}{6}$

22. $\frac{11}{15} - \frac{8}{15} =$ $\frac{1}{5}$

23. $\frac{4}{7} - \frac{2}{7} =$ $\frac{2}{7}$

24. $\frac{3}{8} + \frac{1}{8}$ = $\frac{1}{2}$

25. $\frac{5}{12} + \frac{2}{3}$ = $1\frac{1}{12}$

26. $\frac{4}{9} + \frac{2}{3} =$ $1\frac{1}{9}$

27. $\frac{2}{3} - \frac{1}{2}$ = $\frac{1}{6}$

Use this circle graph for questions 28–30.

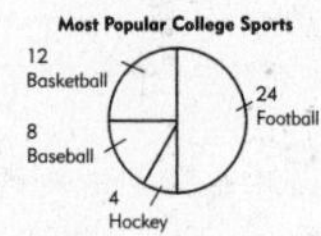

28. How many more people like basketball than hockey?

8

29. How many people like football or baseball?

32

30. How many people were surveyed?

48

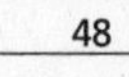

GO ON

Grade 4 367

Name

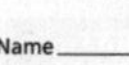

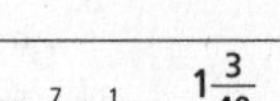

UNIT 12 TEST FORM B PAGE 4

31. $\frac{7}{10} - \frac{1}{3} =$ $\frac{11}{30}$

32. $\frac{7}{8} + \frac{1}{5} =$ $1\frac{3}{40}$

33. $\frac{1}{2} + \frac{5}{9}$ = $1\frac{1}{18}$

34. $\frac{5}{8} - \frac{1}{4}$ = $\frac{3}{8}$

35. $\frac{1}{4} + \frac{5}{9}$ = $\frac{29}{36}$

36. $\frac{7}{13} - \frac{3}{13} =$ $\frac{4}{13}$

37. Elise ate $\frac{1}{3}$ of the pie and Samantha ate $\frac{5}{12}$ of the pie. How much of the pie did they eat in all?

$\frac{3}{4}$

38. Horatio made a mixture of $\frac{2}{3}$ cup apple juice and $\frac{4}{5}$ cup grape juice. How much more grape juice was there than apple juice?

$\frac{2}{15}$ cup

39. Tia used $\frac{2}{3}$ lb of peanuts and $\frac{5}{6}$ lb of walnuts in her recipe. How many pounds of nuts did she use altogether?

$1\frac{1}{2}$ lb

40. Jaoquin had $\frac{1}{2}$ cup of ranch dressing. He used $\frac{1}{3}$ cup on his salad and the rest on his sandwich. How much dressing did he use on the sandwich?

$\frac{1}{6}$ cup

368 Grade 4

STOP

Chapter 25

Name

Read each question carefully. Darken the circle on your answer sheet for the correct answer. Put all answers in simplest form.

1. Write $\frac{4}{10}$ as a decimal.

A. 4.000 **C.** 0.04
(B.) 0.4 **D.** 0.0004

2. Write an equivalent decimal.

0.8

F. 8.0 **H.** 0.080
G. 0.008 **(J.)** 0.80

3. Write $\frac{13}{100}$ as a decimal.

A. 13.00 **(C.)** 0.13
B. 0.013 **D.** 1.3

Use the model for problems 4–5.

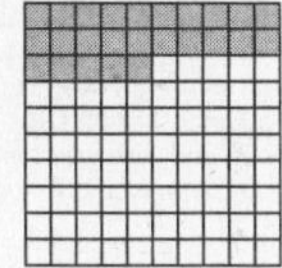

4. Which decimal matches the model?

F. 0.025 **(H.)** 0.25
G. 2.5000 **J.** 25.00

5. Which fraction matches the model?

(A.) $\frac{1}{4}$ **B.** $\frac{1}{2}$ **C.** $\frac{3}{4}$ **D.** $\frac{4}{5}$

6. Write 0.009 as a fraction in simplest form.

F. $\frac{9}{10}$ **(H.)** $\frac{9}{1,000}$
G. $\frac{9}{100}$ **J.** $\frac{9}{1}$

7. Write $\frac{44}{100}$ as a decimal.

(A.) 0.44 **C.** 0.404
B. 0.044 **D.** 0.0044

8. Write $\frac{373}{1,000}$ as a decimal.

F. 373.000 **H.** 3.73
G. 37.3 **(J.)** 0.373

Use the model for problems 9–10.

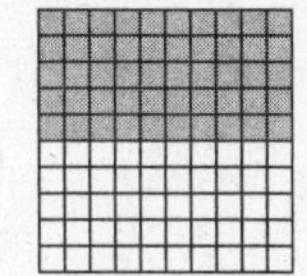

9. Which decimal matches the model?

(A.) 0.5 **C.** 0.005
B. 0.05 **D.** 5.00

10. Which fraction matches the model?

F. $\frac{1}{4}$ **(G.)** $\frac{1}{2}$ **H.** $\frac{2}{3}$ **J.** $\frac{3}{4}$

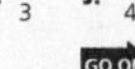

Name

11. Write an equivalent decimal.

0.5

(A.) 0.50 **C.** 0.005
B. 0.050 **D.** 0.0050

12. Write $\frac{12}{100}$ as a decimal.

F. 1.2 **H.** 0.012
(G.) 0.12 **J.** 0.0012

13. Write an equivalent decimal.

0.47

A. 4.700 **(C.)** 0.470
B. 0.047 **D.** 0.0047

14. Write $\frac{33}{100}$ as a decimal.

(F.) 0.33 **H.** 0.0033
G. 0.033 **J.** 3.003

15. Write an equivalent decimal.

0.025

A. 0.0025 **C.** 0.250
(B.) 0.0250 **D.** 0.2500

16. Write $\frac{558}{1,000}$ as a decimal.

F. 5.580 **H.** 0.0558
(G.) 0.558 **J.** 0.00558

17. Rachel starts painting on a canvas and covers $\frac{1}{4}$ of the canvas with paint. Express this as a decimal.

A. 0.75 **(C.)** 0.25
B. 0.025 **D.** 2.5

18. David is buying furniture for his home office. His desk takes up $\frac{1}{10}$ of the area of the room. Express this as a decimal.

F. 1.0 **H.** 0.01
(G.) 0.1 **J.** 0.001

19. Maika polled 100 students about their favorite ice cream. Vanilla was chosen by 27 of the students. Express this as a decimal.

(A.) 0.27 **C.** 0.0027
B. 0.027 **D.** 2.07

20. Blake is competing in a bicycle race. The race is 100 miles long. So far he has bicycled 88 miles. How much of the race has he completed?

F. 88 **(H.)** 0.88
G. 8.8 **J.** 0.088

Name

Read each question carefully. Fill in the correct answer in the space provided.

Put all answers in simplest form.

1. Write $\frac{7}{10}$ as a decimal.

0.7

2. Write an equivalent decimal.

0.2

0.20

3. Write $\frac{67}{100}$ as a decimal.

0.67

Use the model for problems 4–5.

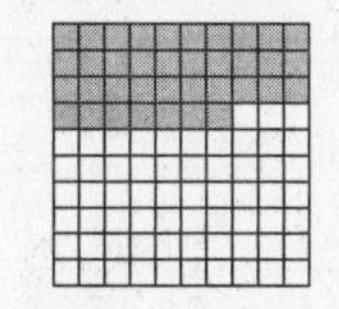

4. What decimal matches the model?

0.37

5. What fraction matches the model? Express in simplest form.

$\frac{37}{100}$

6. Write 0.003 as a fraction in simplest form.

$\frac{3}{1,000}$

7. Write $\frac{41}{100}$ as a decimal.

0.41

8. Write $\frac{519}{1,000}$ as a decimal.

0.519

Use the model for problems 9–10.

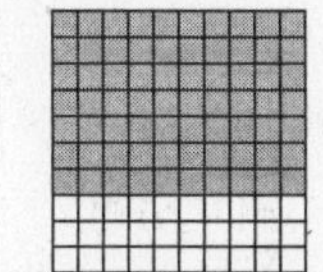

9. What decimal matches the model?

Accept 0.7 or 0.70

10. What fraction matches the model? Express in simplest form.

$\frac{7}{10}$

GO ON

Name

CHAPTER 25 TEST FORM B PAGE 2

11. Write an equivalent decimal.

0.4

0.40

12. Write $\frac{83}{100}$ as a decimal.

0.83

13. Write an equivalent decimal.

0.91

0.910

14. Write $\frac{23}{100}$ as a decimal.

0.23

15. Write an equivalent decimal.

0.099

0.0990

16. Write $\frac{817}{1,000}$ as a decimal.

0.817

17. Terry eats $\frac{2}{5}$ of a pizza. Express this as a decimal.

0.4

18. Richard is building a darkroom for developing photographs. The sinks in the room take up $\frac{3}{10}$ of the area of the room. Express this as a decimal.

0.3

19. Ellen polled 100 students about their favorite sports. Basketball was chosen by 34 of them. Express this as a decimal.

0.34

20. Amy has 100 sheets of photographic paper. She prints 74 photos using a sheet of paper for each photo. Express this as a decimal.

0.74

Chapter 26

Name ____________________

Read each question carefully. Darken the circle on your answer sheet for the correct answer. Put all answers in simplest form.

1. Write $22\frac{34}{100}$ as a decimal.
   (A) 22.34 C. 22.304
   B. 22.034 D. 22.0034

2. Write $9\frac{12}{100}$ as a decimal.
   F. 91.2 H. 9.012
   (G) 9.12 J. 9.0012

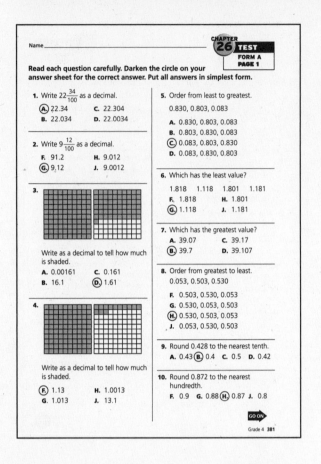

3. Write as a decimal to tell how much is shaded.
   A. 0.00161 C. 0.161
   B. 16.1 (D) 1.61

4. Write as a decimal to tell how much is shaded.
   (F) 1.13 H. 1.0013
   G. 1.013 J. 13.1

5. Order from least to greatest.
   0.830, 0.803, 0.083
   A. 0.830, 0.803, 0.083
   B. 0.803, 0.830, 0.083
   (C) 0.083, 0.803, 0.830
   D. 0.083, 0.830, 0.803

6. Which has the least value?
   1.818 1.118 1.801 1.181
   F. 1.818 H. 1.801
   (G) 1.118 J. 1.181

7. Which has the greatest value?
   A. 39.07 C. 39.17
   (B) 39.7 D. 39.107

8. Order from greatest to least.
   0.053, 0.503, 0.530
   F. 0.503, 0.530, 0.053
   G. 0.530, 0.053, 0.503
   (H) 0.530, 0.503, 0.053
   J. 0.053, 0.530, 0.503

9. Round 0.428 to the nearest tenth.
   A. 0.43 (B) 0.4 C. 0.5 D. 0.42

10. Round 0.872 to the nearest hundredth.
    F. 0.9 G. 0.88 (H) 0.87 J. 0.8

Name ____________________

11. Round 4.345 to the nearest hundredth.
    A. 4.4 (C) 4.35
    B. 4.34 D. 4.5

12. Round 7.085 to the nearest hundredth.
    (F) 7.09 H. 7.08
    G. 7.1 J. 7.9

13. Which has the least value?
    (A) 2.040 C. 2.404
    B. 2.044 D. 2.440

14. Which has the greatest value?
    F. 13.9 H. 13.109
    G. 13.09 (J) 13.91

15. Order from least to greatest.
    0.450, 0.405, 0.045
    (A) 0.045, 0.405, 0.450
    B. 0.045, 0.450, 0.405
    C. 0.405, 0.045, 0.450
    D. 0.450, 0.405, 0.045

16. Round 4.707 to the nearest hundredth.
    F. 4.70 H. 4.708
    (G) 4.71 J. 4.7

17. The distance from Harry's house to school is 3.7 km. The distance from his house to the park is 3.4 km. The distance from his house to the record store is 3.9 km. From the library to his house is 3.8 km. Which is closest to Harry's house?
    A. school C. record store
    (B) park D. library

18. In 2001, a computer company made $32.48 million and in 2002 it made $32.4 million. In 2003, the company made $34.2 million and in 2004 it made $34.48 million. In which year did the company make the least amount of money?
    F. 2001 H. 2003
    (G) 2002 J. 2004

19. In the 100-meter race, Jim had a time of 11.8 seconds. Bobby's time was 12.2 seconds, Ramon's was 11.4 seconds, and Leah's time was 14.3 seconds. Who won the race?
    A. Jim (C) Ramon
    B. Bobby D. Leah

20. Lacy rides 7.8 km to school. George rides 7.83 km, Kelly rides 7.03 km, and Larry rides 7.08 km. Who has the longest ride to school?
    F. Lacy H. Kelly
    (G) George J. Larry

Name ____________________

Read each question carefully. Fill in the correct answer in the space provided. Put all answers in simplest form.

1. Write $22\frac{3}{100}$ as a decimal.
   22.03

2. Write $9\frac{17}{100}$ as a decimal.
   9.17

3. Write as a decimal to tell how much is shaded.
   1.72

4. Write as a decimal to tell how much is shaded.
   1.44

5. Order from least to greatest.
   0.640, 0.643, 0.064
   0.064, 0.640, 0.643

6. Which has the least value?
   1.471 1.174 1.714 1.147
   1.147

7. Which has the greatest value?
   52.13 52.31 52.4 52.09
   52.4

8. Order from greatest to least.
   0.702, 0.072, 2.070
   2.070, 0.702, 0.072

9. Round 0.467 to the nearest tenth.
   0.5

10. Round 0.653 to the nearest hundredth.
    0.65

Name ____________________

CHAPTER 26 TEST FORM B PAGE 2

11. Round 3.781 to the nearest hundredth.
    3.78

12. Round 6.479 to the nearest hundredth.
    6.48

13. Which has the least value?
    3.05 3.055 3.505 3.55
    3.05

14. Which has the greatest value?
    16.2 16.29 16.209 16.19
    16.29

15. Order from least to greatest.
    0.670, 0.607, 0.067
    0.067, 0.607, 0.670

16. Round 5.254 to the nearest hundredth.
    5.25

17. The distance from Lenny's house to school is 4.2 mi. The distance from his house to the movies is 4.7 km. The distance from his house to the gym is 4.7 km. From the library to his house is 4.4 km. Which building is closest to Lenny's house?
    school

18. In 2001, a pet food company made $2.68 million and in 2002 it made $2.4 million. In 2003, the company made $2.25 million and in 2004 it made $2.82 million. In what year did the company make the least money?
    2003

19. In the 200-meter race, Jamal had a time of 27.3 seconds. Eddie's time was 26.8 seconds, Malcolm's was 26.9 seconds, and Juan's was 27.5 seconds. Who won the race?
    Eddie

20. Rosie jogged 8 km yesterday. Danny jogged 8.2 km yesterday, Mickey jogged 8.1 km, and Suzie jogged 8.8 km. Who jogged the least yesterday?
    Rosie

Unit 13

Name____________________________________

UNIT 13 TEST FORM A PAGE 1

Read each question carefully. Darken the circle on your answer sheet for the correct answer.

1. Write $\frac{2}{10}$ as a decimal.

A. 20.000 **C.** 0.02
(B) 0.2 **D.** 0.0002

2. Order from least to greatest.

3.19, 0.319, 0.139

F. 3.19, 0.139, 0.319
G. 3.19, 0.319, 0.139
H. 0.319, 0.139, 3.19
(J) 0.139, 0.319, 3.19

3. Write an equivalent decimal.

0.6

A. 6.0 **C.** 0.06
(B) 0.600 **D.** 0.006

4. Write $6\frac{34}{100}$ as a decimal.

F. 634.000 **H.** 6.034
(G) 6.34 **J.** 0.634

5. Order from least to greatest.

0.702, 0.720, 0.072

A. 0.720, 0.702, 0.072
B. 0.702, 0.720, 0.072
(C) 0.072, 0.702, 0.720
D. 0.072, 0.720, 0.702

6. Write an equivalent decimal.

0.39

F. 3.90 **H.** 0.039
(G) 0.390 **J.** 0.0039

7. Write $\frac{8}{100}$ as a decimal.

A. 800.00 (C) 0.08
B. 0.8 **D.** 0.008

8. Which has the least value?

1.155 1.150 1.105 1.501

F. 1.501 **H.** 1.150
(G) 1.105 **J.** 1.155

9. Write an equivalent decimal.

0.5

A. 0.005 **C.** 0.050
B. 0.05 (D) 0.0500

10. Write $\frac{30}{1,000}$ as a decimal.

F. 30.00 (H) 0.030
G. 0.30 **J.** 0.003

GO ON

Name____________________________________

UNIT 13 TEST FORM A PAGE 2

11. Which has the greatest value?

71.6 71.06 71.16 71.106

A. 71.16 (C) 71.6
B. 71.106 **D.** 71.06

12. Write an equivalent decimal.

0.007

(F) 0.0070 **H.** 0.70
G. 0.070 **J.** 7.0

13. Write $35\frac{15}{100}$ as a decimal.

(A) 35.15 **C.** 35.015
B. 35.105 **D.** 35.0015

14. Round 0.751 to the nearest tenth.

F. 1.0 **H.** 0.7
(G) 0.8 **J.** 0.75

15. Write $\frac{789}{1,000}$ as a decimal.

A. 789.00 **C.** 7.89
B. 78.9 (D) 0.789

16. Round 3.406 to the nearest hundredth.

F. 3.5 (H) 3.41
G. 3.0 **J.** 3.40

17. The distance from Nikki's house to school is 2.4 km. The distance from her house to the post office is $2\frac{9}{10}$ km. From the bakery to Nikki's house is $2\frac{1}{10}$ km and from the grocery store to her house is 3.1 km. Which is closest to Nikki's house?

A. school (C) bakery
B. post office **D.** grocery store

18. In 1995, a jewelry company made \$78.9 million and in 1996 it made \$80.23 million. In 1997, the company made \$77.65 million and in 1998 it made \$80.03 million. In what year did the company make the least money?

F. 1995 (H) 1997
G. 1996 **J.** 1998

19. A movie theater will take up $\frac{3}{4}$ of the available space at a mall. Express this as a decimal.

(A) 0.75 **C.** 0.075
B. 0.34 **D.** 0.034

20. There are 4 floors in an apartment building. Erica lives on the floor between Wen and Alice. Mark lives on the bottom floor. Wen lives on the floor above Erica. Who lives on the second floor?

F. Erica (H) Alice
G. Wen **J.** Mark

GO ON

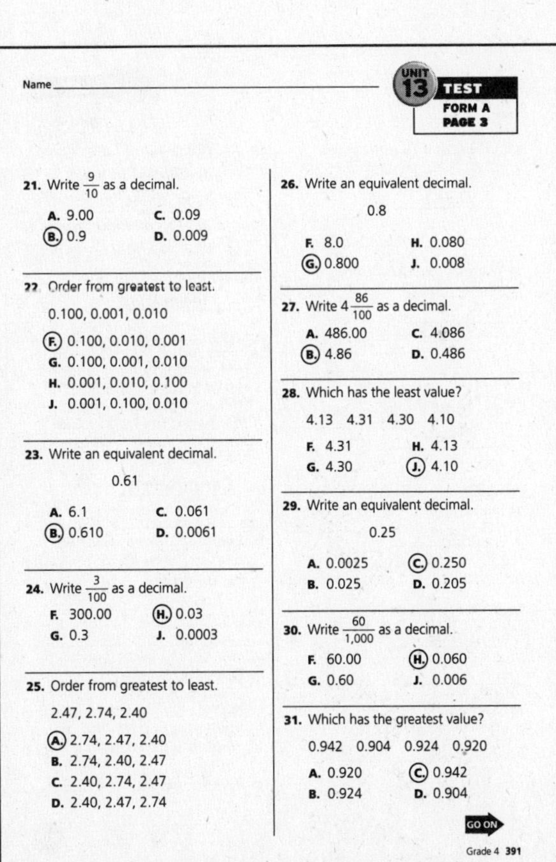

Name____________________________________

UNIT 13 TEST FORM A PAGE 3

21. Write $\frac{9}{10}$ as a decimal.

A. 9.00 **C.** 0.09
(B) 0.9 **D.** 0.009

22. Order from greatest to least.

0.100, 0.001, 0.010

(F) 0.100, 0.010, 0.001
G. 0.100, 0.001, 0.010
H. 0.001, 0.010, 0.100
J. 0.001, 0.100, 0.010

23. Write an equivalent decimal.

0.61

A. 6.1 **C.** 0.061
(B) 0.610 **D.** 0.0061

24. Write $\frac{3}{100}$ as a decimal.

F. 300.00 (H) 0.03
G. 0.3 **J.** 0.0003

25. Order from greatest to least.

2.47, 2.74, 2.40

(A) 2.74, 2.47, 2.40
B. 2.74, 2.40, 2.47
C. 2.40, 2.74, 2.47
D. 2.40, 2.47, 2.74

26. Write an equivalent decimal.

0.8

F. 8.0 **H.** 0.080
(G) 0.800 **J.** 0.008

27. Write $4\frac{86}{100}$ as a decimal.

A. 486.00 **C.** 4.086
(B) 4.86 **D.** 0.486

28. Which has the least value?

4.13 4.31 4.30 4.10

F. 4.31 **H.** 4.13
G. 4.30 (J) 4.10

29. Write an equivalent decimal.

0.25

A. 0.0025 (C) 0.250
B. 0.025 **D.** 0.205

30. Write $\frac{60}{1,000}$ as a decimal.

F. 60.00 (H) 0.060
G. 0.60 **J.** 0.006

31. Which has the greatest value?

0.942 0.904 0.924 0.920

A. 0.920 (C) 0.942
B. 0.924 **D.** 0.904

GO ON

Grade 4 391

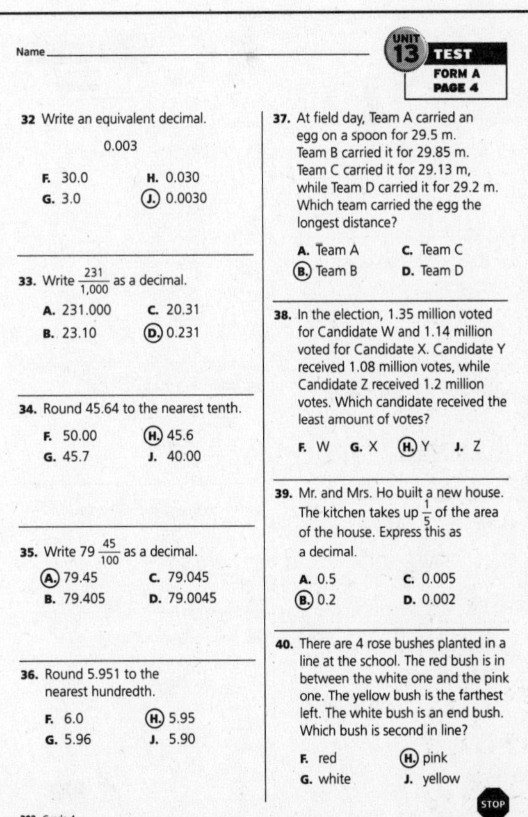

Name____________________________________

UNIT 13 TEST FORM A PAGE 4

32 Write an equivalent decimal.

0.003

F. 30.0 **H.** 0.030
G. 3.0 (J) 0.0030

33. Write $\frac{231}{1,000}$ as a decimal.

A. 231.000 **C.** 20.31
B. 23.10 (D) 0.231

34. Round 45.64 to the nearest tenth.

F. 50.00 (H) 45.6
G. 45.7 **J.** 40.00

35. Write $79\frac{45}{100}$ as a decimal.

(A) 79.45 **C.** 79.045
B. 79.405 **D.** 79.0045

36. Round 5.951 to the nearest hundredth.

F. 6.0 (H) 5.95
G. 5.96 **J.** 5.90

37. At field day, Team A carried an egg on a spoon for 29.5 m. Team B carried it for 29.85 m. Team C carried it for 29.13 m, while Team D carried it for 29.2 m. Which team carried the egg the longest distance?

A. Team A **C.** Team C
(B) Team B **D.** Team D

38. In the election, 1.35 million voted for Candidate W and 1.14 million voted for Candidate X. Candidate Y received 1.08 million votes, while Candidate Z received 1.2 million votes. Which candidate received the least amount of votes?

F. W **G.** X (H) Y **J.** Z

39. Mr. and Mrs. Ho built a new house. The kitchen takes up $\frac{1}{5}$ of the area of the house. Express this as a decimal.

A. 0.5 **C.** 0.005
(B) 0.2 **D.** 0.002

40. There are 4 rose bushes planted in a line at the school. The red bush is in between the white one and the pink one. The yellow bush is the farthest left. The white bush is an end bush. Which bush is second in line?

F. red (H) pink
G. white **J.** yellow

STOP

392 Grade 4

Unit 13

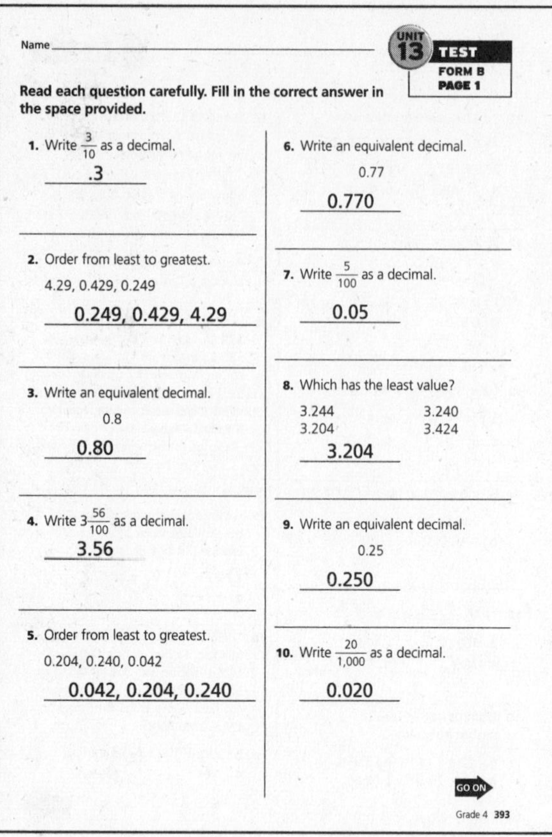

Name ______

UNIT 13 TEST FORM B PAGE 1

Read each question carefully. Fill in the correct answer in the space provided.

1. Write $\frac{3}{10}$ as a decimal.
   .3

2. Order from least to greatest.
   4.29, 0.429, 0.249
   0.249, 0.429, 4.29

3. Write an equivalent decimal.
   0.8
   0.80

4. Write $3\frac{56}{100}$ as a decimal.
   3.56

5. Order from least to greatest.
   0.204, 0.240, 0.042
   0.042, 0.204, 0.240

6. Write an equivalent decimal.
   0.77
   0.770

7. Write $\frac{5}{100}$ as a decimal.
   0.05

8. Which has the least value?
   3.244 3.240
   3.204 3.424
   3.204

9. Write an equivalent decimal.
   0.25
   0.250

10. Write $\frac{20}{1,000}$ as a decimal.
    0.020

GO ON

Grade 4 393

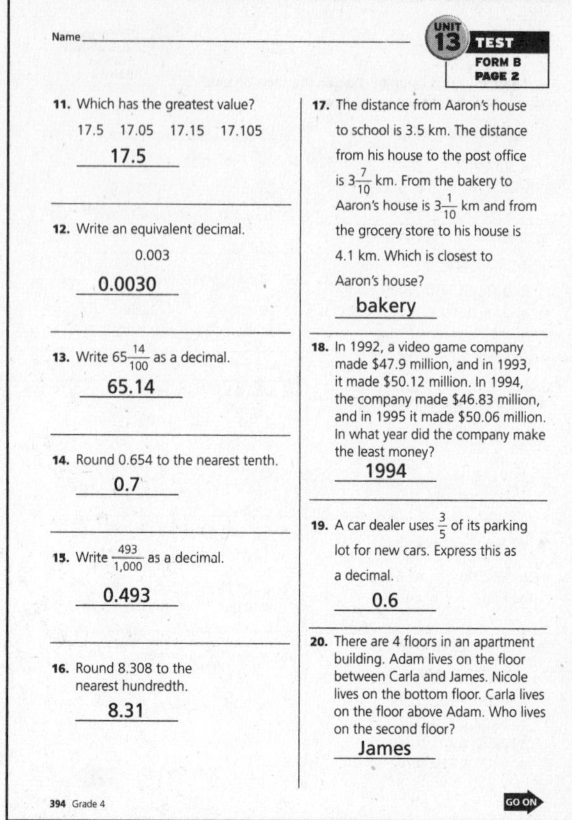

Name ______

UNIT 13 TEST FORM B PAGE 2

11. Which has the greatest value?
    17.5 17.05 17.15 17.105
    17.5

12. Write an equivalent decimal.
    0.003
    0.0030

13. Write $65\frac{14}{100}$ as a decimal.
    65.14

14. Round 0.654 to the nearest tenth.
    0.7

15. Write $\frac{493}{1,000}$ as a decimal.
    0.493

16. Round 8.308 to the nearest hundredth.
    8.31

17. The distance from Aaron's house to school is 3.5 km. The distance from his house to the post office is $3\frac{7}{10}$ km. From the bakery to Aaron's house is $3\frac{1}{10}$ km and from the grocery store to his house is 4.1 km. Which is closest to Aaron's house?
    bakery

18. In 1992, a video game company made \$47.9 million, and in 1993, it made \$50.12 million. In 1994, the company made \$46.83 million, and in 1995 it made \$50.06 million. In what year did the company make the least money?
    1994

19. A car dealer uses $\frac{3}{5}$ of its parking lot for new cars. Express this as a decimal.
    0.6

20. There are 4 floors in an apartment building. Adam lives on the floor between Carla and James. Nicole lives on the bottom floor. Carla lives on the floor above Adam. Who lives on the second floor?
    James

394 Grade 4

GO ON

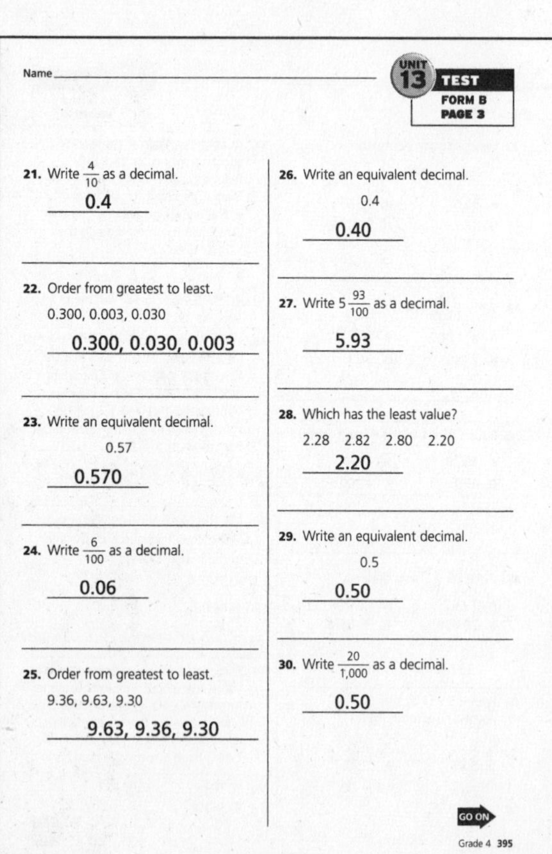

Name ______

UNIT 13 TEST FORM B PAGE 3

21. Write $\frac{4}{10}$ as a decimal.
    0.4

22. Order from greatest to least.
    0.300, 0.003, 0.030
    0.300, 0.030, 0.003

23. Write an equivalent decimal.
    0.57
    0.570

24. Write $\frac{6}{100}$ as a decimal.
    0.06

25. Order from greatest to least.
    9.36, 9.63, 9.30
    9.63, 9.36, 9.30

26. Write an equivalent decimal.
    0.4
    0.40

27. Write $5\frac{93}{100}$ as a decimal.
    5.93

28. Which has the least value?
    2.28 2.82 2.80 2.20
    2.20

29. Write an equivalent decimal.
    0.5
    0.50

30. Write $\frac{20}{1,000}$ as a decimal.
    0.50

GO ON

Grade 4 395

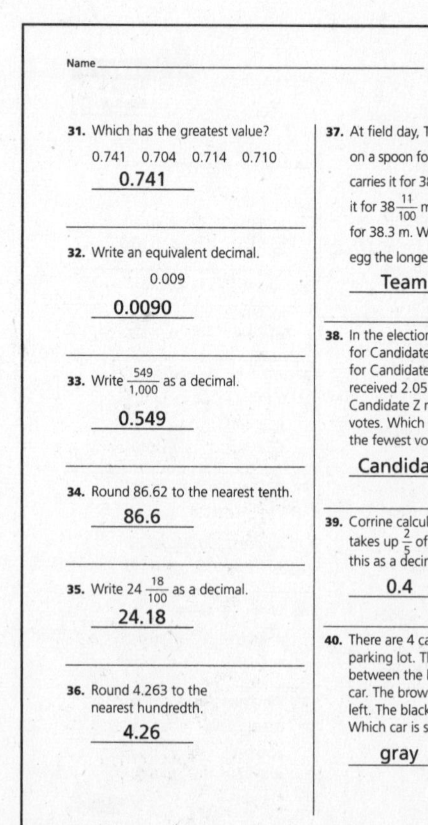

Name ______

UNIT 13 TEST FORM B PAGE 4

31. Which has the greatest value?
    0.741 0.704 0.714 0.710
    0.741

32. Write an equivalent decimal.
    0.009
    0.0090

33. Write $\frac{549}{1,000}$ as a decimal.
    0.549

34. Round 86.62 to the nearest tenth.
    86.6

35. Write $24\frac{18}{100}$ as a decimal.
    24.18

36. Round 4.263 to the nearest hundredth.
    4.26

37. At field day, Team A carries an egg on a spoon for 38.6 m. Team B carries it for $38\frac{18}{20}$ m. Team C carries it for $38\frac{11}{100}$ m while Team D carries it for 38.3 m. Which team carries the egg the longest distance?
    Team B

38. In the election, 2.37 million voted for Candidate W and 2.19 voted for Candidate X. Candidate Y received 2.05 million votes, while Candidate Z received 2.2 million votes. Which candidate received the fewest votes?
    Candidate Y

39. Corrine calculates that her bed takes up $\frac{2}{5}$ of her bedroom. Express this as a decimal.
    0.4

40. There are 4 cars lined up in a parking lot. The blue car is in between the black car and the gray car. The brown car is the farthest left. The black car is an end car. Which car is second from the left?
    gray

396 Grade 4

STOP

Chapter 27

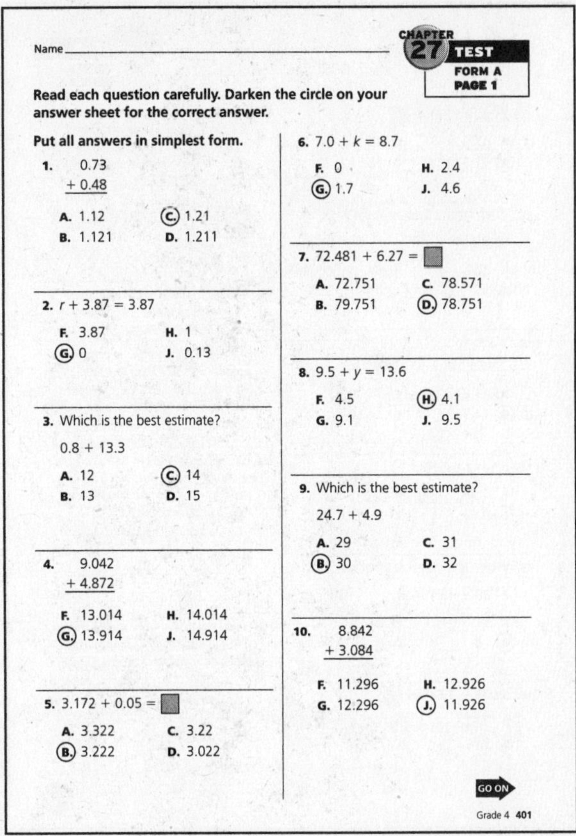
Name

CHAPTER 27 TEST FORM A PAGE 1

Read each question carefully. Darken the circle on your answer sheet for the correct answer.

Put all answers in simplest form.

1. 0.73 + 0.48
A. 1.12 (C) 1.21
B. 1.121 D. 1.211

2. $r + 3.87 = 3.87$
F. 3.87 H. 1
(G) 0 J. 0.13

3. Which is the best estimate?
0.8 + 13.3
A. 12 (C) 14
B. 13 D. 15

4. 9.042 + 4.872
F. 13.014 H. 14.014
(G) 13.914 J. 14.914

5. 3.172 + 0.05 = ▢
A. 3.322 C. 3.22
(B) 3.222 D. 3.022

6. $7.0 + k = 8.7$
F. 0 H. 2.4
(G) 1.7 J. 4.6

7. 72.481 + 6.27 = ▢
A. 72.751 C. 78.571
B. 79.751 (D) 78.751

8. $9.5 + y = 13.6$
F. 4.5 (H) 4.1
G. 9.1 J. 9.5

9. Which is the best estimate?
24.7 + 4.9
A. 29 C. 31
(B) 30 D. 32

10. 8.842 + 3.084
F. 11.296 H. 12.926
G. 12.296 (J) 11.926

GO ON

Grade 4 401

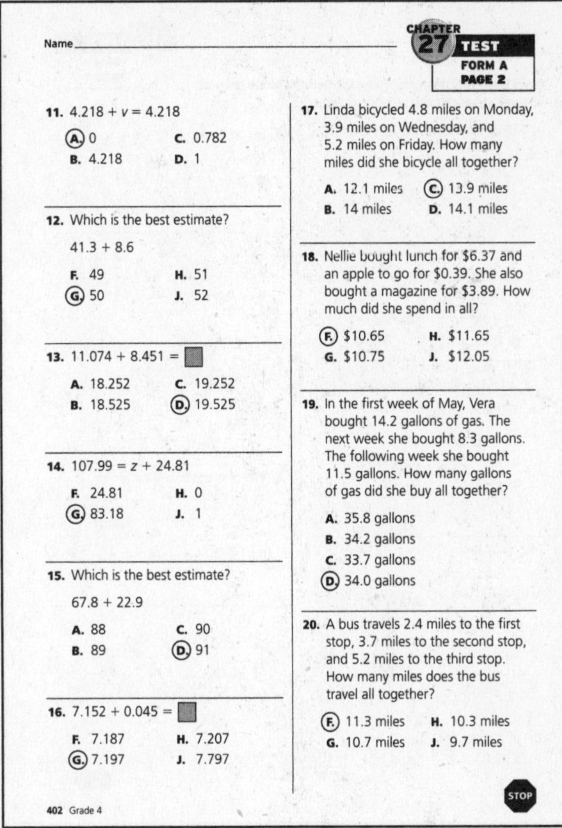
Name

CHAPTER 27 TEST FORM A PAGE 2

11. $4.218 + v = 4.218$
(A) 0 C. 0.782
B. 4.218 D. 1

12. Which is the best estimate?
41.3 + 8.6
F. 49 H. 51
(G) 50 J. 52

13. 11.074 + 8.451 = ▢
A. 18.252 C. 19.252
B. 18.525 (D) 19.525

14. $107.99 = z + 24.81$
F. 24.81 H. 0
(G) 83.18 J. 1

15. Which is the best estimate?
67.8 + 22.9
A. 88 C. 90
B. 89 (D) 91

16. 7.152 + 0.045 = ▢
F. 7.187 H. 7.207
(G) 7.197 J. 7.797

17. Linda bicycled 4.8 miles on Monday, 3.9 miles on Wednesday, and 5.2 miles on Friday. How many miles did she bicycle all together?
A. 12.1 miles (C) 13.9 miles
B. 14 miles D. 14.1 miles

18. Nellie bought lunch for $6.37 and an apple to go for $0.39. She also bought a magazine for $3.89. How much did she spend in all?
(F) $10.65 H. $11.65
G. $10.75 J. $12.05

19. In the first week of May, Vera bought 14.2 gallons of gas. The next week she bought 8.3 gallons. The following week she bought 11.5 gallons. How many gallons of gas did she buy all together?
A. 35.8 gallons
B. 34.2 gallons
C. 33.7 gallons
(D) 34.0 gallons

20. A bus travels 2.4 miles to the first stop, 3.7 miles to the second stop, and 5.2 miles to the third stop. How many miles does the bus travel all together?
(F) 11.3 miles H. 10.3 miles
G. 10.7 miles J. 9.7 miles

STOP

402 Grade 4

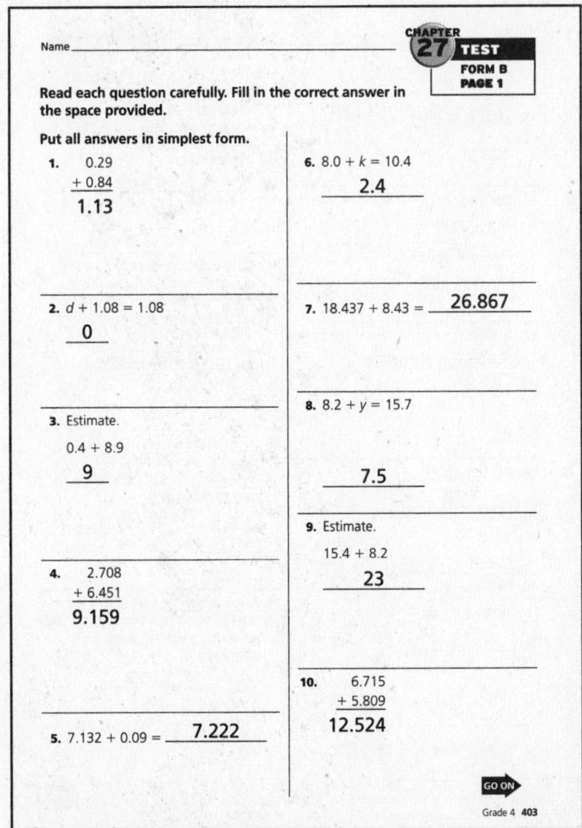
Name

CHAPTER 27 TEST FORM B PAGE 1

Read each question carefully. Fill in the correct answer in the space provided.

Put all answers in simplest form.

1. 0.29 + 0.84
1.13

2. $d + 1.08 = 1.08$
0

3. Estimate.
0.4 + 8.9
9

4. 2.708 + 6.451
9.159

5. 7.132 + 0.09 = 7.222

6. $8.0 + k = 10.4$
2.4

7. 18.437 + 8.43 = 26.867

8. $8.2 + y = 15.7$
7.5

9. Estimate.
15.4 + 8.2
23

10. 6.715 + 5.809
12.524

GO ON

Grade 4 403

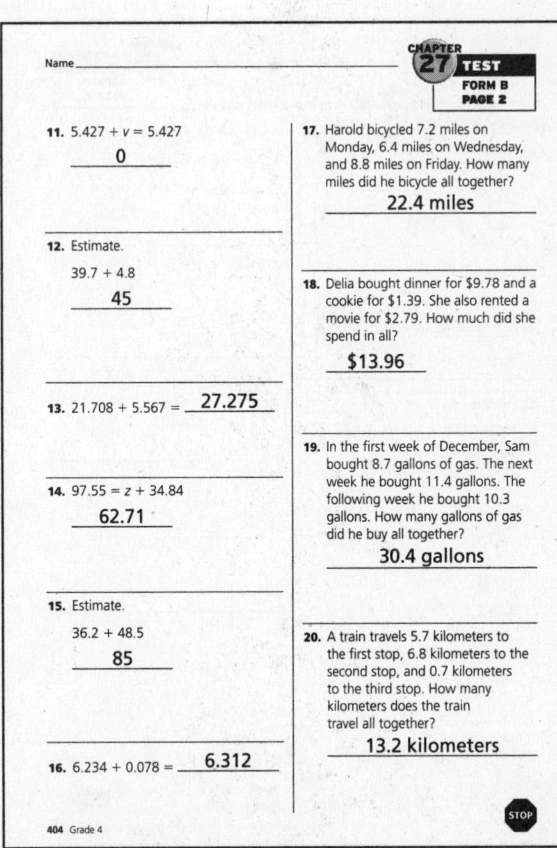
Name

CHAPTER 27 TEST FORM B PAGE 2

11. $5.427 + v = 5.427$
0

12. Estimate.
39.7 + 4.8
45

13. 21.708 + 5.567 = 27.275

14. $97.55 = z + 34.84$
62.71

15. Estimate.
36.2 + 48.5
85

16. 6.234 + 0.078 = 6.312

17. Harold bicycled 7.2 miles on Monday, 6.4 miles on Wednesday, and 8.8 miles on Friday. How many miles did he bicycle all together?
22.4 miles

18. Delia bought dinner for $9.78 and a cookie for $1.39. She also rented a movie for $2.79. How much did she spend in all?
$13.96

19. In the first week of December, Sam bought 8.7 gallons of gas. The next week he bought 11.4 gallons. The following week he bought 10.3 gallons. How many gallons of gas did he buy all together?
30.4 gallons

20. A train travels 5.7 kilometers to the first stop, 6.8 kilometers to the second stop, and 0.7 kilometers to the third stop. How many kilometers does the train travel all together?
13.2 kilometers

STOP

404 Grade 4

Chapter 28

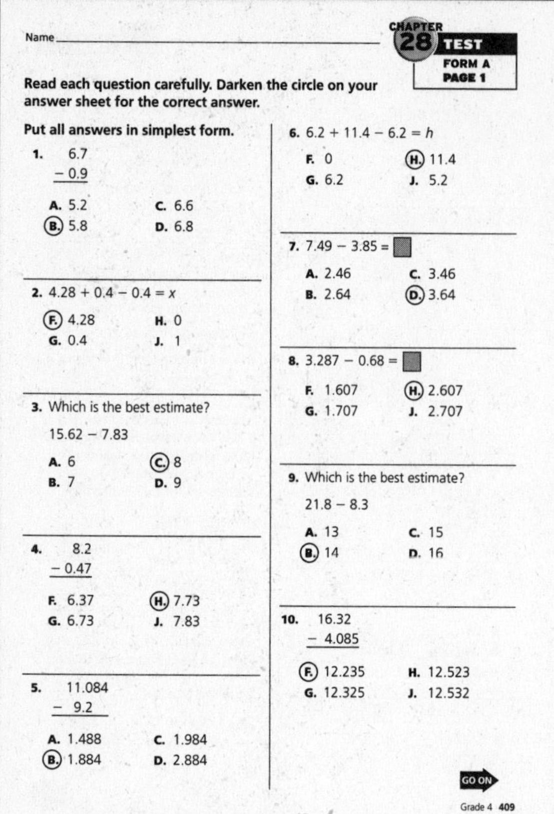

Name____________________

CHAPTER 28 TEST FORM A PAGE 1

Read each question carefully. Darken the circle on your answer sheet for the correct answer.

Put all answers in simplest form.

1. 6.7 − 0.9

A. 5.2 (B.) 5.8 C. 6.6 D. 6.8

2. 4.28 + 0.4 − 0.4 = x

(F.) 4.28 G. 0.4 H. 0 J. 1

3. Which is the best estimate?

15.62 − 7.83

A. 6 B. 7 (C.) 8 D. 9

4. 8.2 − 0.47

F. 6.37 G. 6.73 (H.) 7.73 J. 7.83

5. 11.084 − 9.2

A. 1.488 (B.) 1.884 C. 1.984 D. 2.884

6. 6.2 + 11.4 − 6.2 = h

F. 0 G. 6.2 (H.) 11.4 J. 5.2

7. 7.49 − 3.85 = ■

A. 2.46 B. 2.64 C. 3.46 (D.) 3.64

8. 3.287 − 0.68 = ■

F. 1.607 G. 1.707 (H.) 2.607 J. 2.707

9. Which is the best estimate?

21.8 − 8.3

A. 13 (B.) 14 C. 15 D. 16

10. 16.32 − 4.085

(F.) 12.235 G. 12.325 H. 12.523 J. 12.532

GO ON

Grade 4 409

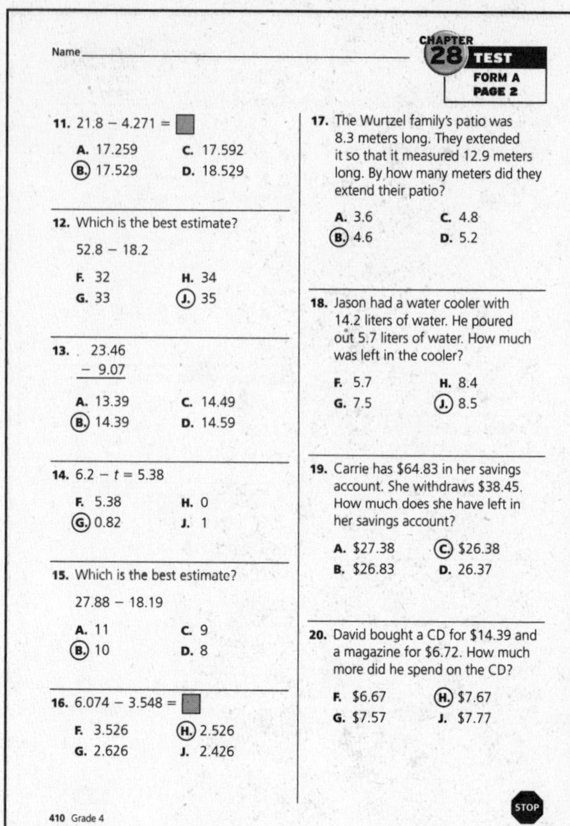

Name____________________

CHAPTER 28 TEST FORM A PAGE 2

11. 21.8 − 4.271 = ■

A. 17.259 (B.) 17.529 C. 17.592 D. 18.529

12. Which is the best estimate?

52.8 − 18.2

F. 32 G. 33 H. 34 (J.) 35

13. 23.46 − 9.07

A. 13.39 (B.) 14.39 C. 14.49 D. 14.59

14. 6.2 − t = 5.38

F. 5.38 (G.) 0.82 H. 0 J. 1

15. Which is the best estimate?

27.88 − 18.19

A. 11 (B.) 10 C. 9 D. 8

16. 6.074 − 3.548 = ■

F. 3.526 G. 2.626 (H.) 2.526 J. 2.426

17. The Wurtzel family's patio was 8.3 meters long. They extended it so that it measured 12.9 meters long. By how many meters did they extend their patio?

A. 3.6 (B.) 4.6 C. 4.8 D. 5.2

18. Jason had a water cooler with 14.2 liters of water. He poured out 5.7 liters of water. How much was left in the cooler?

F. 5.7 G. 7.5 H. 8.4 (J.) 8.5

19. Carrie has $64.83 in her savings account. She withdraws $38.45. How much does she have left in her savings account?

A. $27.38 B. $26.83 (C.) $26.38 D. 26.37

20. David bought a CD for $14.39 and a magazine for $6.72. How much more did he spend on the CD?

F. $6.67 G. $7.57 (H.) $7.67 J. $7.77

410 Grade 4

STOP

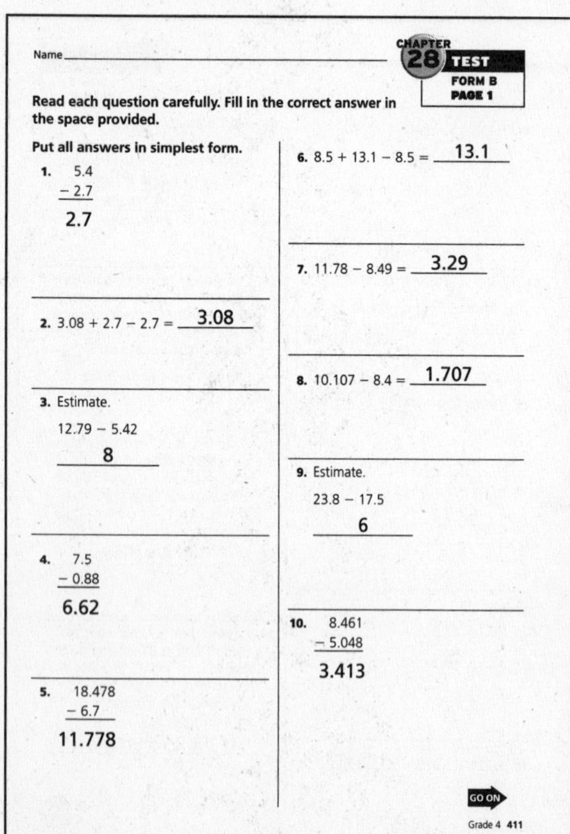

Name____________________

CHAPTER 28 TEST FORM B PAGE 1

Read each question carefully. Fill in the correct answer in the space provided.

Put all answers in simplest form.

1. 5.4 − 2.7 = 2.7

2. 3.08 + 2.7 − 2.7 = 3.08

3. Estimate.

12.79 − 5.42 = 8

4. 7.5 − 0.88 = 6.62

5. 18.478 − 6.7 = 11.778

6. 8.5 + 13.1 − 8.5 = 13.1

7. 11.78 − 8.49 = 3.29

8. 10.107 − 8.4 = 1.707

9. Estimate.

23.8 − 17.5 = 6

10. 8.461 − 5.048 = 3.413

GO ON

Grade 4 411

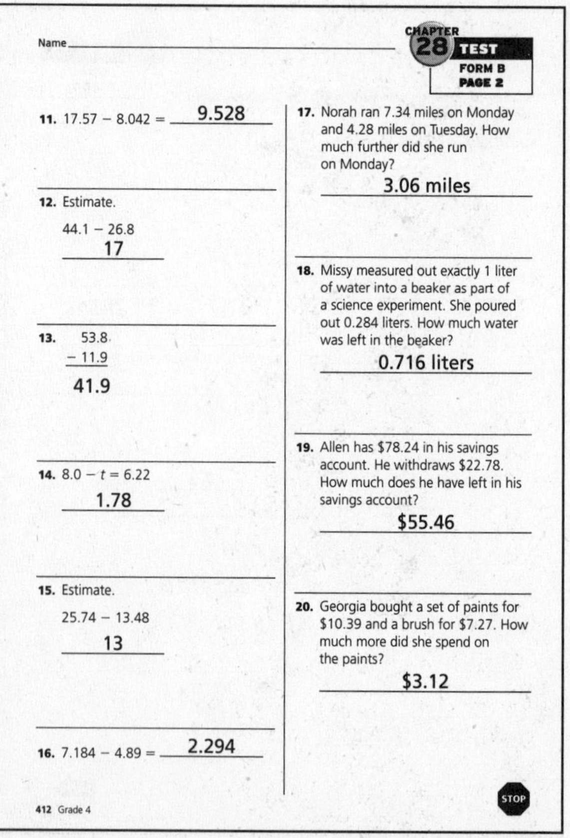

Name____________________

CHAPTER 28 TEST FORM B PAGE 2

11. 17.57 − 8.042 = 9.528

12. Estimate.

44.1 − 26.8 = 17

13. 53.8 − 11.9 = 41.9

14. 8.0 − t = 6.22 1.78

15. Estimate.

25.74 − 13.48 = 13

16. 7.184 − 4.89 = 2.294

17. Norah ran 7.34 miles on Monday and 4.28 miles on Tuesday. How much further did she run on Monday?

3.06 miles

18. Missy measured out exactly 1 liter of water into a beaker as part of a science experiment. She poured out 0.284 liters. How much water was left in the beaker?

0.716 liters

19. Allen has $78.24 in his savings account. He withdraws $22.78. How much does he have left in his savings account?

$55.46

20. Georgia bought a set of paints for $10.39 and a brush for $7.27. How much more did she spend on the paints?

$3.12

412 Grade 4

STOP

Unit 14

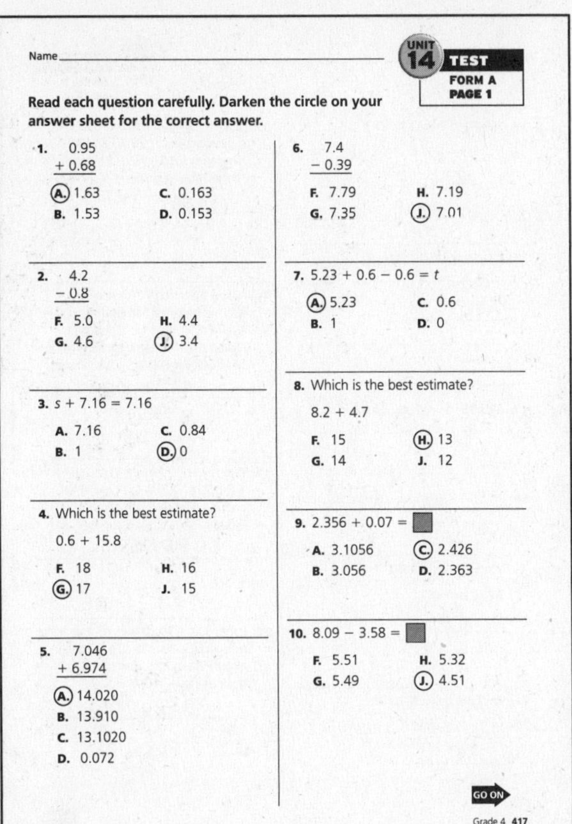

Name______________________________

UNIT 14 TEST FORM A PAGE 1

Read each question carefully. Darken the circle on your answer sheet for the correct answer.

1. $0.95 + 0.68$
   A. 1.63 C. 0.163
   B. 1.53 D. 0.153

2. $4.2 - 0.8$
   F. 5.0 H. 4.4
   G. 4.6 **J. 3.4**

3. $s + 7.16 = 7.16$
   A. 7.16 C. 0.84
   B. 1 **D. 0**

4. Which is the best estimate?
   $0.6 + 15.8$
   F. 18 H. 16
   G. 17 J. 15

5. $7.046 + 6.974$
   A. 14.020
   B. 13.910
   C. 13.1020
   D. 0.072

6. $7.4 - 0.39$
   F. 7.79 H. 7.19
   G. 7.35 **J. 7.01**

7. $5.23 + 0.6 - 0.6 = t$
   A. 5.23 C. 0.6
   B. 1 D. 0

8. Which is the best estimate?
   $8.2 + 4.7$
   F. 15 **H. 13**
   G. 14 J. 12

9. $2.356 + 0.07 = \blacksquare$
   A. 3.1056 **C. 2.426**
   B. 3.056 D. 2.363

10. $8.09 - 3.58 = \blacksquare$
   F. 5.51 H. 5.32
   G. 5.49 **J. 4.51**

GO ON

Grade 4 417

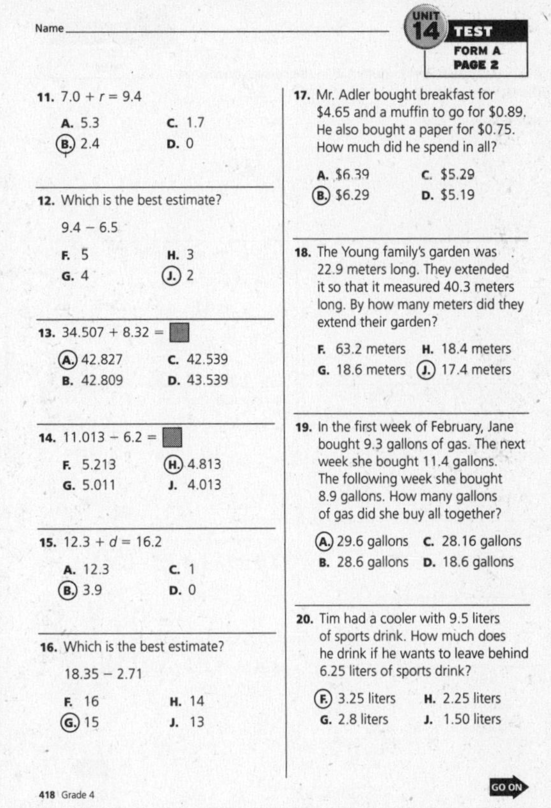

Name______________________________

UNIT 14 TEST FORM A PAGE 2

11. $7.0 + r = 9.4$
   A. 5.3 C. 1.7
   B. 2.4 D. 0

12. Which is the best estimate?
   $9.4 - 6.5$
   F. 5 H. 3
   G. 4 **J. 2**

13. $34.507 + 8.32 = \blacksquare$
   A. 42.827 C. 42.539
   B. 42.809 D. 43.539

14. $11.013 - 6.2 = \blacksquare$
   F. 5.213 **H. 4.813**
   G. 5.011 J. 4.013

15. $12.3 + d = 16.2$
   A. 12.3 C. 1
   B. 3.9 D. 0

16. Which is the best estimate?
   $18.35 - 2.71$
   F. 16 H. 14
   G. 15 J. 13

17. Mr. Adler bought breakfast for $4.65 and a muffin to go for $0.89. He also bought a paper for $0.75. How much did he spend in all?
   A. $6.39 C. $5.29
   B. $6.29 D. $5.19

18. The Young family's garden was 22.9 meters long. They extended it so that it measured 40.3 meters long. By how many meters did they extend their garden?
   F. 63.2 meters H. 18.4 meters
   G. 18.6 meters **J. 17.4 meters**

19. In the first week of February, Jane bought 9.3 gallons of gas. The next week she bought 11.4 gallons. The following week she bought 8.9 gallons. How many gallons of gas did she buy all together?
   A. 29.6 gallons C. 28.16 gallons
   B. 28.6 gallons D. 18.6 gallons

20. Tim had a cooler with 9.5 liters of sports drink. How much does he drink if he wants to leave behind 6.25 liters of sports drink?
   F. 3.25 liters H. 2.25 liters
   G. 2.8 liters J. 1.50 liters

418 Grade 4

GO ON

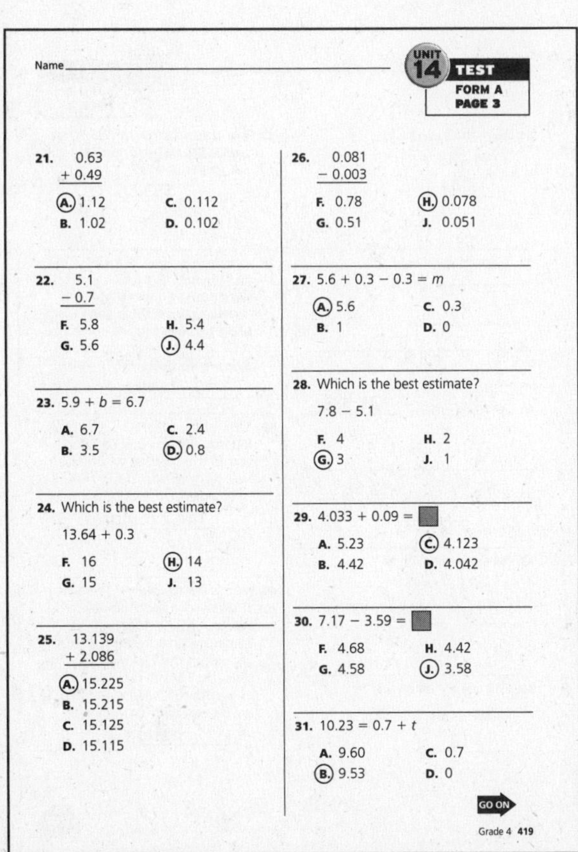

Name______________________________

UNIT 14 TEST FORM A PAGE 3

21. $0.63 + 0.49$
   A. 1.12 C. 0.112
   B. 1.02 D. 0.102

22. $5.1 - 0.7$
   F. 5.8 H. 5.4
   G. 5.6 **J. 4.4**

23. $5.9 + b = 6.7$
   A. 6.7 C. 2.4
   B. 3.5 **D. 0.8**

24. Which is the best estimate?
   $13.64 + 0.3$
   F. 16 **H. 14**
   G. 15 J. 13

25. $13.139 + 2.086$
   A. 15.225
   B. 15.215
   C. 15.125
   D. 15.115

26. $0.081 - 0.003$
   F. 0.78 **H. 0.078**
   G. 0.51 J. 0.051

27. $5.6 + 0.3 - 0.3 = m$
   A. 5.6 C. 0.3
   B. 1 D. 0

28. Which is the best estimate?
   $7.8 - 5.1$
   F. 4 H. 2
   G. 3 J. 1

29. $4.033 + 0.09 = \blacksquare$
   A. 5.23 **C. 4.123**
   B. 4.42 D. 4.042

30. $7.17 - 3.59 = \blacksquare$
   F. 4.68 H. 4.42
   G. 4.58 **J. 3.58**

31. $10.23 = 0.7 + t$
   A. 9.60 C. 0.7
   B. 9.53 D. 0

GO ON

Grade 4 419

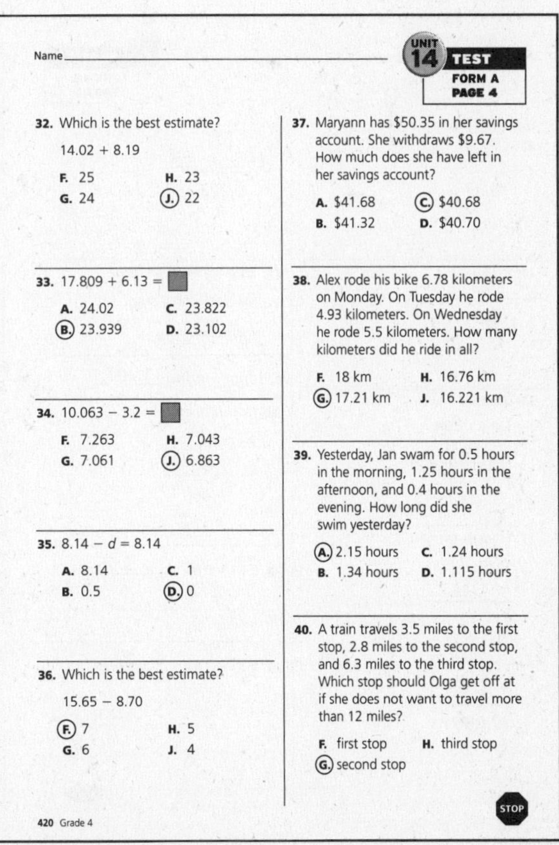

Name______________________________

UNIT 14 TEST FORM A PAGE 4

32. Which is the best estimate?
   $14.02 + 8.19$
   F. 25 H. 23
   G. 24 **J. 22**

33. $17.809 + 6.13 = \blacksquare$
   A. 24.02 C. 23.822
   B. 23.939 D. 23.102

34. $10.063 - 3.2 = \blacksquare$
   F. 7.263 H. 7.043
   G. 7.061 **J. 6.863**

35. $8.14 - d = 8.14$
   A. 8.14 C. 1
   B. 0.5 **D. 0**

36. Which is the best estimate?
   $15.65 - 8.70$
   F. 7 H. 5
   G. 6 J. 4

37. Maryann has $50.35 in her savings account. She withdraws $9.67. How much does she have left in her savings account?
   A. $41.68 **C. $40.68**
   B. $41.32 D. $40.70

38. Alex rode his bike 6.78 kilometers on Monday. On Tuesday he rode 4.93 kilometers. On Wednesday he rode 5.5 kilometers. How many kilometers did he ride in all?
   F. 18 km H. 16.76 km
   G. 17.21 km J. 16.221 km

39. Yesterday, Jan swam for 0.5 hours in the morning, 1.25 hours in the afternoon, and 0.4 hours in the evening. How long did she swim yesterday?
   A. 2.15 hours C. 1.24 hours
   B. 1.34 hours D. 1.115 hours

40. A train travels 3.5 miles to the first stop, 2.8 miles to the second stop, and 6.3 miles to the third stop. Which stop should Olga get off at if she does not want to travel more than 12 miles?
   F. first stop H. third stop
   G. second stop

STOP

420 Grade 4

Unit 14

Name ____________

UNIT 14 TEST
FORM B
PAGE 1

Read each question carefully. Fill in the correct answer in the space provided.

1. 0.45
 + 0.62
 1.07

2. 0.72
 − 0.09
 0.63

3. Solve the equation for *b*.
 $b + 5.37 = 5.37$
 0

4. Estimate the sum.
 0.7 + 12.1
 13

5. 8.391
 + 4.850
 13.241

6. 3.7
 − 0.81
 2.89

7. Solve the equation for *g*.
 $6.41 + 8.2 - 8.2 = g$
 6.41

8. Estimate the sum.
 9.3 + 5.6
 15

9. 3.297 + 0.28 = 3.577

10. 6.32 − 5.21 = 1.11

GO ON

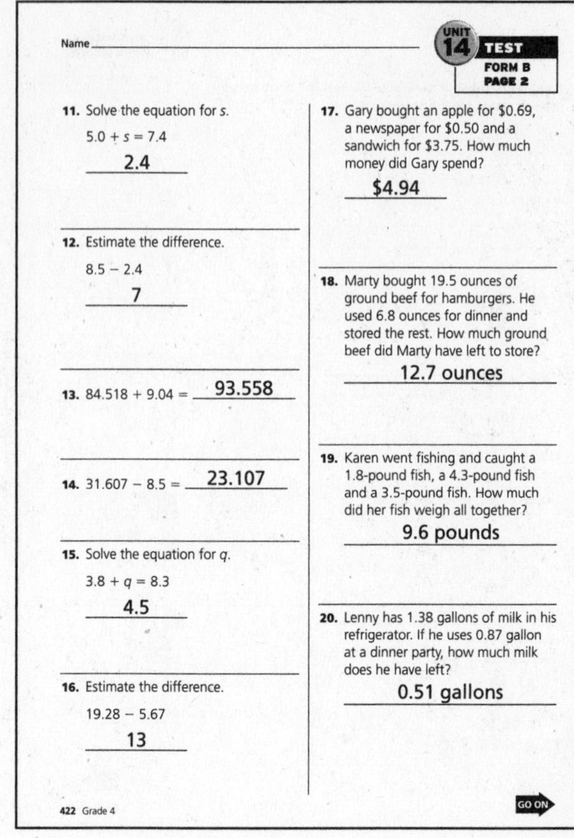

Name ____________

UNIT 14 TEST
FORM B
PAGE 2

11. Solve the equation for *s*.
 $5.0 + s = 7.4$
 2.4

12. Estimate the difference.
 8.5 − 2.4
 7

13. 84.518 + 9.04 = 93.558

14. 31.607 − 8.5 = 23.107

15. Solve the equation for *q*.
 $3.8 + q = 8.3$
 4.5

16. Estimate the difference.
 19.28 − 5.67
 13

17. Gary bought an apple for $0.69, a newspaper for $0.50 and a sandwich for $3.75. How much money did Gary spend?
 $4.94

18. Marty bought 19.5 ounces of ground beef for hamburgers. He used 6.8 ounces for dinner and stored the rest. How much ground beef did Marty have left to store?
 12.7 ounces

19. Karen went fishing and caught a 1.8-pound fish, a 4.3-pound fish and a 3.5-pound fish. How much did her fish weigh all together?
 9.6 pounds

20. Lenny has 1.38 gallons of milk in his refrigerator. If he uses 0.87 gallon at a dinner party, how much milk does he have left?
 0.51 gallons

GO ON

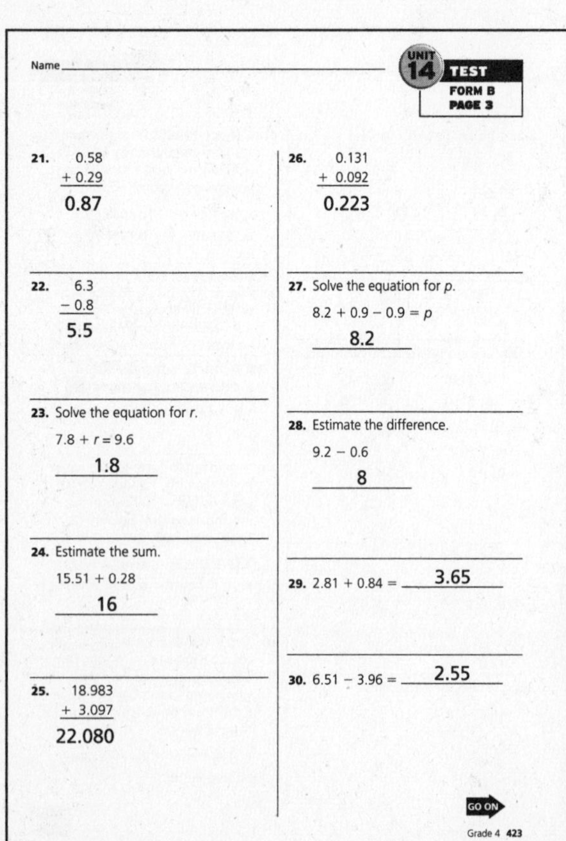

Name ____________

UNIT 14 TEST
FORM B
PAGE 3

21. 0.58
 + 0.29
 0.87

22. 6.3
 − 0.8
 5.5

23. Solve the equation for *r*.
 $7.8 + r = 9.6$
 1.8

24. Estimate the sum.
 15.51 + 0.28
 16

25. 18.983
 + 3.097
 22.080

26. 0.131
 + 0.092
 0.223

27. Solve the equation for *p*.
 $8.2 + 0.9 - 0.9 = p$
 8.2

28. Estimate the difference.
 9.2 − 0.6
 8

29. 2.81 + 0.84 = 3.65

30. 6.51 − 3.96 = 2.55

GO ON

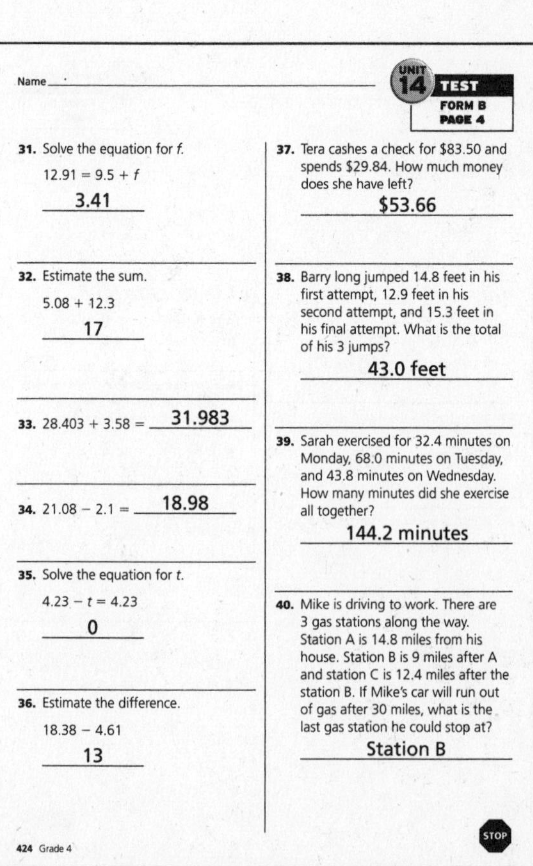

Name ____________

UNIT 14 TEST
FORM B
PAGE 4

31. Solve the equation for *f*.
 $12.91 = 9.5 + f$
 3.41

32. Estimate the sum.
 5.08 + 12.3
 17

33. 28.403 + 3.58 = 31.983

34. 21.08 − 2.1 = 18.98

35. Solve the equation for *t*.
 $4.23 - t = 4.23$
 0

36. Estimate the difference.
 18.38 − 4.61
 13

37. Tera cashes a check for $83.50 and spends $29.84. How much money does she have left?
 $53.66

38. Barry long jumped 14.8 feet in his first attempt, 12.9 feet in his second attempt, and 15.3 feet in his final attempt. What is the total of his 3 jumps?
 43.0 feet

39. Sarah exercised for 32.4 minutes on Monday, 68.0 minutes on Tuesday, and 43.8 minutes on Wednesday. How many minutes did she exercise all together?
 144.2 minutes

40. Mike is driving to work. There are 3 gas stations along the way. Station A is 14.8 miles from his house. Station B is 9 miles after A and station C is 12.4 miles after the station B. If Mike's car will run out of gas after 30 miles, what is the last gas station he could stop at?
 Station B

STOP

Final

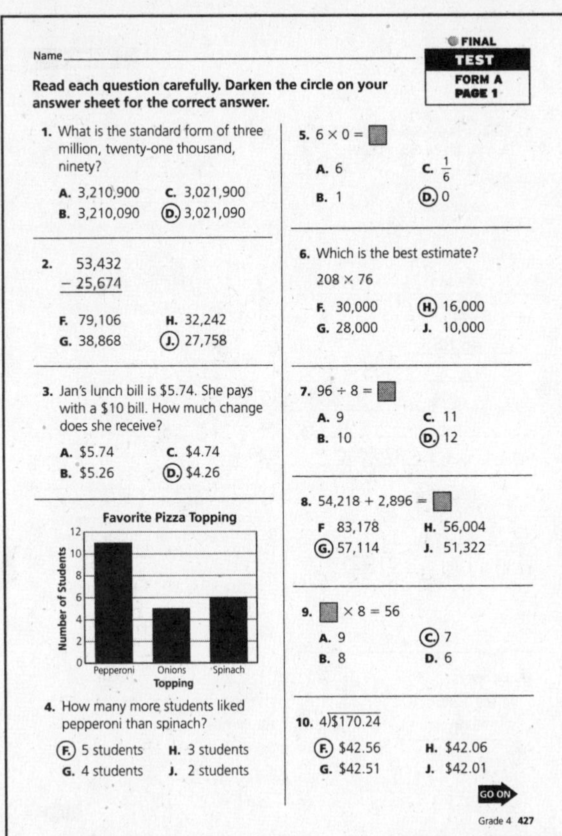

Name ______________________

FINAL TEST FORM A PAGE 1

Read each question carefully. Darken the circle on your answer sheet for the correct answer.

1. What is the standard form of three million, twenty-one thousand, ninety?
   - A. 3,210,900
   - B. 3,210,090
   - C. 3,021,900
   - (D.) 3,021,090

2. 53,432 − 25,674
   - F. 79,106
   - G. 38,868
   - H. 32,242
   - (J.) 27,758

3. Jan's lunch bill is \$5.74. She pays with a \$10 bill. How much change does she receive?
   - A. \$5.74
   - B. \$5.26
   - C. \$4.74
   - (D.) \$4.26

4. How many more students liked pepperoni than spinach?
   - (F.) 5 students
   - G. 4 students
   - H. 3 students
   - J. 2 students

5. $6 \times 0 =$ ▢
   - A. 6
   - B. 1
   - C. $\frac{1}{6}$
   - (D.) 0

6. Which is the best estimate?
   208×76
   - F. 30,000
   - G. 28,000
   - (H.) 16,000
   - J. 10,000

7. $96 \div 8 =$ ▢
   - A. 9
   - B. 10
   - C. 11
   - (D.) 12

8. $54,218 + 2,896 =$ ▢
   - F 83,178
   - (G.) 57,114
   - H. 56,004
   - J. 51,322

9. ▢ $\times 8 = 56$
   - A. 9
   - B. 8
   - (C.) 7
   - D. 6

10. $4\overline{)\$170.24}$
    - (F.) \$42.56
    - G. \$42.51
    - H. \$42.06
    - J. \$42.01

GO ON

Grade 4 427

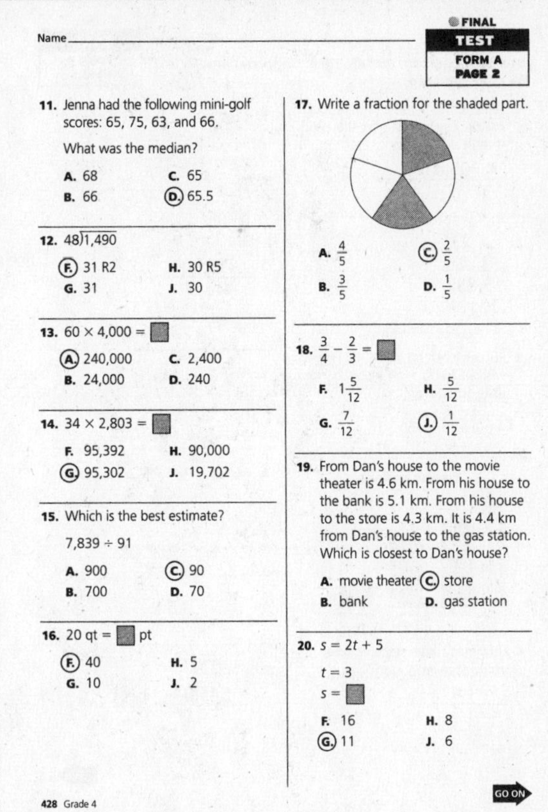

Name ______________________

FINAL TEST FORM A PAGE 2

11. Jenna had the following mini-golf scores: 65, 75, 63, and 66.
    What was the median?
    - A. 68
    - B. 66
    - C. 65
    - (D.) 65.5

12. $48\overline{)1,490}$
    - (F.) 31 R2
    - G. 31
    - H. 30 R5
    - J. 30

13. $60 \times 4,000 =$ ▢
    - (A.) 240,000
    - B. 24,000
    - C. 2,400
    - D. 240

14. $34 \times 2,803 =$ ▢
    - F. 95,392
    - (G.) 95,302
    - H. 90,000
    - J. 19,702

15. Which is the best estimate?
    $7,839 \div 91$
    - A. 900
    - B. 700
    - (C.) 90
    - D. 70

16. 20 qt = ▢ pt
    - (F.) 40
    - G. 10
    - H. 5
    - J. 2

17. Write a fraction for the shaded part.
    - A. $\frac{4}{5}$
    - B. $\frac{3}{5}$
    - (C.) $\frac{2}{5}$
    - D. $\frac{1}{5}$

18. $\frac{3}{4} - \frac{2}{3} =$ ▢
    - F. $1\frac{5}{12}$
    - G. $\frac{7}{12}$
    - H. $\frac{5}{12}$
    - (J.) $\frac{1}{12}$

19. From Dan's house to the movie theater is 4.6 km. From his house to the bank is 5.1 km. From his house to the store is 4.3 km. It is 4.4 km from Dan's house to the gas station. Which is closest to Dan's house?
    - A. movie theater
    - B. bank
    - (C.) store
    - D. gas station

20. $s = 2t + 5$
    $t = 3$
    $s =$ ▢
    - F. 16
    - (G.) 11
    - H. 8
    - J. 6

428 Grade 4

GO ON

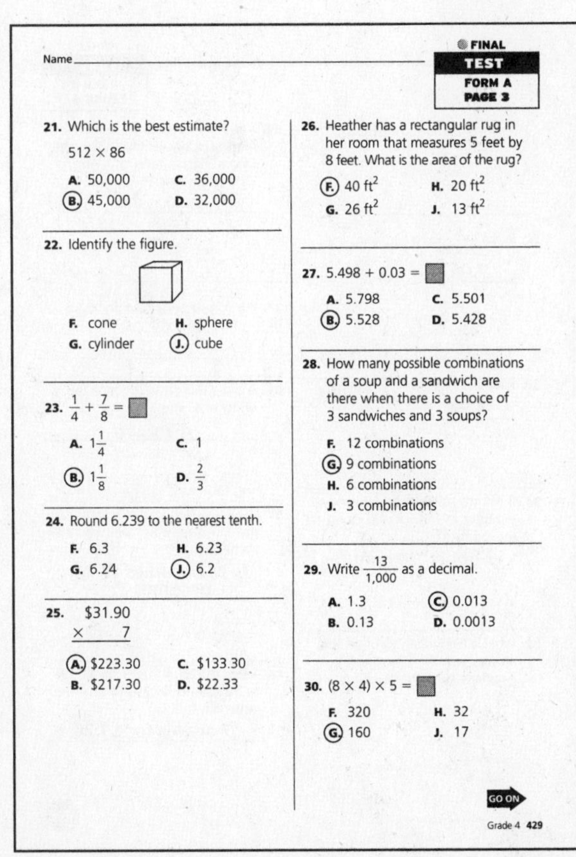

Name ______________________

FINAL TEST FORM A PAGE 3

21. Which is the best estimate?
    512×86
    - A. 50,000
    - (B.) 45,000
    - C. 36,000
    - D. 32,000

22. Identify the figure.
    - F. cone
    - G. cylinder
    - H. sphere
    - (J.) cube

23. $\frac{1}{4} + \frac{7}{8} =$ ▢
    - A. $1\frac{1}{4}$
    - (B.) $1\frac{1}{8}$
    - C. 1
    - D. $\frac{2}{3}$

24. Round 6.239 to the nearest tenth.
    - F. 6.3
    - G. 6.24
    - H. 6.23
    - (J.) 6.2

25. \$31.90 × 7
    - (A.) \$223.30
    - B. \$217.30
    - C. \$133.30
    - D. \$22.33

26. Heather has a rectangular rug in her room that measures 5 feet by 8 feet. What is the area of the rug?
    - (F.) 40 ft^2
    - G. 26 ft^2
    - H. 20 ft^2
    - J. 13 ft^2

27. $5.498 + 0.03 =$ ▢
    - A. 5.798
    - (B.) 5.528
    - C. 5.501
    - D. 5.428

28. How many possible combinations of a soup and a sandwich are there when there is a choice of 3 sandwiches and 3 soups?
    - F. 12 combinations
    - (G.) 9 combinations
    - H. 6 combinations
    - J. 3 combinations

29. Write $\frac{13}{1,000}$ as a decimal.
    - A. 1.3
    - B. 0.13
    - (C.) 0.013
    - D. 0.0013

30. $(8 \times 4) \times 5 =$ ▢
    - F. 320
    - (G.) 160
    - H. 32
    - J. 17

GO ON

Grade 4 429

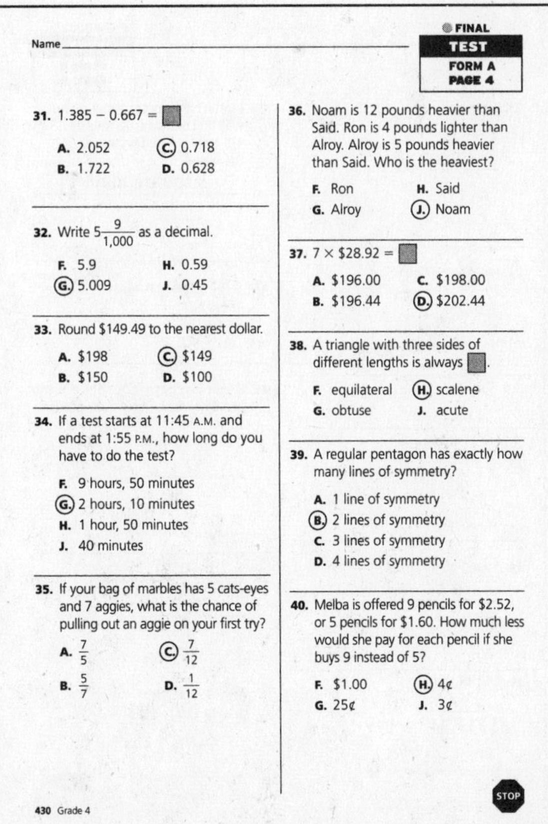

Name ______________________

FINAL TEST FORM A PAGE 4

31. $1.385 - 0.667 =$ ▢
    - A. 2.052
    - B. 1.722
    - (C.) 0.718
    - D. 0.628

32. Write $5\frac{9}{1,000}$ as a decimal.
    - F. 5.9
    - (G.) 5.009
    - H. 0.59
    - J. 0.45

33. Round \$149.49 to the nearest dollar.
    - A. \$198
    - B. \$150
    - (C.) \$149
    - D. \$100

34. If a test starts at 11:45 A.M. and ends at 1:55 P.M., how long do you have to do the test?
    - F. 9 hours, 50 minutes
    - (G.) 2 hours, 10 minutes
    - H. 1 hour, 50 minutes
    - J. 40 minutes

35. If your bag of marbles has 5 cats-eyes and 7 aggies, what is the chance of pulling out an aggie on your first try?
    - A. $\frac{7}{5}$
    - B. $\frac{5}{7}$
    - (C.) $\frac{7}{12}$
    - D. $\frac{1}{12}$

36. Noam is 12 pounds heavier than Said. Ron is 4 pounds lighter than Alroy. Alroy is 5 pounds heavier than Said. Who is the heaviest?
    - F. Ron
    - G. Alroy
    - H. Said
    - (J.) Noam

37. $7 \times \$28.92 =$ ▢
    - A. \$196.00
    - B. \$196.44
    - C. \$198.00
    - (D.) \$202.44

38. A triangle with three sides of different lengths is always ▢.
    - F. equilateral
    - G. obtuse
    - (H.) scalene
    - J. acute

39. A regular pentagon has exactly how many lines of symmetry?
    - A. 1 line of symmetry
    - (B.) 2 lines of symmetry
    - C. 3 lines of symmetry
    - D. 4 lines of symmetry

40. Melba is offered 9 pencils for \$2.52, or 5 pencils for \$1.60. How much less would she pay for each pencil if she buys 9 instead of 5?
    - F. \$1.00
    - G. 25¢
    - (H.) 4¢
    - J. 3¢

STOP

430 Grade 4

Final

Name ______________________

FINAL TEST FORM B PAGE 1

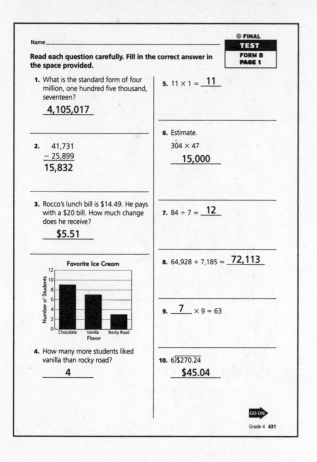

Read each question carefully. Fill in the correct answer in the space provided.

1. What is the standard form of four million, one hundred five thousand, seventeen?
   4,105,017

2. 41,731 − 25,899 = 15,832

3. Rocco's lunch bill is $14.49. He pays with a $20 bill. How much change does he receive?
   $5.51

Favorite Ice Cream

Number of Students: 0, 2, 4, 6, 8, 10, 12
Flavor: Chocolate, Vanilla, Rocky Road

4. How many more students liked vanilla than rocky road?
   4

5. 11 × 1 = 11

6. Estimate.
   304 × 47
   15,000

7. 84 ÷ 7 = 12

8. 64,928 + 7,185 = 72,113

9. 7 × 9 = 63

10. 6)$270.24
    $45.04

GO ON

Name ______________________

FINAL TEST FORM B PAGE 2

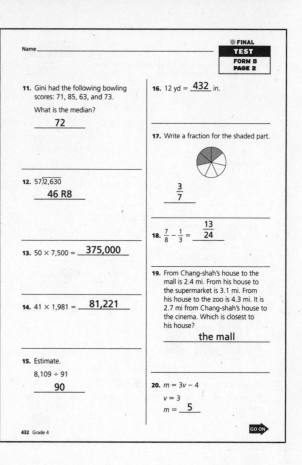

11. Gini had the following bowling scores: 71, 85, 63, and 73.
    What is the median?
    72

12. 57)2,630
    46 R8

13. 50 × 7,500 = 375,000

14. 41 × 1,981 = 81,221

15. Estimate.
    8,109 ÷ 91
    90

16. 12 yd = 432 in.

17. Write a fraction for the shaded part.
    $\frac{3}{7}$

18. $\frac{7}{8} - \frac{1}{3} = \frac{13}{24}$

19. From Chang-shah's house to the mall is 2.4 mi. From his house to the supermarket is 3.1 mi. From his house to the zoo is 4.3 mi. It is 2.7 mi from Chang-shah's house to the cinema. Which is closest to his house?
    the mall

20. $m = 3v - 4$
    $v = 3$
    $m =$ 5

GO ON

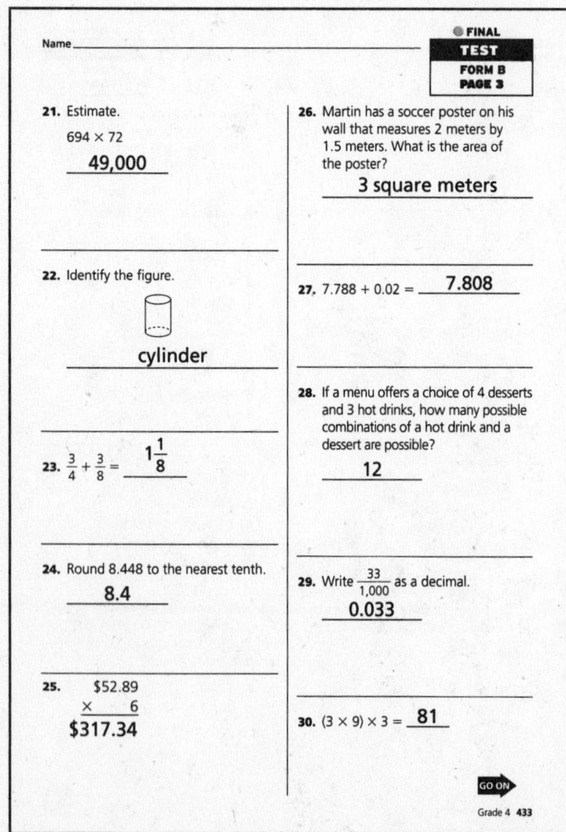

Name ______________________

FINAL TEST FORM B PAGE 3

21. Estimate.
    694 × 72
    49,000

22. Identify the figure.
    cylinder

23. $\frac{3}{4} + \frac{3}{8} = 1\frac{1}{8}$

24. Round 8.448 to the nearest tenth.
    8.4

25. $52.89 × 6 = $317.34

26. Martin has a soccer poster on his wall that measures 2 meters by 1.5 meters. What is the area of the poster?
    3 square meters

27. 7.788 + 0.02 = 7.808

28. If a menu offers a choice of 4 desserts and 3 hot drinks, how many possible combinations of a hot drink and a dessert are possible?
    12

29. Write $\frac{33}{1,000}$ as a decimal.
    0.033

30. (3 × 9) × 3 = 81

GO ON

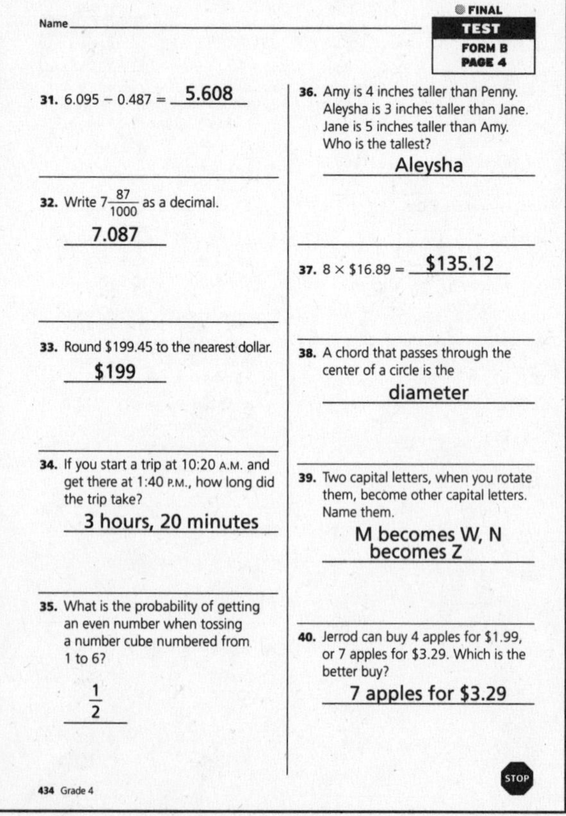

Name ______________________

FINAL TEST FORM B PAGE 4

31. 6.095 − 0.487 = 5.608

32. Write $7\frac{87}{1000}$ as a decimal.
    7.087

33. Round $199.45 to the nearest dollar.
    $199

34. If you start a trip at 10:20 A.M. and get there at 1:40 P.M., how long did the trip take?
    3 hours, 20 minutes

35. What is the probability of getting an even number when tossing a number cube numbered from 1 to 6?
    $\frac{1}{2}$

36. Amy is 4 inches taller than Penny. Aleysha is 3 inches taller than Jane. Jane is 5 inches taller than Amy. Who is the tallest?
    Aleysha

37. 8 × $16.89 = $135.12

38. A chord that passes through the center of a circle is the
    diameter

39. Two capital letters, when you rotate them, become other capital letters. Name them.
    M becomes W, N becomes Z

40. Jerrod can buy 4 apples for $1.99, or 7 apples for $3.29. Which is the better buy?
    7 apples for $3.29

STOP